(Each scale division is 1/10 as great as the last)

10^{-1} 10^{-2} 10^{-3} 10^{-4} 10^{-5} 10^{-6} 10^{-7} 10^{-8} 10^{-9} 10^{-10} 10^{-11} 10^{-12} 10^{-13} 10^{-14} 10^{-15} 10^{-16}

One Inch
Equals
2.54×10^{-2} meter

Wavelength Infrared
(10^{-5} meter)

Wavelength Yellow Light
(5.89×10^{-7} meter)

One Angstrom Unit (10^{-10} met

Wavelength Of 100,000 ev X-ray (1.24×10^{-11}

One Fermi Unit (10^{-15} meter)

Wavelength Of 10 Bev Gamma Ray (1.24×10^{-16} meter)

Understanding

the PHYSICAL SCIENCES

OLAF P. ANFINSON

DEPARTMENT OF PHYSICAL SCIENCE
LONG BEACH STATE COLLEGE

ALLYN AND BACON, INC.

Boston, 1963

Understanding

the PHYSICAL SCIENCES

to my wife, MARY JANE

PREFACE

One necessity of our modern way of life is that we have some understanding of the physical sciences and the interrelated facts which we encounter every day from the fields of physics, chemistry, astronomy, and geology.   Most people are aware of science as an active and dynamic force which is shaping every aspect of contemporary life; however, too often, persons are timid about making a genuine effort to comprehend the nature of science.   There is a widely held misconception that the sciences are far beyond the comprehension of the average individual.   That this is a fallacy is well demonstrated by the interest and understanding in things scientific displayed by children in any neighborhood or household.   Fortunately, we never completely outgrow this characteristic of youth.   For example, curiosity describes the person who browses before selecting his next book to read.   For such a person, an enlightening book on the physical sciences should be of particular interest both as a stimulus to intelligent curiosity and as a practical tool for understanding the events of today.

Curiosity regarding things and events is one of the primary motives supporting progress in the sciences. Intelligent persons want to know more about the world in which they live and achieve great satisfaction from their search for better understandings. They do not always wait for problems to arise before seeking knowledge. They are thinkers. They seek out pertinent problems which obstruct progress. They anticipate the course of meanings and events. They investigate to ascertain the reality of their anticipations. They never cease learning.

What a person learns depends to a large extent upon his purpose for learning and upon the types of observations and experiences which one allows to influence him. In early infancy everyone develops a deep curiosity regarding the objects and events about him. Our curiosity may have diminished somewhat but it has not been completely satisfied. Every day we find ourselves confronted with unexpected results and perplexing situations. These occur largely because even familiar situations may bring forth the unexpected. Therefore, our interpretations of the most commonplace circumstances are constantly undergoing revision as our curiosity becomes aroused by unforeseen outcomes.

One of the purposes of this book is to aid the reader in expanding his world of meanings by re-examining in the light of scientific explanations many of his presently held interpretations. Beginning our inquiry in the realm of sound and light is not by chance. As children we became dependent on the sense organs as our primary means of learning about our surroundings. By these means, we first learned to *locate* objects of interest. Soon, our need for relocating familiar objects gave us an elementary sense of *direction*. As experiences accumulated, certain situations and events took on special meanings in terms of anticipations which we could prepare to deal with successfully. Out of these meanings we have constructed and continue to construct the world in which we must live. That this is a troublesome world is due, at least in part, to incomplete understanding of our channels of information. As a simple example, recall how the apparent location of objects is often confused by echoes and mirror images. Understanding the scientific law of reflection helps to restore order to these otherwise trial and error situations. The area of sight and sound is a productive place to begin our inquiry also because an understanding of the characteristics and processes which describe and explain these primary channels of observation is basic to our study in other areas.

In this book we shall hold to the premise that the purpose of science is *explanation*. It is true that we could limit our discourse to the premise that the purpose of science is *description*. In the event of the second premise, we should have been content to call attention to the visible properties of objects and events and to consider only the facts of science. But facts have a way of becoming so impersonal as to be boring to most people. Hence, we shall go beyond objects, events, and their observable properties to the more exciting personal meanings for situations and phenomena. In this area science becomes a dynamic kind of knowledge which grows and changes as one's meanings grow and change. This does not mean that we shall dispense with facts and measurements. In science our meanings, or concepts, would have no resemblance to actual experience were it not for the insistence in science upon verification by measurements at an operational level. The purpose, rather, of emphasizing explanation is to help the reader to adopt the self-correcting aspects of scientific thinking in which there is a vital interaction between personal concepts—the reader's own meanings for situations and phenomena—and verification involving the logic and methods of scientific problem-solving. It is intended that this book serve as a stimulus and guide in developing understanding of concepts and in improving competence in using the facts and methods of physical science.

OLAF P. ANFINSON

CONTENTS

SOURCE OF SOUND

The source of sound is a vibrating body. Statements such as this have the appeal of being familiar and the crispness of authority. To persons who have lost the zest of curiosity, the opening remark might seem to be an adequate explanation for the source of sound and perhaps also for sound itself. For those students who rely mainly upon memorized statements to gain scholarly success, statements such as this have the appeal of quotations that can be remembered easily. (Let us hope that no reader is that naïve. What could be more boring than the recitation of unchallenged cliches?) Fortunately, most scholars study with the purpose of achieving a meaningful understanding of the subject matter rather than of learning to repeat words like a parrot. For those who still possess the delightful curiosity of youth, statements like that of the opening remark are but invitations to question and to investigate. Do all sounds actually originate in vibrating bodies?

Many sources of sound seem always near at hand. Tracing a few sounds to their origin should not be difficult. After that, the next logical step would be to check for evidences of vibration. For example, the sound of a radio could be traced to the cone of the loudspeaker. Placing one's fingers on the cone would reveal that it was vibrating. Another sound might lead us to a group of rustling leaves. Seeing the motion of the quaking leaves would confirm that they too were vibrating. But what relationships if any exist between the observed vibrations and the sounds being produced? And what of sounds such as the wind whistling through a small crack beneath a window?

We say that the wind is whistling. Checking for wind vibrations with our fingers would lead to nothing, except perhaps causing the sound to stop. To look for visibly vibrating bodies also would be fruitless. Yet one might be able to imagine that the sound originated in a vibrating portion of the air near to the window crack. If so, how could you describe such a vibration and how might you demonstrate that your description explained the facts?

Characteristics that describe All objects and events are known by their characteristics. For instance, a missing person is described in such terms as height, weight, color of eyes, and color of hair. A rain storm might be described in terms of wind directions, wind velocity, inches of rainfall, and temperature variations. Our knowledge about an object or about an event is the composite of all the known characteristics of the subject and all of the expected meanings which accompany those characteristics. It follows that we can never achieve complete knowledge about any object or event. Search for knowledge is always in progress. Curiosity—man's urge to know—is the primary motivation behind this search. In many instances the search is spurred on by the realization that one's freedom of choice is being impaired by inadequate knowledge. An active imagination can aid in the search. The successful search for knowledge is usually limited by the number of useful characteristics with which a person is able to endow the object or event under study.

At this stage and for the purposes of introduction, the descriptive characteristics chosen shall be confined to those which can be measured in a direct manner.

The vibrations of the speaker cone or the rustling leaves can be described in terms of the characteristics of the motions of the moving parts. Other parts, although not in motion, also may be involved in the vibration but for now we shall concentrate upon describing the motion. If a magnified slow-motion, sound movie were available showing the vibrating speaker cone, various parts of the cone would appear to be moving in step with the sound being reproduced. If the sound being reproduced were that of a single, sustained musical note, the motions would be repetitious—each new motion being almost identical with the previous motions. Under these circumstances, the motions of the portions of the cone observed in the movie would be almost identical to the motions observed in a flexible card attached to springs in the manner shown in Fig. 1.1. Because of the similarity of its motion the arrangement in Fig. 1.1 will be used to analyze the vibratory motion. The advantage of transferring the analysis to the motion of the card and springs is that the natural rate of motion here allows a direct measurement of characteristics. The characteristics useful in describing the card's motion might then be recognized and observed with further meaning in the motions of the speaker cone.

When a vibrating system comes to rest as vibrations cease, the system is said to have reached the *conditions of equilibrium.*

The term system as used above refers to all of the materials and parts that in any way contribute to a given phenomenon.

A convenient point of reference which can be marked on a moving part of the system is chosen for purposes of keeping track of the motion. Under conditions of equilibrium the position of the chosen reference point is marked as the *equilibrium position.* This mark is a stationary point of reference when measuring other characteristics of a vibratory motion. Point *E* in Fig. 1.1 represents

A loudspeaker designed for reproduction of voice and music. The sound of a radio can be traced to the cone of the loudspeaker. [*Courtesy of the Radio Corporation of America.*]

Figure 1.1

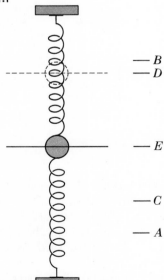

the equilibrium position of a reference point at the edge of the card.

Before a vibration can start, some influence from outside the system must initiate the action. The system represented in Fig. 1.1 could be set into motion by the action of a person pulling the card downward by hand from *E* to *A* and then releasing it. After the initial action the card would be seen to periodically repeat the following set of general motions:

1. An upward motion with increasing speed from *A* toward *E*,
2. After moving past *E*, an upward motion with decreasing speed from *E* toward *B*,
3. A momentary stop at *B*,
4. A downward motion with increasing speed from *B* toward *E*,
5. After again moving past *E*, a downward motion with decreasing speed from *E* toward *A*,
6. A momentary stop at *A*.

The series of motions described above constitute one *cycle* of vibration. The sequence of events which constitutes a cycle repeats with each vibration. Repetitious events, of course, are not confined to vibrating systems. Any series of events (for instance, the apparent revolution of the moon around the earth or the rise and fall of the tides) which repeat themselves over and over may be called cyclic events.

The average number of cycles that are counted during a given unit of time is the characteristic of a cyclic phenomenon called the *frequency*. The unit of measure for frequency of a vibration is *cycles per second* (cps). For example, if 90 cycles of vibration are counted during one minute, the frequency would be computed as follows:

$$\frac{90 \text{ cycles}}{60 \text{ sec}} = 1.5 \text{ cps}$$

The average time required for completing one cycle of events is the characteristic called the *period*. The unit of measure for the period of a vibration is *seconds per cycle*. Under the conditions described in the example above, the period would be computed as follows:

$$\frac{60 \text{ sec}}{90 \text{ cycles}} = \tfrac{2}{3} \text{ sec per cycle}$$

Obviously, the relationship between the frequency and the period of a given vibratory motion is one of reciprocals; that is:

$$(1.1) \qquad \text{period} = \frac{1}{\text{frequency}}$$

$$(1.2) \qquad \text{frequency} = \frac{1}{\text{period}}$$

The general description of the motions which constitute a cycle of vibration indicates that the motion of the reference point is limited to the space between the points of momentary stopping. At any given instant the position of the reference point within this space could be measured by its displacement with respect to the equilibrium position. The term *displacement* denotes the direction and the measured distance between the equilibrium position and the instantaneous location of the reference point. Directions of displacements are conventionally indicated as positive or negative. Directions toward the right of the observer or upward are indicated as positive or (+) displacements from the position of equilibrium. Directions toward the left or downward are indicated as negative or (−) displacements. For example, in Fig. 1.2, when the card is at point C the

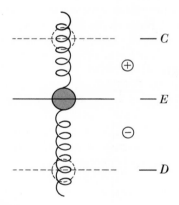

Figure 1.2

displacement might be measured to be 1.2 inches upward from E or simply +1.2 inches. When the card is at point D, the displacement might be measured to be 1.5 inches downward from E or simply −1.5 inches.

The maximum displacements during a given cycle are called the *amplitudes* of the vibration. In Fig. 1.1, the displacement from E to A represents the $(-)$ amplitude. The displacement from E to B represents the $(+)$ amplitude.

Using the descriptive characteristics provided thus far, the motions of the vibrating card during a given segment of time might be described very simply as follows: the card had an up and down motion with a period of $\frac{2}{3}$ sec per cycle and amplitudes ranging from ± 1.9 inches during the first cycle to ± 1.7 inches during the last cycle measured.

Descriptive characteristics are useful only for identifying the phenomenon and for communicating information about the events of the phenomenon. They do not explain, for instance, what was added to the system from the outside source which initiated the action. They do not explain what keeps the motion going, nor why the motion eventually is brought to a halt. More dynamic characteristics are needed to explain the phenomenon. These dynamic characteristics usually involve one or more descriptive characteristics in combination with other characteristics that owe their meaning to relationships found in certain classes of events as, for instance, all events in which objects are moved from one location to another.

Time out for organizing thoughts Before pursuing further the ideas reaching toward explanation, we should be reminded that this pursuit is not an altogether haphazard task. Knowledge is an outgrowth of achieving sets of reliable characteristics with which to identify relationships and to give an integrated meaning with regard to the nature of the matters under study. The related characteristics originate in the minds of men, but the reliability of these characteristics is determined only through a thorough appraisal of the accuracy of their supposed descriptions. In science a systematic reference is made to measured outcomes as compared with the expected outcomes based upon the supposed relationships. The relationships are confirmed or denied as a result of these comparisons. The rapid growth of scientific explanation has been accomplished by activities of invention and verification. In a very real sense each individual must originate and confirm his own sets of meanings in spite of all the available guides, such as this and other books, which outline successful activities of investigation. Each individual through thought and action discovers meanings and confirms them to his own personal satisfaction.

The present investigation was instigated by the remark that the source of sound is a vibrating body. Thoughtful appraisal of the meanings attached to the ideas concerning vibrating bodies led to setting up certain measurable characteristics with which to describe the phenomenon of vibration. It was hoped that demarcating certain descriptive properties of vibratory motion might make other discoveries possible. For instance, when vibratory motion cannot be directly observed accompanying sound, the imaginative mind can make vibratory action a possibility even though invisible media may be involved. The problem of explanation where direct observation is denied necessarily becomes much more abstract. Thus, the confirmation or rejection of supposed relationships depends upon the required certainty that designated conditions are necessary to provide explanation and that these conditions are demonstrated facts in the relationships being investigated.

That measurable characteristics are but anchorage points from which to chart further explorations might be illustrated in the descriptions that follow.

The suggestion has been raised that the periods of vibrating systems are constant and that the amplitudes are symmetrical and are measured from a centrally located position of equilibrium. One must be prepared to vary these supposed conditions to fit observed facts. Not every vibrating system has an unvarying period, nor are centrally located equilibrium positions a requirement. A bouncing ball, for example, has a sequence of motions that is repeated over and over again. The motions are therefore cyclic; but the cycles do not have equal periods. Investigation shows that in bouncing balls as the heights of the bounces diminish so do the periods. Also, the amplitudes during a given cycle are not symmetrical. Under conditions of equilibrium the ball comes to rest in contact with the surface against which it has been bouncing. Therefore, the negative amplitude is equal only to the amount the ball is flattened during contact with the surface as it bounces. The positive amplitude takes the ball into the space above the surface. The negative and positive amplitudes during a given cycle are not equally displaced from a centrally located equilibrium position. The discrepancies in the cycle of the bouncing ball, however, do not upset the meanings attached to the descriptive characteristics used. The meanings, rather, are enriched by the fact that these characteristics can now serve to distinguish between the several types of cyclic motions.

The motion that has been described for the system diagramed in Fig. 1.1 is called *simple harmonic motion*. Obviously, this is not the only possible type of vibratory motion; but it is the only type which may be associated with a musical sound consisting of a single note without overtones. The choice of simple harmonic motion was made because the essential characteristics of this type of vibration are the most easily analyzed. Once given meaning these characteristics can be used to describe more complicated motions.

Continuing the investigation Clues to the conditions necessary for sustaining vibration in a system can be gathered by personal contact with such a system. When supplying the pull which starts a vibration, one learns that some of the materials in the system have the qualities of elasticity. An elastic material not only resists distortion, it also has the faculty of restoring its shape after it has been distorted. The resistance to distortion is measured by the amount of pull needed to increase the displacement. In elastic materials the greater the displacement becomes, the greater must be the pull needed to increase the displacement.

Exerting a push or a pull in order to move an object from one position to another is a very common experience. The word *force* is used to express the idea that a push or a pull has been acting. To exert a force without meeting an opposition is impossible. For example, recall the confusion that results if the rope breaks under the tension of battle in a tug-of-war. The opposition produced by an elastic system, however, has characteristic qualities of its own. First, the force needed to counteract the opposition is directly proportional to the displacement which has been achieved previously. (See the graph in Table 1.1.) Second, if after distorting the system,

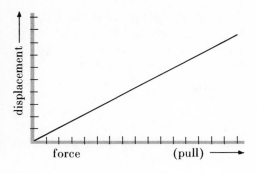

TABLE 1.1

one backs off slowly so as to oppose the restoring process, the restoring force is felt to diminish proportionately as the displacement is reduced until both the force and the motion in the system cease at the position of equilibrium.

In view of these experiences with force and opposition in elastic materials, it would be reasonable to expect that when the system is released to take on its vibratory motion, the restoring force supplied by the springs must be acting against some kind of opposition although different from that which was supplied in the backing-off process mentioned above. A great deal more will be said in later chapters about this type of opposition of objects that are free to move. For the present, an insight into the prevailing conditions can be gained from attempting to stop the vibratory motion abruptly once it has been set into motion, or to start the motion abruptly once it has come to rest. If, as shown in Fig. 1.3, one were to attach a lightweight cotton thread to the central mass of the vibrating system, the distorting force could be exerted by pulling the thread slowly downward. Releasing one's grip on the thread would start the vibration. Seeking to stop the motion abruptly one could grasp the thread and hold tightly. The

result is invariably a broken thread. *When the system is in motion it strongly resists coming rapidly to rest.* In a similar way, had the distorting force been exerted by a rapid jerk downward upon the thread, the thread would have been broken with but a slight effect upon the system. *When the system is at rest it strongly resists a rapid increase in motion.* These qualities of resistance to rapid changes in the state of motion are called *inertia.*

The qualities of elasticity and inertia are essential characteristics to be found among the constituent parts of all vibrating systems.

Composite characteristics The action of a force which moves an opposing object from one location to another is designated as *work.* In a strict sense, a force which

Figure 1.3

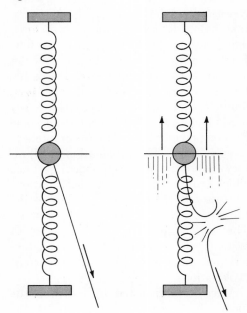

does not produce displacement of an object does not accomplish any work. The amount of work is calculated by multiplying the amounts of the measured quantities of the two characteristics involved—force times displacement. For example, if a pull equal to that needed to lift a 2-pound weight produces a movement of an object through a displacement of 4 feet in the direction of the pull, the amount of work accomplished would be calculated as follows:

(1.3) force $\times$ displacement = work

$$2 \text{ lb} \times 4 \text{ ft} = 8 \text{ foot pounds}$$

The *foot pound* is a unit of work. Other units for measuring work will be introduced when the need arises.

The ability to do work is a definition of *energy*. Energy is a characteristic of a system or a phenomenon rather than of an object. The constituent materials and parts which make up a system determine which of many forms of energy may characterize the system. Energy can take many different forms such as heat, light, and sound, to mention but a few. Energy while changing forms provides a major clue concerning interactions between different systems. It has been found that more often than not many individual but related systems become the component parts of more comprehensive systems. The explanation of vibratory motion involves component systems which provide the energy transformations necessary to do the work of completing the cyclic actions of the vibrating system. The descriptions of the component systems will be limited to those characteristics necessary for the current explanations.

After being distorted, by providing the force which moves components of the system from one place to another, an elastic material is doing work. The distorted material, therefore, has the ability to do work; that is, the material possesses energy. The components containing the elastic materials are, therefore, a system capable of transforming energy. The term *elastic system* shall be used to refer to the components that provide elasticity.

The elastic system does work in overcoming the inertia of the components that are free to move in the total vibrating system. Once in motion, these moving parts in turn do the work of again distorting the elastic system. Hence, the moving components comprise a system capable of transforming energy. The term *inertial system* shall be used to refer to the components that provide inertia.

If the elastic system and the inertial system were the only component systems available to interact during the energy transformations of vibratory motion, the vibrating system, once set in motion, would continue to vibrate indefinitely. Even casual observation, however, reveals that vibrating systems do not continue vibrations indefinitely. But only the most careful observations and critical thinking reveal clues to explain these declining activities.

Careful measurements under controlled conditions have revealed that energy is a constant quantity in the interactions between well-defined systems. This principle of constant quantity of energy has been extended to test for possible relationships in complex systems. These tests have brought under observation a multiplicity of component systems in order to maintain constant energy audits. The clues that reveal the characteristics which define the component systems are the evidences of changes taking place in the vicinity of known energy transformations. For example, careful investigation for changes in the vicinity of vibrating systems reveals changes in the temperature of component parts and of surrounding materials. Changes in air pressure near to the card also are observed. These changes are characteristic properties of systems involved in transformation of the energies of heat and sound, respectively. The conclusion is that the energy becoming unavailable to the elastic and inertial systems has reappeared in other forms that are the properties of other systems. This may be a decisive clue to the investigation we are making with regard to vibrating bodies and sound.

Conservation of energy The evidence persists that energy is a basic entity. Over and over again, energy transformation has been found to be one of the primary conditions leading to the explanation of phenomena taking place in in the universe. Some of the great discoveries in science such as relativity, radioactivity, and nuclear power have been brought about by the conceptual inventions necessary to account for the energy transformation in the given phenomena. The principle prompting these inventions is expressed as the *principle of conservation of energy*: "Energy can neither be created nor destroyed. It only can be transformed from one form to that of another form."

Potential and kinetic energy A study of the graphs in Table 1.2 will introduce several relationships between time, displacements, forces, and velocities in a

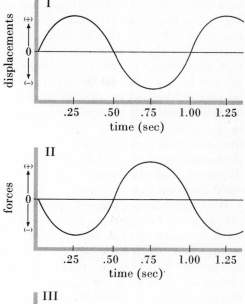

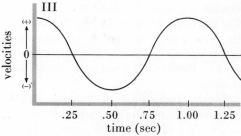

TABLE 1.2

vibrating system. The positive and negative signs shown in the graphs refer to the directions taken by the quantities so indicated on the vertical axis. The quantitative amounts are indicated by the relative distances above and below the central zero line. The horizontal axis is calibrated in units of time as indicated. Zero time was marked at the instant that the reference point while moving upward passed through its equilibrium position.

The data for the graphs was supplied

by a system similar to that diagramed in Fig. 1.1. The indicated period was 1 sec per cycle. Hence, the frequency was 1 cycle per sec. Observing the simultaneous changes recorded in Graphs I, II, and III we find that during the first quarter of the period: (a) the displacement increased from zero to its maximum in an upward direction; (b) the force increased from zero to its maximum in a downward direction; and (c) the velocity decreased from its maximum in an upward direction to zero.

With reference to Fig. 1.1, during the first quarter of the period as the displacement increases upward, the lower spring is stretched. The indicated increase in downward force is the result of the distortion of the lower spring. This downward force opposes the motion of the inertial system reducing the velocity to zero when the point of maximum displacement is reached. The force is always directed toward the equilibrium position.

Under conditions of maximum displacement, maximum distortion has taken place in the elastic system. Therefore, as indicated by the conditions of maximum force, at this time the elastic systems have the greatest potential to do work. This ability to do work resulting from distortion in an elastic system is referred to as *potential energy*. The potential energy of the elastic system is directly proportional to the force and is, therefore, reduced to zero at such times that the combined forces equal zero.

As indicated by the graphs, under conditions of minimum displacement the velocities in the inertial system reach maximum proportions. The ability to do work resulting from the inertial resistance against forces that would reduce the velocities of the parts of the inertial system is referred to as *kinetic energy*. The kinetic energy of the inertial system is reduced to zero when the velocities are zero.

The kinetic energy of an inertial system is greatest when the velocities within that system are greatest. The potential energy of an elastic system is greatest when the restoring forces within that system are greatest. An interpretation of the graphs in Table 1.2 will show that in terms of time the maximum potential energy of the elastic system occurs at the time when the kinetic energy of the inertial system is zero; and the maximum kinetic energy of the inertial system occurs at the time when the potential energy of the elastic system is zero. As one might expect under these circumstances, the energy build-up in one system is always at the expense of an energy depletion in the other system. The work of producing the vibratory motion is the result of the energy transformations occurring between these two component systems within the total vibrating system.

The preceding paragraphs were intended as an introduction to the meanings of potential and kinetic energy rather than as a complete definition of these important energy relationships. Added meanings will accrue as broader applications are made in other explanations involving the energy forms.

Defining energy in terms of the ability to do work is only one of many possible definitions of energy. And this definition, like all of the others, places the meanings of energy in the realm of expectancies rather than of observable quantities. There is no other way to measure amounts of energy than in terms of the changes that take place during the processes of energy transformation.

Hence, by the time measurement is completed, the involved energy has assumed new forms. The transformed energies have new meanings based upon expected outcomes which should take place if certain processes occur.

We have given thought to the meanings of potential and kinetic energies in terms of the ability to do work. The ability to do work is not limited exclusively to transformations of these two energy forms, nor is doing work the only change that can take place when these energies are transformed. The suggestion has been made that temperature changes and pressure disturbances also accompany the energy transformation of vibratory motion. Changes in temperature and pressure disturbances are properties associated with the energies of heat and sound, respectively.

DYNAMIC EXPLANATIONS

Almost everyone has at some time tried to break a length of wire or a piece of metal by flexing it back and forth around a crease at the place one wished to achieve the break. Touching the metal near where it had been flexed gives ample evidence that the flexed materials increased in temperature. This change in temperature occurred because some of the energy being transformed in doing the work of flexing the metal was converted into heat.

In the vibrating system that we have been studying, the distortion of the elastic materials in the springs is a flexing action. Therefore, when the elastic materials are being periodically distorted we should expect that some of the energy being transformed in doing this work would be converted into heat. The fact that the temperature of the springs increases during the time of vibration confirms the above hypothesis. The transformation of energy from the vibrating system into heat contributes greatly to the decreasing action and final stopping of the vibratory motion

Another familiar experience is suggested by the motions of the card attached to our vibrating system. A flat surface such as a piece of cardboard used to fan the air will produce gusts of wind. Wind consists of comparatively large bodies of air that have been set into motion. Therefore, the argument can be made that wind has kinetic energy.

The kinetic energy of the gusts of wind set into motion by the card in the vibrating system has been transformed from the energy of the system. Hence, the fanning by the card also contributes to the decreasing vibratory action and bringing to rest the motion of the vibrating system. By varying the size of the card attached to the vibrating system the amount of wind produced per cycle can be controlled. The larger the area of the card, the greater will be the amount of energy transformed per cycle of a given amplitude. The greater energy transformation of large cards would bring the vibration to rest in a shorter time.

The initial explanation of the major conditions contributing to the observed motions of a vibrating system has now been completed. If any conclusion can be reached from this explanation, it is that energy transformation is a major concept used in explaining phenomena where the ability to do work is gained or lost by a defined system. However, we should be reminded that one's meanings for the characteristics that define the relationships between systems should be held open for additions and corrections of meanings as future observations may demand.

INTERPRETATION—THE RUDDER FOR INVESTIGATION

Our inquiry was not instigated to learn of energy transformations associated with vibrating systems. The goal of our investigation was to discover whether or not there are essential relationships between vibrating bodies and the production of sound. The investigation branched out rapidly from consideration of known locations of sound production to the specific nature of motion in the cone of a loudspeaker; to the similar motions of a more easily analyzed vibrating system; to the descriptive characteristics of vibratory motion, and so on and on. Many explanations were set forth to aid in understanding the relationships encountered as the investigation proceeded and many insights into future procedures of investigation were introduced. But the goal of an investigation is not to accumulate explanations and insights without purpose. Therefore, from time to time, it is proper to take stock of one's progress toward a stated objective. Whenever possible, a trial solution or hypothesis should be made. The relationships one has learned should be extended to attempt an explanation under the conditions specified by the problem. The validity of one's choice of meanings can then be interpreted when used to cope with the given situation so that activities leading either to verification or to redirection can take place.

The goal of our present investigation

has never been completely out of sight. Nevertheless, the time has come to turn our attentions more specifically toward our objective. Do all sounds actually originate in vibrating bodies?

Source of sound In a physical sense sound is a form of energy. For that reason, the source of sound must be an energy transformation. Vibrating systems, such as the loudspeaker cone, are explained in terms of energy transformations. Although we referred to the motions observed in slow-motion movies of the cone as being similar to the motions described for the card in Fig. 1.1, the actual motion of the cone has much shorter amplitudes and a much shorter period than those of the card. For example, our sample calculations for the frequency of the vibrating system containing the card showed a typical value of 1.5 cycles per sec. A loudspeaker cone might have frequencies ranging from 50 to 5000 cycles per sec. The shorter periods of the cone would require comparatively high elastic forces in the elastic system as compared to low inertial components in the inertial system, in order that the more rapid energy transformations could take place. At the present moment our interest does not concern the processes of the energy transformations taking place within the vibrating system of the loudspeaker. It is enough to know that vibration takes place. The vibratory motion requires energy transformation in which possibly some energy might be converted to sound if the required conditions for such a transformation are present.

In our example of vibratory motion, the card fanning the air produced gusts of wind carrying kinetic energy. Wind, however, is not the only possible result of energy transformations that can be supported by air. All materials—gases, liquids, and solids—are composed of molecules which are characterized as particles moving at high speeds in a highly random manner. The motion of molecules is generally confined within the boundaries of the bodies containing them. In gaseous materials, of which air is one example, pressure on the boundary surfaces results from the combined action of the billions of molecules that repeatedly bounce against the surfaces involved. The greater the number of gas molecules that strike a surface per unit of time, the greater is the pressure registered in that region of the body of gas. The randomness of the molecular motions, however, is such that a rapid distribution of molecules occurs which would equalize any pressure variations that might occur within a homogeneous body of gas. Only certain influences by systems outside of the body of gas can produce even momentary discrepancies in the density of numbers of molecules in localized regions of the gas.

Any motion in a system outside the body of gas which would produce a momentary change in the number of molecules in a given region of the gas would accordingly change the pressure in that portion of the gas. Because the average speed of the gas molecules is greater than the speed of the motion producing the disturbance, a ripple of pressure variation would move outward in all directions away from the region disturbed. The ripple would be carried forward at the average speed of the gas molecules involved. Upon striking the boundary surfaces between the body of gas and other systems, the pressure ripple can do work which indicates an energy transformation. Periodic succession of pressure ripples of this type are a characteristic process in systems that support the energy of sound.

The nature of sound is the subject of the investigation in Chapter 2, therefore, no further description of sound will be given at this time.

In a loudspeaker cone the vibrating surfaces that make contact with the air periodically sweep out the molecules from the regions comprising the amplitudes of vibration. These momentary dislocations of air molecules set up the conditions necessary to send periodic pressure ripples into the air. Thus, in the action of sweeping out molecules, some of the energy of the vibrating sections of the cone is transformed into sound.

The essential conditions A meaningful and verifiable relationship has been established between the motions of a loudspeaker cone and the production of sound. The relationship involves transforming some of the kinetic energy of certain sections of the cone into sound. This relationship is not unique to a loudspeaker. It is a matter of common observation that many devices support the production of sound. The numerous types of musical instruments are examples to prove this point. Also, it is obvious that not every situation involving energy transformation produces sound. For example, sound is noticeably absent in situations such as the conversion of electricity to heat in a stove, the exchange of potential and kinetic energies in a swinging pendulum, and the conversion of light to heat from a heat lamp. Furthermore, it can be demonstrated that vibrations by themselves do not assure a transformation of energy into sound. For example, the situation shown in Fig. 1.4 has a ringing bell inside a bell jar from which air can be evacuated. As the air is pumped out of the jar the sound becomes weaker and finally disappears. The motions of ringing are observed to continue inside the jar, but no sound can be heard. The foregoing observations effectively point out the fact that sound is produced only when certain conditions prevail in the situations producing energy transformations. What are these conditions essential to production of sound?

A deductive analysis can be made by the process of deleting all of the unnecessary details from the description of the operations producing sound in the loudspeaker. The following indicates the conditions essential for explaining the production of sound:

1. Periodic changes of short duration in the motions of objects where the materials in motion make contact with the molecular boundary surfaces of a body composed of materials which can transmit sound.

Figure 1.4

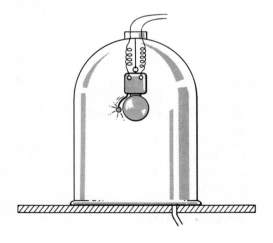

2. A transformation of energy as explained by the work done in increasing and decreasing momentarily the density in numbers of molecules in a region of the transmitting materials.

When the above conditions of contact and energy transformations apply we should expect that some of the energy being transformed would be converted into sound. Whether the energy thus converted becomes sound that can be heard is another matter. We might have to extend our meanings for sound beyond the limited range of human sense organs.

UNFINISHED BUSINESS

The end of a chapter does not terminate the learning with regard to the topics being discussed. Important questions have been raised that have been left unanswered. We have indicated that our thoughts may return to some of these questions at a more opportune time. Raising questions is a natural outgrowth of inquiry. Sorting out the questions which most likely will lead to important explanations is a studied outgrowth of scientific activities. Choosing fruitful questions to guide the inquiries of certain classes of students is one of the functions of books about scientific topics. The function of the student is to use these inquiries to organize for himself a fuller awareness of the world in which he lives and the possibilities for further action which this awareness brings. Curiosity and reasoned search activities lead to a possibility of choices in meanings for given situations and are the more intelligent pathways to the freedom and progress which only awareness can bring about.

If the reader has allowed himself to become challenged by the activities of inquiry, he should now be particularly curious to place to the test of application the essential conditions set forth in explanation of the production of sound. Elementary situations for production of sound such as the beating of a drum, the blowing across the mouth of a bottle, the blowing through a reed, the plucking of a string, and the blowing through the rotating holes of a simple siren should be used in the beginning. The more complex devices of sound production are usually found to be combinations of several of the more elementary situations. A thorough test involves planned activities such as are outlined below:

Observation. Observe or recall a recent observation of the chosen situation.

Reasoned Search Activities. Describe the devices and the phenomena involved in the chosen situation in terms of meaningful characteristics that are known to be useful in showing the relationships likely to support the conditions being tested.

Prediction. Demonstrate by measurement or performance that the related characteristics can and do exist in the situations chosen.

Assimilation or Correction. If verification is demonstrated, recount other devices that are supported by similar situations, thereby expanding the application. If the verification fails, search for and correct possible interferences of the performance, or redirect the search activities to discover more useful relationships than those previously tested.

SUMMARY

The qualities of elasticity and inertia are essential characteristics of some of the constituent parts in all vibrating systems. Vibratory motion is described in terms of the period of vibration, the directions of motion, and the amplitudes of the motion about the position of equilibrium. After receiving energy from an outside source, the elastic system and the inertial system interact during the ensuing vibratory motion, each doing work on the other and thereby transforming the energy necessary to sustain the motion in the vibrating system of which they are a part. The ability to do work resulting from distortion in an elastic system is referred to as *potential energy*. The ability to do work resulting from the inertial resistance in moving bodies to the action of forces which would slow them is referred to as *kinetic energy*. The vibratory motion does not go on indefinitely because the energy is transformed into energy forms which are properties of systems not related to sustaining the vibration. The vibratory motion stops when the energy of vibration is transformed into heat, or other forms such as wind or sound.

The conditions for explaining the production of sound are an interaction between vibrating systems and the molecules of materials which can transmit sound and a transformation of energy when the vibrating system does the work of increasing and decreasing the numbers of molecules interacting.

PROBLEMS

1 A vibrating system similar to that shown in Fig. 1.1 was set into motion. The following data describes the time and displacement from the position at equilibrium of a reference point on the system. Make a graph of this motion similar to Table 1.2.

Time (sec)	Displacement (cm)	Time (sec)	Displacement (cm)
0.00	0.0	0.75	−7.1
0.05	2.6	0.80	−8.7
0.10	5.0	0.85	−9.6
0.15	7.1	0.90	−10.0
0.20	8.7	0.95	−9.6
0.25	9.6	1.00	−8.7
0.30	10.0	1.05	−7.1
0.35	9.6	1.10	−5.0
0.40	8.7	1.15	−2.6
0.45	7.1	1.20	0.0
0.50	5.0	1.25	2.6
0.55	2.6	1.30	5.0
0.60	0.0	1.35	7.1
0.65	−2.6	1.40	8.7
0.70	−5.0	1.45	9.6

2 What was the amplitude of vibration of the reference point used in the above example? How did you determine this value?

3 What was the period and frequency of vibration of the system described in Problem 1? How did you determine these values?

4 From your graph estimate the displacement at 0.075 seconds and at 0.775 seconds.

5 Predict the displacement at 1.60 seconds and at 1.75 seconds. What clues did you use in making your predictions?

6 Explain the conditions which describe the elastic system and the inertial system associated with a vibratory motion. Give examples of these systems and indicate the evidences which prove the stated conditions exist in these examples.

7 What is the relationship between the principle of conservation of energy and explaining vibratory motion?

8 What is the relationship between the principle of conservation of energy and explaining the production of sound?

9 Explain the relationship between molecular motion and the production of sound.

2

NATURE OF SOUND

The word "sound" has two sources of meaning: that associated with the sensation of hearing and that associated with the phenomenon capable of stimulating the sensation of hearing.   Hearing is essential for adequate communication with our surroundings.   Much of what we learn from associating with other people is stimulated by speech.   The world of music is a powerful stimulant affecting our moods and emotions.   An ever increasing recognition is being given to the effect of noise in our lives.   Properly, the meanings associated with the sensation of hearing are in the province of psychology and the arts.   Therefore, in this study of physical science we shall be more directly concerned with the phenomenon that stimulates the sense of hearing, although we cannot completely ignore those meanings associated with the sensation.   Since most of us live in a "booming, bustling" world of sound, our curiosities are continually being aroused as our reactions to sounds help or hinder interpretation of our surroundings.

EVERYDAY OBSERVATIONS ABOUT SOUND

Many characteristics of sound seem almost self-evident after giving the matter some thought. Consider the following examples:

1. Sound travels in straight lines from the source to the observer. We rely on this observation to establish the direction from us to many objects which give off sound. The fact that search in the direction indicated locates the object tends to confirm the straight line motion of sound.
2. Sound travels more slowly than light. This fact is strikingly illustrated in this age of jet planes. The direction indicated by the sound does not lead us to the present location of the plane.
3. All types of sound travel at the same speed in a given material. Loud sounds, soft sounds, high pitched sounds, and low pitched sounds travel at the same rate of speed. Hence, all the sounds from a band or orchestra remain blended in the same sequence at the end of their journey as they had when they left the band shell.
4. The loudness of sound diminishes rapidly as the observer becomes further removed from the source of the sound.
5. Sound can induce resonance. When a person sings or whistles loudly into a piano, we may find that the piano strings have been placed into motion to the extent that we hear the pitch of the sung or whistled sound being repeated back to us from the piano. This sound is not an echo. The piano strings involved were set into motion by the sound directed into the instrument.

Sound as energy Resonance can be demonstrated more simply by mounting two tuning forks of like frequency on resonator boxes as shown in Fig. 2.1. Striking the fork at A with a mallet will produce a sound which travels to B

Figure 2.1

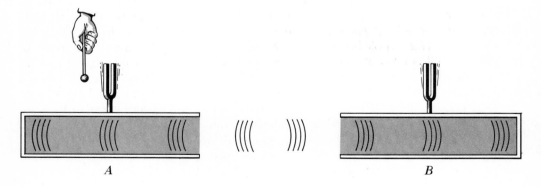

A

B

setting the fork there into vibration. The vibrating fork at B produces sound which can be heard easily if the fork at A is stopped. Because work was done in placing the fork at B into vibrating motion, energy (the ability to do work) must have been transferred from system A to system B. *The propagation of energy from one place to another must be a function of sound.*

This raises the question of the nature of the process by which the transfer can be explained in a manner which also gives meaning to the many observations that one can make relative to the propagation of sound.

Sound and material media Transmission of sound takes place only in material media. The presence of materials whether gas, liquid, or solid is an absolute requirement for sound. The situation of the ringing bell within an evacuated bell jar as was shown in Fig. 1.4 illustrated that sound does not travel through a vacuum.

As to propagation of energy, there can be only two means by which energy of motion could be transferred from one place to another by material means. Either the vibrating source throws chunks of materials in all directions away from itself much like a lawn sprinkler throws showers of water drops through the air; or the vibrating source disturbs an elastic medium much like water waves are sent outward on the surface of water from the place where a pebble was dropped into the pool. In either way, motion could be transferred from the source to other objects not in direct contact with the source.

While there is nothing positively absurd about the idea of a tuning fork throwing chunks of material through the

air from itself to the ear of a listener, the analogous occurrence in water or in a solid would be most difficult to imagine. In view of the greater ease for acceptance, we should choose perhaps to investigate the wave disturbance alternative for a possible explanation of energy transfer through materials. In preparing to understand the possible relationships, it would be wise, therefore, to learn more about wave motions and about the molecular structure of matter.

CHARACTERISTICS OF WAVES IN MATTER

Observe or bring into mind the manner in which water waves spread out upon the water surface around a *point* of disturbance. Expanding circular waves are formed and the advancing wave is characterized by a *circular wave front*. If a straight edged object rather than a point were producing the disturbance, the advancing water waves would have no curvature and hence would be characterized by a *plane wave front*.

When a small segment of a circular wave front is observed after the wave has expanded through a considerable distance from its source, the great curvature of the wave front makes a small segment of it seem almost straight. Therefore, after a wave front has traveled some distance, the wave segments can be looked upon essentially as a plane wave front. This type of relationship will be referred to again in a later section of this book.

Calling upon imagination one could expand the idea of surface waves fitting the pattern into a three dimensional continuum. With the help of imagination one could picture a spherical balloon-like ob-

Wave disturbances on the surface of water.

ject vibrating internally while completely immersed in a material medium. This vibrating sphere would emit spherical waves expanding out in all directions of space away from the source. Because of their shape these waves would be characterized by *spherical wave fronts* moving out as if they were giant expanding balloons.

We shall be called upon to use spherical waves in explaining the distribution of sound.

Types of wave disturbance Observe the motion of a piece of cork floating on water which is supporting waves originating in a periodic vibration. As wave after wave

moves outward, the piece of cork remains relatively unmoved. When observed more critically, the piece of cork is seen to rise with the bulge of each wave front, move forward riding the bulge for a short distance, and then dropping into the trough between succeeding wave fronts while retreating to its original position. This action is repeated with the passing of each wave. When the wave motion stops, the cork is found resting at the position it had before the disturbance began.

Obviously, the cork has followed the motion of the water particles in which it floats. The observed motions of the cork indicate that *only the wave forms proceed continuously outward, the particles of the*

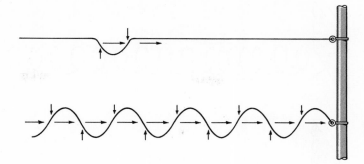

Figure 2.2

medium remain relatively stationary. A wave is but a temporary change in the shape or condition of the materials of the supporting medium. Since the medium is required to restore its shape after the disturbance, the system comprising the medium must have qualities of elasticity.

Waves are classified on the basis of how the particles of the medium seem to move with reference to the direction in which the wave front proceeds.

1. *A transverse wave* is one in which the particles of the medium are displaced at right angles to the direction in which the wave front proceeds. A visual demonstration of a transverse wave can be had by holding one end of a length of rope in the hand as shown in Fig. 2.2 and moving the hand back and forth sidewise. A single sidewise thrust will send a single pulse moving along the rope. A periodic and prolonged back and forth movement of the hand will send a series of transverse waves moving along the length of the rope.

2. *A compressional (longitudinal) wave* is one in which the particles of the medium are displaced back and forth in line with the direction in which the

wave front proceeds. A visual demonstration of a compressional wave can be had by attaching a long spiral spring to supports as shown in Fig. 2.3. If the support at one end is struck a sharp blow with a mallet, the end of the spring will be compressed longitudinally and this compressional pulse will travel along the spring. If the support is struck periodically, a *wave train* of compressions and rarefactions will travel along the spring.

3. The motions described for the piece of cork on water had characteristics of both longitudinal and transverse motion. Actually the line of motion of the water particles near the surface was elliptical with respect to the direction of wave propagation. This motion is referred to as a *gravitational wave.*

COMPRESSIONAL WAVES OF SOUND

In order to transmit a transverse wave the medium must have elastic qualities to restore its shape or condition after a *shearing action.* In other words, the medium

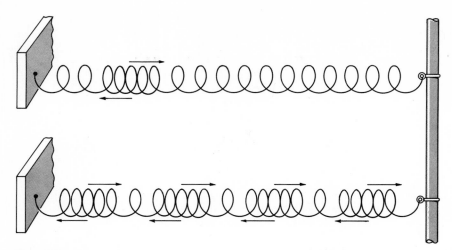

Figure 2.3

Figure 2.4

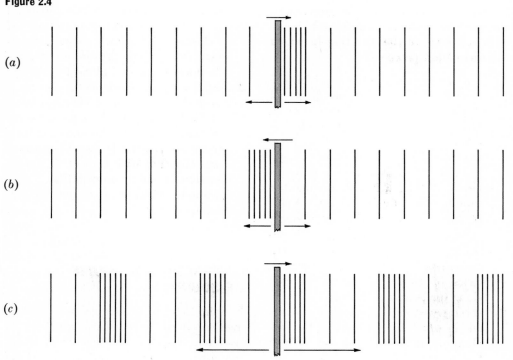

(a)

(b)

(c)

must resist the actions of being flexed or twisted. Only solid materials can resist and restore themselves after a shearing action. Gases and liquids very obviously can not be flexed or support a shearing stress. Transverse waves therefore are transmitted only through solids and are not found moving through gases or liquids.

Since sound generally is heard after transmission through air, it follows as the result of eliminating transverse waves from gases that sound can be explored most logically as a compressional wave. A clue supporting this decision was given in the study of sources of sound in Chapter 1. Fig. 2.4 gives a pictorial illustration of the relationship between the vibratory motions of a source and the resulting compressional wave motions. Fig. 2.4a illustrates the relationship that exists at the instant when the vibrating body passes through the equilibrium position. The motion is toward the right and the speed of the body is at the maximum. The forward surface of the vibrating body has swept out (reducing in number density) the molecules from the region on the left side of the body and has compressed (increasing in number density) the molecules into the region on the right side of the body. One-half cycle later, Fig. 2.4b, the vibrating body is moving toward the left through the equilibrium position. The result is a compression of molecules to the left of the body and a rarefaction of molecules on the right side. After a series of vibrations, the resulting regions of compression and rarefaction move as compressional waves in all directions away from the disturbing vibrator, Fig. 2.4c. As was learned in Chapter 1, some of the energy of the vibrating system is transformed into sound which is transmitted by these compressional waves.

When a more symmetrical vibrating body such as a bell is the indicated vibrator, it is less difficult to imagine that spherical wave fronts are expanding outward from the source. A cross section through such a three-dimensional pattern is represented by Fig. 2.5.

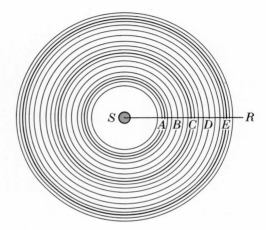

Figure 2.5

Pressure patterns Let us suppose that a series of sensitive pressure detectors have been placed at equal distance intervals along line SR in Fig. 2.5. If at a given instant, simultaneous readings were made of all the instruments, the recorded readings would furnish the data for a graph such as Graph I in Table 2.1. As is indicated in Graph I, the points of minimum and maximum pressures correspond to positions of rarefactions and compressions, respectively, in Fig. 2.5. The linear pressure changes were not abrupt. The pressures follow a pattern similar to that of the velocity changes shown in Graph III, Table 1.2, as well they should, being the results of a similar pattern of velocity. The major difference in the

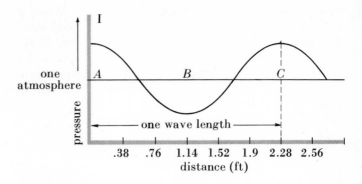

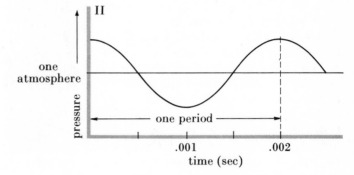

shapes of the graphs is that the pressure variations attenuate rapidly as the compressional waves expand outward from the source.

The pressure patterns indicated by the graphs in Table 2.1 will serve to define certain important descriptive characteristics of wave phenomena.

As shown in Graph I, the distance from one compression peak to the next following compression peak is called a *wavelength*. A wavelength represents the distance sound has traveled during one period of vibration of a stationary source. The distance of a wavelength could be measured between other points on the curve. For example, the displacement between two consecutive points of minimum pressure would also be a measure of the wavelength. Less complicated methods of determining the wavelength of sounds will be described later in this chapter.

Let us now suppose that a continuous record of the pressure variations moving past point *A* was made by one of the pressure detectors. If a stop watch were triggered by the first compressional peak that passed the detector and a count were made of each succeeding peak that passed during a time recorded by the stop watch, the frequency of compressional peaks could be calculated. Each succeeding peak would represent the passing of a wavelength of sound. The average number of wavelengths that pass the detector each second is called the *frequency* of the sound. Musicians might refer to frequency as *pitch*. The higher the pitch the greater are the number of wavelengths per second that reach the ear or other detector of sound.

In the same manner as in vibration, the reciprocal of the frequency of sound is called the *period* of the sound. The period is the time required for a wavelength to pass a given point. Graph II in Table 2.1 is the timed record of the pressure variations moving past point *A* in Fig. 2.5. The time recorded between two consecutive pressure peaks constitutes one period of sound. The relationship between the period and frequency of sound is the same as that recorded for the vibrating system in Chapter 1:

$$period = \frac{1}{frequency}$$

Because Graph I and Graph II are based on the same phenomenon, it would be logical to expect that relationships would be found between the two records. Referring to the units used in measuring wavelengths and periods gives clues to one of these relationships. The wavelength was defined as the distance that sound travels during one period of vibration of a stationary source. The period was defined as the time required for one wavelength to move past a stationary detector. The period of the wave motion must be equal to the period of vibration of the stationary source. The unit for measuring wavelengths could be *ft per wavelength*. The unit for measuring periods could be *sec per wavelength*. From our experiences traveling by automobile we should recall that miles per hour is a unit for measuring speed. Feet per second would be an equally acceptable unit for measuring speed. That is:

$$(2.1) \quad speed = \frac{distance\ traveled}{time\ of\ travel}$$

Dividing feet per wavelength by seconds per wavelength we get the unit for speed:

$$\frac{ft/wavelength}{sec/wavelength} = \frac{ft}{sec} = speed$$

Therefore,

$$(2.2) \quad speed\ of\ waves = \frac{wavelength}{period}$$

From equation (1.2) we know that frequency equals the reciprocal of the period. Hence, we also can use,

(2.3) speed of waves

$$= wavelength \times frequency$$

The speed of sound in air on a warm day, temperature 80°F, is about 1140 ft per second. The speed of sound changes with change in temperature, but at any given temperature the speed of sound in air remains constant.

Doppler effect In forming the definitions of wavelength and period in terms of the records in Graphs I and II, great care was taken to point out that the sound was transformed and detected at stationary points. Which is to say that the stipulation was made that the source and the observer remained a fixed distance apart during the time when the records were being made. Had the source and detectors been moving so that the distance between them was changed during the time of recording, the records would have yielded different measures of wavelength and period. To an observer, the effect of a motion relative to the source is heard as a change in pitch. All persons who can hear can recall some instances when a sounding whistle passed rapidly near at hand and thus recall the sudden shift in the pitch of the sound at the moment of passing. This change in frequency caused by the relative motions between source and observer is called the *Doppler effect*, enunciated by the Austrian physicist and mathematician Johann Christian Doppler (1803–1853).

Graph II in Table 2.2 illustrates the effect upon the wavelength produced by having a source moving toward the detector. Above Graph II is reproduced a replica of Graph I for sound from a stationary source. Graph II is a record of the effect produced when this same source is moving at a constant speed directly toward the detectors. The dis-

TABLE 2.2

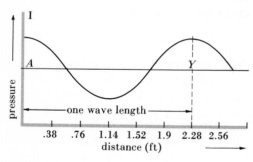

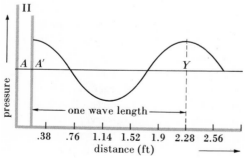

placement between A and A' in Graph II represents the distance through which the source moved during one period of its vibration. The maximum pressure wave front which left the source at the beginning of the recorded cycle, in each of the situations shown, moves forward at the speed of sound and reaches the points marked Y after one period of vibration. The point Y in each graph is of equal distance from the starting point at A. At the end of the period a second maximum pressure wave front would be leaving the stationary source at A. The distance from A to Y should be recognized as a wavelength. At the end of the period a second maximum pressure wave front also would be leaving the moving source, but from its new position at A'. The effect of the moving source was to shorten the wavelength by the displacement between A and A'. All waves leaving the moving source in the direction of its motion would be shortened similarly. Because the speed of sound remains constant at a given temperature, the ratio of wavelength to period of the wave motion would remain constant. Thus, as the wavelength decreases fractionally, the period of wave motion would decrease correspondingly, and the frequency of the sound waves would increase inversely.

In order to illustrate with numerical values the effect of a moving source upon the sound waves given off in the direction of its motion, let us calculate the wavelengths, periods, and frequencies using a typical set of data. We shall stipulate conditions such that the speed of sound in air is 1140 ft per second. The source in each situation has a frequency of 500 cycles per second. In the situation of motion the source is moving toward the detectors at a speed of 90 ft per second.

I. Source at Rest

$$\text{wavelength} = \frac{\text{speed of sound}}{\text{frequency}}$$

$$= \frac{1140 \text{ ft/sec}}{500 \text{ wavelengths/sec}}$$

$$= 2.28 \text{ ft/wavelength}$$

$$\text{period} = \frac{1}{\text{frequency}}$$

$$= \frac{1}{500 \text{ wavelengths/sec}}$$

$$= 0.002 \text{ sec/wavelength}$$

II. Source Moving Toward the Detectors

distance source moved per cycle

$$= \text{speed} \times \text{period of vibration}$$
$$A \text{ to } A' = 90 \text{ ft/sec} \times .002 \text{ sec/cycle}$$
$$= 0.18 \text{ ft/cycle}$$

wavelength = wavelength of stationary source minus distance source moved

$$\text{wavelength} = 2.28 \text{ ft} - 0.18 \text{ ft}$$
$$= 2.1 \text{ ft/wavelength}$$

$$\text{frequency} = \frac{\text{speed of sound}}{\text{wavelength}}$$

$$= \frac{1140 \text{ ft/sec}}{2.1 \text{ ft/wavelength}}$$

$$= 543 \text{ wavelengths/sec}$$

To the nearest whole numbers, the circumstances described above produced a noticeable 8.6 percent increase in the frequency of sound. This is a change in pitch somewhat greater than that of going from middle C to C# on a musical scale.

If the source were moving in the opposite direction, the effect would be to increase the wavelength by 0.18 ft with a corresponding decrease in frequency.

A change in frequency is noticed also when the observer moves toward or away from a stationary source of sound. Fundamentally, the effect here results from changing the apparent period per wavelength rather than changing the wavelengths of the sound. It is left as a problem for the student to explain why the frequency of sound changes for the moving observer.

The Doppler effect is not limited to sound waves in its applications. All waves that travel at constant speeds can show the Doppler effect. The major value of measurement involving Doppler effect is in determining relative speeds of objects when frequencies of wavelengths from the sources are known. We shall refer to these measurements when it suits our purpose.

We shall now return to the everyday observations about sound with which we opened this chapter in order to discuss these apparent facts in terms of the wave characteristics now indicated.

Straight line motion of sound Were it not for diffraction, reflection, and refraction, sound waves always would travel in a straight line path from source to observer.

That sound waves entering through an open window are heard in every part of the room is a well known fact. In situations like this the sound seems to come to the observer from the window opening as if the opening were the source of the sound waves. Apparently, the sound waves must bend around the edges of the window opening. This phenomenon is called *diffraction*. Fig. 2.6 illustrates the relative diffraction effects in small and large openings. Whether an opening is to be considered small or large depends not so much upon the actual size of the opening as it does upon the relative size of the wavelength of the sound with respect to the size of the opening. The

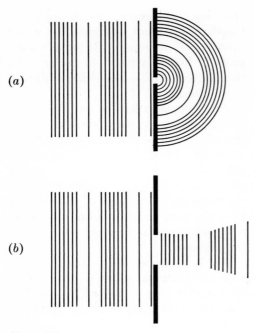

(a)

(b)

Figure 2.6

"small opening" effect as shown in Fig. 2.6a is produced when the opening is small with respect to the wavelength. Had the wavelength been smaller (sound of higher frequency) the opening at *a* would have seemed relatively large as shown at *b*. Although some diffraction is present at *b*, the effect is not as intense as at *a*. The relative size of an opening for diffraction of sound is very strikingly demonstrated if you should find yourself in a narrow alley when a band passes in parade on the adjoining street. As the band approaches the opening to the alley you can hear the bass notes quite distinctly but you must wait until the band is marching directly in front of the opening before the high pitched sounds are heard. For the long wavelength bass notes the opening to the alley resembles situation *a*, but for the shorter wavelength treble notes the

same opening resembles situation *b*. More explanation will be added to the phenomenon of diffraction in Chapter 3.

When sound waves which are traveling through a given material reach the boundary between it and other materials, part of the sound is *reflected* back into the original medium; the remaining sound enters the second medium and may be *refracted*.

The reflected sound might be heard as an echo. Echoes often confuse an observer as to the true direction of the source. Such echoes are observed often while one is situated between tall buildings. Under these circumstances it is difficult, for instance, to locate a plane flying overhead because the echo directs one's attention to an area other than that in which the plane is located. Although the sound may be traveling in straight lines, a reflection changes the direction abruptly. A more specific inquiry into the nature of reflections and refractions will take place with regard to the wave characteristic of light in Chapter 3.

The portion of the sound which enters

Figure 2.7

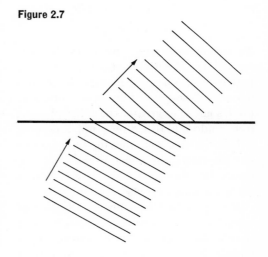

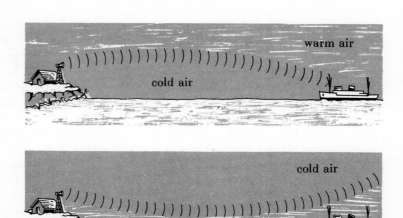

Figure 2.8

the second medium would continue on in its original direction after entering the second medium if the speed of sound in that medium were the same as the speed in the original material. If, however, the speed were to change upon entering the second medium the direction of travel would be changed. The phenomenon of changing directions of wave fronts at the boundary between two media is called *refraction*. Because the wave fronts of the sound waves entering the new medium could not maintain continuity unless the adjoining segments of the fronts on each side of the boundary remained joined together, a change in direction must take place if the speed of motion changes. The only exception would be if a plane wave front were to cross the boundary moving at right angles to the boundary and therefore would move across as a complete unit and continue on in the original direction.

Because sound travels more rapidly in warm air than in colder air, sound would be refracted upward by a layer of colder air lying above a layer of warm air near to the earth's surface. A layer of cold air lying beneath a layer of warm air would refract the sound downward. These effects are often observed by persons stationed on boats anchored out some distance from the shore. As indicated by the diagrams in Fig. 2.8, the sounds from the shore can often be heard quite clearly in the early evening when the air just above the water surface is cooler than the layer of air at greater height above the water. Later in the evening when the air in the top layer has cooled below the temperature of the water, the sounds from the shore are bent upward to such an extent that nothing can be heard from the shore.

Speed of sound and molecular speeds

As previously stated, the speed of sound in air is affected by the air temperature. The most widely quoted value for speed of sound in air is 1087 feet per second at the air temperature of 32 degrees Fahrenheit, the temperature of ice water. The speed of sound increases with increased temperature at the rate of 1.1 ft per second for each increase of one degree Fahrenheit. (Two feet per second is the increase per degree centigrade; the temperature of ice water is zero degrees centigrade.)

The temperature-related variation in speed of sound is accounted for by the kinetic theory of molecules. The kinetic theory pictures a gas to be composed of billions of independent molecules that are moving at high speed in a completely chaotic manner (having no preferred direction of motion). The pressure of air is transmitted by the collisions of the air molecules with each other and with the surface molecules of the substances forming the boundaries of air masses. The greater the number of molecules per unit volume of the gas, the greater the number of collisions per unit time and thus the greater the pressure. When regions of unequal pressures exist within an air mass, the molecules are exchanged rapidly from regions of higher pressure to regions of lower pressure until an equilibrium of pressure is restored. The exchange of molecules between the various regions should occur at the average speed of the molecules involved. Therefore, when the average speed of the molecules is increased, a more rapid rate of pressure exchange will occur. Because compressional waves of sound are pictured as consisting of alternate regions of compression and rarefaction (higher and lower pressure) moving through the molecules of the medium, the kinetic molecular theory of gases would relate the speed of sound to the average speed of the molecules involved.

The increased speed of sound accompanying an increase in temperature would suggest, therefore, that temperature is a measure of the average speed of the molecules in a gas. Investigation has shown that this simple relationship between temperature and speed is not completely true. Molecules are thought to be spinning as well as moving with linear speed. The temperature of gases, therefore, is a measure related to the combined effects of both spin and linear motions rather than the linear motion exclusively. Nevertheless, an increase in gas temperature does indicate an increase in the average speed of the molecules involved. The extent of the change in molecular speed accompanying a temperature change depends upon the type of material.

Pitch and the speed of sound In keeping with the kinetic molecular theory, the speed of sound would not be affected by the frequency of the pressure disturbances. The frequency of waves passing a given point is controlled by the conditions at the source of the sound. Although the wavelength of sound in air for a given frequency would vary with a change in speed of sound, this would not affect the frequency of the sound coming from a stationary source. The Doppler effect from moving sources would be more pronounced when the speed of sound is decreased. For example, if the preceding calculations I and II had been made when the speed of sound was 1087 ft per second, the following results would have ensued: the wavelength of the sound from the moving source would have been 1.994 ft per wavelength instead of the 2.1 ft; and the frequency would have been increased to 545 wavelengths per second instead of the 543.

Loudness versus distance The intensity (loudness) of sound is proportional to the amount of work that can be done by that portion of each wave front that passes through an opening having a given area and placed at the various points of inquiry. Recalling that sound is propagated as spherical wave fronts which are expanding out into space, the total energy potential per wave can be thought to be distributed uniformly throughout the surface area of the expanding sphere. The surface area of a sphere is calculated from the formula, $A = 4\pi r^2$, where A is the area in square feet if the radius r is measured in feet. The available energy potential per square foot of the surface would theoretically be equal to the total energy potential per wave front divided by the area, or

$$\text{total energy potential}/4\pi r^2$$

Since the relationship is determined by the value of the radius squared occurring in the denominator, this shows to be an *inverse square* relationship. The relative intensities of sound at two points displaced r_A and r_B from the source would be:

$$\frac{\text{intensity at } A}{\text{intensity at } B} = \frac{\dfrac{\text{energy potential}}{4\pi r_A^2}}{\dfrac{\text{energy potential}}{4\pi r_B^2}}$$

$$= \frac{\text{energy potential}}{4\pi r_A^2} \times \frac{4\pi r_B^2}{\text{energy potential}}$$

$$= \frac{r_B^2}{r_A^2}$$

Therefore, theoretically, the ratio of the intensities of sound at two locations A and B should be inversely proportional to the ratio of the squares of the distances to the source from A and B. Actual observations of intensities, however, indicate that the intensities are reduced much more rapidly than the theoretical ratios would predict. Since the transmission consists of energy, the rapid reduction in intensity would indicate that transforma-

tion of sound to other forms of energy takes place while the sound waves travel outward from the source.

Because the rate of absorption (energy transformation) is much greater near to the surfaces of the earth, an attempt is made to increase the audible range of boat whistles, fog horns, and emergency warning devices by placing them as far above the absorbing surfaces as practicable.

Sensitivity of the human ear In a strict sense, the term *loudness* should be used only to designate the magnitude of the sensation experienced when sound waves enter the human ear. The sensation is to some extent dependent on the individual ear and the frequency of the sound, and is not directly proportional to sound *intensity*. Under normal conditions and throughout a relatively wide range of intensity, the smallest change in intensity to which an average ear is sensitive is an increase of 1.26 times the previous intensity.

A change in loudness of sound resulting from a tenfold increase in intensity is the unit called a *bel* in honor of Alexander Graham Bell, the inventor of the telephone. This unit indicates that two sounds differ in sound level by one bel when their intensities have a ratio of ten. Each step in this ratio represents an increase of intensity by a factor of about 1.26. Since each of these steps represents a tenth of a bel, the factor of 1.26 is called a *decibel*. The decibel, therefore, represents the smallest change in sound intensity detectable by the normal ear under average circumstances.

In order to reveal some well-known relationships between loudness and sound intensity, several common sounds have been used to make up Table 2.3.

Resonance and measuring the speed of sound Any two vibrators that are capable of vibrating at the same frequency can be said to be in *resonance*. If one of these vibrators produces sound of sufficient intensity to set the second vibrator into motion, the induced vibration is characterized as a *sympathetic vibration*. Sympathetic vibrations are sometimes very annoying. For example, recall the commonly occurring resonant vibrations of picture frames, cabinets, and screens to certain frequencies that occur regularly over radio or TV sets.

The importance of resonance to the study of the nature of sound lies in the use of resonance tubes as a means of measuring wavelength and speed of sound in air. The resonance tube is an arrangement whereby the air column enclosed in a hollow tube may be used as a vibrating system producing audible sound. The most useful type of resonance tube consists of a long hollow tube set upright and provided with a means whereby the length of the air column might be adjusted by raising or lowering the level of water which fills the lower portion of the tube. When a vibrating tuning fork is placed over the open end of this type of resonance tube (Fig. 2.9), the lower prong of the fork produces sound waves which

enter the open tube. When this prong moves downward at maximum velocity through its equilibrium position a compressional wave pulse of greater than average air pressure travels from it down into the tube (a). When the pulse strikes the water surface the pressure wave is reflected back up the tube to the open end (b). Upon reaching the open end the pulse of compressed air pops out into the unconfined space above the tube leaving behind it a region of lowered pressure (c). The resulting pulse of lower than average air pressure moves back down the air column and is reflected at the water surface (d). As this pulse of rarefaction reaches the open air which is at normal air pressure, the higher air pressures above the tube cause an inrush of air into the emerging region of rarefaction creating a new pulse of compression (e). The whole process is then repeated.

If the length of the resonance tube is adjusted so that the first pulse of compression returns to the open end at the instant that the lower prong of the tuning fork is moving upward with maximum velocity through its equilibrium position, the maximum rarefaction produced by the prong at that time will be added to the rarefaction being produced by the popping out of the compressed air. The

TABLE 2.3

Sound	Loudness	Relative intensity
Threshold of hearing	0 decibels	0
Rustling of leaves	20 decibels	100
Quiet home	40 decibels	10,000
Average radio	70 decibels	10,000,000
Automobile horn	90 decibels	1,000,000,000
Loud thunder	110 decibels	100,000,000,000
Sound becomes painful	120 decibels	1,000,000,000,000

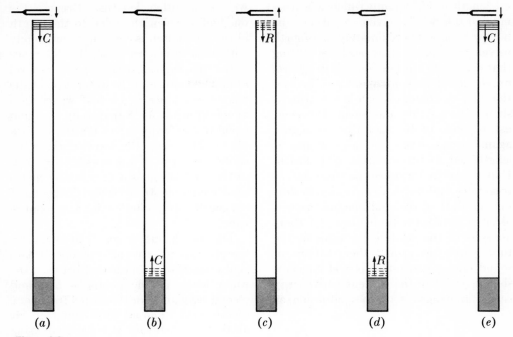

Figure 2.9

energy potential of the pulse is therefore increased. When this more energy-packed pulse reaches the mouth of the tube after reflection, the prong is producing another maximum compression which reinforces the compression produced by the inrush of air into the rarefaction. After several successive additions of energy in this manner, the air at the open end of the tube begins to vibrate and resonance occurs. The sound produced by the vibrating air column has greater intensity than the sound from the tuning fork and can be heard at a distance beyond the point where the sound from the tuning fork becomes inaudible. The air column continues to vibrate producing audible sound for as long as sufficient energy is fed into it from a resonant tuning fork.

The relationship between the resonating air column and the speed and wavelength of sound becomes evident when we review a few of the definitions developed earlier in this chapter. By definition, the time elapsed during the half cycle of vibration starting with a maximum velocity downward through the equilibrium position and ending with a maximum velocity upward through the equilibrium position is one-half period. This distance that sound travels from a stationary source during one-half period is one-half wavelength. The compressional waves being reflected in the resonance tubes move at the speed of sound. Because of the reflection, the actual distance of travel for each pulse described above involves twice the length of the air column within the tube. Under conditions using the shortest length of air column which will resonate to a fork of a given frequency, the hollow tube is approximately one-fourth wavelength long. The need for stating that the length is *approximately one-fourth wavelength* is brought about by the fact that the air column which is vibrating is slightly longer than the tube. However, use is made of the fact that resonance again occurs when the air column is lengthened to three-fourths wavelength. Under this circumstance the sound pulses travel one and one-half wavelengths during the time of one and one-half periods of vibration for the tuning fork. A short analysis of the relative positions of the tuning fork prong and the positions of sound pulses at one-half period intervals should reveal to the student why energy can be exchanged in this new situation, as

Figure 2.10

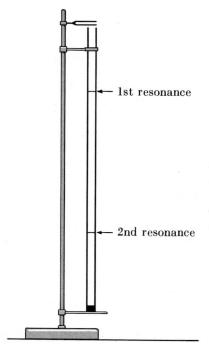

← 1st resonance

← 2nd resonance

well as at other lengths. Because the one-half wavelength added to the length of the air column is contained completely within the resonance tube, the difference in the tube length between the water level at first resonance to the water level at the second resonance is one-half wavelength of sound in air for a frequency of sound equal to the frequency of the tuning fork used. Therefore, the wavelength as described in terms of the pressure recorded in Graph I becomes a more easily measured characteristic of sound in terms of resonating air columns in a resonance tube.

The wavelength of sound in air at the temperature of the air column is two times the distance measured between the water levels at the points of first and second resonance for the stated frequency of the fork. The speed of sound in air at that temperature is calculated using formula (2.3):

(2.3) speed of waves
$$= \text{wavelength} \times \text{frequency}$$

For example, let us specify conditions for resonance using the apparatus diagramed in Fig. 2.10:

frequency = 830 wavelengths per sec
length of space in tube at
   first resonance = 3.75 in.
length of space in tube at
   second resonance = 11.77 in.
temperature = 75°F

The calculated wavelength would be:

$2 \times (11.77 - 3.57 \text{ in.})$
$$= 16.4 \text{ in. per wavelength}$$

The speed of sound would be calculated as follows:

$$\frac{830 \text{ wavelengths}}{\text{sec}} \times \frac{16.4 \text{ in.}}{\text{wavelength}}$$
$$= 13,612 \text{ in. per sec}$$

The fact that the speed of sound can be calculated accurately from the wave characteristics discernible in operating resonance tubes constitutes an important verification of the wave nature of sound.

SYSTEMATIC STRUCTURING

The fact that resonance involves a transfer of energy by means of sound directs attention to a fundamental function of all wave phenomena—that of transmitting energy from one place to another. All wave phenomena are described by the characteristics of period, frequency, wavelength, and speed of propagation. In our study of sound these characteristics have been given meanings in terms of easily demonstrated and readily measured relationships. The meanings thus developed will serve as the foundation for developing further understandings and fuller meanings through applications extending into situations where less easily demonstrated theories of wave action form the basis for explanation. Wave-like functions will be found to be important structural concepts in the organization of our knowledge regarding the physical world.

The occurrence of diffraction, reflection, and refraction in certain situations involving sound should tend to associate these events with wave phenomena. This is not to classify these events as products of wave phenomena by mere association. Further explanation of the events in terms of wave characteristics will be needed to confirm the relationships. But events of this type contain clues to important explanations in other situations which shall be investigated along the way. Each new area of study will contribute its own descriptions and explanations which very often will augment the former meanings of the familiar concepts used, as well as contribute to the exploration of new meanings and applications of meanings that help to bring into sharper focus the processes of nature. The wave characteristics are good examples of how knowledge can take on a semblance of structure, helping greatly in organizing ideas and in analyzing new ideas for possible relationships found in known patterns.

SUMMARY

Energy in the form of sound is propagated from one place to another through a material medium. The transmission usually takes place by means of compressional waves. In a homogeneous medium, sound waves are characterized by spherical wave fronts expanding outward into space. The *wavelength* is the distance measured along a radius of the expanding wave fronts between one compression peak and the next following one. The wavelength is the distance sound travels during one period of vibration of a stationary source. The average number of wavelengths that pass a detector each second is called the *frequency of sound*. The reciprocal of the frequency, called the *period of the sound*, is the time required for a wavelength to pass a given point. The speed of the sound in the given medium can be determined by dividing the measurement of wavelength by the measurement of period. These measurements can be made using a tuning fork of known frequency in conjunction with a resonance tube. The speed of sound in air at the temperature of ice water is 1087 feet per second. The speed is constant over a wide range of frequencies within a given medium at a given temperature. The speed of sound in air increases and decreases with relative increase and decrease in air temperature.

Sound waves exhibit the phenomena of the Doppler effect, diffraction, reflection, and refraction. These phenomena make it necessary to know the nature of any relative motion between source, receiver, and intervening materials; the nature of the intervening materials; and the relation between the placement of sound-producing apparatus, the size of openings through which the sound passes and the wavelengths of the sound. *Loudness of sound* refers to the magnitude of the sensation experiences when sound waves enter the ear. Loudness is measured in units called the *bel* which represents a tenfold increase in intensity. The average ear is sensitive to a minimum intensity increase of about 1.26 times the previous intensity. This factor of increase is called a *decibel* and represents the smallest change in sound intensity detectable by the normal ear.

PROBLEMS

1 Under conditions when the speed of sound was 1130 ft per second, a hammer blow was heard by the person wielding the hammer and he heard the echo from a cliff 3 seconds later. How far away from the listener was the cliff? What assumptions were made in determining your answer?

2 Give several examples of situations which demonstrate diffraction of sound.

3 What is the difference in meaning between the terms "period of the sound" and "period of a vibrating body?"

4 What is the relationship between molecular motion and the speed of sound?

5 On a day when the temperature is 82°F., a given tuning fork produced resonance at 5.68 inches and at 17.10 inches. What is your estimate of the frequency of this fork? What steps did you use to solve this problem and why?

6 Explain the Doppler effect under circumstances of a moving source of sound.

7 Sound waves of 2.28 ft per wavelength were moving at 1140 ft per second in air. The waves were detected by a receiver moving at 90 ft per second toward the stationary source of sound. What was the apparent period per wavelength detected by the receiver? What was the frequency of vibration of the source? What was the frequency of the sound detected by the receiver?

8 What is the relative intensity of two sounds which differ in loudness by 5 decibels?

9 Explain why a resonance tube of a given length can be in resonance to several different frequencies of sound.

3

NATURE OF LIGHT

Almost all known information has been communicated to mankind by means of light in one form or another. Every creature having sight keeps itself informed by means of light concerning the location and the distinguishing qualities of the objects and events in which it is interested. Men of science often use specially designed light gathering devices in their search for information. With the aid of a telescope the astronomer takes pictures which search the outermost depths of space for information about the universe. The biologist with the aid of a microscope probes into the problems of understanding life processes by communicating with light reflected from objects too small to be observed directly. Light is best known as a means of communicating with the physical world in which we live but it has many other important functions.

Light like sound is a form of energy. Evidences of energy transformations involving light are constantly observed. For instance, we can feel the warmth of sunlight changed into heat. Light triggers electric eye circuits which protect machine operators, open and close doors, and do innumerable tasks that can be monitored by light. Light tans the skin, yet it bleaches the hair. Light destroys odors, yet it activates the production of smog. Without light there would be no photosynthesis. Without photosynthesis there would be no grass, no trees, no vegetables, and no life. Light is indeed a requisite and versatile form of energy.

Light while in transit is invisible. To be observed, some of the light must be converted to other forms of energy. Only by observing the energy conversions involving light and by trying to explain the phenomena involved can we become aware of the nature of light.

OBSERVING CHARACTERISTICS OF EVENTS

The accumulated observations of generations of men form the basis for evidence in our study of light. In some instances everyday experiences and simple experiments can provide decisive tests with which to verify an explanation. In other instances, however, carefully devised apparatus and extremely minute measurements provide the crucial tests. The fact that energy is transmitted as light as it was by sound suggests possible analogies between the properties of light and sound. The postulation of wave characteristics proved very productive in explaining phenomena of sound. Perhaps postulation of wave characteristics might also be a good hypothesis for our inquiry about light. Therefore, can we single out events which might suggest

wave motion in the propagation of light? Are there measurable characteristics observed in these events which can be attributed to frequency, wavelength, or variable speeds of propagation? Are there analogous phenomena related to light such as reflection, diffraction, refraction, and resonance which were observed with sound?

At the outset the fact must be recognized that the exact nature of light is not yet evident. We shall consider phenomena which necessitate including particle characteristics as well as wave characteristics to complete an explanation. The dual nature of these properties has inspired the development of totally new concepts in the explanations of modern science. We shall use some of these concepts when the need arises. We shall now call attention to some apparent characteristics in the phenomena of light.

Line of sight A general fact accepted by most persons is that light travels along straight lines. This cannot be accepted as a scientific "law" but belongs to the realm of common-sense interpretations. For example, the perception of location of an object seems to be determined primarily by interpretation of lines of sight. The fact that objects are found where we perceive them to be supports this interpretation. Very early in life we learned to verify our interpretations of location by simply reaching out and touching nearby objects. But as a result, many persons habitually react as if their sense of sight emanates from their eyes, proceeding outward to the object seen, rather than attributing it to incoming light from the object to the eye. Most of these persons revise their reaction patterns after careful observation.

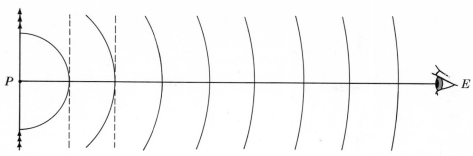

Figure 3.1

If events involving light are to show characteristics of wave motion, our experiences with sound would suggest that we describe the light emitted from a luminous point as forming spherical wave fronts expanding outward into space around that point. If we assume that each observed luminous point on an object is a source of spherical wave fronts, then we must also assume that we perceive these points because our eyes receive portions of these diverging waves, and that we have learned to make sense out of the complex jumble of light waves which enter our eyes. Any attempt at diagraming the confusion of wave fronts which would exist between the eyes and the luminous points on an object would be most unintelligible. Lines of sight, however, can be linked to the proposed wave phenomena as a descriptive characteristic. In this sense, lines of sight become an orderly approach to our investigation.

Your attention is drawn to Fig. 3.1. Line *PE* represents the line of sight between point *P* on the object and point *E* of the eye. In terms of the proposed spherical wave fronts forming a train of waves moving from the point source to the eye, each segment of line *PE* which originates at *P* and ends at a wave front

is a radius of that particular sphere. Thus, the line *PE* describes the path along which a particular spherical wave segment expands before entering the eye. The term *ray* is used to designate a line, such as *PE*, which describes the direction of motion of a wave segment in moving from one place to another. In consideration of later uses to be made of rays, we point out that a radius of a sphere is perpendicular to the lines tangent to the point on the sphere's surface at which the radius terminates. The lines tangent to a point on a curved surface form a plane tangent to the curved surface. In geometry any line perpendicular to a tangent plane at the point of tangency is called the normal line or just simply the *normal*. Hence, the ray *PE* is normal to all the wave fronts moving along the path which the ray represents. It can be shown that a ray is always a normal of the wave phenomenon it described.

Tracing rays of light from representative points of an object to the receiver greatly simplifies diagraming the directions along which waves of light travel in the phenomena we choose to observe.

Depth perception The location of an object with respect to two points of

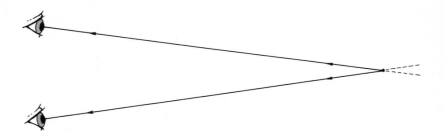

Figure 3.2

reference can be diagramed using two converging rays which originate at the points of reference and intersect at the position of the object. We are able to judge distances and to see objects in three dimensions because our two eyes function as a range-finding system. The ray diagram in Fig. 3.2 shows how each eye has a slightly different line of sight. The point of intersection of these sight lines is the location of the object.

The ability to judge reliably the location of objects with respect to our own position is called *depth perception*. Each person's safety on the public streets and highways depends to a large extent upon the reliability of his depth perception and upon this ability in the persons with whom he must associate. Reliable depth perception is an essential for successful participation in most sports. All occupations which involve manipulation of objects around obstacles require well-developed depth perception. For example, highly developed depth perception is a prerequisite for pilots of aircraft.

The physical conditions fundamental to perception of location are intersecting sight lines. If for some reason light does not travel along a single straight line for the entire distance between the object and the eyes, judgement of location becomes very difficult.

Reflection—the law of reflection We have mentioned previously the confusion resulting when echoes interfere with locating objects by means of sound. Similar effects are produced by reflection of light. However, by using lines of sight we can observe more precisely the conditions present in reflection of light than was possible for echoes.

There are in effect two types of reflection, both described by the same rules of ray tracing. The more common effect is called *diffused reflection* which accounts for the light by which we see all objects

Figure 3.3

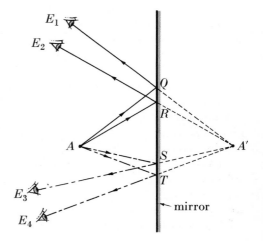

not giving off their own light. The more confusing effect is called *regular reflection* which gives rise to mirror images. The general properties of all reflections can be determined by examining the conditions for regular reflection.

The rays of light traced in Fig. 3.3 describe the conditions for regular reflection based on lines of sight. The diagram indicates how the eyes at E_1 and E_2 apparently see the object at A' when the object is actually located at A. The lines of sight converge at A' located behind the mirror. Our knowledge of the fact that the object is not situated behind the mirror should prompt immediate curiosity as to the reason for the deception. The answer can be demonstrated quite reasonably by anyone possessing a pocket mirror.

That which seems to be located at A' is classified as a *virtual image*. It is an illusion. The virtual image does not exist; it is merely the effect brought about, in this situation, by the regular reflection of the light coming from the real object. Retracing the diagramed rays from A to Q to E, and from A to R to E_2 establishes why, under these particular circumstances, a virtual image appears to be at A'. Does the virtual image of the object at A always appear to be at A'?

Fig. 3.3 suggests an affirmative answer. When the points representing the eyes are moved to E_3 and E_4 the rays entering the eyes again converge at A'. Of course, in a printed diagram this need not be a true coincidence; the diagram could be constructed purposely to produce this effect. The proof is found if a measured correspondence occurs when similar lines of sight from the object to a plane mirror and to an eye result from actual observations. It is hoped that the reader is curious enough to investigate by tracing lines and measuring angles produced from actual use of mirrors.

Measurement of the indicated angles in Fig. 3.3 will reveal that the angle between the mirror surface and ray AQ (the *incident ray*) is equal to the angle between the mirror surface and ray QE, (the *reflected ray*). The condition of equality, also, is true for the angles between the mirror surface and the *incident ray AR* and between the mirror surface and the *reflected ray RE_2*. This

Figure 3.4

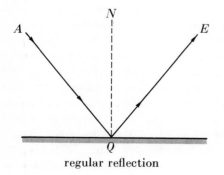

regular reflection

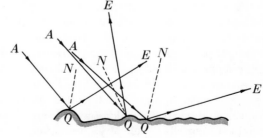

diffused reflection

condition applies to the corresponding angles formed by the rays from A to the mirror and from the mirror to the eyes at E_3 and E_4. The measured equalities existing between these related angles formed when actual lines of sight are established between an object, a plane mirror, and an eye are the basis for a generalization called the *law of reflection.*

The angles designated in Fig. 3.4 are more universally applicable for describing all types of reflection than the angles used in Fig. 3.3. The line QN in each situation is a *normal* to the reflecting surface involved. In order to more easily designate angles, the angle AQN between the incident ray and the normal is called the *angle of incidence*, and the angle NQE between the normal and the reflected ray is called the *angle of reflection.* Using these angles instead of the angles between the mirror surface and the rays is permitted because the normal is perpendicular to the plane surface and subtracting equals from equals results in equal quantities. The law of reflection can be stated as follows: *The angle of reflection is equal to the angle of incidence; and the incident ray, the normal and the reflected ray lie in the same plane.*

Guide lines to truth   Thus far, the only assumption we have used has been that light travels along straight lines; and, to the extent of our investigation, the assumption has been adequate for the needs of description. Underlying our investigation, however, is the hypothesis that phenomena of light have properties of wave motion. In this regard we have made no crucial tests. The line-of-sight situations described could have been explained equally well by assuming straight line flight of particles. The

choice of ray diagrams was made in order to remain consistent with the chosen hypothesis of wave motion. Our common-sense logic in this regard seems to have served us well. But if carried too far, the use of common-sense logic to explain observations can lead to erroneous conclusions. The following situations are used as an illustration of this possibility.

Shadows—umbra and penumbra   Shadows are well-known observations which seem to support the assumption that light travels along straight lines. Several representative situations involving formation of shadows are illustrated by ray diagrams in Fig. 3.5. When, as shown in Fig. 3.5a, the rays diverge from a point source of light, the shadow is larger than the object intercepting the light. When, as shown in Fig. 3.5b, the source of light is so far removed from the object that for all practical purposes the wave fronts are plane and, therefore, the rays are parallel, the shadow is the same size as the object. When, as shown in Fig. 3.5c, the light source has an extensive surface which provides myriads of points from which rays can diverge, the shadow has two regions. The dark region where the rays are totally blocked off is called the *umbra.* The grey region surrounding the umbra where the rays are only partially blocked off is called the *penumbra.* When, as shown in Fig. 3.5d, the object intercepting the rays is small compared to the apparent size of the light source, the umbra takes on the appearance of a cone converging to a point in space and is not observed unless an intervening object presents itself in the cone upon which the shadow can be seen. In the space outside of the cone, only those parallel

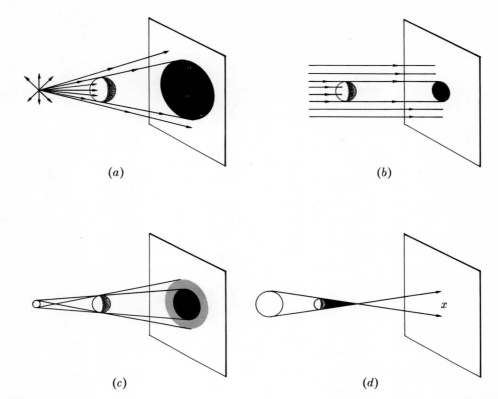

Figure 3.5

rays along a given line of sight would be blocked off by the object. For instance, a person at point x in Fig. 3.5d would see near the center of the light source a dark spot having the general shape of the object.

If for our tests of wave properties we now depended exclusively upon everyday observations of wave propagations such as water waves entering a harbor or sound waves entering a room through a window, a characteristic phenomenon observed would be the tendency of waves to expand and to move around behind any obstacles in their path. The water waves entering a harbor fan out and fill the entire harbor with waves of reduced amplitude. Sounds produced on one side of a building are heard on the opposite side of the building with only reduced loudness the consequence of the barrier. Obstacles only partially block off a region from a wave motion. Therefore, the apparently sharp shadows cast by light seem to contradict the hypothesis that phenomena of light show evidence of wave motion. Thus, at this stage, were we to rely only upon our personal observations and common-sense logic in making decisions we very likely would reject the wave hypothesis in favor of the flight-of-particles hypothesis in explaining

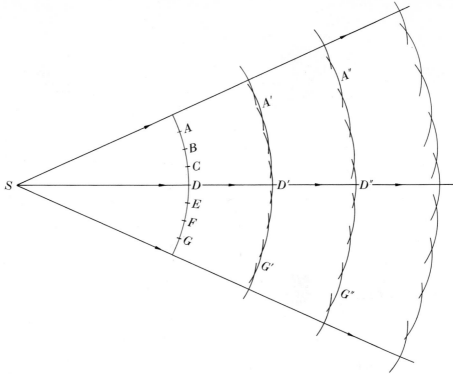

Figure 3.6

the propagation of light. The truth remains, however, that since no crucial test has been made with regard to wave properties of light, judgment would be premature at this stage. Before suggesting a crucial test concerning wave characteristics of light, we shall discuss a very successful plan for describing wave front propagations of any form.

Huygens' principle Propagation of sound was explained by having each part of the transmitting medium transfer pressure variations to the parts of the medium adjacent to it. Therefore, the pressure variations were transferred from one set of parts to the parts adjacent to them, and the new set transferred the effect to the next set in line, and so on through the entire medium. This apparent transfer of the wave motions from part to part in media is involved in all observable wave phenomena.

In 1690, Christian Huygens (1629–1695) generalized this observed fact into a principle describing all wave propagations. The essential feature of the description produced by *Huygens' principle* is that *every point on a wave front acts as a new source of a small wavelet which spreads out in all directions.* Fig. 3.6 illustrates the construction of a two-dimensional model based upon Huygens'

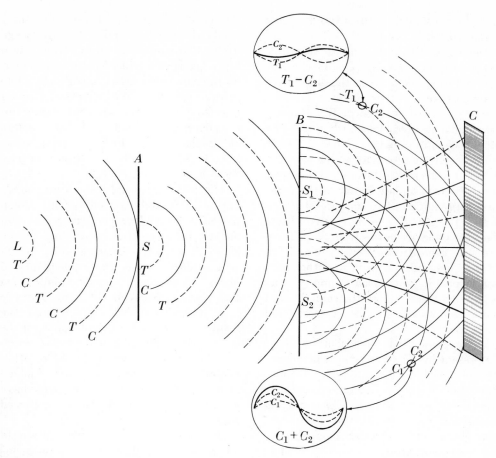

Figure 3.7

principle. The wavelets from points A, B, C, D, E, F, and G spread out to form the envelope indicated by line $A'D'G'$. This envelope is the advancing wave front from which a new set of wavelets can be constructed to designate the motion of the wave. For spherical waves the model must be expanded into three dimensions and the wavelets become small sections of spheres which spread out in all directions.

Adding and subtracting wave motions
A crucial test as to whether phenomena of light show characteristics of wave motion is embodied in a famous experiment first performed by Thomas Young (1773–1829) in 1801. Fig. 3.7 is a diagram of Young's apparatus design. The theory of operation was based on Huygens' principle of wave propagation. Wave characteristics are postulated for the light leaving the lamp at L. The

light is represented by the alternate wave fronts forming crests, shown as solid curves marked C, and troughs, shown as dotted curves marked T. The terms *crest* and *trough* come from the descriptive nomenclature of water waves. The distance from crest to crest or from trough to trough measured along a ray represents one wavelength of light. When the wave fronts reach the screen at A, the segment of each front passing through the narrow slit at S acts as a point source of Huygens' waves spreading out to the second screen at B. The slits S_1 and S_2 in screen B are placed at equal distances from S. Therefore, the wave fronts from S reach slits S_1 and S_2 simultaneously, and the wave fronts spreading out from S_1 and S_2 start away from these slits at the same instant and in identical sequence of crests and troughs.

If the postulated wave characteristics are present in the described phenomenon, the relationships indicated by the diagram should apply. Take notice of how everywhere along the solid lines cutting across the wave fronts the crests and troughs respectively from S_1 coincide with the crests and troughs from S_2. These conditions would intensify the effects of the wave fronts momentarily because an addition takes place momentarily as represented by the connected insert in Fig. 3.7.

The addition of wave effects causing intensification is called *reinforcement*. In the diagram, maximum reinforcement is localized to the points along the solid lines. Partial reinforcement would apply to regions nearby these lines. From the same point of view, everywhere along the dashed lines cutting across the wave fronts the crests from S_1 coincide with the troughs from S_2 and the troughs from S_1 coincide with the crests from S_2. These conditions would diminish the effects of the wave fronts momentarily because a subtraction takes place momentarily as represented by the connected insert in Fig. 3.7. The subtraction of wave effects is called *interference*. In the diagram, maximum interference is localized to the points along the dashed lines. Partial interference would apply to regions nearby these lines.

The fact that bright and dark bands appear alternately on the viewing screen placed in front of properly placed slits in an apparatus designed according to the above diagram was interpreted by Young as a confirmation of the wave theory of light. Measurements can be made upon the distance between slits, the distance from the slits to the screen, and the distance between the bright bands on the screen which correctly indicate the wavelengths of the light used. No other explanations except those which include characteristics of waves for light have adequately explained these observed results.

But what of the shadows produced when light is blocked off by an obstacle? These shadows only seem to be sharp. Careful observation would reveal at the edge of each shadow a region where the light noticeably invades. Interpretations too complex to be described here indicate how, when the openings between the obstacles greatly exceed the wavelengths involved, interference annuls the observation of wave effects beyond an extremely small extension of the size of the openings through which the waves flow. However, the waves actually do spread into the space behind the obstacles because the predicted extensions of wave effect beyond the straight-line limits do appear.

INTERPRETING FURTHER OBSERVATIONS

The preceding inquiry has revealed a notable parallel between the wave characteristics of sound and light. As yet, however, nothing has been said about transmitting media or the nature of the wave disturbances related to transmission of light. Herein the properties of sound and light are strikingly different. Whereas sound cannot be transmitted through a vacuum, light travels unhindered through the vacuum of space at the tremendous speed of 186,300 miles per second. Sound is transmitted by compressional waves superimposed upon the ordinary motions of the molecules in the transmitting medium. Light waves manifest a combination of interdependent electric and magnetic effects in which changes occurring in each of the effects give rise to a compensating projection of the other into the surrounding space. Thus each effect acts as the simultaneous source for the other in a manner described by Huygens' principle, and without any apparent need for a medium in which to flow.

Although there are basic differences in the fundamental natures of sound and light, there are also many analogous situations involving the two forms of energy which have enlightening characteristics worth further investigation.

Refraction of waves Light changes direction of motion if it moves obliquely from one medium into another. This effect was also observed for sound. The phenomenon in both instances is caused by an abrupt change in the speed of transmission for the portion of the waves which enter the new medium. The *ratio* of the speed of transmission in one medium to the speed of transmission in the adjoining medium is called the *relative index of refraction*. The ratio is of constant value for any two specified media and is a function of the two media when they are in contact. Table 3.1 lists the relative index of refraction for light as a function of air and each of the designated media.

TABLE 3.1   Relative index of refraction for air and the specified medium

Water	1.33	Crown glass	1.50
Quartz	1.54	Flint glass	1.65

Because determination of ray directions for light is possible by establishing sight lines, greater refinement in measuring the extent of change in direction is available for light than for other wave phenomena.

In 1621, almost a half-century before scientists would reach the stage of measuring the speed of light in space, Willebrord Snell (1591–1626) formulated a law with which the change in direction of light between two known media could be ascertained, and then predicted reliably. Snell's discovery was that the change in direction of waves passing from one medium to another is governed by a ratio of sine values.

(3.1)   sin angle of incidence/sin angle
        of refraction = a constant for
        the given media

We shall now define the terms used above.

With reference to Fig. 3.8, the angle of incidence $\angle i$ is the angle between the incident ray and the normal. The angle of refraction $\angle r$ is the angle between the refracted ray and the normal. The normal in each case is the line normal to the surface of the adjoining media at the

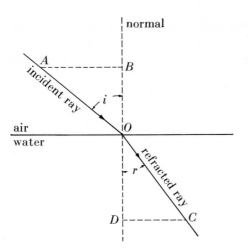

normal

A

incident ray

air
water

i

B

O

r

refracted ray

D

C

Figure 3.8

point where the rays intersect the surface.

The sine of an angle is defined by the ratio of the *side opposite* an angle to the *hypotenuse* as measured in a *right triangle* containing these parts. In Fig. 3.8, right triangles were constructed in the following manner:

1. From the point O at the intersection equal segments were measured off on the incident ray and on the refracted ray making $OA = OC$.
2. From point A a line was constructed perpendicular to the normal at B forming the right triangle ABO.
3. From point C a line was constructed perpendicular to the normal at D forming the right triangle CDO.

By definition, therefore, the sine of the angle of incidence $= \sin \angle i = AB/OA$, and the sine of the angle of refraction $= \sin \angle r = CD/OC$. The constant of Snell's law for the two media is

$$\frac{\sin \angle i}{\sin \angle r} = \frac{AB/OA}{CD/OC}$$

$$= \frac{AB}{OA} \times \frac{OC}{CD} = \frac{AB}{CD} = \text{constant}$$

where $OA = OC$.

The relative index of refraction is equal to the constant of Snell's law. Before it was possible to measure the speed of light in different media, the ratio of velocities stipulated in the index of refraction was only an interesting hypothesis based upon geometric proof and the wave theory of light. Let us inspect the arguments of the hypothesis.

Let line EF, Fig. 3.9, be the surface adjoining air and water. Wave fronts WV and OR are moving toward the surface at the speed of light in air. Wave fronts SQ and XY are moving away from the surface at the speed of light in water. These wave fronts are small segments of waves so far removed from their source that for all practical purposes the waves have plane wave fronts traveling at right angles to their respective rays. When wave front OR moves forward, the portion of the wave at O immediately enters the water and slows down; the portion at R continues on to Q at the speed of light in air. Therefore, during the time the portion at R moves from R to Q, the portion at O moves from O to S. The change in direction of the wave portion in the water must take place in order to preserve the continuity of the wave front during the transition. The distance traversed by a wave front in each medium equals the speed multiplied by the travel time. If the travel time is t and the speed of light in air and in water is c_a and c_w, respectively, the distance RQ in air is equal to $c_a \times t$ and the distance OS in water is equal to $c_w \times t$. The indicated equal angles shown in the diagram make angle i' equal to angle i and angle r' equal to angle r so that the following substitutions can be performed in Snell's law:

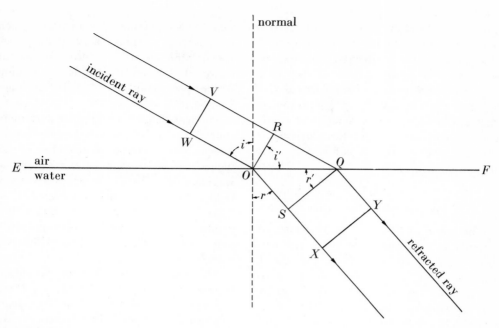

Figure 3.9

$$\frac{\sin i}{\sin r} = \frac{\sin i'}{\sin r'} = \frac{RQ/OQ}{OS/OQ} = \frac{RQ}{OS}$$

$$= \frac{c_a \times t}{c_w \times t} = \frac{c_a}{c_w} = \text{a constant}$$

The relative index of refraction, therefore, is expressed as follows:

(3.2) relative index of refraction

$$= \sin i/\sin r = \frac{c_i}{c_r}$$

where c_i equals the speed of light in the incident medium and c_r equals the speed of light in the refracting medium.

Until 1850 when Jean Foucault (1819–1868) demonstrated that the speed of light in water is less than the speed in air, the above-stated equality was a matter of mathematical speculation. Since the time Foucault reported his results, explaining refraction on the basis of speeds

of propagation has been on the firm foundation of measured verification. The success of explaining refraction by speeds of wave propagation along with Young's earlier diffraction experiment and other verifications of wave phenomena have left very little doubt in the minds of scientists concerning the wave characteristics attributed to light.

Frequency, wavelength and color Just as frequency of sound is the physical explanation for the pitch heard in musical tones, frequency of light is the physical explanation for the observed colors in objects. One value of discovering the relationships among the characteristics of a given physical action is the pattern it affords for postulating analogous characteristics in phenomena showing signs of similar type actions. For example, the wave actions of sound have the related characteristics of frequency, wavelength, and speed of propagation. If any two of these properties can be measured the third can be computed. The knowledge that light has wave characteristics, then, leads to postulating a similar relationship for light which is stated as follows:

(3.3)   frequency

$$= \frac{\text{speed of light in a vacuum}}{\text{wavelength of light in a vacuum}}$$

The speed of light has been measured directly to be 1.863×10^5 miles per second ($1.863 \times 10^5 = 1.863 \times 100,000 = 186,300$). In the metric units more often used in scientific measurement the equivalent measure for the speed of light is 2.998×10^8 meters per second ($2.998 \times 10^8 = 299,800,000$). By using the denary system to show relative accuracy of measurement we have indicated that the values quoted above have been rounded off to four significant figures. When rounded off to three significant figures, the speed of light is 300 million meters per second (2.998×10^8 becomes 3.00×10^8).

The wavelengths of light are extremely short but can be measured nevertheless. A space the length of 1 meter (39.37 inches) can accommodate over 1.5 million wavelengths of a standard, red colored light. Measuring the wavelengths of light involves using instruments which produce visible interference patterns. One such instrument is the Michelson interferometer.

The essential features of an interferometer are shown in Fig. 3.10. Plane wave fronts from S enter the glass plate at N which is partially silvered on the side toward the observer. About half of the light goes through the silvered surface and the other half is reflected by

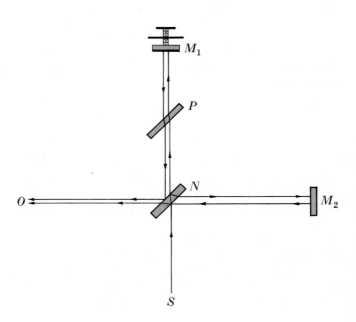

Figure 3.10

the silvered surface. The light that goes through continues on through the glass plate at P to the mirror at M, where the light is reflected back through P to N. A useful amount of the returning light is reflected from N to the observer at O. Meanwhile, the reflected portion of the original light from the source travels to the mirror at M_2 where this light is reflected back through N. A useful amount of this light also proceeds through the silvered surface and to the observer at O. Thus, the light from a single source is split into two parts each traveling along a separate path which brings the parts back together again in such a manner that interference can be achieved and observed. The glass plate at P is of the same thickness as the plate at N in order for the light traveling along each path to pass through the same thickness of glass before reaching the observer.

When the mirrors at M_1 and M_2 are at equal distances from the observer's side of N, the wave fronts from the two routes will reach the observer with the crests and troughs respectively from one route coinciding with the crests and troughs from the other route so that reinforcement results. Reinforcement would also occur when the distance to M_1 is one-half wavelength greater or less than the distance to M_2, or whenever the distances differ by whole number multiples of one-half wavelength. However, when the distance from N to M_1 is one-quarter wavelength greater or less than the distance to M_2, the wave fronts from the two routes will reach the observer with the crests from one route coinciding with the troughs from the other so that maximum interference results. Maximum interference would also occur whenever the distances differ by an odd number of quarter wavelengths. To the observer the conditions of reinforcement make the surface at N appear bright, and the conditions of maximum interference make the surface appear dark.

In operation a source emitting monochromatic light (light having a single frequency) is used. One of the mirrors is attached to a high precision micrometer screw so that the mirror can be moved slowly through a precisely known distance. As the mirror is moved slowly toward N the observer sees the surface at N change alternately dark and bright. The number of dark surfaces which take place during a known forward displacement of the mirror equals the number of wavelengths shift taking place in the wave patterns at N. Because a change of one-half wavelength in the displacement of the mirror produces a whole wavelength shift in the wave patterns, the wavelength of the monochromatic light is calculated as follows:

(3.4)   wavelength = 2 × displacement of mirror/number of dark surfaces observed

For instance, if 500 dark surfaces were observed as the mirror is moved 15 thousandths of a centimeter, the wavelength would be

2 × 0.015 cm/500 wavelengths
    = 0.00006 cm/wavelength

Placing the known values of speed and wavelength into the relationship expressed by Eq. 3.3, the frequency is computed.

$$\text{frequency} = \frac{30{,}000{,}000{,}000 \text{ cm/sec}}{0.00006 \text{ cm/wavelength}}$$

= 500,000,000,000,000 wavelengths/sec

The above frequency identifies light from the central part of the orange band in the rainbow.

Dispersion and colors of the rainbow
Unlike the observed conditions for sound where all frequencies travel at the same speed in a given medium, the observed "rainbow" display of colors produced when a narrow beam of sunlight is spread out by a prism is explained on the basis of light of different frequencies traveling at uniquely different speeds while in the prism. The separation and distribution of white light into constituent colors by a refraction device is called *dispersion*. The array of colors produced is called a *spectrum.*

The explanation for dispersion is illustrated by the ray diagram in Fig. 3.11. A narrow beam of white light (sunlight) is directed to the surface of the prism. The light is refracted as defined by the index of refraction in passing from air

With regard to the ratio of velocities expressed in the index of refraction and the constant angle of incidence, the greater the angle of refraction the greater the change in speed of the light upon entering the second medium. Tracing the various rays from the source and through the diagram, while giving thought to the meaning of the refractions involved, supports the idea that while in the glass the red light has a greater speed than the violet light. The other colors are dispersed between red and violet in the order of their decreased speed while in the glass. The index of refraction determined for any given frequency of light could be used in computing the speed of that light in glass.

The conditions which produce the rainbow are illustrated in Fig. 3.12. The

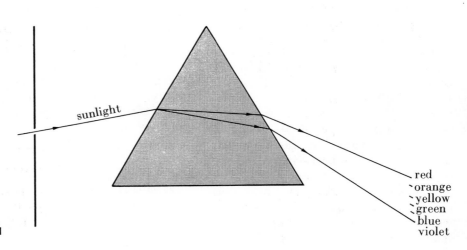

Figure 3.11

into glass and from glass into air. As illustrated, the light of lowest frequency (red) is refracted the least at the two surfaces, and the light of highest frequency (violet) is refracted the most.

rainbow is seen only when the sun is behind the observer. The spectrum is produced by a combination of reflection within the raindrops and refraction at the surfaces where the light enters and leaves.

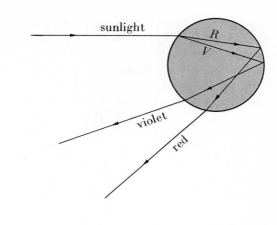

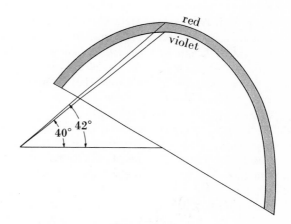

Figure 3.12

The messages of spectra Again, at this point the reader should be reminded of the atomic structure of matter. In a later section of this book we shall inquire more specifically into the atomic theory. However, an important consideration with regard to our present inquiry and the atomic structure of matter is the discovery that atoms of each element can emit light of characteristic frequencies which identifies the elements involved. Not only does the emitted light identify the elements but it also reveals other information about the structure of the matter involved.

If the atoms are held closely together as would occur in solids, liquids, and in gases that are under extremely high pressures, such as in the sun and the stars, the mutual interference between these closely packed atoms would prevent them from emitting their own characteristic frequencies. The result is that a continuous sequence of frequencies is emitted which is referred to as a *continuous spectrum*. When the light emitted from this sort of material is dispersed the result is a characteristic continuous sequence of colors ranging from red to violet. Common examples of sources producing continuous spectra are the filaments of incandescent lamps, the white hot materials in a glazing furnace, and the glowing electrodes of an arc light.

In contrast to the above result, if the atoms are comparatively far apart as would occur when molecules are dissociated into the atoms of their constituent elements by high temperature flames, each of the atoms emits comparatively few frequencies. Each of these frequencies would appear in the resulting spectrum as a narrow and sharply defined bright line. Thus, the results show a group of characteristically different bright lines with frequencies that identify each element involved. These sets of lines are called *bright line spectra* or, perhaps more descriptively, *atomic spectra*.

Molecules also emit characteristic spectra. At first glance, light from molecular origins seems to form wide bands of colors as if they were portions of a continuous spectrum. Upon greater dispersion the bands are found to consist of groups of lines arranged very closely together but having great regularity. The general appearance of the groups of lines characteristic of given molecules leads these to be called *band spectra*; however, because they are really composed of well defined groups of lines, the term *molecular spectra* is more meaningful.

Just as tuning forks and other systems that emit sounds can absorb waves of their own frequency in resonance, so an atom or molecule can absorb light of those frequencies to which it is resonant. This absorption of these particular frequencies is the exact reverse of emission. When atoms and molecules absorb particular frequencies from light emitted by a source giving off a continuous spectrum, the frequencies absorbed show up as dark lines in the continuous spectrum and occur at the positions of the characteristic bright lines emitted by these atoms or molecules in their atomic or molecular spectra. These dark lines seen against a background of a continuous spectrum are called *dark line spectra* or, more meaningfully, *absorption spectra*.

We have come far into study of the nature of light on the hypothesis of wave characteristics for light. The straight-line propagation suggested by phenomena such as reflection, refraction, and shadows were successfully explained in terms of ray diagrams describing the motion of wave fronts. Diffraction, reinforcement, and interference phenomena were interpreted with the aid of Huygens' principle as evidence supporting the postulated wave motions. Furthermore, nothing about these events would suggest anything but harmony between defining light as energy propagated by wave motion and the actions in any selected phenomenon of light. Measurements to support the predicted wave characteristics such as wavelength, frequency, and speed of propagation were described. Measurements of phenomena beyond the limits of visual sensation indicate that identical wave phenomena extend to extremely short wavelengths such as ultraviolet and X-ray and to extremely long wavelengths such as infrared and radio. The entire spectrum from longest to shortest waves is called the *electromagnetic spectrum*. Fig. 3.13 gives a comprehensive overview of the constituent radiations which make up this spectrum. The reader should notice how the visible spectrum makes up but an insignificant narrow band of this much more extensive range of radiations having characteristics identical to visible light.

Nowhere as yet, however, have we involved the dynamic concepts of energy

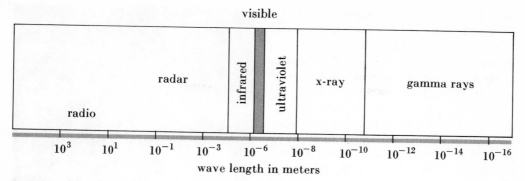

visible

radio

radar

infrared

ultraviolet

x-ray

gamma rays

| 10^3 | 10^1 | 10^{-1} | 10^{-3} | 10^{-6} | 10^{-8} | 10^{-10} | 10^{-12} | 10^{-14} | 10^{-16} |

wave length in meters

Figure 3.13

in our inquiry. We have reserved this to the end because we must extend our means of explaining things into a realm far removed from everyday common sense. We shall have to choose concepts that are in harmony with observed events.

CONSERVATION OF ENERGY

At the outset we prepared you for a possible need for modification of meanings to explain some of the phenomena involving light. These expanded meanings do not contradict any of the basic characteristics we have referred to above, but they do place limitations on the assumptions based upon light being propagated by continuous wave motions.

The photoelectric effect Heinrich Hertz (1857–1894) in 1887 discovered that an electric spark starts more readily between electrodes that are exposed to ultraviolet light. Since the spark includes transfer of electrons, further investigation of phenomena involving electrically charged objects proved that the light was liberating electrons from the surface of metals. The fact of electron liberation by light was not in itself inconsistent with the assumed wave characteristics of light propagation because light waves were known to have properties similar to the electric and magnetic effects produced in many electrical phenomena. But assuming continuous flow of energy by wave propagation led to difficulties which could not be resolved.

Assuming wave propagation of light, energy should flow without interruption through every cross-sectional area illuminated by the light. The amount of energy flowing through each unit of area should be directly proportional to the intensity of the illumination and should be directly proportional to the time of exposure. If, therefore, the photoelectric effect were explained by the wave theory of light, the kinetic energy of the electrons coming from the illuminated surface should be proportional to the intensity of illumination. The facts do not support this prediction. The maximum energies of the liberated electrons are independent of the intensity of illumination. Also, if the wave theory of light were to explain the photoelectric effect, light of low frequency should be just as effective as light of high frequency in providing the energy to liberate electrons. Even if the energy content of low frequency were less than that of high frequency, an increase in the intensity of illumination should restore the balance. Again, the facts do not support this prediction. Observations indicate liberation of electrons only when the frequency of light exceeds a sharply defined threshold frequency and the higher the frequency goes beyond this threshold frequency, the greater becomes the maximum energies of the liberated electrons. The accumulated or combined energy attributed to intense illumination is not transferred to the electrons liberated in the photoelectric effect. Furthermore, when the relative intensity of illumination is very low, if the wave theory applied, long periods of time to accumulate energy would be needed to supply the calculated relative energy needs to eject electrons with the observed energies. The fact that electrons are liberated immediately although not in great numbers under these conditions is not consistent with the idea of continuous flow of waves; and the fact that the liberated electrons have energies equal to those coming from surfaces under intense illumination with the same frequency of light called for serious restudy of the phenomena of light.

Einstein's hypothesis To the brilliant mind of Albert Einstein (1879–1955) the observed conditions characteristic of the photoelectric ejection of electrons did not present a problem calling for modification of the wave propagation concepts of light, but, rather, presented proof that

Albert Einstein. [*Courtesy of the Bettmann Archive.*]

light possessed a corpuscular structure. In 1905 Einstein introduced a fundamental change in the concepts explaining propagation of light. With the admirable simplicity which so often characterized his work, Einstein derived a successful interpretation of the photoelectric effect. Instead of assuming a continuous flow of energy propagated by spherical waves emitted by the source of light, Einstein assumed that the energy of light is concentrated in a discrete packet having an energy content equal to a constant elementary quantity of action multiplied by the frequency of the light. The elementary quantity of action is the universal constant discovered earlier by Max Planck, and the frequency is that predicted by the wavelength and speed of propagation of light.

According to Einstein's hypothesis, if

an electron must have expended upon it an amount of work W in order to be released from a surface, the electron can be ejected only if the energy of the light packet (called a photon) supplying the energy is greater than $W = h\nu_0$. (When W equals the work of liberation, h equals Planck's constant and ν_0 equals the threshold frequency for electron ejection.) If the frequency of the photon energy is ν of higher frequency than ν_0, the electron is ejected with a kinetic energy equal to $KE = h\nu - W$. Therefore, as the frequency of light is increased, the maximum kinetic energy of the ejected electrons becomes increasingly greater. And, because these packets of light (photons) are discrete concentrations of energy, the undivided amount of energy in each photon can be transferred to a single electron. Hence, the immediate liberation of energetic electrons by light of extremely low intensity of illumination. The explanation is complete. Predictions made in accord with Einstein's hypothesis have been found to be in nearly perfect accord with measurement from careful experiments.

The complete theory of photons did not spring forth fullfledged from the mind of Einstein. Some of the cleverest thinkers of his time had contributed to the development of the theory. In fact, Einstein's successful interpretations were an important extension of the quantum hypothesis developed a few years earlier by Max Planck. The conventional wave theory of light also had failed to account for the observed intensity pattern of the various light frequencies emitted by sources at known temperatures.

Planck based his quantum hypothesis upon the assumption that matter can *emit* light only by finite quantities in packets. This did not necessarily mean

that light was propagated in packets. After emission of light in packet form at regular intervals, Huygens' principle made it possible to provide propagation in patterns of homogeneous waves. Planck favored this point of view. Einstein's extension of the quantum idea to *absorption* as well as emission made it also necessary for light to be *propagated* in a discontinuous structure. The success of the photon hypothesis has changed the entire outlook of science and its methods. Let us recount our own procedures.

EXPLANATION VERSUS WISHES

At the outset we invoked our own sensory experiences. We suggested that for light, as for sound, apparent conditions made possible only two means by which energy could be transferred from one location to another; namely, chunks of material could be thrown outward in all directions from the source to be intercepted by the receivers or a wave disturbance could account for the propagation of energy. We fashioned a model based upon postulated wave disturbances.

We now find that for light the propagation is not an "either . . . or" proposition. Nor can we state explicitly that it is a combination of both chunks and waves. Photons are neither chunks nor waves. They are no more one or the other or both than they are red, white, and blue, or long or short. It simply doesn't make sense to ask or to attempt to answer such inquiries.

What we have been learning in this chapter is that our explanations for phenomena in nature are intrinsically uncertain when based upon sensory models. We must not extend our models beyond the realm of verified knowledge, except in attempts for verification. In truth let us admit that these models are but mental images around which we attempt to integrate our understandings. When we have made this admission, we find ourselves more free to do without images, especially when their sensory qualities blur our acceptance of indisputable facts. It happens that science uses a dynamic kind of explanation, one that grows and changes as our understandings grow and change.

SUMMARY

Light, like sound, is a form of energy. The exact nature of light is not yet known. Light has wave characteristics but it is not wholly a wave phenomenon. The wavelengths of light are extremely short but can be measured with an interferometer. The model presented by Huygens' principle is useful in describing and predicting the events in wave propagations. The wave nature of light was confirmed by Young on the basis of observed constructive reinforcement and destructive interference of light waves as predicted by Huygens' principle.

The term *ray* is used to designate the direction of motion of a wave segment in moving from one place to another. The law of reflection generalizes the observed fact that the angle of incidence equals the angle of reflection in regular reflection. The refraction of light is explained on the basis of the ratio of the speed of waves in two adjoining media. The ratio is called the relative index of refraction and is determined by computing the ratio of the sines of the measured angle of incidence and the angle of refraction.

The light does not need a medium of transmission. The speed of light in a vacuum is 186,300 miles per second. The speed of light in transparent media is uniquely different for different frequencies of light, the change in speed in a given medium is greater for the higher frequencies than for the lower frequencies. This variation of speed of transmission with frequency of light explains dispersion of light by prisms. The resulting spectra give important clues to the atomic elements and the atomic structures which constitute the light emitting materials.

The principle of conservation of energy requires that light be emitted, transmitted, and absorbed in quanta of discrete amounts of energy as described by Planck's quantum equation: $E = h\nu$.

PROBLEMS

1 Present five or more evidences of energy transformation which establish light as a form of energy.

2 A sample of flint glass reveals a relative index of refraction of 1.65 for yellow light. To three significant figures what is the speed of the yellow light in the glass?

3 Draw to scale the path of a ray of light through a cube of crown glass 2 inches thick if the ray enters the surface with an angle of incidence of 30° at such a position that the ray passes completely through the parallel surfaces of the cube. Explain the method you used to determine the direction of the refracted ray.

4 Explain the various conditions in the rain drops which produce the rainbow as illustrated in Fig. 3.12.

5 To three significant figures, what is the range of frequencies expressed by the range of wavelengths shown for the electromagnetic spectrum in Fig. 3.13?

6 In a Michelson interferometer, monochromatic light produced 500 dark surfaces as the mirror was moved one-hundredth of a centimeter. What was the wavelength and frequency of the light? What steps did you use in solving these problems and why?

7 Summarize the facts involved in the photoelectric effect which cannot be explained by the continuous wave theory of light.

8 How did Einstein's hypothesis explain the above-mentioned facts?

4

ASPECTS OF SCIENTIFIC THINKING

When we give thought to the variety of sounds we hear and the world of light and color which surrounds us, we realize that we are equipped with sensory apparatus of great discrimination. We are sensitive to reception of communication signals from a great variety of sources. Although thoughts about our sensory apparatus cause us to marvel, the human capacity to give meanings to these diverse signals is infinitely more remarkable. Our ability to organize our thinking into something more than bare observations of fact expands our world. Increasing our world of meanings is the great adventure of intelligent living.

The resourcefulness used in extending the range of communication with the world and in giving meanings to these communications is truly the central gate to expanding knowledge. Giving meanings involves reasoning. The more consistently our meanings have roots in the verifiable predictive aspects of the systems observed, the more free we become to question with hope of success the meanings of the processes of nature. We soon learn of limitations in our interpretive meanings as well as those in our sensory apparatus. The more we learn the more we find to question. The problem is to distinguish fact from fiction, scientifically acceptable explanation from that which is wishful thinking.

KNOWLEDGE BEGETS KNOWLEDGE

A well-known professor of philosophy used to introduce this thought in these words: Ideas are like people; they have ancestors. The adventure of knowing is that valid knowledge prepares the way for further ventures into the world of the unknown. The advantage of science is that by using the methods of science we know what we are doing. No one can hand you knowledge in a neat package ready for use as needed. Each person must develop his own fund of knowledge by constantly using his ideas in such a manner as to refine their meanings, thus making them worthy "ancestors" of ideas yet "unborn." Our ideas take on shades of meaning from the relationships which are given to the situations to which the ideas belong. The meanings are derived not so much from the events anticipated but from the relationships which link past events to present situations in such a manner as to make prediction of future events a possibility. The ideas expressed in science are greatly colored in this regard because they have origins traceable to both observed fact and exploratory thought. The meanings of science are guides for action in the immediate future

based upon interpretation of past and present conditions. The success of scientific meaning lies in the self-corrective nature of basing meanings *only* upon interpreting what is observed fact. When we recognize how ideas are expressed in words and symbols which derive their meanings from the interpretations of both those who speak and those who listen, the value of science is found in its organization of meanings (concepts) so that a more uniform sense of usefulness applies to the interpretations held in common. Thus, critical thought rather than misunderstanding attends the interplay of ideas. The rapid growth of scientific knowledge has its roots in this fertile field of critical thought and self-corrective verification in observed facts. Our personal adventure in knowledge also can have roots of this kind.

There are no well-defined steps of a so-called "scientific method" which we must follow. We cannot divorce one aspect of scientific procedure from the many aspects which might be involved in discovering and organizing the facts and interpretations belonging to an explanation. We color what we observe with our meanings for the situation. We color our interpretations with meanings based on past performances. We color our anticipations and the verifications in terms of judgments whose meanings have roots in the past and the present and have buds extending into the future. It is questionable whether we ever observe, interpret, anticipate, or verify without involving every one of these aspects. Therefore, let us be more critical of our meanings than of a formal method. Let us organize our concepts into useful explanations; useful because they are becoming more compatible with the ideas of others who are interpreting science and useful because they lead to anticipations which are becoming more congruous with the facts observed in natural processes.

Situational meanings   It was suggested that the language of science derives its meanings from the situations to which the words and symbols apply.   For example, the word "frequency" when used in descriptions of sound brings to mind the number of cyclic pressure variations occurring each second at a point of observation in a given medium.   In descriptions of vibrating bodies, the word "frequency" refers to the average number of vibrations per seconds observed in a vibrating object.   In describing light, the word "frequency" brings forth ideas of color and of the energy content of the photons involved, and is quantitatively "measured" by the ratio between the speed of light and a measured wavelength.   Each of these meanings was based upon a growing pattern of observations, interpretations, anticipations, and verifications which belong to explanations of a specific phenomenon.   Therefore, the meaning for the term "frequency" must be couched in words which identify the characteristics discovered and verified by observation in the phenomenon involved.

The unifying concepts of science grow by means of the constant interplay between observed facts and rational interpretations.   For example, our meanings for phenomena involving properties of wave motion stem from observations of water waves.   The interference and reinforcement patterns of overlapping waves, the diffraction patterns of waves entering a harbor, the patterns of equal distances (wavelengths) between crests of waves are all matters of direct observation of water waves.   These patterns, therefore,

become a model useful in interpreting wave-like events observed in the phenomena of sound and light.   The observed fact that sound is propagated through air and reasoning that only compressional waves are possible in media which do not resist a shearing action related sound propagation specifically to cyclic pressure variations moving as waves through media which transmit sounds.   The wavelength of sound was interpreted as the distance between identical conditions of the cyclic pressure variations in a medium, and was verified by observing the measured lengths of air columns which resonate to sounds from sources of known frequency.   The postulated relationship:

speed of propagation
$$= \text{wavelength} \times \text{frequency}$$

was verified by comparing computed results to the results achieved by direct observation of time for sound to travel a measured distance through air of specified temperature.   It is true that our references to observed facts were largely vicarious experiences, but it is hoped that the reader would become curious enough to experience the observations directly when possible.

More obscure from direct observation are the wave characteristics of light. Fundamental similarities with regard to energy transmission suggested analogous phenomena for light and sound.   The wave model for propagation of light was enhanced by the application of Huygens' principle in interpreting the observed results of Young's diffraction experiment. The measurement of wavelengths of monochromatic light by using Michelson's interferometer plus the direct measurement of the speed of light allowed the stipulation of frequency to the phenomenon involved in propagation of light.   The relationship between frequency, wavelength, and speed of propagation in wave motions was again the guide for interpretations. But observations involving the phenomenon of photoelectric effect forced a redefinition of the nature of light propagation.

Waves in water and sound waves have the continuity of cycle after cycle of the wave disturbance which transmits an uninterrupted flow of energy from source to receiver. The particle-like characteristics of photons make the continuity of wave motion impossible. Thus, it was found that any model used for interpretation has only limited usefulness, and the limits established by observed results are as important to adequate interpretation as is the knowledge of the useful characteristics of a model. As our knowledge increases, the interrelationships of our concepts become more useful sources of interpretation than the individual models. It can be said that we do not build *our* world out of experiences but rather that we become aware of *the* world in our experiences of observation and interpretation. Therefore, let us get on with the adventure of observation and interpretation in the hope that along with our search for better choices of concepts to interpret the processes of the world we also may acquire the habit of following through to observed consequences the interpretations we use in everyday life.

THE REWARDS OF CURIOSITY

The immediate consequence of an intelligent curiosity is to have more scientifically acceptable meanings for the natural occurrences which we observe. This knowledge does not reduce the enjoyment we find in our experiences but, rather, it enhances the enjoyment because of better understanding. For instance, knowledge about sound does not reduce our enjoyment of music and the use of musical instruments; it makes enjoyment of good music more probable because of understanding the nature of sound and the production of sound.

Today, music is an important part of most persons' lives. Musicians and listeners to music are primarily interested in it as an art. However, their experiences would be much enhanced were they to become more curious about the scientific explanations of the natural phenomena involved in their art.

Musical phenomena Enjoyment of music involves natural phenomena related to sources of sound, the propagation of sound, and the mechanisms for receiving and interpreting the signals of sound. A musical sound may be characterized as a group of simple musical tones each having a frequency which is a multiple of the *fundamental frequency*. The fundamental frequency is called the *pitch*. The multiples of the fundamental frequency which make up a musical sound are called *overtones* or *harmonics*.

This complex of several frequencies occurring together produces a very complicated series of wave patterns in the wave envelopes which transmit the sound from source to receiver. Fig. 4.1 shows a pat-

Figure 4.1

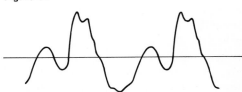

tern of the pressure variations in a wave train as reproduced by a microphone and made visible on a television screen. The combined pattern of pressures does not always indicate only the frequencies produced by the source or sources because interference and reinforcement take place between sounds of different frequencies which produce pulsations called *beats*. The vibrato effect produced in organs is an illustration of this phenomenon. The phenomenon of beats can be demonstrated by two tuning forks of the same frequency. If the forks are sounded simultaneously they produce a single tone that is materially louder than when one fork is sounded alone. If we now were to loop a strong rubber band tightly around the prongs of one of the forks and then sound the two forks again, the sound which before was continuous will now periodically rise and fall in strength. The number of beats per second is determined by the difference between the respective frequencies of the two sources producing the sound.

(4.1) beat frequency equals frequency source *1* minus frequency source *2*

When the beat frequency is not greater than six or seven vibrations per second, the listener perceives a tone halfway between the source frequencies but also hears the beat as a steady rise and fall in intensity. When the beat frequency is increased from six to about twenty vibrations per second the listener hears the rise and fall change to a succession of pulsations which become increasingly annoying until finally he hears clearly the two source frequencies. If the two sources have the same frequency the beat frequency will be zero. This effect is used in piano tuning. A tuning fork of a standard pitch is used as one of the sources. The corresponding string on the piano is tuned to a frequency which produces "zero beats" when sounded with the fork.

The amount of energy carried through a unit area in one second by sound waves is called *intensity*. The differences in the

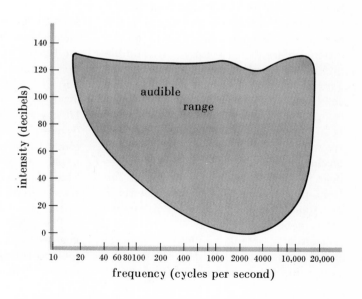

Figure 4.2

relative intensity of the audible harmonics which comprise the wave train is called the *quality* of tone. Different individuals vary greatly as to upper and lower limits of frequency heard. The listener is also unable to distinguish the separate overtones which make up a musical sound. It takes long training and skill to acquire the ability to distinguish the sounds emanating from each of the various instruments of an orchestra. However, the sounds can be analyzed and sound reproduction is today a growing business. Science awaits only a greater interest and curiosity by musicians as scientists to make sound production a growing field of applied science.

The musical instrument as a machine

A musical instrument is a machine for imparting energy to the air in the form of sound. The first essential feature of an instrument is the *generator* which vibrates in a highly complex blend of frequencies. For example, in the clarinet the generator is the single reed in the mouth piece. The second essential is the *resonator* which amplifies certain of the generated frequencies up to an audible intensity. In the clarinet resonance occurs in the cylindrical air column inside the barrel of the instrument. The musical quality of an instrument is produced in both generator and resonator. A defective generator fails to produce overtones having frequencies which are pleasing to hear. A defective resonator would fail to amplify to the proper intensities those overtones which characterize a quality instrument.

To a large extent the pleasing blend of frequencies required by the composer of music and the conductor who interprets the music is produced only by a skilled musician playing a quality instrument. The musician, however, can learn much from a careful study of the characteristics of his instrument and the sound it is capable of producing in order to improve its application to his art.

A musician's choice of instruments for interpreting a given composition will depend upon the effect he wishes to produce and upon his knowledge of the possible characteristics of the instruments at his command. With the modern facilities for study of instruments' qualities, it would seem that modern composers could invent and use many new and refreshingly different combinations of instruments with pleasing effects. Most of today's artists lack the curiosity of the musical giants of yesteryear and lag far behind the scientific instrument makers in producing an art out of the physical phenomena available to them. A basic interest and understanding in the science of sound would arouse progress in the art of music making.

Music—the mathematical art

Blends of musical sounds that seem pleasing to hear are largely a matter of learned appreciation and are closely related to the musical knowledge of the listener. We shall not dwell long upon musical appreciation. However, it should be pointed out that frequencies which comprise the blends found to be pleasing are not formed by a haphazard joining together of just any kind of sound; pleasing blends are recognized to have frequencies that form simple arithmetic ratios.

The growth of musical scales had its genesis in the recognition of these arithmetical ratios. Musical scales were produced to make available these pleasing combinations of sound as the basic tools for the musician. The ratio between the frequencies of two tones is called an *interval*. Although there are an unlimited number of possible intervals, a pleasing result is produced only when the interval is a relatively simple fraction. Discovering pleasing intervals was fundamental to the grouping of frequencies into musical scales.

128). The second triad would consist of G ($768 = 4 \times 192$), B ($960 = 5 \times 192$), and D ($1152 = 6 \times 192$). The third triad would consist of F ($682\frac{2}{3} = 4 \times 170\frac{2}{3}$), A ($853\frac{1}{3} = 5 \times 170\frac{2}{3}$) and C' ($1024 = 6 \times 170\frac{2}{3}$). The D in the second triad is an octave above tone II in the table. The reader should also notice how the intervals between successive notes are simple ratios. For the scale in Key of C

TABLE 4.1

Tone	I	II	III	IV	V	VI	VII	VIII	IX
Ratio (triad)	4		5		6				
					4		5		6
				4		5		6	
Frequency	$4f$	$\dfrac{9f}{2}$	$5f$	$\dfrac{16f}{3}$	$6f$	$\dfrac{20f}{3}$	$\dfrac{15f}{2}$	$8f$	
Name	do	re	mi	fa	sol	la	ti	do'	
Key of C	C	D	E	F	G	A	B	C'	
Frequency	512	576	640	$683\frac{2}{3}$	768	$853\frac{1}{3}$	960	1024	
Intervals		9:8	10:9	16:15	9:8	10:9	9:8	16:15	
Key of D	D	E	F	G	A	B	C	D'	
Frequency	576	648	720	768	864	960	1080	1152	
Intervals		9:8	10:9	16:15	9:8	10:9	9:8	16:15	

The diatonic scale A very pleasing effect is produced when a group of three notes with frequencies in the ratio of 4:5:6 are sounded together. Three notes having frequencies in this ratio are called a *triad*. Reference to Table 4.1 will indicate the diatonic musical scale is composed of three sets of triads. Tone I, the *tonic*, is chosen as the basis for the scale. A triad is produced using this tone as the note of lowest frequency. For example, if C of frequency 512 is the tonic, the first triad would consist of C ($512 = 4 \times 128$), E ($640 = 5 \times 128$) and G ($768 = 6 \times$

these are 9/8, 10/9, and 16/15 repeated always in the order indicated. The first two of these intervals are called *whole tones* and the 16/15 interval is called a *half-tone*. The intervals in the octave consist of five whole tones and two half-tones.

The major drawback in the diatonic scale is easily observed by comparing the frequencies which make up the scale Key of D to the frequencies which make up the scale Key of C. An organ or piano tuned to the diatonic scale Key of C could not be used to play music written in the

Key of D. Anyone who has owned and played a simple harmonica has made this discovery. Music cannot be transposed from one key to another without retuning such an instrument to the second key.

The tempered scale The piano keyboard contains twelve, not seven, intervals to the octave. This scale is based on a sequence of thirteen notes consisting of eight whole tones and five semitones which correspond to the eight white keys and five black keys of the piano octave. This *scale of equal temperament* sacrifices true pitch for the sake of flexibility. Johann Sebastian Bach established the scale in 1722 by publishing his composition "Twenty-four Preludes for the Well-tempered Clavier." These compositions sound pleasing only when played with a tempered scale. The tempered scale as used today has the 2:1 interval of an octave divided into twelve equal intervals. We must recall that an interval is a ratio and not an additive arithmetical difference between two frequencies. Therefore, each of the twelve intervals is not one-twelfth of the 2:1 octave interval, but is the twelfth root of two ($\sqrt[12]{2}$) or 1.059. Since the interval between successive notes is always the same, transposition from one key to another is easy. Fundamentally, however, since these ratios are not simple but irrational ratios, some concessions have to be made in the preferred, pleasing effect of true triad intervals for the sake of ease in transposition. A little thinking and some simple computations will show that the consequences made possible by these concessions far outweigh the sacrifice of pure tones. It has been said that the reason why the tempered scale happens to work so well is that the tempered fifth turns out

to have an interval of 1.4983 which has a difference of only 17 parts in 15,000 from the true fifth whose ratio is 3:2 (1.5). Very few musicians can detect a difference in pitch as small as this. The tremendous growth in musical arts since 1700 can be largely attributed to the discovery and adoption of the equally tempered scale. This growth, it should be pointed out, was made possible by application of mathematical and scientific discoveries which preceded the growth. Progress in the art of music is still going on. Invention in the field of producing music has not stopped, but need for research is evident.

SCIENCE GENERATES ACTION

Who can be so crass as to feel that the age of adventure is past or is so inaccessible as to be out of one's reach? There are more opportunities for adventure today than at any other age in history. Adventure is here for those who seek it. These adventures can start now in the world of everyday living.

Exploration, invention, and expression are activities which enrich the lives of all who partake. These are not the passive, leisurely, or submissive activities so often pictured as the "good life" by magazine and TV advertisements. These are exciting, forward-looking, and tenacious activities which smack of the pioneering spirit. Of course, these activities are not without frustrations. The going is slowed almost to a standstill at times. It takes courage to see a tedious task of learning and discovery through to the finish. However, it is not necessary for one to be out at the fringes of the unknown to partake of this spirit. All that one needs to get started is the curiosity of a child and the willingness to be guided by the fruitful practices of science. Anyone who can think and who can communicate with natural processes and with other persons who are interested in science can find himself engrossed in activities that continually bring new meanings and new promises into his life.

One need not search far for questions to ask. The insight is not in finding questions to ask but in asking questions which are crucial tests of our knowledge. For instance, there are several conditions in nature which produce rainbow-like displays of color. Is our knowledge of the phenomena of light adequate to observe critically and to explain these conditions?

Coronas and halos Under certain conditions faint rainbow-like rings may be observed around the sun or the moon. If the red section is on the outside of the ring, like in the primary rainbow, the ring is called a *corona*. The corona is generally observed at such times as when a fog or light cloud cover is dispersing or when a thin layer of fog persists. It is explained by the diffraction of light around the tiny droplets of the fog which produces reinforcement of some frequencies and interference of others so that the reinforced colors are observed. Most people refer to the corona as "the ring around the sun" or "the ring around the moon." Some people even go so far as to predict rain by it. Although moisture is involved in the phenomena, the prediction must be classified as wishful thinking.

If the red section of the ring is on the inside of the ring, like in the secondary rainbow, the ring is called a *halo*. Two halos are often observed, the brighter one at an angle of 22° from the direction of the sun or moon and the fainter one at an angle of 46°. The halo results from the refraction and dispersion of light by tiny ice crystals floating in the upper stratosphere.

In the polar regions, when the sun is near the horizon, and cold weather produces millions of tiny ice crystals to flutter through the upper portions of the atmosphere, four radial streaks of white light are seen in addition to the halos. The streaks, two vertical and two horizontal, are the result of reflections from the crystal surfaces. The directions of the streaks represent angles where reflecting power of all transparent solids is high. A similar pattern may be observed upon viewing a street lamp through a clean screen door or viewing a study lamp through a silk scarf.

Because of the increased intensity of light where the white streaks cross the halos, the colors are greatly intensified at these regions and form what are called *sundogs*. At times when the sky light is too brilliant for easy observation of the faint halos, the sundogs stand out as spectacular color displays near the horizon just after sunrise and before sunset on cold winter days.

The reader should at this time diagram the conditions of diffraction around droplets and refraction and dispersal through crystals in an attempt at explaining why the colors are seen in reversed order in the corona and halos. (Hint: red light has the longest wavelength of visible light and has the highest speed in ice.)

Polarized light—transverse waves The evidence presented in support of wave characteristics of light propagation made no reference to the type of wave motion involved—longitudinal, transverse, or other possible patterns. The phenomenon of *polarization* of light demonstrates the transverse wave characteristics of light propagation. The light entering an open window may be thought to consist of billions of photons having transverse waves vibrating in all possible directions in the planes perpendicular to the direction of the light rays. (Fig. 4.3.) This

The blue sky The blue of a clear sky is produced by a phenomenon called *scattering*. The light coming to the earth's surface from the sky is not direct sunlight but is scattered light which is predominantly blue. A theory explaining scattering would have the electromagnetic nature of light waves induce transverse

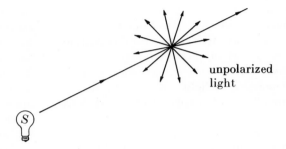

unpolarized light

Figure 4.3

light is largely unpolarized. If the light is exposed to a polarizing situation, all the modes of vibration except one are removed. The remaining light would contain vibrations only in the selected direction. If then the remaining light was exposed to a situation where the favored direction was crosswise to that of the light, the effect would be to extinguish the light completely. A mechanical illustration of the events referred to above can be had by producing a transverse vibration in a rope as indicated in Fig. 4.4. When the slit in the board is in line with the direction of the transverse motion, the pattern of waves continues on to the other side of the board. When the slit is turned at right angles to the transverse motion, the pattern of waves stops at the board. The type of polarization produced in situations affecting light often provides clues to the phenomenon involved.

vibrations in the electrons of the scattering particles, thus absorbing the energy of the photon. A similar photon would be re-emitted almost immediately. However, the emission would be in random directions so that the original direction of the light propagation would be broken up. Because particles as small as air molecules scatter high frequency photons more readily than those of lower frequency, the violet and blue light is scattered the most giving the whole sky a blue appearance.

When larger particles are involved, light of lower frequency is also scattered giving the scattered light a white appearance. This effect is most noticeable in the strong beams of light produced by klieg lights and the "searchlights" so familiar at new business openings in our cities.

Because the electrons involved in emitting the scattered light were those transverse to the ray, the light emitted in any

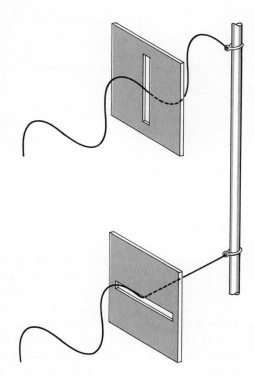

Figure 4.4

given direction should be largely plane polarized. This is a fact found both in the sky light and in the light scattered from searchlight beams. If the blue sky is observed through the polaroid film, a 90° rotation will cause a considerable change in brightness of the blue light observed. This observation is partial evidence in support of the theory of scattering by particles.

The red sunset is attributed to the fact of dust and smoke particles in the lower portion of the atmosphere having scattered out all but the red colors when sunlight is observed after a long journey in the lower portion of the atmosphere.

INTELLIGENT OBSERVATION— ASKING CRUCIAL QUESTIONS

Obviously, things are not always the way they seem to be. This fact was brought to our attention directly with regard to shadows and to the photoelectric effect. Our interpretations of events must bring into play all factors which explicitly explain the phenomena involved. We must be careful not to over-extend our meanings into areas where our anticipations are not congruous with the facts. In other words, what we have learned is useful only if our anticipated outcomes prove to be valid. Scientists have strived and are striving to devise the means which reveal the characteristics useful in explaining physical phenomena. Their discoveries chart a course which we can follow in gaining insights into meanings for our own use and verification.

Mirages and looming One of the most intriguing situations involving atmospheric refraction is the mirage. When one drives along a level highway on a hot day the black asphalt at a distance in front of the car seems to be covered with water. A similar situation plagued the old prospectors walking across the hot desert sands. The water is just a reflected image of the sky. The effect is called a *mirage*, and our knowledge of refraction makes the mirage a predictable fact.

On hot sunny days the air in contact with the highway or the sand has been heated to a high temperature and because the heated air has expanded, light in it is propagated at a slightly greater speed than in the cooler air above. For the light coming from the cooler air and entering the heated air, the index of refraction equals the ratio of the slower speed in cool air to the faster speed in warm air. Thus, the angle of incidence is smaller than the angle of refraction.

index of refraction

$$= \frac{\text{sine angle of incidence}}{\text{sine angle of refraction}}$$

If the angle of incidence is made larger, the angle of refraction increases. When the angle of incidence is increased sufficiently, the angle of refraction becomes 90° and the refracted ray travels along the surface separating the two media. The incidence angle for which the angle of refraction is 90° is called the *critical angle* for the two media involved. If the angle of incidence is made larger than the critical angle, *total reflection* occurs at the surface separating the two media. For example, Fig. 4.5 illustrates total reflection by an isosceles right-angled prism. If the index of refraction glass to air were

$$0.67 = \frac{\text{sine angle of incidence}}{\text{sine angle of refraction}}$$

and the angle of refraction were increased to 90°, the sine angle 90° equals unity and

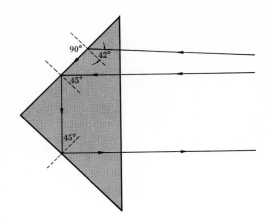

Figure 4.5

the sine angle of incidence would equal 0.67. A table of sines would reveal this angle of incidence to be about 42°. Therefore, incident angles greater than 42° would produce total reflection.

When light approaches the hot air layer at a large angle of incidence, as indicated in Fig. 4.6, it is totally reflected giving rise to a mirage.

When the air next to the surface is substantially colder than the air at a higher

Figure 4.6

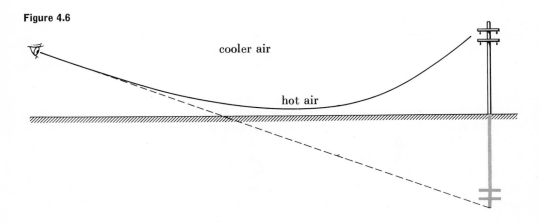

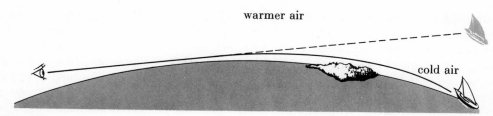

warmer air

cold air

Figure 4.7

level, the rays of light are reflected downward as indicated in Fig. 4.7. Frequently, the persons aboard ships in waters near the coastal islands of California see images of distant ships sailing over the tops of the channel islands. This phenomenon is called *looming.*

When one looks at an object across the top of a camp fire or across a stretch of hot sandy beach, one often sees a wavy, shimmering effect. This arises from the refraction of the light as it passes from colder to warmer to colder air. The twinkling of stars in part is due to a similar effect.

Events such as have been mentioned above are parts of everyday observations made more interesting when they are understood. But scientists are generally more interested in questions more baffling than these. One such question led to an unexpected outcome and became the basis for formulation by Einstein of the theory of relativity.

The ether   We have become accustomed to the idea of waves in terms of disturbances moving in a tangible medium. In considering the Doppler effect we found apparent changes occurred in the wave characteristics of sound when the source and observer were moving with regard to the transmitting medium. If the reader successfully explained how the apparent frequency of sound changes for the moving observer, he realizes that the apparent frequency depends upon the relative speed between the sound waves and the observer. That is, if the speed of sound were 1140 ft per second and the observer were moving toward the source at 114 ft per second, the relative speed obtaining would be 1140 ft per second + 114 ft per second = 1254 ft per second. The apparent frequency of sound known to have wavelengths of 2.28 ft per wavelength would be computed to be:

$$\text{apparent frequency} = \frac{\text{relative velocity}}{\text{wavelength}}$$

$$= \frac{1254 \text{ ft/sec}}{2.28 \text{ ft/wavelength}}$$

$$= \frac{550 \text{ wavelengths}}{\text{sec}}$$

If the observer did not know that he was moving toward the source but did know that the source was emitting sound of wavelength 2.28 ft at an apparent frequency of 550 wavelengths per second, he would compute the speed of sound to be 1254 ft per second. Had the observer been moving away from the source at the same speed, the apparent frequency would have been 450 wavelengths per second, and he would have computed the speed of sound to be 1026 ft per second.

Only when the observer is at rest with respect to the medium, would he observe a frequency of 500 wavelengths per second and compute the speed to be 1140 ft per second. It follows that, in general, the apparent frequency and computed speed of sound depend upon the relative speed between the observer and the medium. Had the observer known that he was in motion, he would have tried to determine the relative motion between himself and the medium so that he could compensate in computing the speed of sound in the medium.

The verification of wave properties for light propagation and the apparent fact that light is transmitted through the vacuum of space brought into focus the need to learn the nature of the postulated medium in which light waves were thought to be propagated. The scientists of the nineteenth century could not conceive of light being propagated without a medium and, therefore, postulated an all-pervading medium which they called the *ether*. It was held that when instruments of proper refinement were devised, the apparent effects of motions with regard to the ether would be measured as had been done for sound. Instruments of desired refinement were available in 1881. Between 1881 and 1887 experiments were performed by Albert Michelson (1852–1931) and Edward Morley (1838–1923) to detect the relative motion of a source of light and the medium through which it was moving. A Michelson interferometer was used which could detect an effect more than ten times as small as was expected.

The experimental design can best be understood with reference to Fig. 3.10. The interferometer was set for a maximum interference when the light to mirror M_1 moved north and south and that to mirror M_2 moved east and west. The instrument was then rotated through 90°, and any change in transit time along the two paths would have become apparent in an interference shift. The earth's orbital speed of 18.3 miles per second was great enough to produce a calculated amount of shift in the interference pattern. The expected shift was never found, and the experiment was repeated at intervals of time which should have revealed maximum changes in the predicted results.

Only two interpretations could be made of the observed facts: first, a propagating medium does not exist and the measured speed of light will be the same regardless of apparatus used or the motions of the apparatus, the observer, or the source of light; second, nature conspired against the observers by causing the ether to move always in such a way as to negate the results or by causing the apparatus to change in length just enough to compensate for the speed of its motion. Neither of these conclusions were very popular. The first interpretation seemed equally as ridiculous as the second. However, all experimental facts agree to the first explanation; it has become a basis for logical development of several important insights into physical processes.

One of the first scientists to accept the factual interpretation was Albert Einstein (1879–1955) who in 1905 offered his special theory of relativity. Einstein recognized two fundamental principles: the laws of nature are the same for all systems moving with uniform speed in a given direction, and light moves through a vacuum with a constant speed whether emitted from a stationary or moving source. The arguments used by Einstein to justify his new concepts are too intricate to develop in this book, but they are perfectly sound and no successful criticism has been directed against them. Einstein showed that everything takes place as if any object in motion with respect to an observer will seem to be shorter in the direction of motion than it would seem to a second observer riding along with the object. In the same manner, the second observer would view the first also shortened in the direction of his apparent motion. The apparent shortening of lengths has as a complement a required slowing of clocks or apparent time. The differences observed in length and time become more noticeable as the relative speeds approach that of light in a vacuum. The speed of light in a vacuum is the greatest speed attainable for material objects. The reason why we are not aware of these effects is that the differences are immeasurably minute for bodies moving at speeds which are small compared to that of light in a vacuum.

Other consequences of special relativity will be mentioned in appropriate places throughout this book. Crucial tests are still being made with regard to many of the consequences predicted by the theory of relativity. The reader can share in this adventure. Curiosity should prompt the reader to keep an eye open for news about the experiments and the interpretation of the outcomes which are reported in newspapers and magazines.

The success of Einstein was the success of an approach which relied only upon observed facts as a basis for developing explanations. The predicted consequences of the special theory of relativity have been found to be valid in all of the conclusive tests performed thus far and the validated consequences are accepted as fact. Those aspects of the theory still untested will stand or fall upon the outcomes of facts measured in phenomena where predicted consequences, if present, can be revealed.

SUMMARY

There are no well-defined steps to the so-called scientific method. We must continually observe, interpret, anticipate, and verify in order that our anticipations may become more congruous with the facts observed in natural events. Knowledge enhances enjoyment of living in a world of natural phenomena which gain reliable meaning only through scientific explanations.

Music involves the natural phenomena related to the production, propagation, and reception of sound. The musical instrument is a machine for imparting energy to the air in the form of sound. It consists of a generator and a resonator which together control the pitch and quality of the sound produced. Music is a mathematical art. The musical scales are determined in terms of ratios of frequencies which are pleasing to the ear and which are convenient to use in building versatile musical instruments and in composing and interpreting sounds which express the art of music.

Nature is an ever-present source of events which prompt curiosity. The colors found in coronas and halos take on meaning when explained by means of diffraction, refraction, and dispersion of light by water droplets and ice crystals in the atmosphere. The phenomenon of polarization of light demonstrates the transverse wave characteristics of light propagation. Scattering of light by the molecules and dust particles in the air explains the blue sky and red sunsets. Refraction and total reflection at incident angles greater than the critical angles explain the phenomena of mirages and looming.

Continued curiosity led to valid understandings of natural events. The interpretations used to explain the results of the Michelson-Morley experiments led to the abandoning of the idea of the ether and to the development of Einstein's special theory of relativity. The theories and concepts of science change and develop on the basis of outcomes of facts measured in phenomena where comparison of anticipations and actual events can be made.

PROBLEMS

1 Being specific about the facts and interpretations involved, describe an example of a concept which *for you* has been shaped by an interplay of observed facts and rational interpretations.

2 Determine the beat frequency produced by sounding E in Key of D (648 cycles per second) and E in Key of C (640 cycles per second). How would this beat sound to the listener? Do the same for F in Key of D (720 cycles per second) and F in Key of C (682⅔ cycles per second).

3 On the basis of Table 4.1 compute and arrange one octave (Key of G) based on the tonic G of frequency 768 cycles per second. Indicate the triads. Show the arithmetic used in computing the frequencies. Explain the musical reasonings for the diatonic scale and indicate how your computations are based on this reasoning.

4 What interpretations of evidence support the assumption that light waves are transverse?

5 A ray of light falls at the midpoint of a surface of a prism and at an angle of incidence of 33°. Make a diagram to scale showing the path of this ray within an equilateral prism made of glass having a relative index of refraction of 1.59.

6 Explain the phenomena of the mirage and of looming.

7 Why were the results of the Michelson-Morley experiments on the motion of light so difficult to interpret?

5

EARTH IN SPACE

In this age of space exploration the daily rotation of the earth on its axis generally is accepted without question. But mankind has not always been so willing to accept this idea. In ancient times, those who pondered upon the subject thought of the earth as the immovable center of the universe. They observed that everything in the universe seemed to revolve around the earth. The earth was thought to be the exalted center of all creation. To relegate the earth to a lesser role seemed degrading and almost unthinkable. The earth seemed to be the center of all cosmic activity. Even today casual observations would tend to support this contention. Even when we know the truth we often find it difficult to defend the accepted relationships. Ask yourself what evidence would you put forth in proof that the earth *is* spinning through space?

We experience the procession of night and day. We know that the rotation

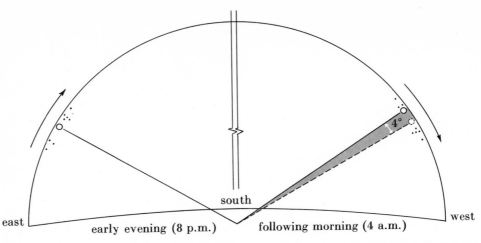

Figure 5.1 The eastward drift of the moon among the stars. Moonrise occurs approximately 50 minutes ($12\frac{1}{2}°$) later each day.

of the earth with respect to the sun brings forth this effect. But the fact of belief would hardly constitute final proof of earthly motion. The ancients, including their most learned men, believed that the sun moved around the earth. Even today we speak of sunrise and sunset as if the sun were in motion.

We also experience the diurnal (recurring every day) motion of the stars. This apparent motion is also attributed mostly to the earth's rotation and in part to the earth's motion in its revolution around the sun. And yet, the fact that all of the stars maintain their relative positions to each other year after year is convincing proof of the earth's motion only when coupled with the knowledge that the stars have tremendous variation in their distances from the earth. The ancients located all the stars on a sphere so large in size and so distant from the earth as to make the earth an immovable point at its center. They also invented an ethereal weightless substance for the stars,

thereby making it possible to imagine them moving in space without opposition. Thus, the ancients produced an explanation which did not tamper with the sensation of seeing the stars apparently moving around the earth. Even though we know better, it is difficult to feel that we and the earth are doing the moving and not the sun and the stars. Indeed, for the practical purposes of time-keeping and navigation, the earth-centered model often is preferred because of its simplicity.

We observe the monthly sequence of the phases of the moon and attribute this to the earth and the moon revolving around a common center once each 27.322 days as measured with respect to the stars. The time interval of this motion is called the sidereal month. From an earth-centered point of view the moon appears to move around the earth each day and at the same time to advance eastward among the stars overtaking the same star groups each sidereal month. In the same sense, the sun can be thought

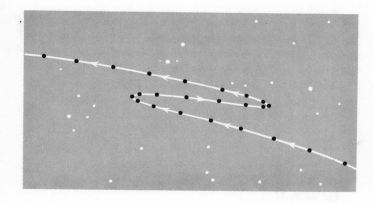

Figure 5.2 Periodically the planets seem to reverse their directions of motion among the stars. For Mars the retrograde motion occurs at intervals of about 780 days.

to move eastward among the stars overtaking the same star groups each sidereal year (365.256 days). (This is, of course, the time it takes for the earth to complete one revolution around the sun with respect to the stars.) Because of these independent motions of the moon and earth with respect to each other and of the moon and earth with respect to the sun,

it takes a somewhat longer time for the moon position to overtake the apparent position of the sun than to overtake the star groups. The interval between moon-sun conjunctions is called a synodic month, the duration of which is about 29.531 days. The moon phases from new moon to new moon correspond to the synodic month. Again, the everyday de-

The moon 19 days after new moon. The phases of the moon are attributed to the earth and moon revolving about a common center once each 27.3 days. [*Courtesy of the Mount Wilson and Palomar Observatories.*]

INSTITVTIO
ASTRONOMICA

Iuxta Hypotheseis tam Veterum quam

COPERNICI ET TYCHONIS BRAHEI,
CAPVT PROOEMIALE.

QVAM Plato Astronomiam , alij plærique Veterum etiam Astrologiam dixere. Ex quo autem Chaldæi suas nugas in Doctrinam hanc invexerunt , est ferè Astrologiæ nomen tribuum Genethliacæ (quæ & Iudiciaria ferè appellatur.) Astronomia verò nuncupata est, quæ in contemplandis, dimetiendisque Astrorum motu, distantia, ordine, magnitudine, luce, adjunctisque cæteris consimilibus occupatur.

Originem ipsi fecit admiratio ; tum nimirùm, cùm homines præter splendorem, varietatem, multitudinem, amplitudinem Siderum, obseruârunt in ipsis motum tam constantem, tam regularem , tam incessanter diei , ac no-

ctis, æstatisque, & hyemis vicissitudines inducentem.

Commendat illam summoperè dignitas subiectæ materiæ, quæ non alia est,quam amplissima,nobilissimáque totius Mundi regio ; Cælestis nempe, quam homines vt contemplentur, tum obtinere oculos, tum erectos habere vultus à Sapientioribus dicuntur.

Certant de eius inuentione , & antiquitate Babylonij, ob authorem Belum ; Ægyptij , ob Mercurium ; Mauri , ob Atlantem , & Herculem;Græci,ob Iouem,Orpheum,& Atreum, Scythæ, ob Prometheum, &c.

Quorum supersunt Obseruationes , antiquissimi Babylonij sunt ; nimirùm habet Ptolomæus aliquot Eclipseis ab iis obseruatas annis paullò plus ante Christum septingentis. Quod de vlterioribus memorant , aut nullo probatur monumento, aut fabulam sapit.

The Ptolemaic Universe as shown by Gassendi, 1658. [*Courtesy of the Yerkes Observatory.*]

Sunt verò Obseruationes eorum , quæ in ætris apparent (ac Phænomena idcircò vo- *(gajendi Obseruationes)*

cantur) germana totius Astronomiæ fundamenta : quatenus factis comparatísque Obseruationi

net, in quo terram cum orbe lunari tanquam epicyclo contineri diximus. Quinto loco Venus nono mense reducitur. Sextum deniq; locum Mercurius tenet, octuaginta dierum spacio circu currens. In medio uero omnium residet Sol. Quis enim in hoc

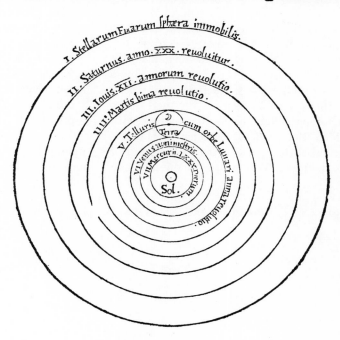

pulcherrimo templo lampadem hanc in alio uel meliori loco po neret, quàm unde totum simul possit illuminare? Siquidem non inepte quidam lucernam mundi, alii mentem, alii rectorem uo cant. Trimegistus uisibilem Deum, Sophoclis Electra intuentē omnia. Ita profecto tanquam in solio regali Sol residens circum agentem gubernat Astrorum familiam. Tellus quoque minime fraudatur lunari ministerio, sed ut Aristoteles de animalibus ait, maximam Luna cum terra cognationē habet. Cō ipit interea à Sole terra, & impregnatur annuo partu. Inuenimus igitur sub
hac

The Copernican System as shown in *De revolutionibus orbium coelestium*, 1556. [*Courtesy of the Yerkes Observatory.*]

scription of these observations made from the earth seem more natural when made from the point of view of a geocentric model. But of course we have now become accustomed to the idea that things aren't always the way they seem to be.

For those curious enough to attempt the location of the planets, the sunlight reflected from five planets can be observed from the earth with the naked eye. As viewed from the earth these planets seem to follow very nearly the same path in the sky as the sun. But there is an annoying difference in the manner with which the planets "wander" when observed with regard to the background of fixed stars. Where the moon and sun seem to move among the stars at a fairly constant speed on simple circular paths, the planets seem to travel in complicated variations of speed and on seemingly erratic paths. The planets at times seem to reverse their directions of motion temporarily—a phenomenon known as *retrograde motion*. Inventing a logical explanation for these apparent motions occupied the lifetimes of several of the most learned men of antiquity. The most successful explanations were presented in the form of models invented to represent the observed motions.

Let us examine two models, one based upon concepts prevalent in ancient times and the other which revolutionized man's

Figure 5.3   The Ptolemaic scheme of cycles and epicycles turning about a stationary earth.

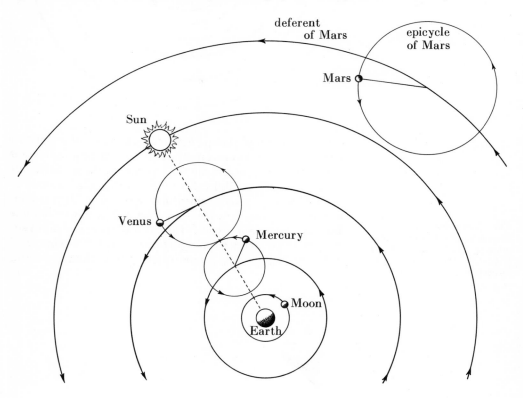

whole trend of thinking. The first model successfully satisfied men's curiosities for almost 1400 years. The second model helped to usher in the age of science. In each model, let us try to discover the useful insights as well as the errors.

CONCEPTUAL MODELS

For approximately 18 centuries (300 B.C. to 1500 A.D.) the accepted theories about the nature of the universe were based on such "common-sense" principles as the following:

1. The earth is the center of the universe and is the only solid thing in the universe and hence is immovable.
2. The heavenly bodies are the abode of the gods or is a creation of God and, therefore, must have the "perfect" form, spherical and unblemished.
3. The heavenly bodies must move around the earth in circular paths or in combinations of circular motions— the circle being the "perfect" curve.
4. The heavenly bodies are in continuous motion made possible because they are composed of a spirit-like substance which is weightless and subject to none of the "defects" of earthly materials.

Ptolemy's geocentric model The most successful conceptual scheme set forth to describe and to permit prediction of the heavenly motions on the basis of these ancient principles was invented by Ptolemy of Alexandria. Ptolemy lived in the second century after Christ. His knowledge of ancient astronomy and previous attempts at astronomical models was encyclopedic. His monumental book on astronomy, the *Almagest*, was introduced into Western culture by the Arabs who transmitted so much of ancient knowledge to Western Europe. As a part of his book Ptolemy devised an ingenious system of *cycles* and *epicycles* used in conjunction with *eccentric paths* and the *equant* to account for all known motions in the universe. Fig. 5.3 represents a model based on Ptolemy's system. Because of size, the figure shows only the innermost celestial bodies. The scheme placed all of the fixed stars on the surface of a large sphere which formed the outermost periphery of the universe. Beyond this outermost sphere there was nothing. The sphere was so large that the immovable earth at the center could be considered geometrically as a single point. The entire sphere turned in a westward direction around the earth once each sidereal day. The stars, therefore, moved in circular paths.

The sun and the moon were the only other bodies placed on purely circular paths. The moon was placed on the circle nearest to the earth and the sun was placed on a circle beyond the paths of the planets Mercury and Venus. In order to account for the observed periodic changes in the motions and the apparent sizes of the sun and moon, the centers of the circular paths of these bodies were offset slightly from the earth. Therefore, as viewed from the earth these bodies would seem to move along *eccentric* paths (Fig. 5.4). The fact that eccentrics violated the ancient doctrine of completely geocentric motion did not seem to detract from the usefulness of this device in accounting for observed motions.

The troublesome retrograde motions of the planets were solved by use of *epicycles* which also violated the doctrine of completely geocentric motion. Each planet was represented as moving in a small circle (*the epicycle*) whose center moved simultaneously in a larger circle (*the deferent*) around the earth (Fig. 5.5). The observed rates of planetary motion could not be properly represented if these epicycles were assumed to roll along steadily on an earth-centered deferent, therefore, eccentrics were introduced to bring the model into harmony with observed data. Thus, the Ptolemaic system was not strictly geocentric, although the earth was assumed to be immobile and the paths were represented as combinations of pure circles. One striking feature of the model was that the centers of the epicycles of Mercury and Venus remained always in a line connecting the earth and the sun.

In view of the complexity of the scheme, there is no evidence that Ptolemy ever regarded the represented motions as being physically real. The model was an abstract geometric device set forth to describe his own observations as well as the recorded observations of his predecessors in Greece and Babylonia. A tribute to the methodic excellence of the device is the thousand years of acceptance with only slight modification. At wide intervals of time, some features of the model had to be changed to restore harmony between the model and observations. For example, eccentrics and the sizes and rates of the epicycles had to be changed and a greater reliance was placed upon a device called the *equant*. Fig. 5.6 illustrates the effect produced by the equant. The center D of an epicycle was usually represented as moving at a uniform rate of rotation about the deferent's center at O. Discrepancies were often adjusted by placing the center of the deferent away from the earth to produce eccentrics. But even this did not always faithfully

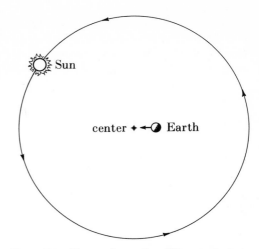

Figure 5.4 Eccentric path. The path is a circle with its center offset from the earth.

represent observed motions. In some cases it was necessary to represent D revolving at a uniform angular motion with respect to another point such as C, called the *equant*. That is, the angle DCB was made to change at a constant rate while D moved along the deferent. Thus, the motion of D was uniform as viewed from C and circular as viewed from O; when viewed from the earth, the motion was a complicated combination of motions which described the observed celestial motions involved. In time the number of additional motions became excessive. By the time of the American Colonial period the geocentric system required more than 70 simultaneous motions to describe the paths of the seven celestial bodies then known. But, you might ask, why did it take so long to discover the erroneous nature of the scheme?

It must be remembered that the Ptolemaic system was remarkably more flexible than most of the dogmatic doctrines adhered to during the Middle Ages. It served very well for predicting the future

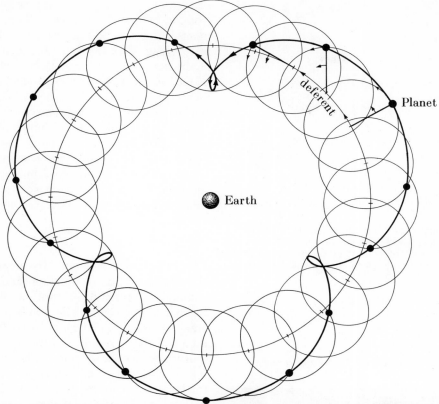

Figure 5.5 Tracing the path of a planet moving in an epicycle whose center is moving along a deferent.

positions of almost all the celestial bodies and when infrequently discrepancies developed, new epicycles and equants were added to bring the system back into harmony with observations. The world of the medieval thinker was a static one of clinging to the collected wisdom of the ancients rather than attempting original interpretations of their own. The question was not how to gain a rational explanation of phenomena, but rather to seek the authority of ancient wisdom. For instance, when changes were made in the celestial scheme, the idea of the stationary earth was defended as a matter of course because since antiquity such arguments had always formed a part of written accounts on astronomy. Although the Ptolemaic scheme was not strictly in accord with the geocentric criteria which predominated in the doctrines of the early philosophers, it was in accord with most of the Greek philosophic doctrine and it was given theological acceptance by the medieval Christian Church. One of the strongest arguments for the Ptolemaic scheme was its "common-sense" answer to why the fixed stars

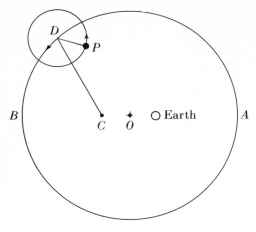

Figure 5.6 The effect of an equant. The center of the epicycle moves at a constant angular rate around the equant at C, but on a circle about the center at O offset from the earth.

Nikolaus Copernicus. [*Courtesy of the Bettmann Archive.*]

showed no change in relative positions from one season to another. (This argument supporting the geocentric scheme lasted long after the general acceptance of the heliocentric scheme.) The above-stated arguments were seemingly overpowering reasons why the Ptolemaic scheme should be maintained. Nevertheless, after 1400 years of influence, the geocentric scheme began giving way to a heliocentric (sun-centered) system, not because of indisputable proof, but because the heliocentric idea gave a vastly more simplified model for the observed celestial motions.

The heliocentric system By depicting all celestial motion as being relative to an immobile sphere of fixed stars and placing the sun at the center, the number of required motions could be reduced to less than half the 70 required of the sixteenth-century geocentric scheme. The name of the scholar who successfully formulated the heliocentric system was Nikolaus Copernicus (1473–1543). Copernicus, who did most of his work in Poland, was educated in Italy. He, like many scholars throughout the years, became annoyed at the complexity of the accepted scheme of astronomy, but unlike the others Copernicus devoted much of his efforts in mathematics and astronomy toward working out a *new* system for describing celestial motions. In the new system the earth lost its exalted position at the center of the universe but in turn gained prominence by virtue of the fact that the earth's motions figured heavily in the explanations of all apparent celestial motions. The Copernican model was in no greater accord with actual observation than the Ptolemaic scheme, but its greater simplicity soon became apparent to anyone who possessed an open-minded freedom to choose between the schemes. Fig. 5.7 is a schematic model of the Copernican system indicating the relationship of celestial bodies out to the distance of Mars. Copernicus, like Ptolemy, placed the fixed stars on a distant sphere, but the Copernican sphere was stationary. The fixed stars became the background against which the celestial bodies were viewed from the rotating earth. All the planets including the earth were indicated as moving on concentric spheres with but a small number of epicycles and eccentrics needed to account for the details of observed motions. The moon, as in the Ptolemaic scheme, made a monthly revolution around the earth. All the motions in the heliocentric system were made to go counterclockwise as viewed from the north. The most revolutionary concept of the Copernican system was the effect

Figure 5.7 The Copernican heliocentric system. Motions are counterclockwise as viewed from a positon in space toward the celestial north pole.

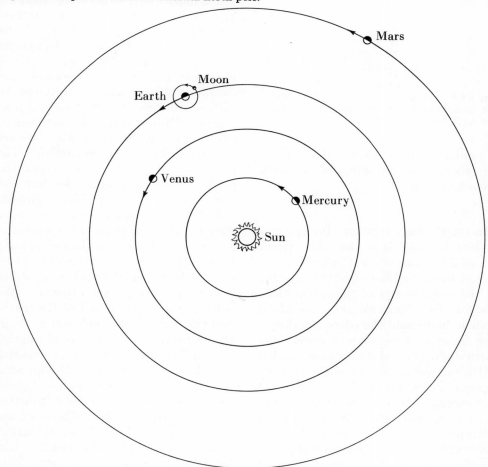

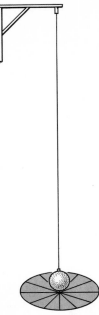

Figure 5.8 Foucault pendulum. The pendulum maintains its orientation in space while the earth turns beneath it.

of combining the rotation of the earth on its axis and the revolution of the earth around the sun.

The earth's daily rotation Because our present-day models of the solar system are modifications of the Copernican system, it should be interesting to note some of the consequences of the assumptions made in the Ptolemaic and Copernican systems in the light of modern knowledge. For instance, if we were to assume the earth stationary and the apparent motion of the sun and stars to be caused by their motions around the earth, the sun would be required to move with a speed in excess of 24 million miles per hour, or over 6,700 miles per second. The most remote planets would require speeds greater than the speed of light, and the nearest star beyond

the sun would require a speed 9000 times the speed of light. Therefore, for us the assumption of daily star circuits around the earth is absurd. The apparent motions of the sun and stars must result from the rotation of the earth as was assumed in the Copernican system, but it is not proof of that rotation.

A direct and convincing proof of the earth's rotation is the Foucault pendulum which is demonstrated to the public in many museums and planetariums. The pendulum is merely a heavy iron ball suspended on a long wire attached at the top in a manner which leaves it free to swing in any direction. The proof was first demonstrated under the dome of the Panthéon at Paris by the French physicist Foucault in 1851. Those who watched the demonstration saw the area under the pendulum slowly turn in a clockwise direction with respect to the swinging pendulum. The rotation of the earth has no effect on the pendulum which continues to swing in its original orientation. The rate of turning of the area under the pendulum depends upon the latitude. For example, let us consider a circular area 30 ft in diameter with its center directly below the point of suspension of a Foucault pendulum and located in Long Beach, California, 33° 46′ north latitude. Once each 24 hours the whole area rotates around the earth's axis. However, the point at the southern end of the north-south diameter of the circle will be about 16.7 feet further from the axis of rotation than the northern end of that diameter (Fig. 5.9). Thus, during a 24-hour rotation, the southern point will travel about 2π times 16.7 ft or about 104.8 ft further than the northern point. Therefore, not only does the circle travel on the earth's surface eastward around the earth's axis, but it is also rotating slowly counterclock-

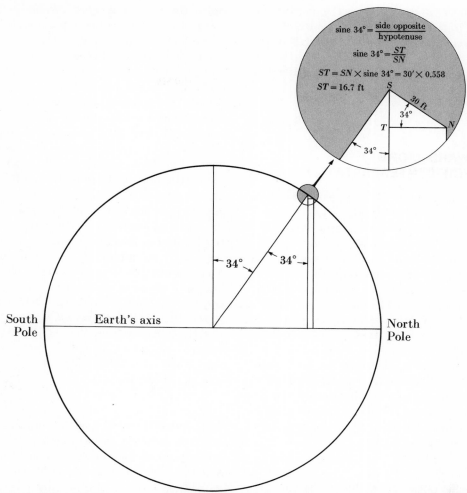

Figure 5.9 The rate with which the earth rotates beneath the Foucault pendulum depends upon the latitude of its location.

wise around a vertical axis through its own center. At Long Beach, California, the time for one complete rotation is about 1.8 days.

Circumference ÷ motion of north and south points with respect to the center

$2\pi15$ ft ÷ $2\pi(15 \sin 33° 46')$ ft per day

$= \dfrac{1}{\sin 33° 46'}$ days $= 1.8$ days

This means that the pendulum would seem to turn through 360° in 1.8 days or 360° ÷ (1.8 × 24) = 8⅓ degrees per hour in a clockwise direction. At the equator the rotation of the pendulum stops. The nearer the latitude is to the poles of the earth's axis, the greater is the hourly rotation until at the poles the Foucault pendulum appears to rotate through 360° per day or 15° per hour. These observations are proof positive that the earth is rotating about an axis.

TOWARD MORE SPECIFIC INTERPRETATION

The usefulness of the geometric patterns established in the Ptolemaic and Copernican systems is still recognized today. The apparent motion east to west of the fixed stars each sidereal day gives the impression that the stars are located on the inside of a hollow sphere. For purposes of locating celestial objects and for navigation, the scheme of a celestial sphere of the fixed stars is a reliable standard for making observations and measurements. In order to speak more intelligently about our observations of celestial motions, including our own movements in space, let us establish meanings for some of the often used reference points on the celestial sphere.

Specific observation guides If you were to sight upward along a vertical line such as a plumb line, you would be looking toward the *zenith*, the point directly overhead in the sky. The point of the celestial sphere directly beneath you is called the *nadir*. The great circle of the celestial sphere situated halfway between the zenith and nadir is called the *horizon*. The horizon is situated at right angles to the plumb line and does not very often coincide with the visible horizon. The points of the celestial sphere directly above the poles of the earth's axis are

called the *north* and *south celestial poles;* and just as the earth's equator is halfway between the earth's poles, the *celestial equator* is halfway between the north and south celestial poles. At any given location the *celestial meridian* is that great circle of the celestial sphere which passes through the zenith and nadir of the given location, as well as the north and south celestial poles (Fig. 5.10). The *astronomical latitude* of any given location in the northern hemisphere is the number of degrees measured on the celestial meridian between the north celestial pole and the northern horizon. Because the celestial horizon is affected by any condition such as a mountain or an ore deposit which would alter the direction of a plumb line at a place of observation, the *geographical latitude*, which has been corrected for "station errors," may be slightly different from that of the astronomical latitude. Except for very precise work the two latitudes may be considered identical.

Apparent motions of celestial bodies If an observer were at the north pole, the north celestial pole would be at the zenith and the celestial equator would coincide with the horizon. From this vantage point the stars would be seen to move in circles parallel to the horizon. The stars would never appear to rise or set. The sun would appear to rise at about March 21 and be above the horizon until about September 23. The moon would rise and set about once each month.

At latitude zero, the earth's equator, the north and south celestial poles would be on the horizon and the celestial equator would pass through the zenith from east to west. An observer at the equator would see all the stars of the celestial

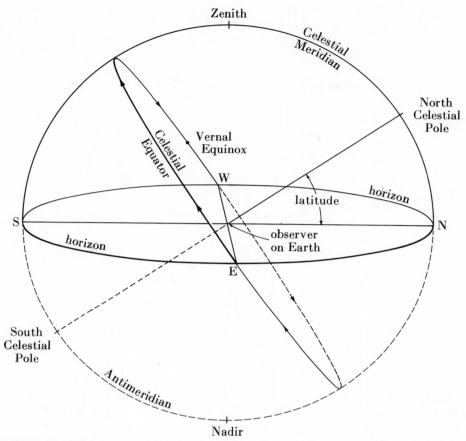

Figure 5.10 The celestial sphere. The observer sees only the portion of the sphere which is above the horizon.

sphere during each sidereal year. The stars would appear to cross the horizon at right angles. The sun would pass across the celestial equator on March 21 and September 23 and would be north of the celestial equator from March 21 to about September 23 and south of the celestial equator from September 23 to March 21. Each new moon would be about the same distance north or south of the equator as the sun at that time.

Full moons occur when the moon is directly opposite the sun and therefore would be about as far on the opposite side of the celestial equator as the sun at any given time.

At Long Beach, California, latitude north 34°, the north celestial pole is on the celestial meridian about 34° above the horizon. The celestial equator arches from the east point of the horizon to the west point and is inclined so as to make

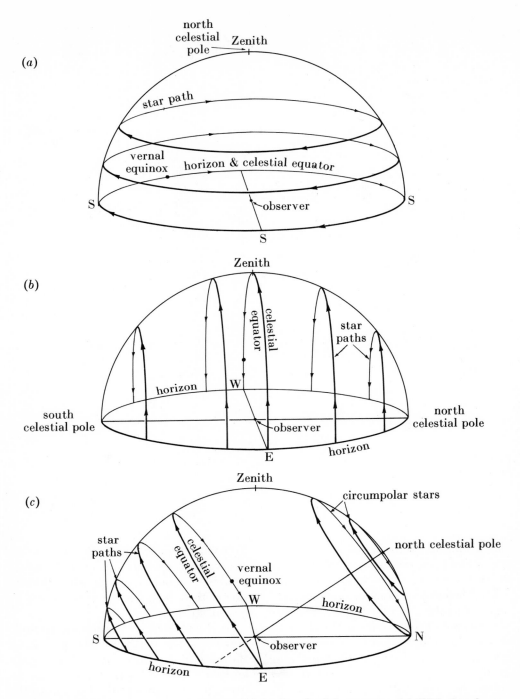

Figure 5.11 Apparent star motions are parallel to the celestial equator. (*a*) With the observer at the earth's north pole the horizon coincides with the celestial equator. (*b*) With the observer at the earth's equator the celestial equator is normal to the horizon. (*c*) The observer is at 34° N. latitude.

its highest point cut the celestial meridian 34° south of the zenith. An observer in Long Beach, California, sees the apparent paths of the stars inclined parallel to the celestial equator. Looking toward the far north, the stars within a radius of 34° are above the horizon at all times and seem to turn around the celestial north pole. When the area of observation is shifted from the zenith southward, the star paths are depressed more and more toward the horizon until they disappear completely. The sun arches across the sky also on paths nearly parallel to the celestial equator. If the observer could disregard displacement due to atmospheric refraction, the sun's path would cross the celestial meridian at about the same point as the celestial equator on March 21 and September 23. On June 22 the sun's inclined path reaches a point of the meridian about (34° − 23½°) 10½ degrees south of the zenith. On December 22 the sun's path is depressed to a

point (34° + 23½°) 57½ degrees south of the zenith.

A person needs only to determine the latitude of his location to make comparable notations with respect to observations for his latitude as were made in the example. Practical applications are sometimes made of these facts. With regard to the location of the noonday sun, architects sometimes design overhanging roofs which shade windows from the noonday sun from late March to late September. The overhang produces an angle at the window bottom (measured between the vertical window and a line from the bottom of the window to the edge of the overhang) which is equal to the degrees latitude of the location of the building.

A brief explanation should be made at this point concerning the 23½° which were involved in the computations shown above. The earth revolves in its orbit with respect to the stars once each sidereal year and rotates on its axis once each

Figure 5.12 Principal points on the ecliptic. The ecliptic is in the plane of the earth's orbit. The celestial equator is in the plane of the earth's equator.

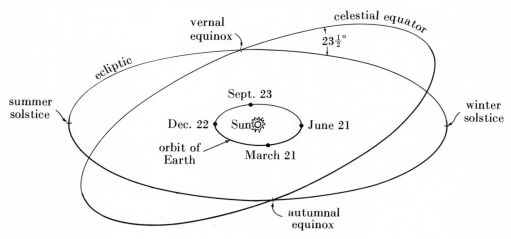

sidereal day. The earth's axis is inclined $23\frac{1}{2}°$ from the line through its center perpendicular to the plane of its orbit; therefore, the sun's apparent annual path around the celestial sphere is a great circle which is inclined $23\frac{1}{2}°$ to the celestial equator. The name given to the apparent great circle path of the sun is the *ecliptic*. The ecliptic is in the plane of the earth's orbit, just as the celestial equator is in the plane of the earth's equator.

Four points on the ecliptic need special mention. The *vernal equinox* is the point where the sun seems to cross the celestial equator on about March 21. The *summer solstice* is the northernmost point of the ecliptic reached by the sun on about

June 22. The *autumnal equinox* is the point where the sun seems to cross the celestial equator on about September 23. The *winter solstice* is the southernmost point of the ecliptic reached by the sun on about December 22. (Fig. 5.12)

Interpreting the celestial clock Although the sidereal day is almost constant, the time between the daily sun transits across the celestial meridian varies throughout the year. Practical reasons dictate that our clocks keep step as closely as possible with the sun; therefore, our 24-hour day is the average time between sun transits for the year. This 24-hour period measuring the earth's average period of rota-

Figure 5.13 Vertical stick sundial. The figure traces the positions throughout the year of the end of the sundial shadow as marked each day at noon mean solar time.

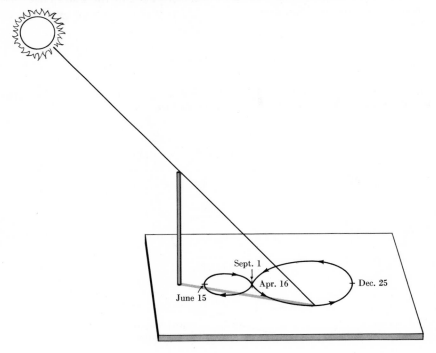

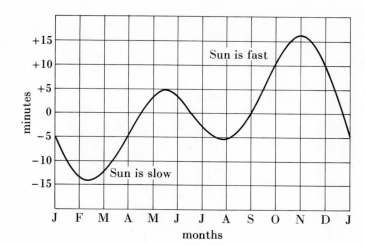

Figure 5.14 Differences between solar transit of the meridian and mean solar noon throughout the year.

tion with respect to the sun is called the *mean solar day*. A simple vertical stick sundial can be used to verify the fact that our clocks are not in step with the sun.

If for a year we marked the end point of the sundial shadow each day when our clock reads 12 noon, we would have traced on the sundial table a figure eight having its long axis running north and south (Fig. 5.13). Four times during the year the sun transit of the meridian occurs at 12 noon by the clock: April 16, June 15, September 1, and December 25. The point of the sundial shadow marked on those days would be situated on the long axis. The rest of the shadow-end tracing is offset from the axis and is not symmetrical about the long axis. A graph of the differences between the sun transit and our clock indicates why this is true. In Fig. 5.14 you should note that the greatest discrepancy occurs on about November 1; on this day the sun transit occurs 16 minutes and 20 seconds before the hour of 12 noon. The greatest delay of transit occurs on about February 8 and is about 14 minutes and 10 seconds slow.

There are two principal reasons for this discrepancy between the sun transit and our clocks: first, the earth revolves in an elliptical orbit and, second, the ecliptic is inclined to the celestial equator.

Let us first give proof of the earth's revolution around the sun and then discuss the effect of this revolution on time-keeping.

Definite proof of the earth's revolution around the sun was furnished in 1726 by James Bradley (1693–1762) when he discovered *aberration* of starlight. Aberration can be illustrated by the situation shown in Fig. 5.15. If rain is falling vertically, the drops will fall directly through the stationary vertical tube. However, if the tube is moving it must be inclined in the direction of the forward motion in order for the drops to fall freely through the tube. The situation of light reaching the earth from a star which is at a right angle to the ecliptic is very similar. If this star were observed from a stationary earth, the telescope would be pointed directly at the pole of the ecliptic; but since the earth is traveling in its orbit

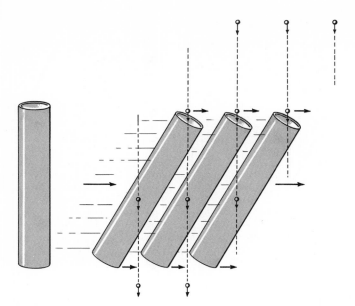

Figure 5.15 Illustrating aberration with regard to falling raindrops. The moving tube must be inclined in order that the drops may fall freely through the tube.

at an average speed of 18.5 miles per second, the telescope must be inclined by a very small angle (0.00569°) in the direction of the earth's motion to allow the ray of light from the star to pass through the instrument. The star would therefore appear to move around in a small orbit of exactly the shape of the earth's orbit.

The most noticeable effect of the earth's revolution is a solar day which is nearly four minutes greater than the sidereal day. The earth rotates once with respect to the stars each sidereal day. During one day the earth also revolves through nearly 1° of its orbit around the sun. Hence, after completing a rotation with

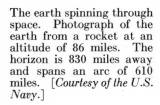

The earth spinning through space. Photograph of the earth from a rocket at an altitude of 86 miles. The horizon is 830 miles away and spans an arc of 610 miles. [*Courtesy of the U.S. Navy.*]

respect to the stars the earth must rotate 1° further to bring the sun again to the meridian. The earth rotates through 1° in about 4 minutes. The average solar day is 3 minutes 56 seconds longer than the sidereal day. A star is so far removed from the earth that for all practical purposes the rays of light are parallel for all orbital positions of the earth. The star would appear to cross the celestial meridian at the same sidereal time throughout the year. By solar time, however, the star transit would be about 4 minutes earlier each day; therefore, on successive nights the stars appear to move further toward the west and each season brings its own characteristic display of stars.

Had the orbit of the earth been circular, the time periods between sun transits would have been equal from day to day and no variation in solar day would have been recorded. The orbit of the earth, however, is elliptical and therefore the speed of the earth varies from day to day. (The explanation of this effect will be discussed in Chapter 6.) Because of the variation in the earth's speed, the distance it travels per day in its orbit varies so that the difference between the variable solar day and the nearly constant sidereal day varies with the speed of the earth. The greatest difference because of the earth's speed occurs on about January 3 when the earth is nearest the sun, the point in the orbit called *perihelion*. The least difference because of the earth's speed occurs on about July 4 when the earth is furthest from the sun, the point in the orbit called *aphelion*. Had varying speed been the only effect involved in sun transit periods, the mean solar day would have varied between the extremes so produced and the sundial tracing of Fig. 5.14 would have been an oval showing agreement with clock time only twice

each year. But the actual tracing is a figure eight; hence, we must consider with care the second reason for the discrepancies in order to account for the observed facts.

In preparation for discussing the second major reason for time discrepancies, we must add *hour circles* to our model of the celestial sphere; then, we can indicate the time effect of the apparent motion of the sun along the ecliptic between these circles. The hour circles on the celestial sphere are like meridians on the earth; they are not full circles. They are half circles which connect the celestial poles, and they are normal (perpendicular) to the celestial equator. As the name implies, there are 24 hour circles spaced to coincide successively with the observer's celestial meridian at intervals of an hour. These circles share in the apparent rotation of the celestial sphere.

As previously explained, the ecliptic is inclined $23\frac{1}{2}°$ to the celestial equator. Once a year, at summer solstice, an observer at only one point along the 23.5° N latitude (Tropic of Cancer) could observe the sun passing through the zenith. Again, at winter solstice, an observer at only one point along the 23.5° S latitude (Tropic of Capricorn) could observe the sun passing through the zenith. At all latitudes between 23.5° N and 23.5° S observers at two locations at some time each year could observe the sun passing through their zenith. Fig. 5.16 is a diagram of the earth's surface indicating the locations of the observers referred to above. The meridians of the observers whose sun transit through the zenith also coincided with an hour circle transit are indicated. Two conditions affecting the time between apparent sun transits can be interpreted from this diagram. First, the hour circles come closer together as

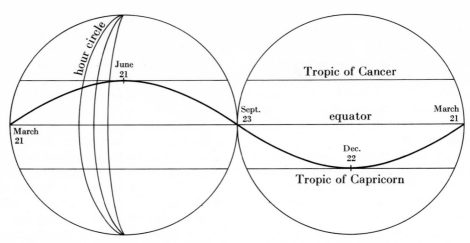

Figure 5.16 The sun reaches zenith positions along the indicated path during a given year.

the latitudes increase; therefore, the time between apparent coincident hour circle and sun transits is decreased.   Second, the apparent path of the sun is more nearly perpendicular to the hour circles as the latitudes increase; therefore, the apparent motion of the sun brings it on a more direct path between hour circles when at higher latitudes than when the sun is above the equator.   Thus, each of these conditions tends to decrease the time between sun transits of hour circles during the seasons when the sun is moving away from the equator, and tends to increase the time between sun transits of hour circles during the seasons when the sun is moving toward the equator.

The effects resulting from the earth's orbital motion and those resulting from the inclination of the earth are not in step. The first effect tends to produce a single cycle of variation each year; the second effect tends to produce two cycles of variation each year.   The cumulative variations in the solar day are indicated in the diagram of Fig. 5.14.

Exposing a hoax Before closing this chapter on the motions of the earth in space, we should touch upon astrology which is one of the remaining cults of superstition concerning the stars.   Astrology is a cruel hoax and is not a science. There are several instances recorded in history when superstitious interpretations of celestial observations have resulted in futile forecasts of disasters such as the end of the world, the fall of empires, and deluge.   For instance, in 1524, the planets Saturn, Jupiter, and Mars all appeared together in the Sign of Pisces (the Fishes). This brought forecasts of floods similar to Noah's flood, and many persons built arks like Noah's in preparation for a deluge which of course never materialized. To have faith in astrology is impossible after one has gained some exact knowledge of the actual motions of objects in the universe.

Astrology was developed in ancient times when a special significance was attached to the fact that the moon and the five "naked-eye" planets were found never to depart more than 9° from the ecliptic. The belt in the celestial sphere containing these apparent motions is called the *zodiac*. Twelve constellations of stars, each outlining the skeleton of an imaginary figure in the sky, were found to be about equally spaced in the zodiac. The zodiac was divided into twelve zones beginning at the point of the vernal equinox and extending through 30° per zone. Each zone was named for the constellation it contained and the entire group was called the *signs of the zodiac*. It was firmly believed the positions of planets, moon, and sun in the constellations of the zodiac controlled the course of history and the lives of those born under the "influence" of a given sign of the zodiac. Belief in astrology is still prevalent in our "age of science" as is evidenced by the popularity of astrology charts in our daily newspapers and the astrology magazines on our public newsstands. How gullible indeed are the uninformed! At best the astrology charts should be read for amusement.

More stagnant than the scholars of the Dark Ages, the serious minded astrologers cling to ancient beliefs without question and without even a glimpse at the sky to discern whether the basic star positions still can be measured off as they were in the past. The basic locations of the signs of the zodiac as measured with respect to the vernal equinox have changed and anyone interested enough to inquire of the night sky can become aware of this fact; but astrologers are not interested in facts. The ancient star charts they use are those ascribed by an earth-centered universe. Astrologers must still cling to the Ptolemaic scheme. Let us explore a motion of the earth which has made astrology a cult based upon a total falsehood.

Everyone can recall seeing a toy top

spinning when off balance so that wobbling took place. The spinning motion kept the top from falling over; but the pull of gravity, tending to tip it over, produced the slow wobbling motion called *precession*. A similar action occurs in the spinning earth.

Because the earth is inclined to its orbit and because the earth bulges somewhat at the equator, the gravitational attraction of the sun and moon is greater for the equatorial bulge than for the rest of the earth; therefore, there is a periodic tendency for these bodies to force a change in the direction of the earth's axis. The long-term result is a slow precessional motion of the spinning earth. About 25,800 years are required for completing one period of this wobble.

This slow precessional motion has the effect of changing the position of the celestial poles and the celestial equator on the celestial sphere. As a direct result, the precession of the vernal equinox is slowly westward along the ecliptic at the average rate of about 0.0139° each year. During the past 2000 years the vernal equinox has moved westward so far that the first sign of the zodiac, Aries, now coincides with the constellation Pisces. Since "modern" astrologers still hold to the original determinations for the signs of the zodiac, it would seem that something has gone wrong with astrology; the signs of the zodiac and the constellations for which they were named no longer coincide. Could it be that astrologers refuse to face the truth?

Setting our house in order Before we castigate too severely the actions of those who have faith in astrology, we should ask ourselves what we have to offer in its stead. We also refuse to face facts if we find it easy to sit back and to denounce something by simply learning to use the "proper" words, when beneath it all we are using nothing of greater worth as a basis for our own actions. If we are beginning to understand a few explanations for the apparent motions of celestial bodies, of what worth is this understanding if we use it only to denounce astrology and go on making our own decisions upon premises which are equally absurd?

The answer is of course very clear. Astrology is still with us today because those who have the power to replace ignorance with understanding do not recognize that their actions speak louder than words. Of what importance is knowing about the precession of the vernal equinox along the ecliptic? It surely will not make life more easy for the knower; it won't help him to build a better automobile, or a better washing machine, or to earn a million dollars. But it can make a person's life more worthwhile because in the knowing one realizes that his concepts stem from an unending process of ferreting out the secrets of nature rather than a life based upon unchanging adherence to unproductive conventions. Concepts based upon science hold promise of a life of progress instead of the stagnation of waiting for a preordained future. The concepts of science assure growth. For instance, the precession of the vernal equinox is an effect resulting from natural laws which as yet are not completely known, nor can the laws ever be known in their entirety. The exploration of precession does not stop with the knowledge that astrology is ill based; it leads to other explanations of problems which have plagued men since the dawn of civilization. For example, the interval between successive vernal equinoxes is the *tropical year*. This is the time period which we

commonly refer to when we use the word *year*. Our calendars attempt to keep in step with the tropical year. During the 1960's the time required for the sun to apparently move on the ecliptic from vernal equinox to the next vernal equinox (the tropical year) is, to the nearest second, 365 days, 5 hours, 48 minutes, and 46 seconds of mean solar time. The time required for one revolution of the earth around its orbit with respect to the stars (the sidereal year) is 365 days, 6 hours, 9 minutes, and 10 seconds of mean solar time. Because of the precession of the vernal equinox along the ecliptic, the tropical year is about 20 minutes less than the sidereal year. The problem of keeping track of our motions in space on the basis of the calendar year is not accurate. Counting the number of days from a predetermined starting date irrespective of calendar years is more acceptable to astronomers than counting calendar years.

The problem of accurate time-keeping is becoming more difficult. Fundamentally, all man-made clocks are synchronized to some "master clock" in nature. At present, the official "master clock" is the rotating earth. But the length of the day is irregular. Even when corrections are made for all known irregularities in the apparent motions of the stars, there remains the fact that the earth's rate of rotation itself fluctuates unpredictably. Therefore, the problems of time-keeping are about to be diverted to a synchronization with atomic oscillations which are revealed by the resonance to, or emission of, radiation from specific atoms or molecules.

The earth keeps on spinning through space providing problems for scientific explanation. The practical applications of earthly motions shift with the needs of each age; but freedom of choice in these matters belongs only to those who can gain knowledge. This is the spirit of adventure in science. Science develops because of uncertainties instead of reliance upon "absolute knowledge." Science offers to everyone interested—to people from all walks of life and not to scientists exclusively—the freedom of directing an unbounded curiosity into channels of progress in knowledge instead of being stifled by boredom and by the fear of impropriety.

SUMMARY

The observed motion of the earth beneath the Foucault pendulum proves that the earth is rotating. The earth's revolution about the sun is proved by the measured aberration of starlight. The sequences of the apparent motions of objects in the solar system may be measured from the earth with respect to the apparent position of the sun or with respect to the apparent positions of the stars. The apparent motion with respect to the positions of the sun and the earth is designated by the term *synodic;* the apparent motion with respect to the positions of the stars is designated by the term *sidereal.* The 24-hour period measuring the average time of the earth's rotation with respect to the sun is called the *mean solar day.* The sidereal day is 23 hours, 56 minutes, and 4 seconds of mean solar time. The motion of the moon-earth system has a sidereal interval of rotation of 27.322 days. The synodic interval between moon-sun conjunctions is 29.531 days. The moon phases from new moon to new moon correspond to the synodic period. One revolution of the earth about the sun with respect to the stars is the sidereal year which has 365 days, 6 hours, 9 minutes, and 10 seconds of mean solar time. Our calendar year, called the *tropical year,* is the time required for the apparent motion of the sun on the ecliptic from vernal equinox to the vernal equinox again and has a period of 365 days, 5 hours, 48 minutes, and 46 seconds of mean solar time.

The apparent positions of objects in the universe as viewed from an observation point on the earth are measured with regard to a fictitious celestial sphere. The points on the celestial sphere directly above the poles of the earth's axis are called the *north* and *south celestial poles.* The *celestial equator* is the great circle situated half-way between the celestial poles. The apparent motion of the sun among the stars is along the great circle called the *ecliptic* which is inclined $23\frac{1}{2}°$ to the celestial equator. The ecliptic is in the plane of the earth's orbit. The ecliptic crosses the celestial equator at the points of the vernal equinox and the autumnal equinox. The sun is in these positions respectively on March 21 and on about September 23.

The inclination of the ecliptic and the earth's elliptical orbit combine to produce apparent motions of the sun which account for the discrepancies between the daily sun transits and the mean solar day. The measured difference between the tropical year and the sidereal year is explained by the precession of the vernal equinox along the ecliptic because of the slow precessional motion of the spinning earth to compensate for the gravitational attraction of the sun and moon upon the earth's equatorial bulge.

PROBLEMS

1 What evidence would you use to prove that the earth is spinning on its axis?

2 What evidence would you use to prove that the earth is revolving around the sun?

3 What is the difference in meaning between the terms "sidereal month" and "synodic month"? Between the terms "sidereal year" and "tropical year"?

4 Make a diagram of the celestial meridian from horizon to horizon for your latitude showing the positions of the following points: the zenith, celestial equator, celestial pole, and the sun at transit on June 22 and December 22.

5 Make a diagram of the celestial meridian from horizon to horizon for a location on the Tropic of Capricorn showing the positions of the following points: the zenith, celestial equator, celestial pole, and the sun at transit on June 22 and December 22. Repeat for a location on the Tropic of Cancer.

6 Make a diagram of the celestial meridian from horizon to horizon for a location on the equator showing the positions of the following points: the zenith, celestial equator, celestial poles, and the sun at transit on June 22 and December 22.

7 Summarize the explanations for the sun dial tracings shown in Fig. 5.13.

8 What would be the apparent rate and direction of rotation in degrees per hour of a Foucault pendulum placed at 45° N latitude? Show your computation and explain the reasons for the steps used. What difference would be noted in the apparent rotation if the pendulum were placed at 45° S latitude and why?

9 Why have the signs of the zodiac moved westward so that the astrology charts have become 2,000 years out of phase with the constellations they are supposed to represent?

6

NATURE OF PLANETARY MOTION

A basic condition that applies to all known systems in the universe is the state of motion. Nothing conceivable is without motion of some kind. Because the earth is in motion, nothing on it can be thought of as at rest. Because the sun is in motion with respect to its galaxy, nothing in the solar system can be thought of as at rest. Even the galaxy as a whole is moving through space. We shall discover that the motions of objects and, particularly, the changes in their motions give important clues to the actions taking place in the systems under scrutiny.

All changes in motion—wherever they occur—are explained essentially in the same manner. The changes vary greatly: a baseball settles into the right field bleachers for a home run, a high jumper clears the bar at a track meet, a stream cascades down a mountain side, a pendulum keeps a clock on time, a satellite goes into orbit around the earth, a planet revolves around the sun, the solar system moves in the galaxy—but the explanation applied to one such change in motion must apply to all similar changes.

But, one might ask, what do these systems have in common which subjects them to the same rules of nature?

The descriptions and explanations of these common properties have been a long time in evolving and a long sequence of questions needed answering before a question such as the one proposed above could be conceived. The process involved more than observing nature and questioning the observed events; it involved abandoning one intellectual frame of reference and creating another. The process of defining the "new" intellectual frame of reference is in part the purpose of courses in science for general education. The process of definition must begin with intelligent questions.

Contemporaries of Copernicus questioned why an earth in motion did not leave the air behind and so cause objects to fall on a diagonal rather than on a vertical. Of course, our answer would be that the air and the objects share in the earth's motions, being parts of the same system. Copernicus would perhaps have answered likewise, but for us the questioning would not end there. We might also ask for an explanation of the fact that the earth revolves in an elliptical orbit. Copernicus would not have asked such a question. Copernicus believed in circular orbits as the "perfect" paths. In his time it was thought to be "natural" for all celestial objects to move in "perfect" paths. This was plain common sense and not worth questioning further. In fact, to question the so-called "natural" events was to mingle the "real" with the "abstract," a practice held by Aristotle to be most dangerous to intellectual lucidity. It is said that the eminent Danish astronomer Tycho Brahe (1546–1601) did question circular orbits, because his observations of comet paths could not be made circular in any sense. But Tycho did not attempt a scientific explanation of observed facts; rather, he publicly described comets as "supernatural" events. This was perhaps a choice prompted by hard-earned wisdom concerning popular opinion toward those who dared to question "natural" events. Tycho Brahe's great service to science was a set of exact and meticulously recorded data on the positions of 777 stars, including an unusually accurate and detailed history of the movements of the planet Mars.

THE QUESTION OF ACCURACY

In 1563, when Brahe was only 17 years old, he realized that the standard references of astronomy were grossly in error. The Alphonsine tables based upon the Ptolemaic geocentric scheme and the Prutenic tables based upon the Copernican heliocentric system made predictions of planetary position with supposedly great accuracy, but Tycho found the Alphonsine tables in error by almost a full month in predicting the conjunction of two planets. The Prutenic tables were in error by several days. At the age of 17, Brahe determined his life's work would be to establish an accurate basis for astronomical studies. He set out to discover the exact location of the stars and planets in the celestial sphere. Later, the project was greatly enhanced by royal grants by Frederick II of Denmark.

Like most men of his day, Brahe dis-

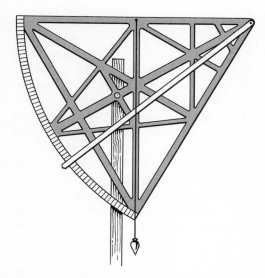

Figure 6.1 The astronomical sextant. An example of Tycho Brahe's mechanical ingenuity in building instruments which yielded highly accurate measurements.

agreed completely with the Copernican heliocentric system. But, unlike many others, Brahe had a good reason for his rejection of Copernicus. He could not accept the idea of an earth moving in an orbit around the sun because his careful measurements of star locations made from opposite sides of the proposed orbits did not reveal an annual parallactic shift in star positions. If the earth really were moving, Brahe reasoned, the background star field should have shifted somewhat with respect to objects nearer the earth such as the sun, much in the manner as we observe the background scene apparently shift with respect to objects on a nearby shore when we ride in a boat.

A theoretical answer to Tycho's objection was offered in the late sixteenth century by Thomas Digges and Giordana Bruno. In this theory the peripheral sphere of stars which formed the outer limits of the universe for both the Ptolemaic and Copernican schemes was dissolved and the stars were scattered throughout an infinite space, so far distant that parallax could not be observed easily. This was not a popular answer. Bruno was burned at the stake, in 1600, for his "dangerous" beliefs. Verification of this scheme had to wait until the latter part of the eighteenth century when suitable telescopes were produced for establishing crucial measurements of star distances.

For over 20 years Brahe measured star locations from his observatory of Uraniborg on the little island of Huen. His observatory became the scientific center of the world. However, Brahe's disregard for the political maneuvering of his enemies left him, near the end of his career, without the support of the Danish Crown; he was forced to flee Denmark and accept the patronage of Emperor Rudolph II at Prague. Brahe lived only two years after his move to Prague in 1599, but long enough to bequeath his unique collection of celestial data to the brilliant imaginative mind of his newly found assistant, Johannes Kepler.

THE QUESTION OF CONTINUOUS PATHS

Brahe had mapped out in detail the motions of the celestial bodies. This was a crucial innovation. Formerly only special points of the motions in assumed circular orbits were observed. The need for closer observation was deemed superfluous. Brahe's data were detailed from point to point and accurate to about 0.07° of modern measurements. However, Brahe made no prolonged attempts at explaining his observations. Kepler,

IOANNIS KEPPLERI
Mathematici Cæfarei
hanc Imaginem.

ARGENTORATENSI BIBLIOTHECÆ
Confecr.

Johannes Kepler. [*Courtesy of the Bettmann Archive.*]

on the other hand, who was a confirmed Copernican seemed always to be working from some imaginative hypothesis. Thus, the collaboration between a supplier of accurate evidence and a man capable of independent reasoning provided a great turning point in human thought. Kepler's empirical laws of the planetary orbits stand out as a monumental breakthrough in mankind's search for reliable explanations of natural phenomena. We shall investigate these laws in some detail.

Kepler's laws of planetary motion After four years of analyzing Brahe's data concerning Mars, Kepler made the discovery now known as *Kepler's second law:* The line joining a planet to the sun sweeps out equal areas in equal intervals of time.

After this discovery and recognizing no authority on the matter as final except the observational records of Brahe, Johannes Kepler tried to find the geometric expression of the exact path in which Mars had moved. He tried the circle, with and without equants, and abandoned it because his best calculations on this basis were in error by approximately 0.13° from Brahe's measured location. Kepler's faith in the accuracy of Tycho's observations made an error as great as this a reason for seeking a more exact expression for the orbit of Mars.

Kepler realized that if the earth were behaving as a planet and circling the sun, the apparent motions of Mars and the other planets would be the result of the combined effects of the earth's motion and the planet's motion. Brahe's data made possible the determination of the sidereal period of the earth. The synodic periods of the planets could also be determined. (A *sidereal period* is the time required for any planet to complete its revolution around the sun with respect to the stars. A *synodic period* is the time required for an inner planet to gain a lap on the earth or for the earth to gain a lap on an outer planet.) Geometrical logic discloses how the fraction of a complete circle through which a planet moves in one day is equal to the ratio of 1 over the sidereal period of the planet, and that the difference between the average daily motion of any planet and the average daily motion of the earth is the fraction of a circle which an inner planet gains on the earth in one day or the fraction of a circle which the earth gains on an outer planet in one day. In the form of an equation, the sidereal period of a planet can be written

$$(6.1) \quad \frac{1}{\substack{\text{sidereal} \\ \text{period}}} = \pm \frac{1}{\substack{\text{earth's} \\ \text{sidereal period}}}$$

$$\mp \frac{1}{\text{synodic period}}$$

where the upper signs are used for the outer planets and the lower signs are used for the inner planets. For instance, the earth's sidereal period is 365.26 days and the synodic period of Mars is 779.94 days. Thus, the sidereal period of Mars is computed to be 686.98 days.

$$\frac{1}{\substack{\text{Mars' sidereal} \\ \text{period}}} = \frac{1}{365.26 \text{ days}}$$

$$- \frac{1}{779.94 \text{ days}}$$

$$= \frac{779.94 \text{ days} - 365.26 \text{ days}}{284{,}880 \text{ days}^2}$$

$$\text{Mars' sidereal period} = \frac{284{,}880}{414.68} \text{ days}$$

$$= 686.98 \text{ days}$$

Fig. 6.2 illustrates how information about the relative size and shape of the orbits of both Mars (M) and the earth (E) could have been plotted. A time was chosen when Mars initially was in opposition (crossing the midnight meridian). A fixed star, designated x, was also observed crossing the midnight meridian in

Figure 6.2 A method of plotting the relative sizes and shapes of planetary orbits from astronomical data.

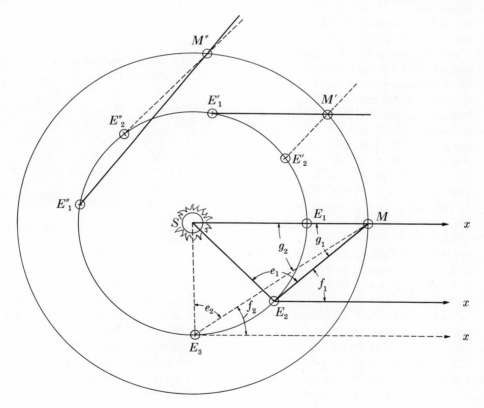

conjunction with Mars. When Mars had completed one sidereal period it was again at position M. The earth during this time had completed one period plus 321.72 days in the second period, and was at some point E_2 of its orbit. Careful measurement was made of the *angle of elongation* of Mars from E_2. This is angle e_1 in Fig. 6.2. The angle between the line toward star x and the line to Mars from E_2 is designated angle f_1. Since star x is at a very great distance from the solar system, the line from E_1 toward star x is virtually parallel to the line from E_2 toward star x, and angle g_1 equals angle f_1. Therefore, all the angles of triangle SE_2M are known. In any plane triangle the ratio of any two sides is equal to the ratio of the sines of the angles opposite those sides. Therefore the ratio of any two sides, such as SM/SE_2, of the triangle can be determined from the known angles. If now Mars is allowed to complete a second sidereal period, the earth will have reached some other point E_3 of its orbit. A similar measurement of angles will establish triangle SE_3M with side SM being common to both triangle SE_2M and triangle SE_3M. Let the ratio of sides $SM/SE_2 = R_1$ and let $SM/SE_3 = R_2$. Dividing the first ratio by the second gives $SE_3/SE_2 = R_1/R_2$. Thus, the ratio of the distances between the earth and the sun at two different points in the earth's orbit are calculated. After repeated determinations, enough of the ratios can be known to describe the relative size and shape of the earth's orbit exactly.

Having described the earth's orbit, the positions of the earth in its orbit are plotted at two times, E_1' and E_2' in Fig. 6.2, such that a sidereal period for Mars separates the two positions. A definite point on the orbit of Mars is defined by measuring the elongation of Mars at the two designated positions of the earth. Again, with repetition the relative size and shape of Mars' orbit is found. Not only would the size and shape of orbits become evident in this process, but also the relative speed with which the planets were moving in each segment of the orbits.

In some such manner, Kepler discovered that the planetary orbits were not circles. After almost two years of exhaustive computations involving ovals of various shapes, he hit upon the truly descriptive curve. As stated in *Kepler's first law:* The orbits of the planets in the solar system are elliptical with the sun at one of the foci.

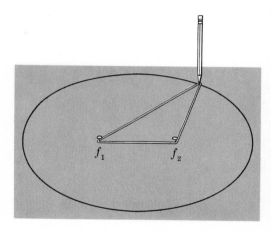

Figure 6.3 How to produce an ellipse about two focal points f_1 and f_2.

Fig. 6.3 illustrates how to draw an ellipse. Place two tacks at f_1 and f_2, respectively, to represent the two foci of the ellipse. Place a loop of string of proper length across the two tacks and move a pencil inside the loop in such a way that the string is kept taut. The figure drawn will be an ellipse.

In 1609 Kepler announced the first and second of the laws which have made him famous. Ten years later, in 1619, he announced *Kepler's third law:* The squares of the periods of the planets are in ratio as the cubes of their mean distances from the sun.

The third law gives a mathematical relationship between the mean radii of planetary orbits and the sidereal periods of the respective planets. Thus if R_E and R_M are the mean distances between the sun and the planets Earth and Mars, respectively, and if T_E and T_M are their respective sidereal periods, the following ratios are equal:

$$(6.2) \quad \frac{R_E^3}{T_E^2} = \frac{R_M^3}{T_M^2} = 8.03 \times 10^{23} \frac{\text{miles}^3}{\text{years}^2}$$

The mean radius of the earth's orbit is 9.29×10^7 miles and its sidereal period is 1.00 year.

$$\frac{(9.29 \times 10^7 \text{ miles})^3}{(1.00 \text{ year})^2} = 8.03 \times 10^{23} \frac{\text{miles}^3}{\text{years}^2}$$

Kepler's third law established a beautifully simple and correct means for computing either the sidereal period or the mean distance from the sun for any planet if one of the two quantities can be measured.

The need for explanation It should be evident by now that we have come a long way beyond the dictates of common-sense observation. But, although the laws of Kepler *describe* planetary motion with great clarity, they do not *explain* how such motions are brought about nor why these motions have such an invariable nature. Kepler was not entirely unaware of this lack, but he could not free himself entirely from the many prevailing common-sense ideas of his time. For instance, the fact that planetary speeds change with changing distances from the sun led Kepler to postulate magnetic forces from a rotating sun which would push "magnetic" planets enough to maintain the observed motion. However, the prevailing idea about forces was that a force must be acting continuously in the direction of motion; hence, Kepler's forces were thought to be pushing the planets along their prescribed paths without explaining how the planets were guided throughout their elliptical orbits. The next bold step in speculative thought toward interpreting the nature of motion came from Isaac Newton (1642–1727).

THE QUESTION OF CAUSES AND EFFECTS

In 1687 Newton's *Principia Mathematica* was first published. It was the culmination of over 20 years of assimilating related ideas from his predecessors and contemporaries, discovering useful relationships, and inventing mathematical tools. Here was the basis for explaining how the celestial bodies are retained in their orbits and for uniting the concepts of planetary motion to the observed motions of everyday objects on the earth. Newton's creative reasoning brought a new degree of order to the concepts of physical science. The central precept was this: given a definite set of conditions affecting inanimate things, a definite kind of event will always follow. The universe became a machine which was influenced only by the simple laws which defined its events.

A useful set of quantitative properties for describing the mechanics of the solar system was laid down by Newton's law of universal gravitation and his laws of motion as explained in the *Principia*. These laws have great usefulness if not carried beyond the limits of their acceptable verification in nature. We must not lose sight of the fact that science is a dynamic kind of explanation which changes as we grow and change. By stating the laws in modern terms we acknowledge that both language and ideas change their meanings with time.

Isaac Newton.　[*Courtesy of the Bettmann Archive.*]

Universal gravitation The law of universal gravitation may be stated as follows:

Every particle of matter in the universe attracts every other particle with a force which varies directly as the product of their masses and inversely as the square of the distance between their centers of mass.

The meaning for the term *mass* as used here is the quantity of matter contained in each particle as measured by weight. The center of mass is that point in the particle toward which the force seems to be directed when the particle is rotated to several different orientations.

Everyone has experienced personal weight. Strictly speaking, weight is the force which a scale or other support must supply to hold up an object. We shall find that weight is very nearly equal to the force of gravity and, therefore, manifests the amount of attraction between the person and the earth. In this sense, weight is directly proportional to the amount of gravitational mass possessed by the person. What is not so apparent to a person is that his weight is also proportional to the mass of the earth and that his weight is inversely proportional to the square of the distance between him and the center of the earth.

On a planet equal in size to the earth but of lesser density so that the planet's mass were one-half the earth's mass, a person weighing 180 lb on the earth would weigh 90 lb. Because the planet had one-half the earth's mass, the person's weight would be one-half that on the earth. If he were transported to a position 8000 miles above the earth, the centers of mass would be separated by three times the distance of the 4000-mile radius of the earth; hence, the person's weight would be one-ninth $(1/3^2)$ that on the earth; that is, 180 lb/9 = 20 lb.

When the first person sets foot on the moon, which has a mass 0.0123 times that of the earth and a radius 0.273 times that of the earth, he will experience a weight of 0.165 times his weight on the earth.

wt × relative mass of moon

(relative distance between
center of mass)²

$$= \frac{1 \times 0.0123}{(0.273)^2} = \frac{0.165 \text{ times weight}}{\text{on the earth}}$$

A person who has a weight of 135 lb on the surface of the earth would have a weight of 0.165 × 135 lb, or 22.3 lb, on the surface of the moon.

There seems to be no way of varying or changing the effects of gravitation. No screening effect can be detected with regard to an object's weight that can be attributed to placing a substance between the object and the earth. Newton's successful calculation, as early as 1666, of the moon's motion with regard to the earth assumed a force of gravity acting through empty space between the moon and the earth.

The law of gravitation was verified in 1797–8 by Henry Cavendish. As suggested by Fig. 6.4, Cavendish suspended by a fiber a lightweight rod carrying a small metal sphere at each end. When the two lead spheres were brought into the positions shown, the resulting gravitational effects rotated the rod slightly out of position. This made possible the determination of the gravitational constant and so changed the law of gravitation from a statement of proportion to a statement of a quantitative effect. Using mathematical symbols the law of gravitation can be stated as follows:

(6.3) $$F = \frac{Gm_1m_2}{d^2}$$

where F = force measured in newtons
if G = the gravitational constant
$$6.673 \times 10^{-11} \frac{\text{newtons–meters}^2}{\text{kg}^2}$$

m_1 and m_2 = masses in kilograms

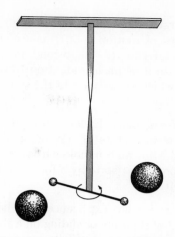

Figure 6.4 The Cavendish method of measuring the gravitational effects of two large lead spheres.

d = distance in meters between the centers of mass

With a known value for G, the mass of the earth can be calculated; this quantity is of fundamental importance to many astronomical calculations. A 1-kg mass at the surface of the earth is known to have a weight of 9.8 newtons. The radius of the earth is 6.38×10^6 meters. Therefore, using Eq. (6.3) the mass of the earth is calculated to be 6×10^{24} kilograms (6 followed by 24 zeros).

$$F = \frac{Gm_1m_2}{d^2}$$

9.8 newtons

$$= \frac{6.67 \times 10^{-11} \text{ newtons–meters}^2}{\text{kg} \times \text{kg}}$$

$$\times \frac{1 \text{ kg} \times \text{mass of earth}}{(6.38 \times 10^6)^2 \text{ meters}^2}$$

(*Note the cancelling of units*)

Solving for mass of the earth,

mass of earth

$$= \frac{9.8 \times (6.38 \times 10^6)^2 \text{ kg}}{6.67 \times 10^{-11}}$$

$$= 6 \times 10^{24} \text{ kg}$$

The first and second laws of motion The first law of motion is often considered as a special case of the second law. We shall use it as an introduction to several ideas which are explicit in the second law of motion.

The First Law: Every material object persists in a state of rest or of uniform straight-line motion unless it is compelled to change that state by a force impressed upon it.

Everyone has experienced the helpless feeling of skidding or sliding on a slippery surface. If you originally were at rest any attempt at making a sudden start was futile. Chances are if you tried to start running you found yourself prone on the slippery surface with nothing but a ruffled dignity to show for your effort. Similarly, if you were in motion when you contacted the smooth surface, you found it futile to attempt a sudden stop or even a change of direction.

Implicit in the above state of affairs is a characteristic common to all material objects, that of *inertia*. The more massive the object, the greater is its inertial resistance to change of motion. The quantitative assessment of inertia will be shown later.

For all objects in motion two conditions persist or tend to be conserved: *direction* and *speed*. The direction of motion can be measured only with an adequate system of references. Straight up, for instance, refers to the system which defines *up* as the direction toward the zenith or the direction opposite that of a plumb line. South is the direction along the earth's meridian toward the south pole. Opposite this is north. When facing south, east is the direction measured 90° counterclockwise from the meridian. Opposite this is west. Measurement is usually made in terms of the number of degrees of rotation with respect to a reference line. For instance, the direction from a place of observation to a stationary balloon might be given as 60° above the horizon and 40° north of east.

The speed of a moving object is defined as the distance traversed per unit of time. Generally, at prescribed times, marks are made of the locations of an object moving along a known path. The length of the path between two marks is measured, and the measured length divided by the measured time interval is the quantity called speed.

The term *velocity* (*v*) combines the ideas of speed and direction into a single characteristic describing objects in motion. Because precise knowledge of the actual path of motion is often denied an observer, velocity is expressed either in terms of an instantaneous value which implies using a time interval so small that no change in speed or direction could take place or in terms of an average value which assumes that if a change in speed and/or direction were taking place, the changes took place at a constant rate. The first meaning referred to is a very useful mathematical concept when precise conditions are known. The second meaning is a very good approximation which can be used when the assumption of no change in direction or speed or a definite time rate of change in these values is tenable. For example, if a sprinter is clocked at 3.4 sec over a 25-yd stretch at the start of the 100-yd dash, his velocity in the direction of the track is 22 ft per second.

$$(6.4) \quad \text{average velocity} = \frac{\text{distance}}{\text{time}}$$

$$= \frac{25 \text{ yd}}{3.4 \text{ sec}} \times \frac{3 \text{ ft}}{\text{yd}} = \frac{75 \text{ ft}}{3.4 \text{ sec}} = \frac{22 \text{ ft}}{\text{sec}}$$

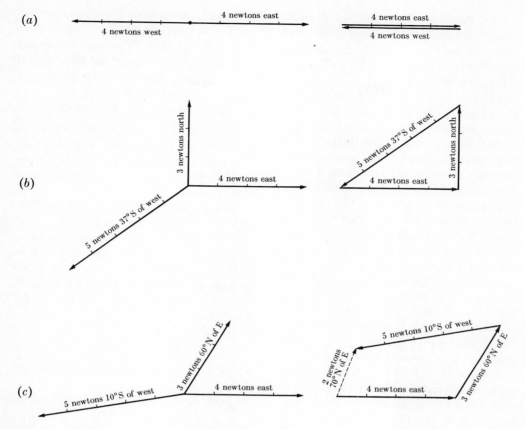

Figure 6.5 Geometrical addition of vector quantities. (*a*) Two equal and oppositely directed forces. (*b*) Three forces which are in equilibrium. (*c*) Three forces which produce an unbalanced force.

The assumption was made that no change in speed or direction occurred during this interval.

Newton's second law of motion explains the conditions that produce a change in motion.

The Second Law: An unbalanced force acting on a material object produces an acceleration that is proportional to the force and takes place in the direction of the unbalanced force.

Unbalanced force Force and velocity have one condition in common: they both include the direction of action. Characteristics that include the direction of action are called *vector quantities*. Nondirectional quantities, such as length or volume, are *scalar quantities*. The term *unbalanced force* implies that two or more forces could oppose each other in such a manner as to become balanced. When such a balance does occur, we say the forces are held in *equilibrium*.

The simplest situations to illustrate forces in equilibrium occur when two forces of equal magnitude are directed opposite to each other. Fig. 6.5a indicates how a vector diagram is used to represent equal and opposite forces. Each force is represented by a line whose length indicates the magnitude of force according to a scale of length per unit of force, such as 1 cm equals 1 newton. Directions of force are determined by a stipulated reference system, such as map coordinates of directions. The arrow at the end of each line indicates the direction. When the assumption can be made that all forces are acting at a given point, the vector diagram consists of a succession of lines. Each new line is started at the arrow end of the preceding line. If the end of the last line coincides with the starting end of the first line the forces are in equilibrium. Fig. 6.5b shows a diagram of three forces in equilibrium.

A state of unbalanced forces is indicated by a force diagram in which the end of the last vector does not coincide with the start of the first (Fig. 6.5c). The amount and the direction of the unbalanced force is indicated by the dotted line and arrow. The unbalanced force is the sum, or *resultant*, of the indicated forces. When the length of the resultant is measured in the proper scale units and converted into force units, the unbalanced force indicated in Fig. 6.5c equals 2 newtons directed 70° N of E.

Acceleration The time rate of change in velocity is called the *acceleration* (a). Expressed symbolically the relationship is as follows:

$$(6.5) \qquad a = \frac{v_2 - v_1}{t}$$

where a = acceleration in meters per second per second

if v_2 = velocity in meters per second at the end of the time period

v_1 = velocity at the beginning of the time period

t = time period in seconds

The units shown here are based upon the fundamental measurement units of meter, kilogram, and second (often referred to as the MKS system). Other systems may also be used.

Observations confirm the fact that for objects of macroscopic size (the size of ordinary objects such as baseballs, automobiles, human beings, aircraft, and so forth) the ratio of accelerations produced in a given object is equal to the ratio of the respective forces producing them. That is:

$$\frac{a_1}{a_2} = \frac{F_1}{F_2} \quad \text{so that} \quad \frac{F_1}{a_1} = \frac{F_2}{a_2}$$

where a_1 is the acceleration produced by F_1

a_2 is the acceleration produced by F_2

Thus the ratio of a force to the acceleration it produces in a given object is a constant for all forces. That is:

$$(6.6) \qquad \frac{F_1}{a_1} = \frac{F_2}{a_2} = \frac{F_3}{a_3} = m$$

The constant indicated by m for the given object is the measure of the object's resistance to change in motion, the object's characteristic of inertia called *inertial mass*. We shall learn later of Newton's hypothesis which revealed an equality between gravitational mass and inertial mass and enabled him to explain planetary motion successfully.

Definition of force As seen in Chapter

1, from the standpoint of human sensations, force may be defined qualitatively as a push or a pull. In situations where a given force can be balanced by another force—such as is produced by the extension of the spring in a spring balance—the relative magnitude of forces can be described quantitatively. But in a dynamic universe involving unbalanced forces, the second law of motion provides the most useful definition of force. In effect, the amount of force is defined by the changes it produces.

The second law of motion as stated by Newton implied that the measurable change which defines quantitatively an unbalanced force is the time rate of change in *momentum*. Momentum expresses the quantity determined by multiplying inertial mass m by velocity v. Hence, convenient units of measure for forces were devised which would express unitary changes in momentum. For instance, a force of 1 newton produces a momentum change of 1 kg-meter per second during 1 sec of time. The kilogram is the unit of inertial mass, a meter per second is the unit of velocity, and the second is the unit of time in which the change took place. Therefore, if an object of mass 5 kg changes its velocity from 5 meters per second to 20 meters per second during an interval of 3 sec, the force producing this change is 25 newtons.

$$\frac{5 \text{ kg} \times (20 \text{ meters/sec} - 5 \text{ meters/sec})}{3 \text{ sec}}$$

$$\times \frac{1 \text{ newton}}{\text{kg-meter/sec}^2} = \frac{5 \text{ kg} \times \overset{5}{\cancel{15}} \text{ meters}}{\cancel{3} \text{ sec}^2}$$

$$\times \frac{1 \text{ newton} \times \text{sec}^2}{\text{kg-meter}} = 25 \text{ newtons}$$

The force relationship stated above can be written:

(6.7)
$$F = \frac{\Delta m v}{\Delta t}$$

where Δ (the Greek letter *delta*) indicates "change in"

F = force (in appropriate units)
m = inertial mass
v = velocity
t = time

When velocities are far below the speed of light the inertial mass can be considered constant. A change in mass actually does accompany all such changes of velocity. This was revealed by Einstein's theory of relativity. However, the change in mass is immeasurably small until velocities reach values near the velocity of light. Therefore, the equation may be written as follows for most low-velocity situations:

$$F = \frac{m \Delta v}{\Delta t}$$

Solving for the quantity of force in the equation $F_1/a = m$ gives $F = ma$. Combining the last two formulas for force shows that

$$\frac{m \Delta v}{\Delta t} = ma$$

and

$$a = \frac{\Delta v}{\Delta t}$$

The above expression for acceleration is exactly equivalent to Eq. (6.5):

$$a = \frac{v_2 - v_1}{t}$$

Types of acceleration Acceleration, like force and velocity, is a vector quantity. Because of this, four different types of acceleration might be produced by unbalanced forces.

1. If the unbalanced force is directed in the same direction as the object's original velocity, the acceleration consists of an increase in speed.

2. If the unbalanced force is directed opposite to the direction of the object's original velocity, the acceleration consists of a decrease in speed; if the force persists for a long enough period of time the speed will decrease to zero, then the object will reverse direction, then the speed will increase in the direction of the force.

3. If the unbalanced force remains always directed at right angles to the object's velocity, the acceleration consists of change in direction without change in speed; if the force persists, the object will assume a circular path. In this special case the circular path will have a radius equal to the product of the inertial mass and the square of the speed divided by the unbalanced force:

$$(6.8) \qquad R = \frac{mv^2}{F}$$

4. If the unbalanced force has a direction other than those specified above, the acceleration consists of both a change in speed and a change in direction, the amounts of each change being determined by the force components available for producing each type.

Just as several forces can be added geometrically as indicated in Fig. 6.5, any given force can be broken up into component parts indicating quantity and direction such that the geometric sum of the parts adds up to the original force. This fact is extremely useful for determining the force component which produces each type of acceleration in the fourth situation above. These com-ponents may change from one instant to the next, however, and therefore the values determined must be considered instantaneous ones. For example, at *the given instant* when an object of 10 kg mass is moving east with a velocity of 4 meters per second, a force of 5 newtons directed 30° N of E is acting on the object. Fig. 6.6 illustrates how the force of 5 newtons at 30° N of E can be resolved into two rectangular components—one "in line" with the direction of velocity (east) and the other at right angles to the velocity (north). The figure, drawn to a scale of 1 cm = 1 newton, indicates the "in-line" force component equals approximately 4.3 newtons and the force component at right angles to the velocity is 2.5 newtons. These force components can be thought to act independently of each other. Therefore, the type of acceleration produced by the "in-line" force component would be a time rate of increase in speed of 0.43 meters per second per second.

$$a = \frac{F}{m} = \frac{4.3 \text{ newtons}}{10 \text{ kg}} \times \frac{1 \text{ kg-meter}}{1 \text{ newton sec}^2}$$

$$= \frac{0.43 \text{ meter}}{\text{sec}^2} \quad \text{or} \quad \frac{0.43 \text{ meter/sec}}{\text{sec}}$$

The right-angle force component would

Figure 6.6 Replacing a vector quantity by appropriate rectangular components.

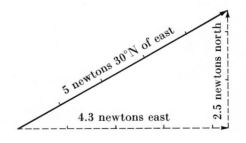

produce an acceleration consisting of a change in direction equivalent to motion in a curve having a radius of 64 meters.

$$R = \frac{mv^2}{F}$$

$$= \frac{10 \text{ kg} \times 4 \text{ meters/sec} \times 4 \text{ meters/sec}}{2.5 \text{ newtons}}$$

$$\times \frac{1 \text{ newton sec}^2}{1 \text{ kg-meter}} = 64 \text{ meters}$$

The combined effect is an instantaneous acceleration in the direction of the unbalanced force; the amount of this acceleration would be 0.5 meters per second per second at 30° N of E.

$$a = \frac{F}{m} = \frac{5 \text{ newtons}}{10 \text{ kg}} \times \frac{1 \text{ kg-meter}}{1 \text{ newton sec}^2}$$

$$= \frac{0.5 \text{ meter}}{\text{sec}^2} \text{ at } 30° \text{ N of E.}$$

The third law of motion Newton's statement of the third law as translated from his *Principia* is the following:

The Third Law: To every action there is always opposed a reaction; or, the mutual actions of two bodies upon each other are always equal and directed to contrary parts.

The terms *action* and *reaction*, at first thought, must refer to forces; but in view of the second law, a much broader interpretation can be made. Anyone who has suffered the discomfort of having a slushy snowball disintegrate while he was attempting to throw it can well remember that as the inertial opposition of the snowball was reduced rapidly to zero, the action transferred to the throwing arm which remained the only source of reaction. Had the snowball remained intact, its inertial reaction would have

prevented the "run away" action and the resulting discomfort.

Another example of the third law in action is that of a water skier being towed by a motor boat. As stated in the third law, the force exerted upon the tow line by the boat is exactly counteracted by an oppositely directed force of equal magnitude exerted by the skier. This question might then be asked: If the forces are equal and opposite, why then is the boat able to pull the skier across the water? A look at the motion of the water in the wake of the boat would give the answer. The propeller of the motor boat is setting great quantities of water into motion directed oppositely to that of the boat's motion. The action and reaction between the propeller and the water is not duplicated by the skier and the water. Therefore, the interlocked system of boat and skier is propelled forward with a force equal to the resistance offered by the water in being propelled backward by the propeller.

Conservation of momentum In situations where two objects collide or where two objects interact at a distance because of gravity, the average force F_1 exerted by the object having mass m_1 would be opposed by an average force F_2 of equal magnitude exerted by the second object having mass m_2. According to the third law

$$F_1 - F_2 = 0$$

According to the second law F_1 acting on m_2 would produce a change in momentum,

$$F_1 = m_2 \frac{\Delta v_2}{\Delta t}$$

during the time interval of action. Similarly, the change in momentum in m_1 would be

The question of prediction and verification brought with it the need for international standards of measurement. The National Bureau of Standards is responsible for maintaining the accuracy of the United States standards of measure. *Above*, Kilogram No. 20, the national standard of mass, a cylinder 39 mm in diameter and 39 mm high, with slightly rounded edges, made of an alloy of 90 percent platinum and 10 percent iridium. Kilogram No. 4, a secondary standard and a duplicate of No. 20, is shown with the bell jars in place. Both standards rest directly on quartz plates. *Below*, intercomparison of standards of mass. *Opposite page top*, this platinum-iridium bar, Prototype Meter Number 27, has been replaced as the national standard of length by the wavelength of the orange-red light emitted by the krypton isotope 86. The meter bar, shown here with the national standard of mass, Prototype Kilogram Number 20, will remain important as a secondary standard because of the ease with which it can be used for certain types of measurement. *Opposite page below*, a National Bureau of Standards scientist adjusts a krypton-86 lamp in its nitrogen bath. The wavelength of the orange-red light emitted by the lamp has just been adopted as the international standard of length. [*Courtesy of the National Bureau of Standards.*]

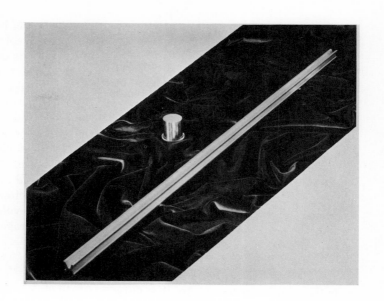

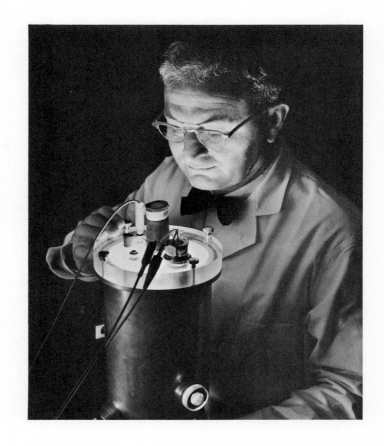

$$F_2 = m_1 \frac{\Delta v_1}{\Delta t}$$

during the same time interval. Therefore

$$\frac{m_2 \Delta v_2}{\Delta t} - \frac{m_1 \Delta v_1}{\Delta t} = m_2 \Delta v_2 - m_1 \Delta v_1 = 0$$

In other words, the total change in momentum during the interaction equals zero. This does not mean that the velocities of each of the masses remain unchanged; it simply means that if we had made two vector diagrams to discover the sum of the velocities before the interaction and again after the interaction, the resultant sums would have remained of equal length and in the same direction in both. All observations to this date support this principle of interaction. *When interactions occur between objects the total change in momentum of the objects involved equals zero.* This statement expresses the *principle of conservation of momentum.*

THE QUESTION OF PREDICTION AND VERIFICATION

Descriptive characteristics such as force, inertial mass, velocity, acceleration, and momentum cannot be measured directly. However, they have been interrelated by definitions of cause and effect to other characteristics which are measurable. The crowning value of Newton's laws was that they established means for mathematical expression of conceptual schemes so that prediction and verification in terms of measurable characteristics were made possible. This produced a revolution in science and, to a great extent, in the whole pattern of human thought.

Explanation of Kepler's third law   We restate here Kepler's third law: the squares of the periods of the planets are in ratio as the cubes of their mean distances from the sun. Applying the stipulated condition that mean distance from the sun is the mean radius of the planetary orbit, the planet would revolve in a circular orbit with a circumference of 2π times that distance. The average speed of the planet would be equal to the distance around the circumference divided by the period of revolution. Stated symbolically the average speed would be:

$$v = \frac{2\pi R}{T}$$

where R = the mean distance from the sun
$\quad\; T$ = period of revolution

Applying Newton's third law of motion to the revolving planet, the gravitational force between the sun and the planet would be exactly counteracted by the inertial reaction of the planet to the change of its direction of velocity. Newton's law of gravitation is stated by Eq. (6.3):

$$F = \frac{G m_1 m_2}{d^2}$$

Newton's second law stipulates that the inertial reaction in the above situation be stated by solving Eq. (6.8) for force, giving

(6.9) $$F = \frac{m v^2}{R}$$

Therefore, the action and reaction may be equated as follows:

(6.10) $$\frac{G m_s m}{R^2} = \frac{m v^2}{R}$$

where G = gravitational constant
$\quad\; m_s$ = gravitational mass of the sun

m = gravitational and inertial mass of the planet

(note: no distinction is made between gravitational and inertial mass)

v = average speed of the planet

R = mean radius of revolution of the planet

Substituting $(2\pi R/T)^2$ for v^2 in Eq. (6.10) gives

$$\frac{Gm_s m}{R^2} = m \times \frac{4\pi^2 R}{T^2}$$

and

$$\frac{Gm_s}{4\pi^2} = \frac{R^3}{T^2} = \frac{R_{\rm E}^3}{T_{\rm E}^2} = \frac{R_{\rm M}^3}{T_{\rm M}^2}$$

and is a constant for any planet.

The subscripts E and M refer to the planets Earth and Mars. Thus, the last two quantities in the above equations:

$$\frac{R_{\rm E}^3}{T_{\rm E}^2} = \frac{R_{\rm M}^3}{T_{\rm M}^2}$$

restates Kepler's third law. Using Newton's laws of gravitation and motion not only leads to the same predictions as does Kepler's law but goes a step further by explaining the actions in terms of cause-and-effect relationships.

Figure 6.7 The guinea and feather tube demonstrating the constant acceleration due to gravity.

The motions of falling objects Most persons have heard that all objects regardless of weight would fall at the same rate if it weren't for air resistance. The "guinea and feather tube" (Fig. 6.7) is a familiar demonstration of this fact. However, personal belief is often hampered by the intrusion of common-sense judgments. It would seem, perhaps, that the greater the weight the greater should be the acceleration, but this line of reasoning disregards the inertial effect of the objects that are being accelerated. Our inquiry into the motions of falling objects should reflect an understanding of Newton's laws of motion. Combining Newton's law of universal gravitation and the second law of motion we discover the following relationship.

$$\frac{Gm_{\rm E}m}{R_{\rm E}^2} = mg$$

where $m_{\rm E}$ = mass of the earth

m = gravitational and inertial mass of the object

$R_{\rm E}$ = distance between the object and the center of the earth

g = acceleration due to the force of gravity

Since we can divide both sides of the above equation by the mass of the object, the resulting equation indicates that the amount of mass, and therefore weight, in the falling object does not affect the accelerated rate of falling. The acceleration of objects due to the force of gravity is constant within the limits expressed by the following equation:

$$(6.11) \qquad g = \frac{Gm_{\mathrm{E}}}{R_{\mathrm{E}}^2}$$

The acceleration due to the force of gravity does vary somewhat from one location on the earth to another. However, the most commonly used value for g is 9.8 meters/sec². Other forces caused by air resistance and the rotation of the earth counteract some of the gravitational force. The remaining unbalanced force would produce accelerations which vary from the value quoted above. Measurements related to bodies falling in evacuated tubes confirm the value predicted for g by Eq. (6.11).

Combinations of free-fall and horizontal velocities Fig. 6.8 is a graph plotting to scale the paths of three objects falling through the space near the surface of the earth. Object (a) had no horizontal velocity; its vertical velocity was accelerated from rest by gravity. Object (b) had a horizontal velocity one-half that of object (c); the vertical velocities of (b) and (c) were accelerated from rest by gravity. The positions of the objects are indicated at the end of three equal time intervals. We assume that the air resistance was negligible.

As you would expect in view of the vector nature of acceleration and velocity, the horizontal and vertical components of velocity acted independently. Therefore, the vertical displacements of (a), (b), and (c) are equal at the end of each time interval and the horizontal displacements of (b) and (c) are simply multiples of each horizontal velocity times time. The vertical velocity at the end of each time interval can be predicted from the definition of acceleration,

$$a = \frac{v_t - v_0}{t}$$

where a = a constant acceleration

v_t = the instantaneous velocity at the end of the time interval t

v_0 = the instantaneous velocity at the beginning of the time interval t

t = the time duration of the interval

Multiplying both sides of the equation by t:

$$at = v_t - v_0$$

and if v_0 is zero,

$$v_t = at$$

The average velocity for a given time interval can also be written in terms of the above symbols.

$$\bar{v} = \frac{v_0 + v_t}{2}$$

The bar above the first symbol indicates "average." If v_0 is zero, $\bar{v} = \frac{v_t}{2} = \frac{at}{2}$

The predicted vertical displacement is given by solving Eq. (6.4) for distance, giving

$$s = \bar{v}t = \frac{gt^2}{2}$$

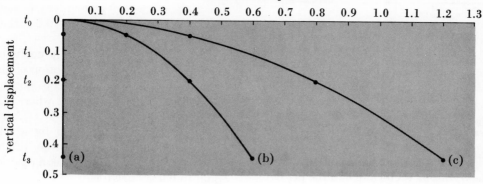

Figure 6.8 Constant rate of vertical displacement of three falling objects. (*a*) Object having no horizontal velocity. (*b*) and (*c*) The object at (*c*) having twice the horizontal velocity of the object at (*b*).

where s = displacement from point of rest

g = acceleration due to gravity

t = time elapsed since acceleration began

For example, if t_2 occurred two-tenths of a second after the start of motion, the vertical displacement (s_v) of object (a) in Fig. 6.8 would be 0.196 meter.

$$s_v = \frac{gt^2}{2}$$

$$= \frac{9.8 \text{ meters} \times \overset{0.10}{\cancel{0.20 \text{ sec}}} \times 0.20 \text{ sec}}{\cancel{\text{sec}^2 \times 2}}$$

$$= 0.196 \text{ meter}$$

The object would have fallen 0.196 meter in 0.20 sec.

The vertical velocity (v_v) of object (a) at this point would be 1.96 meters per second.

$$v_v = gt = 9.8 \text{ meters/sec}^2 \times 0.20 \text{ sec}$$
$$= 1.96 \text{ meters/sec}$$

The position and velocity for each of the objects (b) and (c) can also be predicted. For example, if object (b) has a horizontal velocity of 2 meters per second, the horizontal component of displacement (s_h) of (b) after 0.20 sec would be 0.4 meters.

$$s_h = \bar{v}t = 2 \text{ meters/sec} \times 0.20 \text{ sec}$$
$$= 0.4 \text{ meters}$$

In combining the horizontal component of displacement of 0.4 meters with the vertical component of displacement of 0.196 meters, we perform a vector addition, as indicated in Fig. 6.9. Measuring and converting the resultant vector, we find the predicted displacement for object (b) is 0.445 meters at an angle 26.1° below the horizon as measured from the starting point.

The combined velocity of (b) at this point of travel would be equal to the vector addition of 2 meters per second horizontal velocity and 1.96 meters per second vertical velocity as determined in

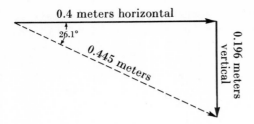

Figure 6.9 Vector addition of horizontal and vertical displacements.

Fig. 6.10. Measuring and converting the resultant vector, we find the predicted velocity for object (b) is 2.8 meters per second directed 44.4° below the horizon.

Verification of the positions of objects in motion at given time intervals can be achieved by photography or by other means of tracing the flight. The agreement between prediction and measured results are almost exact. Thus, Newton's laws not only invite intelligent questions but also lead to convincing results.

At this point, one might ask: Since the earth is spinning on its axis, and the objects on the earth's surface share in the surface velocity, does not the inertial

Figure 6.10 Vector addition of horizontal and vertical velocities.

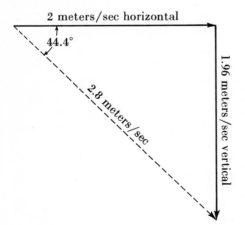

reaction to this constant changing of the direction of velocity counteract some of the gravitational force upon these objects?

The answer is *yes*, but by a negligible amount. The maximum reaction of this type would occur for objects located along the earth's equator where the rotational velocity is greatest. Calculating the reaction produced by a 1-kg object moving as part of the earth's surface at the equator indicates a reaction equal to 0.0339 newton.

$$F = \frac{mv^2}{R}$$

$$= \frac{1 \text{ kg} \times 465 \text{ m/sec} \times 465 \text{ m/sec}}{6.38 \times 10^6 \text{ meters}}$$

$$\times \frac{1 \text{ newton–sec}^2}{\text{kg–meter}} = 0.0339 \text{ newton}$$

where 465 meters/sec = velocity of the earth's surface at the equator
6.38 × 10⁶ meters = radius of the earth at the equator

(The denary system of expressing very large numbers was used: 10^6 is equivalent to moving the decimal point six places to the right. Therefore, $6.38 \times 10^6 = 6,380,000$.)

The force of gravity upon a 1-kg mass is 9.8 newtons; consequently, the reaction of 0.0339 newton is less than 0.35 percent of this force, a reduction of about 3.5 parts in a thousand. But let us investigate this reaction further for situations when velocities eastward (including the surface velocity) are boosted to 1000, 2000, or 4000 meters per second. We can see that the inertial reaction would increase in proportion to the square of the velocity. The inertial effect of an increased horizontal velocity would be that the instantaneous radius of revolution for the object would become greater as the velocity increased. Respectively, the velocities of 1000, 2000, and 4000 meters per second would produce instantaneous radii of 1.02×10^5 meters, 4.08×10^5 meters, and 16.32×10^5 meters.

$$R = \frac{mv^2}{F}$$

$$R_1 = \frac{1 \text{ kg} \times 1000 \text{ m/sec} \times 1000 \text{ m/sec}}{9.8 \text{ newtons}}$$

$$\times \frac{1 \text{ newton-sec}^2}{\text{kg-meter}} = 1.02 \times 10^5 \text{ meters}$$

$$R_2 = \frac{1 \text{ kg} \times 2000 \text{ m/sec} \times 2000 \text{ m/sec}}{9.8 \text{ newtons}}$$

$$\times \frac{1 \text{ newton-sec}^2}{\text{kg-meter}} = 4.08 \times 10^5 \text{ meters}$$

$$R_3 = \frac{1 \text{ kg} \times 4000 \text{ m/sec} \times 4000 \text{ m/sec}}{9.8 \text{ newtons}}$$

$$\times \frac{1 \text{ newton-sec}^2}{\text{kg-meter}} = 16.32 \times 10^5 \text{ meters}$$

Each time the horizontal velocity component is doubled, the radius of revolution becomes four times as great. One might profitably recall this relationship when tempted to drive an automobile around a turn in a road at increasingly greater speeds.

The *minimum* skid-free *turning radius increases as the square of the velocity.*

Fig. 6.11 illustrates the comparative flight paths of the objects referred to above. Notice that the lengths of the flights increase greatly with increased velocity because of the curvature of the earth. It should be obvious that were the initial horizontal velocity great enough, the object would continue to fall

indefinitely without reaching the earth's surface. In other words, under these conditions the inertial reaction to the change in direction would equal exactly the force of gravity; and the radius of revolution would be equal to the distance

Figure 6.11 Comparative flight paths of objects starting out with horizontal velocities of 1000 m/sec, 2000 m/sec, and 4000 m/sec.

from the object to the earth's center of mass.

At what horizontal velocity would the inertial reaction to change in direction equal the force of gravity?

The relationships expressed in Eq. (6.10) can be extended to include this situation:

$$\frac{Gm_E m}{R_E^2} = \frac{mv^2}{R_E}$$

where v and R_E are at right angles to each other. As indicated in the equation, the symbol for mass can be cancelled out which indicates that the mass of the objects in flight have no effect upon the velocity needed for going into an orbit. If the objects were to revolve in circular orbits near the earth's surface, the values for m_E and R_E in the equation would be those of the earth's mass and radius, respectively. Since Gm_E/R_E^2 also equals g,

$$g = \frac{v^2}{R_E}$$

and

$$v = \sqrt{gR_E}$$

If the calculation is performed using the

mean radius of the earth for R_E, the horizontal velocity needed for an object to orbit in a circular path near the earth's surface would be 7900 meters per second.

$$v = \sqrt{gR_E}$$
$$= \sqrt{9.8 \text{ meters/sec}^2 \times 6.37 \times 10^6 \text{ meters}}$$
$$= 7900 \text{ meters/sec}$$

This is equivalent to 4.9 miles per second or about 17,600 miles per hour. Because of air friction, velocities of this magnitude could not be attained near the earth's surface without serious consequences caused by heating. However, similar calculations could be used to stipulate

Mercury-Atlas 6 carrying John H. Glenn, Jr. in the Friendship 7 spacecraft which made three orbits around the earth. [*Courtesy of the National Aeronautics and Space Administration.*]

the horizontal velocity needed for circular orbits at distances beyond the earth's atmosphere. The fact that satellites and space capsules go into orbit as calculated is a verification of these laws of motion.

Explaining elliptical orbits Logically, the next question would be: What would be the effect if the horizontal velocity near the earth were greater than the 7900 meters per second required for a circular orbit?

The cause-and-effect relationships expressed by Newton's laws again provide the answer. Horizontal velocities greater than that needed for a circular orbit would change the orbit to an ellipse. At positions near the earth's surface, an object having greater horizontal velocity than 7900 meters per second would assume a curved path having a radius R_c which at the instant is greater than R_E. The instantaneous effect can be predicted from the following relationships:

$$\frac{Gm_E m}{R_E^2} = \frac{mv^2}{R_c}$$

in which the term to the left of the equal sign represents the force of gravity and the one to the right, an inertial reaction equal in amount. Because of this greater radius of revolution, the object's velocity would be directed slightly above the earth's horizon and, as is indicated in Fig. 6.12, the resultant vector of gravitational force can be resolved into rectangular components such that the *centripetal* component F_c is directed at a right angle to the velocity, and the *tangential* component F_t is directed oppositely to the velocity. The centripetal component determines the position of the center of curvature for the segment of the orbit

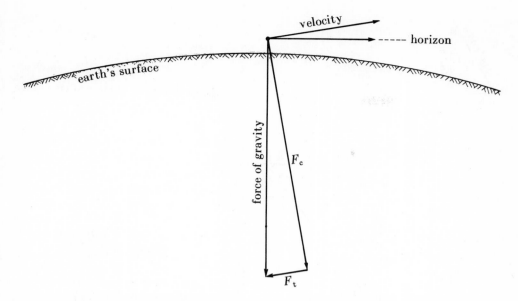

Figure 6.12 Resolution of gravitational force into centripetal and tangental components.

occupied by the orbiting object at that instant and the tangential component determines the rate by which the object's speed is decreasing at that instant. The force of gravity and its components change for every point along the orbit. The combined effect, as shown in Fig. 6.13, would be for the object to begin revolving around the earth in an elliptical path.

Kepler discovered certain facts about orbital motions which he expressed in his first and second laws of planetary motion. First, the orbits are elliptical; this does not exclude circular orbits because the circle is a special form of the ellipse. Second, the line between the centers of the massive central object and its orbiting companion sweeps out equal areas during equal periods of time; this implies that the product of the line distance between the objects' centers and the velocity remains constant ($vR_E \simeq k$) at all points of the orbit.

The vector diagrams shown in the inserts of Fig. 6.13 illustrate how Newton's laws explain these events. As illustrated, at points A, B, and C, the forces due to gravity are resolved into centripetal and tangential components. Changes in the amount of the tangential component, F_t, depends upon two variable factors, R_E and angle θ. F_t varies inversely with R_E^2 at each location and directly to the sine of angle θ (sine = side opposite/hypotenuse). The combined effect explains how the velocity changes inversely with R_E so that the product vR_E remains a constant as required by Kepler's second law.

Changes in the amount of the centripetal component, F_c, depend upon a single factor. F_c varies inversely as the cosine of angle θ (cos = side adjacent/hypot-

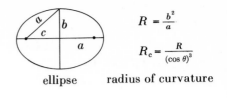

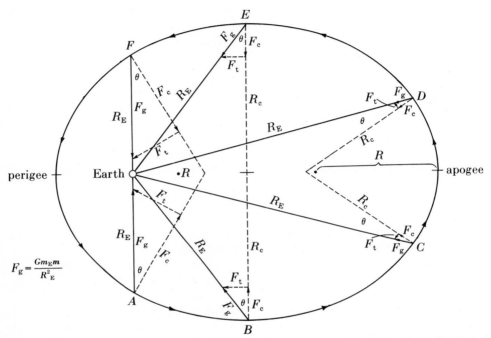

Figure 6.13 Comparative force and radius components at various locations of an elliptical orbit.

enuse). This fact becomes evident in the following logical development: at all points of the orbit the illustrations show

$$\frac{mv^2}{R_c} = F_g \cos \theta$$

Consequently,

$$\frac{mv^2}{R_c} = \frac{Gm_E m}{R_E^2} \cos \theta$$

When we solve for R_c,

$$R_c = \frac{v^2 R_E^2}{Gm_E \cos \theta}$$

By Kepler's second law,

$$vR_E \simeq k.$$

Squaring the terms on both sides of this equation gives:

$$v^2 R_E^2 \simeq k^2$$

Also, Gm_E is a constant which can be expressed as K.

Substituting the proper constants into the above equation for R_c we get

$$R_c = \frac{k^2}{K} \times \frac{1}{\cos \theta} \simeq \frac{\text{a constant } R}{\cos \theta}$$

When θ equals zero, the $\cos \theta$ equals 1; consequently, at perigee and apogee·

$$R_c = R \equiv \frac{k^2}{K}$$

The cosine effect explains why R_c increases in length, hence decreasing the curvature of the orbit between the point of perigee to the point B where angle θ is greatest; and why R_c decreases in length, hence increasing the curvature of the orbit between point B to the point of apogee where angle θ becomes zero again.

As illustrated, at points D, E, and F, tangential components equal in amount to those at C, B, and A, respectively, produce instantaneous accelerations which increase the velocity; hence, at perigee the horizontal velocity is restored to its original amount each time the object returns to that point. From perigee, the process and its explanation repeats itself. This explanation of elliptical orbits can of course be profitably related to the orbits of the planets in the solar system and of the moon around the earth.

Planets falling through space around the sun Kepler's model of the solar system describes, with only a very small amount of error, the predictable paths of the planets revolving around the sun. Newton's laws of motion and universal gravitation explain these motions in terms of measurable characteristics such as mass,

time, and displacement, which can then be related to cause-and-effect concepts such as force, velocity, and acceleration. The results are predictable explanations for all directly observable motions. The accelerations of planets are explained in terms of gravitational forces between the sun and the various planets. The agreement between prediction and observed events is very good, but not exact. A most serious discrepancy occurred between predictions and observations for the motions of the planet Mercury. The perihelion of Mercury does not occur at precisely the same point of its orbit during each revolution as would be predicted by the explanation examined above; it moves forward about 0.00028° during each revolution. This discrepancy puzzled astronomers for many years.

In 1915, Einstein published a new law of gravitation based upon his general theory of relativity. Einstein's theory accounts for the motions of Mercury to a high degree of exactness. We shall not attempt in this book to explain the relationships expressed by the theory of relativity, but we do point out that the question of cause and effect was again re-opened by Einstein's study. The precept that causes are always followed by specific and inevitable effects has been found to be only an excellent approximation of what is really happening in nature. The idea that we can stipulate inevitable effects as the result of observing related conditions has given way to a more realistic view of nature where inherent uncertainties make absolute predictions untenable. However, in the world of planets, satellites, baseballs, automobiles, and other objects of macroscopic size, Newton's laws are a highly valid means of explanation which lead to reliable, but not perfect, predictions.

SUMMARY

Tycho Brahe's meticulous data on star and planet locations enabled Johannes Kepler to discover the descriptive laws of planetary motion. The mathematical prediction and explanation of the motion of all macroscopic bodies moving under the influence of measurable or predictable forces were made possible by Isaac Newton's laws of motion and of gravitation. The relationships expressed by vector as well as scalar quantities involved in Newton's cause-and-effect explanations of natural events became the meaningful language of physical science. Forces are defined in terms of the time rate of change in momentum of the bodies interacting. The principle of conservation of momentum has become a central concept in explaining all changes of motion in the universe.

The agreement between predictions based on Newton's laws and the observed motions are very good but are not exact. The notable precession of the perihelion of Mercury was solved by the more encompassing relationships expressed in Albert Einstein's general theory of relativity. The new relationships show the laws of Newton to be excellent approximations. Newton's laws are highly valid means of predicting motions of objects within those limits of the mass and velocity characteristics where the laws lead to reliable results.

PROBLEMS

1 What was the significance of the Cavendish experiment on gravitation?

2 Indicate several situations in which you have experienced the actions stated in each of Newton's three laws of motion.

3 Compute the sidereal period of Venus which has a synodic period of 584 days. Explain the reasons for using the steps in your computation.

4 Mars has a mass 0.108 times the earth's mass and a radius 0.520 times the earth's radius. A person having a mass of 80 kg steps out of his rocket on Mars. On the basis of the law of gravitation, compute the force of gravity on this person on Mars. Explain the steps used in the computation. What is the ratio of this person's weight on Mars as compared to his weight on the earth?

5 By means of a force diagram similar to Fig. 6.5c, compute the resultant of 136 newtons directed east and 102 newtons directed north.

6 Construct a graph similar to Fig. 6.8 showing the predicted path of an object falling through space near the surface of the earth after being given a horizontal velocity of 5 meters per second. What would be the object's predicted velocity 0.5 sec after leaving the starting point? What would be its predicted displacement at that time with regard to the starting point?

7

THE SUN—A CENTER OF COSMIC ACTIVITY

Our sun is the dominant factor in phenomena which involve the solar system. The sun is a star, not much different from any other star except it is so near to the earth that detailed investigation of its characteristics is possible. Because life on earth depends upon the light and consequent heat reaching us from the sun, it has been one of the principal objects of man's curiosity.

Compared to the earth the sun has tremendous proportions. Among stars, however, the sun is of about average size. The photographed surface of the sun indicates a diameter of 1.39×10^9 meters (864,000 miles), 109 times the diameter of the earth. The earth-moon system is dwarfed by the sun (Fig. 7.1). If the center of the sun were placed at the earth's center, the moon's orbit would be situated only about half-way to the sun's surface. It is not surprising therefore to find the area of the sun's luminous surface is about 109^2 (about 11,900) times the area of the earth's surface. In volume the

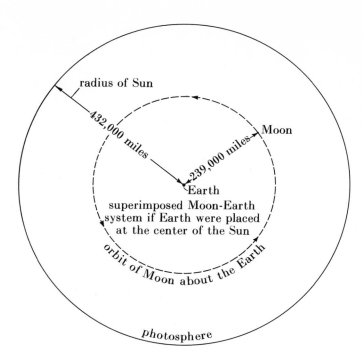

Figure 7.1 The proportions of the visible sun. The moon-earth system is dwarfed by the sun.

sun is 109³, or about 1.3 million, times as large as the earth. The solar mass is 1.986×10^{30} kg as compared to 5.983×10^{24} kg for the earth.

The sun rotates counterclockwise on its axis, but in a manner which reveals its gaseous composition. The sun's surface rotates at different speeds at different latitudes. The fastest rotation is near the solar equator where the sunspots show a rotation period of about 25 days. Sunspot activity extends to latitudes between 35° north and south of the equator. Rotation in latitudes of 35° has a period of 27 days. The slowest rotation is at the poles where the period is about 35 days. The gases at the surface of the sun near the equator seem to flow across a more slowly turning interior region of the sun.

The source of solar energy was not explained until comparatively recent times. In 1938, Hans Bethe outlined a series of nuclear reactions which operate in stars to release atomic energy. We shall study these reactions in more detail later, but now let us examine the concepts of energy that are the keys to understanding most physical phenomena.

A UNIVERSE WITH UNVARYING ENERGY

The solar system represents a huge concentration of energy with the sun as the central figure in that concentration. According to modern theories, energy is the basic entity involved in explaining natural processes. We should reiterate that energy cannot be created or destroyed; it can merely be transformed from one form to another. At the outset, as was intimated in Chapter 1, we shall measure energy in terms of work units. Fundamentally, energy cannot be measured except in terms of what happens when it is transformed from one type of energy to another. Work represents what happens when energy is transformed through action of a force which moves an opposing object from one place to another.

Energy in terms of work Energy transformations that do work must satisfy certain essential conditions. First, the force and the displacement achieved must have vector components in the same direction. Second, the opposition to the force must be in the form of either an oppositely directed force or an inertial reaction. Both conditions must be satisfied in order that work be done. For instance, no work is done when the only inertial reaction is that of change in direction. In this case the opposing object is always moving at right angles to the force and hence no component of the motion is in the direction of the force.

amount of work accomplished is measured by the following relationships.

(1.3)   work = force × displacement in the direction of the force

$$W = FS$$

For example, a wheelbarrow of mass 40 kg is rolled up an inclined ramp a distance of 17.3 meters, as indicated in Fig. 7.2. A force of 69.3 newtons is required to move the wheelbarrow up the incline. The work done is 1198 joules.

$$W = FS = 69.3 \text{ newtons} \times 17.3 \text{ meters}$$
$$= 1198 \text{ newton–meters}$$

The unit of energy transformed in doing 1 newton-meter of work is the *joule*. Thus, 1198 joules of energy were transformed in performing the above work. The joule is a comparatively small unit of energy. We buy electrical energy in unit quantities of the *kilowatt-hour* which is equivalent to 3,600,000 joules.

Although both force and displacement are vector quantities and must have components in the same direction for work to be performed, the product of two vector quantities is a scalar quantity and has no directional qualities. Thus, work and energy are scalar and non-directional. It also should be pointed out that energy is attributed to situations where work

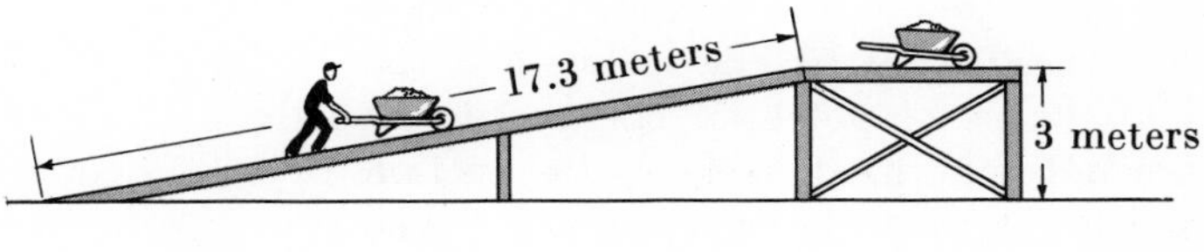

Figure 7.2 Energy relationships of force times displacement. The work done in pushing the wheelbarrow is converted to potential energy.

17.3 meters

3 meters

Also, no work is done if an object moves at constant velocity from one place to another when no opposition is involved.

If a force produces a displacement of an object in the direction of the force, the

could be done even if the work may never actually be accomplished. An often-quoted definition is: *energy is the ability to do work.*

The wheelbarrow shown at the top of

the incline in Fig. 7.2 is said to have *potential energy*. The work done in moving it to the top was accomplished by a force that moved the object against the opposition of a component of the force of gravity upon it. The force of gravity is capable of returning the wheelbarrow to the level from which it started. If the wheelbarrow fell off the platform, the force of gravity acting on the 40-kg mass would be 392 newtons.

$$F = mg$$
$$\text{force} = 40 \text{ kg} \times 9.8 \text{ meters/sec}^2$$
$$\times 1 \text{ newton-sec}^2/\text{kg-meter}$$
$$= 392 \text{ newtons}$$

The force of 392 newtons acting through a displacement of 3 meters in the direction of the force of gravity would represent a transformation of 1176 joules of energy.

Two important questions may now have entered your mind: Why is the potential energy not equal to the work done in pushing the wheelbarrow up the incline? What form of energy results when the energy is transformed by a falling body?

The principle of conservation of energy operates as strictly as the principle of conservation of momentum. There are, however, so many forms of energy that accounting for all possible transformations is very difficult. In the example above, the 22 joules difference between the 1198 joules transformed in moving the wheelbarrow up the incline and the 1176 joules of potential energy can be accounted for most likely by the friction which retarded the wheelbarrow. The energy transformed to overcome friction was probably transformed into heat.

In answering the second question, let us predict the probable action of a falling object. Obviously, the resulting acceleration will increase the velocity of the

object as it falls. The potential energy being transformed was measured in terms of force times the displacement. In terms of change in velocity, we can apply the relationships expressed by Eq. (6.7), $F = m\Delta v/t$.

If the original velocity were zero, the change in velocity is equal to the final velocity and the above relationship is expressed:

$$F = \frac{mv_t}{t}$$

where v_t = the velocity at any instant of time t.

In terms of displacement and velocity, the relationships expressed in Eq. (6.4) are $s = \bar{v}t$,

where
s = the displacement
$\bar{v}$ = average velocity
t = time of action

If the original velocity were zero, the average velocity would be equal to one-half the velocity achieved during the time acceleration was taking place.

Figure 7.3 The action of a simple pendulum illustrates energy transformation in an isolated system.

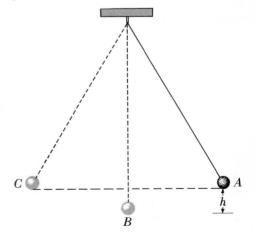

Under these circumstances the above relationship can be expressed:

$$s = \frac{v_t t}{2}$$

Substituting the appropriate expressions for force and displacement, the energy (E) transformed becomes:

$$E = Fs = \frac{mv_t}{t} \times \frac{v_t t}{2} = \frac{mv_t^2}{2}$$

or:

(7.1) $$KE = \tfrac{1}{2}mv^2$$

The relationships expressed by Eq. (7.1) are those of *kinetic energy (KE)*.

Action in terms of potential and kinetic energy A simple pendulum consisting of a small but massive ball tied to the end of an almost weightless string illustrates the equivalence of kinetic and potential energy. The action is illustrated in Fig. 7.3. To start the pendulum swinging the ball is pulled out from its equilibrium position B to position A. In so doing the ball was lifted through a displacement h against the opposition of the force of gravity. The amount of work done was equal to the amount of the force of gravity upon the ball multiplied by the displacement h. Hence, the potential energy (PE) of the ball at A may be expressed as follows:

$$PE = F_g h = mgh$$

If the ball has a mass of 0.1 kg, and h is 0.05 meter, the potential energy at A equals 0.049 joule.

$$PE = mgh$$

$$PE = 0.1\,\text{kg} \times 9.8\,\text{meters/sec}^2$$
$$\times 1\,\text{newton-sec}^2/\text{kg-meter}$$
$$\times 0.05\,\text{meter}$$

$$\times 1\,\text{joule/newton-meter}$$
$$= 0.049\,\text{joule}$$

When the ball is released at A and swings back to position B, the total available potential energy has been transformed into kinetic energy. The conservation principle dictates the kinetic energy at B to be equal to the potential energy at the outset. Therefore:

$$PE = KE = \frac{mv^2}{2} = 0.049\,\text{joule}$$

From this relationship we can predict that the velocity of the ball when it reached point B was 0.99 meter per second.

$$KE = \frac{mv^2}{2}$$

$$v^2 = \frac{2(KE)}{m} \quad \text{or} \quad v = \sqrt{\frac{2(KE)}{m}}$$

$$v = \sqrt{\frac{2 \times 0.049\,\text{joule}}{0.1\,\text{kg}} \times \frac{1\,\text{kg-meter}^2}{\text{joule-sec}^2}}$$

$$= \sqrt{\frac{0.98\,\text{meter}^2}{\text{sec}^2}} = 0.99\,\text{meter/sec}$$

At any point in the arc of swing the sum of the potential energy and the kinetic energy is equal to 0.049 joule. Since the vertical displacement of the ball can be measured at any point of the arc, the potential energy could be calculated as the product of force times the displacement at any given point. Then the kinetic energy is found by subtracting the remaining potential energy from the 0.049 joule total energy. Hence, the velocity of the ball can be predicted for all points of the arc.

If there were no air resistance nor other factors leading to energy transformation during the pendulum swing, the simple pendulum could continue its swinging

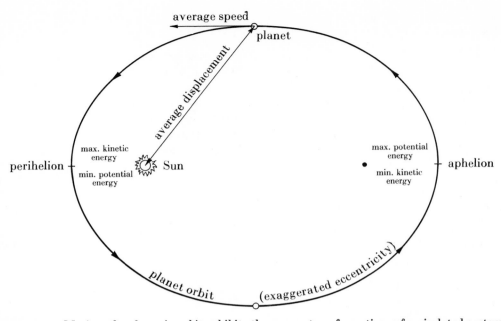

Figure 7.4 Motion of a planet in orbit exhibits the energy transformations of an isolated system.

indefinitely. But just as the vibrating systems we studied in Chapter 1 were transforming energy into forms other than the kinetic and potential energies involved in the vibration, the pendulum also has other systems that disturb its regular swinging and eventually the pendulum comes to rest. Only where there are no disturbing systems present does the transformation from kinetic to potential to kinetic energy go on indefinitely. Because of the great distances involved, disturbances from outside the solar system have only very minor influence upon internal actions within the solar system.

Energy and planetary motion In a manner similar to the energy relationships of the simple pendulum, the earth, as each of the other planets in the solar system,

possesses an almost unvarying amount of energy which is related to its orbital positions and motion. (See Fig. 7.4.) At perihelion the planet reaches its greatest speed and therefore its greatest kinetic energy. Since perihelion marks the planet's nearest approach to the sun, the potential energy is at its minimum. After moving past perihelion the planet is being slowed down by the component of gravity opposing the velocity. The action during this stage transforms kinetic energy into potential energy by the amount of work done in displacing the planet further from the sun. At aphelion the planet is furthest from the sun and therefore possesses its greatest potential energy. Since aphelion marks the point of slowest planetary speed, the kinetic energy is at its minimum. At each point in the planet's orbit, the sum of the potential and kinetic energies is constant. After moving past aphelion the direction of tangential acceleration of the planet is reversed so that speed increases. The action during this stage transforms potential energy into kinetic energy. When the planet reaches perihelion the action repeats.

Unlike the pendulum, the planetary motion in space meets very few conditions that transform energy to other forms such as heat or work upon objects in other systems. The planetary systems of the sun are very stable. Even when small disturbances do occur, the enormous energy binding the planets to the sun makes these actions seem inconsequential. For example, it would require an enormous and prolonged disturbance to change the earth's orbital motion. The kinetic energy of the earth at points of average speed is 2.652×10^{33} joules. Great as this is, an energy of twice this amount binds the earth gravitationally to the sun.

Weighing the sun The binding energies of the solar system are a consequence of the gravitational effects of the sun's mass. Calculating the mass of the sun is relatively simple in terms of the relationships expressed in Newton's laws. The accuracy of these calculations depends upon the precision with which the displacement between the earth and the sun can be measured. In terms of action and reaction effects between the sun and the earth,

$$(6.10) \qquad \frac{Gmm_s}{R^2} = \frac{mv_E^2}{R}$$

from which:

$$m_s = \frac{v_E^2 R}{G}$$

where m_s = mass of the sun

v_E = average orbital speed of the earth

R = average displacement between the earth and the sun

G = gravitational constant

Substituting known values, computation indicates the mass of the sun is 1.986×10^{30} kg.

$$m_s = \frac{v_E^2 R}{G}$$

$$= \frac{(2.977 \times 10^4)^2 \, m^2 \times 1.495 \times 10^{11} \, m}{sec^2 \times 6.673 \times 10^{-11} \, newton\text{–}m^2/kg^2}$$

$$\times \frac{1 \, newton\text{–}sec^2}{kg\text{–}meter} = 1.986 \times 10^{30} \, kg$$

Gravitational potential Because the mass of all the planets combined is only about one-thousandth that of the sun, the influence of the planets upon each other can be ignored except for the most minor effects. However, the planets do produce localized effects upon objects situated on their surfaces or within a comparatively short distance from their surfaces. The concept of gravitational potential can aid in understanding these effects better.

Without going into the mathematical derivation of the concept of gravitational potential, we can accept the idea that if enough energy were available to do the work, an object of unit mass could be transported so far out into space away from the earth that the force of gravity between the object and the earth would be zero. The gravitational potential with respect to the earth of an object having a unit quantity of mass is equal to the amount of work the earth's gravitational effect has done in bringing the unit of mass from a position in outer space having zero gravity down to its present position near to the earth. The gravitational potential is expressed by the following relationships:

$$(7.2) \qquad P = \frac{Gm_E}{R}$$

where P = gravitational potential with regard to the earth
G = gravitational constant
m_E = mass of the earth
R = displacement between the center of the object and the center of the earth

At the earth's surface the gravitational potential is 6.25×10^7 joules per kilogram.

$$P = \frac{Gm_E}{R} =$$

$$\frac{6.67 \times 10^{-11} \text{ newton–m}^2 \times 5.98 \times 10^{24} \text{ kg}}{\text{kg}^2 \times 6.38 \times 10^6 \text{ m}}$$

$$\times \frac{1 \text{ joule}}{\text{newton–meter}} = \frac{6.25 \times 10^7 \text{ joules}}{\text{kg}}$$

The units of the result indicate that gravitational potential is equivalent to energy per unit mass.

Escape velocity and binding energy In space travel the most fundamental energy problem is how to overcome the *binding energy* which massive objects in space effect by virtue of their gravitational influence. This binding energy is equal to the gravitational potential multiplied by the mass of the space vehicle. For example, the energy needed to remove a 5000-kg (11,000 lb) rocket vehicle beyond the gravitational influence of the earth is 3.125×10^{11} joules.

$$\frac{6.25 \times 10^7 \text{ joules}}{\text{kg}} \times 5000 \text{ kg}$$
$$= 3.125 \times 10^{11} \text{ joules}$$

This is equivalent to 86,800 kilowatt-hours of energy, and does not include the energy needed to transport the fuel used during the flight.

In order to reduce to a minimum the energy needed for transporting fuel, a rapid conversion of fuel energy to kinetic energy is attempted in the early stages of space flights. The required speed of an object having enough kinetic energy to overcome the binding energy is referred to as *escape velocity*. The relationships are expressed in the following manner:

$$\text{kinetic energy} = \text{binding energy}$$

$$(7.3) \qquad \frac{mv^2}{2} = mP$$

$$v = \sqrt{2P} = \sqrt{\frac{2Gm_E}{R}}$$

The escape velocity from the earth's surface is 1.12×10^4 meters per second.

$$v = \sqrt{2P}$$

$$= \sqrt{\frac{2 \times 6.25 \times 10^7 \text{ joules}}{\text{kg}} \times \frac{1 \text{ kg–meter}^2}{\text{joule–sec}^2}}$$

$$= \frac{1.12 \times 10^4 \text{ meters}}{\text{sec}}$$

This is equivalent to 11.2 kilometers per second or about 25,000 miles per hour. Regardless of mass, all objects that reach an instantaneous velocity of 11.2 kilometers per second when near the earth's surface can escape from the influence of the earth's gravitational effects unless influenced by outside disturbances such as air friction.

Binding energy between planets and sun

Because of its great mass, the sun has a much greater gravitational potential than the earth. Even at positions as far removed from the sun as is the earth's orbit, the sun's gravitational potential is more than ten times that acting at the earth's surface. At the distance of the earth's orbit, the sun's gravitational potential is 8.865×10^8 joules per kilogram as compared with the gravitational potential of the earth of 6.25×10^7 joules per kilogram at its surface.

$$P_s = \frac{GM_s}{R} = \frac{6.673 \times 10^{-11} \text{ newton-m}^2}{\text{kg}^2}$$

$$\times \frac{1.986 \times 10^{30} \text{ kg}}{1.495 \times 10^{11} \text{ meter}} \times \frac{1 \text{ joule}}{\text{newton--meter}}$$

$$= \frac{8.865 \times 10^8 \text{ joules}}{\text{kg}}$$

The escape velocity (v_e) from the solar system measured for a position on the earth's orbit is 4.2106×10^4 meters per second.

$$v_e = \sqrt{2P_s} =$$

$$\sqrt{\frac{2 \times 8.865 \times 10^8 \text{ joules}}{\text{kg}} \times \frac{1 \text{ kg--meter}^2}{\text{joule--sec}^2}}$$

$$= 4.2106 \times 10^4 \text{ meters/sec}$$

This is equivalent to 26.1 miles per second or almost 94,000 miles per hour.

The binding energy between the earth and the sun is 5.304×10^{33} joules.

$$E_b = P_s m_E = \frac{8.865 \times 10^8 \text{ joules}}{\text{kg}}$$

$$\times 5.983 \times 10^{24} \text{ kg} = 5.304 \times 10^{33} \text{ joules}$$

It is interesting to note that the kinetic energy of 2.652×10^{33} joules due to the average orbital speed provides the earth with one-half of this energy. This relationship between kinetic energy and binding energy is true of all objects in orbit around a massive body.

Solar radiation

Great as are the binding energies between the sun and the planets, this energy fades almost into insignificance compared with other energy attributes of the sun. The earth, for instance, intercepts about 10 billion billion (10^{19}) joules of radiant energy from the sun each minute. A simple exercise in arithmetic reveals the enormous energy output of the sun. Each square centimeter of area placed perpendicular to the incoming solar radiation at a position just outside the earth's atmosphere intercepts about 8.12 joules of energy each minute. To intercept the total solar output we project this value per unit area to the total area of a sphere with the sun at its center and having a radius equal to the distance from the earth to the sun. A sphere of this size has a surface area of 2.81×10^{27} cm^2.

$$A = 4\pi R^2 = 4\pi \times 1.495 \times 10^{13} \text{cm}$$
$$\times 1.495 \times 10^{13} \text{cm}$$
$$= 2.81 \times 10^{27} \text{cm}^2$$

The energy flowing through this sphere at 8.12 joules per minute per square centimeter is 2.28×10^{28} joules per minute. This means that in one year the sun transforms about 12×10^{33} joules of its nuclear energy into radiant energy.

Quantities as great as these are difficult to appreciate. The energy output from the sun in a single minute could supply the energy needs of the United States at present levels for over 50 million years. Of course, most of this radiant energy is transmitted into the open spaces of the universe and thus is lost from the solar system. However, the energy content of the universe is not being altered by this process because the sun's energy has always been a part of the total energy content of the universe.

CONCEPTS FOR SOLAR EXPLORATION

Although the ultimate source of solar energy is nuclear fusion, the immediate effect in the sun is the transformation of heat energy to radiant energy. Heat energy is measured in the laboratory in terms of its effects in changing the temperature of given quantities of water. A useful unit of heat energy is the *calorie*. One calorie is the energy needed to raise the temperature of 1 gram of water 1°C. This unit calorie should not be confused with the Calorie spelled with a capital "C" which is used in measuring food energy. The food Calorie is equivalent to 1000 calories. The equivalence of calories to joules is as follows:

$$1 \text{ calorie} = 4.186 \text{ joules}$$

The importance of thinking of radiant energy in terms of heat energy is that in laboratory experiments the temperature of the radiating bodies has been found to indicate the rate of radiation as well as the frequency of the most intense radiation. As a consequence, the intensity of the various colors emitted by a radiating body becomes an effective means of measuring its temperature and its rate of energy radiation. Applying these findings to solar radiation indicates the surface temperature of the sun is between 5700°K and 6100°K. The temperature most generally used is 6000°K. The absolute *Kelvin scale* of temperature is used in these designations. The graduations on this scale are equal to those in the centigrade scale but the Kelvin places the freezing point of water at 273° instead of 0°.

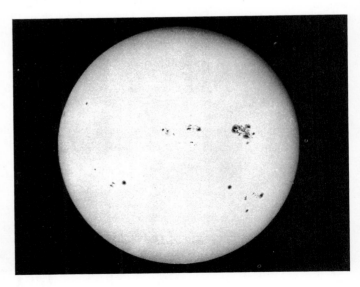

Direct photograph of the sun showing sunspots in both the northern and southern hemispheres of the sun. [*Courtesy of the Mount Wilson Observatory*.]

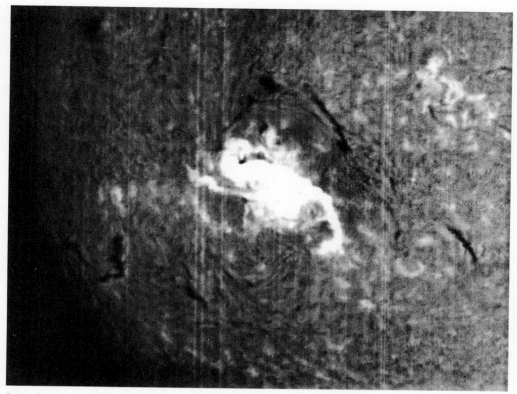

Solar flare. [*Courtesy of the Mount Wilson and Palomar Observatories.*]

Structure of the sun Photographs of the sun indicate that its surface is not of uniform brightness. High-altitude photographs show that the face of the sun is covered with comparatively small, constantly changing, and very bright nodules. They are about 150 miles in diameter, and are thought to be the tops of rising columns of gases boiling up from the hotter interior regions. The sunspots and solar flares are also regions that vary from the average brightness of the sun. The sunspots appear dark because their temperature is about 4500°K, about 1500°K cooler than the average. The solar flares, on the other hand, show momentary increases in temperature as the hot gases stream outward from the sun at speeds as great as 450 to 1000 miles per second with high temperature surfaces reaching altitudes of 100,000 miles from the sun's luminous surface.

The sun is a region of great turbulence. The unbalancing forces which produce this turbulence are largely of four types: gravitational, inertial, electrical, and magnetic. Before we investigate the effects of these forces, it will be useful to describe in general the structure of the sun.

The sun is wholly gaseous, even to its center where it is estimated that the temperature reaches 13 million degrees and the density is about 50 times that of

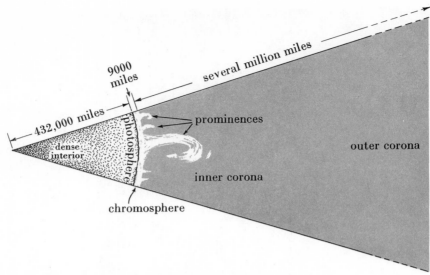

Figure 7.5   A cross section of the sun and solar atmosphere.

water, or about 4.4 times the density of lead. The previously stated dimensions of the sun are those of the *photosphere* (Fig. 7.5). This is the lowest level to which we can make direct observations of the sun and is the region from which most of the sun's light is emitted. But the sun does not end at the photosphere; it has an outer atmosphere that recent studies indicate may extend to regions beyond the earth's orbit. The lower part of the sun's atmosphere up to a height of about 14,000 kilometers (9000 miles) above the photosphere is called the *chromosphere*. The portion of the atmosphere beyond the chromosphere is called the *corona*. At the time of a total eclipse of the sun, the chromosphere is seen as a thin, brilliantly red shell. Also, ever-changing eruptions and clouds of luminous gas extend outward from the sun and at times appear to be falling inward to the chromosphere. These irregularities are called *prominences*. They extend

to heights ranging from a few thousand miles to several hundred thousand miles above the chromosphere.

The appearance of the corona varies with the eleven-year half-cycle of sunspot activity in the photosphere. The visible portions of the corona are highly irregular in outline, forming jetlike projections reaching radially outward in thin streams and also forming archlike, wide-angled jets called *flares* which are associated with the sunspots. The polarized nature of coronal light indicates scattering. That is, the coronal light is produced mainly by scattering of sunlight by dust particles and electrons in this region of the sun's atmosphere.

Before the invention a few years ago of the coronagraph by the French astronomer Bernard Lyot, study of the corona was limited to the brief periods of total eclipse of the sun. The coronagraph creates an artificial eclipse allowing observation of the inner part of the corona

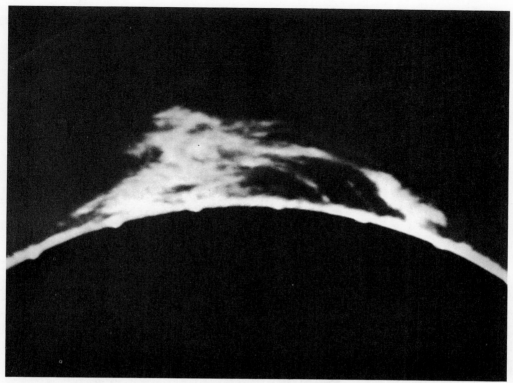

Large solar prominence 132,000 miles high. [*Courtesy of the Mount Wilson and Palomar Observatories.*]

without an actual eclipse of the sun by the moon. The greatly increased study of the corona and chromosphere have revealed some rather astonishing facts concerning the temperature of the materials at the various levels of the solar atmosphere. To help in understanding the new data, we shall review some ideas about temperature and heat before continuing our solar exploration.

Temperature and heat Difference in temperature is one of the fundamental sensory experiences in our lives. We can recognize by touch when one material is warmer than another; that is, when one material has a higher temperature than another. When the temperature of a body is increased, some of its physical characteristics are changed. These changes may be visible. For instance, we can see that the liquid in a thermometer expands when temperature is increased and therefore occupies a greater volume in the tube. The thermometer is calibrated to make use of this uniform expansion and contraction of a liquid to measure changes in temperature.

In a general sense, temperature is simply the measure of the relative tendency for heat to flow from one region to another region in contact with it. Heat tends to flow from regions of higher temperature

Solar corona photographed during the total eclipse of the sun, 1932. The coronal light is produced mainly by scattering of sunlight by particles in the sun's atmosphere. [*Courtesy of Science Service, Inc.*]

to regions of lower temperature until equal temperature conditions of equilibrium are achieved. In ideal gases the temperature has been defined as proportional to the average kinetic energy of the gas molecules. In Chapter 2 the molecular motions of a gas were described as moving randomly in all directions at a variety of speeds. This concept of molecular motions was also suggested as a descriptive characteristic for other materials. In other words, a high temperature corresponds to a highly agitated state of molecular motion. However, temperature does not measure the energy of the body. We again bring to mind that the sensory models of particles in random motion are but mental images and our

experiences in Chapter 3 remind us to keep an open mind to evidence that might materially change those models or even make them obsolete.

Earlier in this chapter we indicated that a relationship exists between temperature and the intensity and frequency range of radiations emitted by materials. Therefore, the word "temperature" is also used with respect to measured intensity and frequency ranges of radiated energy. When we spoke of spectroscopically determined radiation temperatures, we used the word "temperature" in this significance. To distinguish between these aspects, when we speak of temperature in terms of random particle motion, we shall use the term *kinetic temperature;*

and when we speak of temperature in terms of radiation data, we shall use the term *radiation temperature.*

Heat is a form of energy and to identify it too closely with a sensory model may do an injustice to the general concept of energy as a fundamental property of objects that enables them to do work on their surroundings. It is sufficient at the moment to associate heat with energy conditions of the constituent parts of matter. When we study the relationship between energy and the structure of matter it would be logical perhaps to do so in terms of the energy of motion in the constituent particles, including the molecules of the materials, the atoms making up the molecules, and the electrons, protons, and neutrons making up the atoms. But to attempt to parcel out and evaluate the energy associated with each particle constituent of matter would lead only to frustration and to no useful understanding. Hence a general approach is used in evaluating changes in the *internal energy* of a substance. We simply assume that if heat is added to a substance, the change in its total internal energy is equal to the heat added, providing no external work or other energy conversion takes place on or by the substance.

Evidence indicating change of internal energy includes changes in temperature, changes in pressure, changes in physical states (as, for instance, from solid to liquid or liquid to gas), and changes in levels of radiation. Because conversion to and absorption of radiant energy is always possible to a greater or lesser degree and is very difficult to measure, the measured relationships are always a matter of some approximation.

We have already stated that heat flows between regions that are at different temperatures. The processes by which heat is transmitted are generally classified into three types: *conduction, convection,* and *radiation.* Various combinations of these processes may operate simultaneously.

The process of *heat conduction* can be illustrated by means of a metal kettle placed on a stove for the purpose of heating water. Heat is conducted from particle to particle from the stove to the kettle with which the stove is in contact and from the metal of the kettle to the water with which the kettle is in contact. The molecular motion is believed to be transferred from particle to particle in accord with Newton's laws of motion. Since the particles have a wide variety of speeds, the transfer is not limited to a single direction. Occasionally some energy is transferred from the cooler body to the warmer body, but the predominant direction of transfer is from the warmer to the cooler regions. The over-all amount of heat transferred from the warmer to the cooler region by conduction is found to be directly proportional to the area of contact and to the difference in temperature between the two regions; it is inversely proportional to the length of materials that separate the two regions in question.

Convection is the process by which heat is transferred from one part of a fluid (that is, a liquid or a gas) to another part by mixing of warmer portions of the fluid into the cooler portions. In the example of the kettle, the water in contact with the metal is heated by conduction. Upon being heated the water expands and becomes less dense; the warmer, less dense water rises to the top of the kettle while the cooler, more dense water sinks to replace it. When this colder water in turn is heated, it too begins to rise. The resulting *circulation* of the fluid mixes the warm with the cool water and continues until all of the fluid is of equal temperature and density. Certain factors may act to prevent this circulation, as we shall see later.

The process of transformation of energies to radiant forms has been considered previously. The rate of radiation and absorption depends upon the radiation temperature of the material involved and upon the nature of the exposed surfaces. A *black body* is defined as an object whose surface would absorb all the radiant energy that falls on it. There are no perfect black bodies. Under actual conditions some of the radiant energy is absorbed, some is reflected, and the remainder is transmitted. In general, a good absorber is also a good radiator. The difference between the amount of radiation absorbed and that radiated from an object is the heat converted in either increasing or decreasing the internal energy of the object.

Temperature relationships in the sun

The sun is very nearly a perfect black body. As such, the sun's rate of energy radiation is found to be proportional to the fourth power of its absolute (Kelvin) temperature (T^4). It was in using these applications of laboratory-discovered relationships between temperature and rate of radiation that the radiation temperature of about 6000°K was attributed to the surface of the photosphere.

Data from the chromosphere and corona reveal that in the first 2000 kilometers (3200 miles) of height above the photosphere, the kinetic temperature is not very far different from that of the radiation temperature in the photosphere. But above this level the kinetic temperature—instead of decreasing, as one might expect—actually begins to increase. At the height of 8000 kilometers (5000 miles) above the photosphere, the kinetic temperature is probably as high as 7000°K. At about 10,500 kilometers (6500 miles), kinetic temperatures reach 20,000°K or more. At the top of the chromosphere 14,500 kilometers above the photosphere, the rapidly rising kinetic temperature approaches 100,000°K. This increase continues on into the corona. At heights of 40,000 kilometers (25,000 miles) above the photosphere, the kinetic temperature reaches values of 1 to 2 million degrees Kelvin. Because of the extremely low probability of particle interaction at these levels, the temperatures are kinetic rather than radiation temperatures.

This does not exclude all radiation from being emitted at these levels. Some radiation does originate here and its high-frequency photons support the kinetic temperature relationships. Photographs taken from rockets above the earth's atmosphere show the presence of X-rays

Figure 7.6 The pattern produced in iron filings placed on a glass cover resting upon a bar magnet. The compass needles are pointing in the directions of the magnetic lines of force.

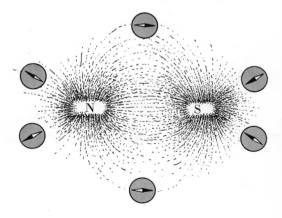

coming from the higher levels of the corona and a lower energy ultraviolet radiation coming from the lower levels. These radiations give supporting evidence for the above-stated temperature gradient. When these high-energy photons are absorbed in the upper levels of the earth's atmosphere, they ionize the layers of air found there.

A completely satisfactory explanation for the increased temperature at high levels in the solar atmosphere is not yet known. Several theories having to do with the turbulence observed at or near the photosphere attempt to explain some of the more prominent observations.

Changing magnetic fields of the sun
Anyone who has played with a pair of magnets can recall that, depending upon the orientation, the forces between magnets can produce repulsion as well as attraction. This bipolar characteristic in forces of magnets gives the directional qualities to the magnetic compass. The compass consists of a magnetized needle which is free to line up in the direction of attraction between the magnetic force centers of the needle and the magnetic force centers of the earth. In an ordinary bar magnet the force centers seem to be situated near the ends of the magnet. Fig. 7.6 shows the pattern in which iron filings become arranged around an ordinary magnet. The filings become arranged in loops or partial loops which suggest that lines of force lead out of the magnet at one end and return to the magnet at the other end. If a small magnetic compass is placed at various locations near a magnet, the positive or north-seeking end of the compass needle will become oriented as indicated in the diagram. Thus it is apparent that like

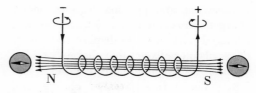

Figure 7.7 Electromagnetism. A magnetic field is produced by the electron flow in a coil of wire.

magnetic poles repel each other and unlike poles attract each other.

Solid magnets like a bar of steel, the compass needle, or the earth are not the only objects which display magnetic properties. Fig. 7.7 indicates how a coil of wire through which electricity is flowing also produces magnetic lines of force. Lines of force cannot be seen; they are only imaginary lines of a model which is helpful in orienting our thinking. That electric currents produce magnetic effects suggests that magnetism is associated with electrical charges which are in motion with respect to the measured magnetic field.

Figure 7.8 Characteristic forces between charged particles. The smaller particles also affect each other but these smaller forces have not been indicated.

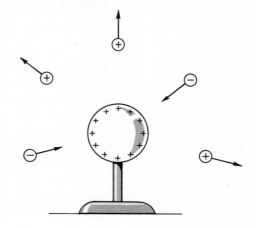

Electrons and protons are electrically charged constituent particles of atoms. Charged particles also display the effects of repulsion between like charges and attraction between unlike charges (Fig. 7.8). The terms positive charge and negative charge are used to distinguish between the unlike electrical charges which attract each other. Electrons are negatively charged and protons are positively charged. These fundamental particles therefore attract each other and bind the atoms and molecules together.

objects moving *across* the magnetic lines of force. Charged particles can move along paths *parallel* to established lines of magnetic force without producing interaction. The interaction which occurs when charged particles move across the imaginary lines of magnetic force involves doing work and therefore indicates a transformation of energy and results in acceleration of the particles involved.

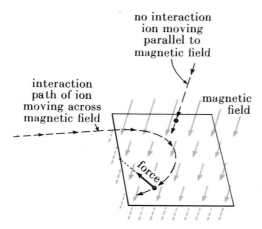

Figure 7.9 Characteristic motions of charged particles moving with respect to a magnetic field. The curved path is that of a negatively charged particle.

The concept of force field and lines of force are used to aid in orientation of the directions of force between charges. Lines of force near electrical charges are directed in the manner with which a positively charged object would tend to move if placed at the various points of space around a charged object. (See Fig. 7.9.) As might be expected, there is interaction between the magnetic field and charged

This magnetic map of the Sun's disk shows the location, field intensity, and polarity of weak magnetic fields. The records are made automatically by a scanning system that employs a polarizing analyzer, a powerful spectrograph, and a sensitive photo-electric detector for measuring the longitudinal component of the magnetic field by means of the Zeeman effect. The calibration strip at the bottom of the picture shows how the recording line slants to right or left to indicate magnetic polarity, and how it changes brightness and form to indicate seven different levels of magnetic field intensity. The extended magnetic areas on the solar disk are characteristically bipolar, and usually produce sunspots as well as other solar activity. [*Courtesy of the Mount Wilson and Palomar Observatories.*]

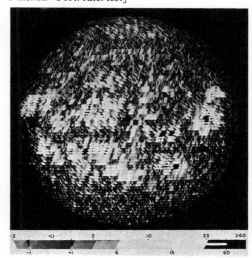

An important effect of magnetic fields upon light was discovered in 1897 by the Dutch spectroscopist Pieter Zeeman (1865–1943). When light-emitting atoms are placed in a magnetic field, the emitted spectral lines are split; that is, each single spectral line becomes a group of three or more lines having slightly different frequencies. The amount of splitting, which means the spread between the lowest and the highest frequency in the group, depends predictably upon the strength of the magnetic field. Furthermore, the light at each of the different frequencies is polarized so that the direction of the magnetic field can be ascertained.

During the few years between the above-mentioned discovery and the year 1908, George Ellery Hale, at the Mount Wilson Observatory, demonstrated that spectral lines of the light coming from sunspots were split and polarized. Thus, he detected magnetic fields on the solar surface. Systematic and precise measurements of the Zeeman effect in the light emitted from sunspots have disclosed that strong magnetic fields accompany the sunspots. The field strengths range from a few hundred times to over 6000 times the strength of the earth's magnetic field. These studies also disclosed opposite magnetic polarity for the usual pairs or groups of sunspots which rotate with the sun. During a given cycle of sunspots, the leading and trailing members of the group, in the sense of their apparent motion across the solar surface, maintain the same order of polarity. This observed regularity has given rise to the stipulation of a 22-year sunspot cycle rather than the 11-year periods of cyclic variation in sunspot number. During the half-cycles beginning in 1913, 1933, and 1954, the leading sunspots in the groups of the northern solar hemisphere of the sun had positive polarity and the trailing sunspots had negative polarity. In the southern hemisphere, the leading spots were negative and the trailing sunspots, positive. During the half-cycles beginning in 1923 and 1943, the situations were reversed.

Weaker magnetic fields have been found in numerous regions of the sun. These patterns change appreciably from day to day depending on the strength of the fields and the general turbulence of the photosphere. Weak poloidal (near the axial poles) fields have also been detected. Reversals seem to take place in the polarity of the poloidal fields at about the time of maximum activities of the sunspot cycle.

ORGANIZING CONCEPTS INTO EXPLANATION

From inspired speculations that apply newly discovered principles and thus often gain observational support, and from bold, sometimes unjustified, anticipations which have withstood the critical tests of scientific research, scientists continue to organize their expanding fund of explanations for natural processes. All scientific explanation must be looked upon as tentative. Science frequently offers more than one alternative theory for a natural phenomenon, particularly when a study is in its early stages. We shall find this is so in the explanations involving the newly discovered solar activities and again in later inquiries. This perpetual growth of ideas is what keeps scientific curiosity alive. Science is an active and critical quest for truth; it never reaches the state of absolute certainty.

Effects of magnetic fields The theory that seeks to explain the newly found evidences of magnetic variations and turbulence in the sun assumes an interaction between solar turbulence and the components of two distinct types of magnetic field. One is the *poloidal field*, similar to the earth's magnetic field; the other consists of two submerged *toroidal* (doughnut-shaped) *fields* running parallel to the equator, one each in the northern and southern hemispheres. Because of the non-uniform rates of spin in the various regions of the sun, an initial poloidal field is believed to be broken up and drawn out to become a pair of toroidal fields. These newly formed fields, one in the southern hemisphere and the other in the northern hemisphere of the sun, are oppositely directed and are greatly strengthened as the differential rotation continues. These

fields first appear at the outermost edges of the sunspot belt and migrate toward the equator. The natural tendency for these doughnut-shaped fields is to remain submerged in the material below the photosphere surface. The highly ionized materials (having a high percentage of atomic particles carrying an electric charge) in the main body of the sun are not subjected to magnetic opposition when their motion is parallel to the lines of magnetic force. However, opposition develops when their motion is directed across the magnetic fields because of the interacting forces between the magnetic field produced by the moving charge and the toroidal field. Therefore, when the strong convection currents carrying the hot gases from the interior to the surface force the materials across the toroidal magnetic fields, the interacting magnetic

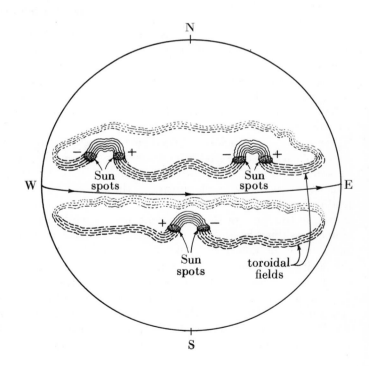

Figure 7.10 How sunspots might be explained in terms of toroidal magnetic fields within the sun.

forces tend to carry the toroidal field upward to the surface. When the toroidal field reaches the surface some of the lines of force break away from the photosphere and arch up into the sun's atmosphere (see Fig. 7.10). This gives rise to the associated positive and negative magnetic regions which may develop into sunspots. Several of these surface loops may develop, forming a number of sunspot groups at the same latitude.

New pairs of toroidal fields are assumed to be formed in the regions of 30° to 40° latitudes north and south at the beginning of each 11-year half-cycle. They then migrate toward the equator and disappear at the end of the cycle. The reversal of field each half-cycle is attributed to a postulated but still unobserved slow, periodic, clockwise and opposing counterclockwise twisting action superimposed upon the differential rotation of the sun. This could produce a forth and back oscillation having a period equal to 22 years, thus accounting for the changes observed during the alternate 11-year half-cycle of the sunspots.

The dark color of the sunspots is produced by the cooling of gases beneath the surface of these areas. In terms of the theory of toroidal fields, when the lines of force break through the surface of the photosphere the magnetic fields leaving and entering the surface are nearly vertical. This allows the convection currents in the hot ionized gases to move freely upward alongside the lines of magnetic force but inhibits any motion horizontally across the lines. Therefore, the transfer of heat to the areas directly below the lines of force is disrupted. The area cools, radiation is reduced, and the region darkens into a sunspot.

Solar prominences, those formations in the corona which appear like luminous cloud condensations of relatively cool hydrogen within the high-temperature corona, may also be explained, at least in part, by the magnetic fields that arch above the photosphere. The appearance of some of the prominences suggest that hydrogen is being collected and cooled near the top of the magnetic arches. This gas pushes down into a hammocklike sagging of the magnetic arch, giving rise to an equilibrium of forces which might exist for days or even weeks. The cloud may dissipate by a falling-in process, but more often it seems to be propelled outward at high speed, possibly by an increase in the magnetic field strength.

The explanation of solar turbulence theoretically supported by magnetic force theories adds plausibility to the idea that the high kinetic temperatures of the solar atmosphere arise from magnetic processes within the sun. Observable evidence tends to support this point of view, but not completely. Two major discrepancies exist. First, although the conditions in the solar atmosphere do fluctuate with the sunspot cycle, the atmospheric changes are not as great as the ebb and flow of sunspot activity suggest and the temperature changes actually take place in the reverse sequence, being at higher temperature at low sunspot incidence and at lower temperature at high sunspot incidence. Secondly, the dominant features of the corona are its radial structure and irregular form. If the coronal gas clouds were formed by flow of materials up from the photosphere along the lines of magnetic force, we should expect a general horizontal flow of materials away from these areas. No evidence of this has been found. Thus, although we shall not abandon the magnetic theory it would seem wise to suspend judgment until other theories and evidence are evaluated.

Gravitational effects of the sun The sun's atmosphere can be said to end at the points where the solar gas density equals the density of the gas in interstellar space. Evidence suggests the probability that the solar gas density in the vicinity of the earth's orbit is about 530 protons (hydrogen nuclei) and 530 electrons per cubic centimeter. This is, of course, a very sparse gas, more sparse than the best vacuum produced in laboratories. But the solar density at this level is, nonetheless, many times more dense than the gas in interstellar space.

Calculations based on evidence of gas densities in the lower regions of the corona place the density of gas in the interstellar space through which our sun is traveling at about 30 atoms per cubic centimeter. If the sun were in fact passing through this interstellar gas, as opposed to the idea that the gas and the sun are moving with equal speeds as part of the same galactic arm, the sun's gravitational field would effect a capturing of gas from the space through which it travels. Assuming these conditions, the gravitational force would do work in compressing the gas and in accelerating the molecular velocities in the direction of the solar mass. Assumptions such as these form the basis for the *infall theory* explaining the coronal temperatures and the solar prominences.

According to this theory, the sun is tunneling through the interstellar gas and scooping up the gas from a tubular space having a cross section equal to the radius of the orbit of Saturn. The gases are pictured streaming in toward the sun from all directions. The speed of the approaching particles is accelerated increasingly as the force of gravity increases with the decreasing displacement of the particles to the sun. Because the gas is largely atomic and is not ionized, the magnetic force fields have little effect upon the incoming gas. Therefore, until the infalling materials reach regions where collisions with solar materials are frequent, the kinetic temperature (random motion) remains comparatively low although the kinetic energy of the particles is very high. The normal kinetic temperature of the interstellar gas is about $-170°C$ or $+103°K$. In the regions of the solar atmosphere where the kinetic energy of infalling materials are converted to kinetic temperature, the kinetic temperature of the gases is found to be 1 to 2 million degrees Kelvin. This can explain the observed region of the corona found to have this temperature.

Questions have probably occurred to the reader concerning why energy from these high temperature outer regions of the sun does not seem to be transmitted downward into the sun in view of the principle that heat flows from regions of high temperature to regions of lower temperature. The infall theory provides an answer. Except where turbulence occurs, only somewhat localized convection and conduction of heat downward seem to occur. However, the atoms upon gaining kinetic temperature also become ionized and magnetic forces distort the normal flow of convection currents. This may account for the reverse sequence of high temperature and sunspot activity mentioned earlier. The action of magnetic forces is thought to prevent the free boiling action of the materials and thus the energy transmission downward would be sealed off. The energy therefore accumulates in localized pockets of the solar atmosphere. This gives rise to greatly increased kinetic temperature in these localities. With increased kinetic temperature, the average speed of the random motion of the particles is increased to the point where an energy sufficient to escape the sun is attained. However, if infall of materials does occur, only the escaping particles that move radially outward have the best probability of avoiding collision with the inward moving particles. Therefore, we would expect that the successful outward moving particles would form jets directed radially outward from the localized pockets of energy accumulation. That such jets or streamers are often seen in photographs of the corona is further evidence for the infall theory.

A great variety of energy transformations are involved in explaining coronal characteristics by the infall theory. The gravitational effects of the sun do work in attracting interstellar gas toward the sun; thus this energy is converted into the kinetic energy of the high-speed particles falling toward the sun. The kinetic energy is transformed into heat when the infalling particles collide with the solar particles in the corona. Some of the heat and kinetic energy is transformed in doing the work of removing electrons from the atoms that collide and so ionization occurs. The ionized particles, carrying electrical charges, produce magnetic fields which interact with the magnetic fields of the sun, thereby producing turbulence in some regions and equalized balance of forces in others which prevent further transfer of energy inward by convection and conduction. Thus accumulation of heat energy takes place in localized pockets as indicated by high kinetic temperatures. Finally, the accumulated energy produces an expulsion of particles from these localized pockets carrying the energy away from the sun by doing the work of overcoming the binding energy between the particles and the sun, and the particles are removed from the influence of solar gravity.

The basic assumptions of the infall theory which may be questioned are the assumed density of interstellar gas and the assumed extent of random motion of this gas.

The rapid accumulation of new data resulting from space probes by rockets and satellites beyond the regions of the earth's atmosphere will make possible more complete and comprehensive theories to explain solar activities and, consequently, the activities of other stars.

SUMMARY

The sun is an average sized star. The energy transformations in the motions of the planetary systems are dwarfed by the energy output of the sun. Ten billion billion joules of radiant energy from the sun reach the earth each minute. The source of the solar energy is conversion of nuclear energy into radiant energy.

The sun is wholly gaseous, even though the density of the gaseous material near its center may be 50 times greater than the density of water. The most prominent visible portion of the sun is the photosphere which has a diameter of 1.39×10^9 meters. Above the photosphere, the chromosphere extends upward about 14,000 kilometers forming the lowest stratum of the sun's atmosphere. Irregular prominences erupt outward from the chromosphere.

The corona extends outward from the chromosphere to great heights. The solar atmosphere may extend outward to regions beyond the orbit of the earth. The visible portions of the corona are highly irregular in shape and feature jetlike projections reaching radially outward and also wide-angled flares associated with the sunspots.

Contrary to general expectation, the temperature of the solar atmosphere increases with increased height above the photosphere. The average surface temperature of the photosphere is about 6000°K. At heights of 25,000 miles above the photosphere, the kinetic temperature reaches values of more than a million degrees Kelvin.

The discovery of the Zeeman effect associated with the sunspots revealed magnetic fields of variable proportions. A 22-year sunspot cycle was revealed with the polarity of the sunspot pairs reversing at 11-year intervals. The processes involved are still unsolved.

Theoretical explanations of solar turbulence on the basis of either the magnetic force theory or the infall theory hold many clues to possible cause-and-effect relationships involved but leave many vital questions unanswered. The present-day accumulation of evidence from varied sources of solar information holds promise of important discoveries and insights into the explanations of solar activities as interpretations take on more meaning from observed facts.

PROBLEMS

1 An iron ball used in a Foucault pendulum has a mass of 45 kg. When in operation the ball has a maximum vertical displacement of 10 cm. What is the velocity of the ball when it reaches the lowest point of its swing? (See Fig. 7.2). Show your computation and explain the reason for using each step.

2 At the earth's surface the gravitational potential is 6.25×10^7 joules per kg. The space capsule *Friendship Seven*, which carried the first American astronaut into orbit, had a mass of about 1720 kg. Compute an estimate of the energy converted in lifting this capsule up to the average height of its orbit using the relationships expressed in Eq. (7.2) and determining the change in gravitational potential between the earth's surface and a level 6.38×10^6 meters from the center of the earth.

3 It is estimated that the energy output from the sun in a single minute could supply the energy needs of the United States for 50 million years. On the basis of this estimate, what are the energy needs of the United States each year?

4 Indicate several situations where conduction of heat takes place and several where convection of heat takes place.

5   Each square centimeter of area placed perpendicular to the incoming solar radiation intercepts 8.12 joules of energy each minute.   This is called the *mean solar constant*.   Express the solar constant in terms of heat energy in calories.

6   The solar constant at the earth fluctuates between 7.87 and 8.41 joules per minute per cm².   Express these energy constants in terms of calories.

7   Find out about some other recent interpretations of solar activities besides those given in the text.   Compare them with the magnetic and the infall theories.

8

THE SOLAR SYSTEM

The solar system moves through interstellar space as a beautifully proportioned assemblage of cosmic materials whose existence and activities form the basis for man's curiosity about natural laws.   The energy-rich sun is the central figure of this system.   The nine known planets revolve around the sun in elliptical paths; however, the eccentricities of these orbits are so slight that in models and diagrams the orbits appear circular with the sun somewhat off-center.

The regularity of the planetary orbits makes it almost inconceivable that such a system could have existed for an infinite time.   Any close encounters with other stars would have disrupted the circular nature of the orbits. Studies of interstellar distances and the probability of encounters between stars place an upper limit of about a million million (10^{12}) years to the age of our solar system.   Studies of energy transformation in stars place an upper

159

limit of about 6 billion years for age of our sun. The planets could not have formed before the sun. Evidence which we shall find in our study of the earth indicates that the earth was formed between 5 and 6 billion years ago. Therefore the sun and the planets are believed to have been formed at about the same time by one all-inclusive process. Before we inquire into the probable processes which evolved the solar system, we should become better acquainted with its principal bodies.

SIZING UP THE PLANETS

Useful comparisons can be learned from measurements of vital characteristics of the planets. Some of these are tabulated in Table 8.1.

The astronomical unit When the distance between one planet and the sun is accurately measured, the distances from the sun to the other planets can be calculated from their observed periods of revolution by applying Kepler's third law. Because all observations have been made from the earth, the average distance from the earth to the sun is used as a unit of astronomical measurement. This is called the *astronomical unit* (A.U.). Accurate measurement of this distance is one of the important problems of astronomy. Measurements before 1958 predominantly involved the asteroid Eros.

The asteroids are a group of small solid bodies revolving around the sun; their average distances from the sun fall between those of the orbits of Mars and Jupiter. The asteroids often have very eccentric orbits which bring some of them

TABLE 8.1 Physical characteristics of the planets

Planet	Mean distance from the sun (in A.U.)	Mass (earth = 1)	Mean diameter (earth = 1)	Mean density (grams/cm³)	Mean surface gravity (earth = 1)	Escape velocity (km/sec)	Period of axial rotation	Inclination of equator to orbit	Albedo	Temp. (°K)
Mercury	0.387	0.056	0.39	4.1	0.38	3.8	87.97^d	$7°$	0.07	446
Venus	0.723	0.817	0.973	4.9	0.86	10.2	30^d ?	$32°$	0.59	326
Earth	1.000	1.000	1.000	5.52	1.000	11.2	23^h56^m	$23°\,27'$	0.29	277
Mars	1.524	0.108	0.532	3.85	0.39	5.0	24^h37^m	$25°\,12'$	0.15	225
Jupiter	5.203	318.35	10.97	1.33	2.64	60	9^h55^m	$3°\,7'$	0.44	121
Saturn	9.539	95.28	9.03	0.71	1.17	36	10^h38^m	$26°\,45'$	0.42	90
Uranus	19.191	14.58	4.00	1.26	1.05	21	10^h40^m	$98°$	0.45	63
Neptune	30.071	17.36	3.90	1.61	1.23	23	15^h50^m	$151°$	0.52	50
Pluto	39.518	0.7 ?	0.4 ?	3.3 ?	0.9 ?	11.?	?	?	0.16 ?	44

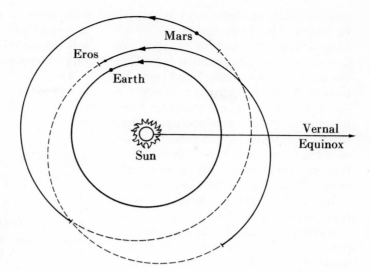

Figure 8.1 The orbit of the asteroid Eros. Approaching within 14 million miles of the earth, Eros provided data for measurement of celestial distances.

very close to the earth at times. The asteroid Eros approaches within 14 million miles of the earth (Fig. 8.1). In astronomical relationships this is very close indeed. Because of its size and displacement, Eros has been extremely useful in measurement of celestial distances. By simultaneously comparing the apparent position of the asteroids with the positions of the fixed stars from two widely separated positions on the earth, accurate determinations can be made of the asteroid's distance from the earth. The nearness of Eros to the earth when the asteroid is at perihelion makes the possible separation of the observation posts a significant portion of the distance to be measured. Very painstaking programs of observation and analysis have been used to increase the preciseness of the astronomical unit. The most notable of these was carried out in 1950 by Eugene K. Rabe of the Cincinnati Observatory, who arrived at a value of 92,914,800 miles with an uncertainty of about 4 parts in 10,000.

In 1958 and again in 1959, echoes of radar signals reflected from the planet Venus were used to determine the astronomical unit (Fig. 8.2). The results indicated values of 92,874,000 and 92,876,000

Figure 8.2 Recent improvements in measurement of celestial distances were accomplished by using radar echoes reflected from the planet Venus.

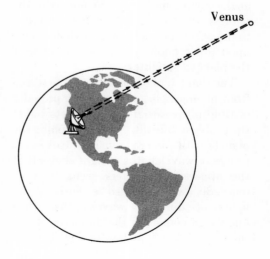

miles with uncertainties of 1 to 5 parts in 10,000. In 1960, the space vehicle Pioneer V was tracked for 108 days and to a distance of 22.46 million miles from the earth. Calculations based upon the path it traced supported the value determined by Rabe. The astronomical unit based upon the space vehicle's trajectory was 92,925,100 miles with an uncertainty of about 8 parts in 10,000. No explanation can be given at this time for the apparent discrepancy between values determined from radar echoes and those from orbits of objects in space. Advancements in radar astronomy and more powerful signals from space vehicles will undoubtedly lead to increasing precision in this field.

Mass and density Density is the ratio of mass per unit volume, and this ratio aids in hypotheses concerning the material make-up of the planets. The mean densities of the planets are calculated from the measurements of mass and diameter.

The mass of the earth is 5.976×10^{24} kg, as calculated from the force of gravity at the earth's surface. The masses of the planets are determined by their gravitational effects on each other or their effects upon other bodies, such as asteroids or the planet's satellites.

The diameters of planets are measured from photographs, although the presence of atmospheres around most planets makes the problem difficult. Photographing the planets with cameras sensitive to specific ranges of wavelengths of light shows that the apparent diameters seem to vary markedly when viewed exclusively by lights of different wavelengths. Best known, of course, is the diameter of the earth: 12,742 kilometers or 7,918 miles.

Measurement of earth diameters have uncertainties of only 200 ft and are therefore among the most precise of all planetary measurements.

The densities recorded in Table 8.1 have not been corrected for pressure variations and therefore may be somewhat misleading when comparisons are made.

Surface gravity and escape velocity
Measurements of planetary mass and diameter can be used also to calculate surface gravity and escape velocity by applying Newton's laws. The following relationships expressed symbolically should refresh the reader's memory:

(6.3) $\quad F_g = \dfrac{Gm_1m_2}{R^2}$ and (7.2) $\quad P = \dfrac{Gm_2}{R}$

Therefore

$$F_g = \frac{Pm_1}{R}$$

and

$$P = \frac{F_g R}{m}$$

Since $F_g = mg$, we substitute in this equation and obtain:

$$P = gR$$

But by Eq. (7.3):

$$v = \sqrt{2P}$$

Therefore

$$v = \sqrt{2gR}$$

This means the escape velocity is calculated by finding the square root of the product of the planet's acceleration due to gravity and the planet's diameter ($D = 2R$). In the calculation process the planet's surface gravity and gravitational potential can also be determined.

Albedo—reflecting power of a surface
The albedo number indicates the ratio of

the light reflected from a planet's surface compared to the sunlight illuminating the surface. In other words, the earth's albedo of 0.29 indicates that 29 percent of the sunlight illuminating the earth is reflected into space while 71 percent is absorbed. By way of comparison, the white paper of this book has an albedo of 0.70, which is just about the reverse condition to that found on the earth's surface as viewed from outer space.

CHARACTERISTICS OF PLANETARY ORBITS

The orbital paths of the planets are defined in terms of shape, position, and size. Again, the earth's orbit is established as a standard for comparison because all measurements are made from the earth. The plane of the earth's orbit as extended outward into space is referred to as the *plane of the ecliptic*. It is the platform, so to speak, upon which the model of the solar system is erected.

Geometrical characteristics According to Kepler's first law, the geometric figure formed by all planetary orbits is an ellipse with the sun at one of the foci. The sun is the only point held in common by all the planets because although they all revolve about the sun as a focus, the orbit of each is in a different plane. Descriptive relationships between a given planetary orbit and the plane of the ecliptic are illustrated in Fig. 8.3. The line *DN* marks the intersection of the planet's orbital plane with the plane of the ecliptic. This line of intersection is called the *line of node* and passes through the sun. Angle *i* measures how far each orbit is inclined to the ecliptic and is called the inclination to the ecliptic.

We adopt the usual mode of viewing models from an imaginary point far above the earth toward the north celestial pole. From this vantage point the planets appear to revolve in a counterclockwise direction. Then the point *D*, called the *descending node*, marks the point at which

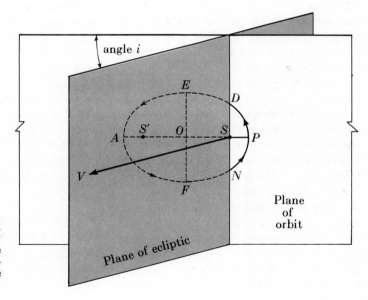

Figure 8.3 Geometrical characteristics of planetary orbits. All the orbits are elliptical and slightly inclined to the plane of the earth's orbit.

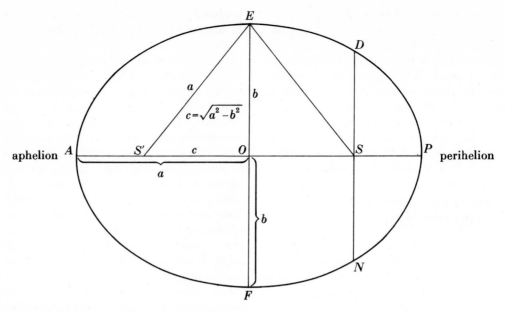

Figure 8.4 Descriptive characteristics of an ellipse.

the planet moves from the northern to the southern side of the ecliptic plane. Point N, called the *ascending node*, marks the point at which the planet moves from the southern to the northern side of the ecliptic plane. In the illustrations here broken lines are used to indicate the portion of the orbit south of the ecliptic, and solid lines the portion north of the ecliptic plane.

Certain characteristics of an ellipse are useful in describing planetary orbits. In the ellipse shown in Fig. 8.4, which is labeled similarly to the orbit shown in Fig. 8.3, line AP represents the *major axis* and line EF the *minor axis*. Point O is the midpoint of both the major and minor axes. The line segments $AO = OP = a$ are called the *semimajor axes*, and the line segments $EO = OF = b$ the *semiminor axes*. In an elliptical orbit the length of the semimajor axis is equal to the average

displacement of the planet from the sun. Recall the method of constructing an ellipse by running a pencil along a loop of string placed around tacks at S and S'. It is apparent that $2(AO + OS) = S'E + ES + S'O + OS$ and that $ES = AO = a$. Therefore, when the planet is at point E or F it is at its mean displacement from the sun.

As indicated in the ellipse in Fig. 8.3, the line segment OS is the displacement of the sun from the common center. In Fig. 8.4, this distance equals c, which forms the base of a right triangle. Therefore by the Pythagorean theorem,

$$c = \sqrt{a^2 - b^2}$$

where a = semimajor axis
b = semiminor axis

The ratio $c/a = e$ indicates the extent that an ellipse differs from a circle and is referred to as the *eccentricity* of the ellipse. The eccentricity of a circle is zero because *e* would equal zero. In terms of orbital components the eccentricity equals OS/AO. (Remember that $ES = AO$.) For example, the eccentricity of the earth's orbit equals 0.01674 which means that the sun is displaced $0.01674 \times 9.291 \times 10^7$ miles or 1,555,000 miles from the center of the ellipse. It also means that the earth is over 3 million miles further from the sun when at aphelion than when at perihelion.

A standard base line from which to measure orientation in space is the line between the sun and the vernal equinox. Again with respect to Fig. 8.3, the line *SV* in the plane of the ecliptic represents the direction of the vernal equinox from the sun. The angle *VSN* is called the *longitude of the ascending node*. The angle *VSP* is called the *longitude of the perihelion*.

Knowledge of a planet's mean displacement from the sun, the eccentricity of its orbit, the inclination to the ecliptic, the longitude of the ascending node, and the longitude of the perihelion fixes the size, shape, and position of the planetary orbit

in space with respect to the sun, the vernal equinox, and the plane of the earth's orbit. Table 8.2 supplies pertinent information about the orbits and the apparent periods of revolution of the planets with regard to the earth and the sun.

Elongation and synodic period The *elongation* of a planet is the angle at the earth formed by the line from the earth to the planet and the line from the earth to the sun. In Fig. 8.5 let the inner circle represent the orbit of an inner planet such as Venus, the middle circle the orbit of the earth, and the outer circle the orbit of an outer planet. We define the position of the planets when the earth is at *E*. When the inner planet is at *I*, the planet is said to be in *inferior conjunction;* when it is at *S*, it is said to be in *superior conjunction.* The points *G* and *G'* mark the planet's possible locations to be at *greatest elongation.* The outer planet is in *conjunction* when at *C* and in *opposition* when at *O*, and it is in *quadrature* when the elongation is 90° as occurs at *Q* and *Q'*. The elongation of a planet is designated

TABLE 8.2   Characteristics of planetary orbits

Planet	Sidereal period of revolution	Synodic period of revolution	Eccentricity of orbit	Inclination to the ecliptic	Longitude of ascending node
Mercury	87.97d	115.88d	0.206	7° 0′	47° 32′
Venus	224.7d	583.92d	0.007	3° 24′	76° 5′
Earth	365.256d	—	0.017	0° 0′	—
Mars	686.98d	779.93d	0.093	1° 51′	49° 2′
Jupiter	11.86y	398.88d	0.048	1° 18′	99° 46′
Saturn	29.46y	378.08d	0.056	2° 29′	113° 4′
Uranus	84.01y	369.66d	0.047	0° 46′	73° 39′
Neptune	164.79y	367.48d	0.009	1° 46′	131° 2′
Pluto	248.43y	366.73d	0.249	17° 8′	109° 56′

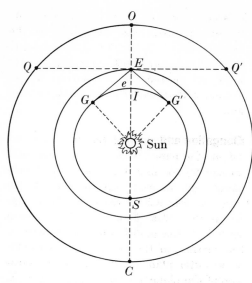

Figure 8.5 Measurement of planetary positions with respect to the earth and the sun.

as east or west elongation depending upon whether the planet rises before the sun (west elongation) or whether the sun sets before the planet (east elongation) during a given calendar day.

The *synodic period* of a planet is the time required between a given elongation of the planet and the same point of elongation of the planet next following. The specified conditions most often used for this measurement are the time between superior conjunctions for an inner planet and between oppositions for an outer planet.

THE INNER PLANETS

The first four planets in the order of their distances from the sun—Mercury, Venus, Earth, and Mars—are distinctly different in many ways from the more distant members in the solar system. First, they are relatively near to the sun. Second,

their average densities are much greater than the outer planets. Third, their average temperatures are relatively high. And, perhaps their most distinctive quality is that the earth is a member of this group and our home in space.

We all have a natural curiosity as to how the earth came into being. Perhaps an inquiry into the characteristics of our nearest neighbors in space might offer some clues. We shall need a bountiful imagination to create meaningful models to aid our understanding. We shall try to interpret information in terms of things that we can experience and then apply these meanings to regions far removed from the earth and to conditions that cannot be easily duplicated in our environment.

Fig. 8.6 represents the orbits of the inner or *terrestrial* planets. The plane of the page is the plane of the ecliptic. The portions of the orbits above the ecliptic plane are shown in solid lines and the portions below, in broken lines. In order to give a better perspective of the relative distances, Fig. 8.7 shows the orbits of the inner planets to a scale of 1 A.U. equals 12.2 map scale miles, with the Los Angeles Sports Arena representing the location of the sun. Table 8.3 gives relative values for planet sizes and orbits set to this scale.

TABLE 8.3 Relative planetary values. Scale: 12.2 miles = 1 A.U.

Planet	Diameter to scale	Radius of orbit in A.U.	to scale
Mercury	24 inches	0.387	4.74 miles
Venus	63 inches	0.723	8.8 miles
Earth	66 inches	1.000	12.2 miles
Mars	33 inches	1.524	18.6 miles

Sun (diameter to scale): 600 ft

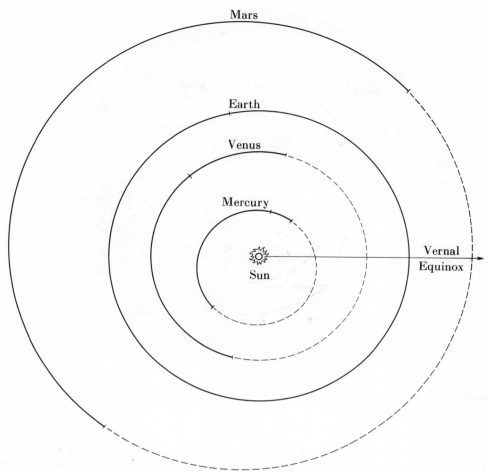

Figure 8.6 The orbits of the terrestrial planets. The portions of the orbits shown in dotted lines are below the plane of the earth's orbit. The cross line is the point of perihelion.

Mercury The planet nearest the sun is Mercury; its average displacement from the sun is 0.387 A.U. (36 million miles). Because Mercury is so near the sun, observation of it is confined, at best, to a period of less than two hours before sunrise and two hours after sunset during periods when the planet is near its greatest elongation. The greatest elongation of Mercury is about 28°.

Mercury's surface is subjected to great contrasts of temperature and solar illumination. The solar tides produced on it by the nearby sun have slowed the planet's rotation until the period of rotation is equal to the period of revolution. We shall discuss later in the chapter the form of energy converted in doing the work of slowing the rotation.

Mercury presents the same surface to-

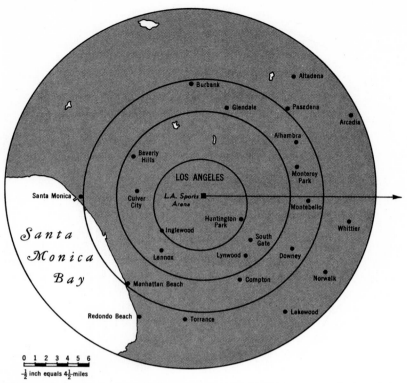

Figure 8.7 Comparison of planetary distances to the scale of 12.2 miles equals 1 A.U.

ward the sun at all times. Therefore it is believed to be the coldest as well as the hottest planet in the solar system. The estimated temperature of the surface facing the sun is about 750°F, hot enough to melt solder. On the opposite side, where sunlight never strikes, the temperature would be near to absolute zero, −459.4°F.

The average illuminance (the amount of light falling on a unit area) on the surface of Mercury as compared with that on the earth can be estimated in terms of the law of inverse squares:

$$\frac{I_M}{I_E} = \frac{R_E^2}{R_M^2}$$

where I_M = illuminance on Mercury

I_E = illuminance on earth
R_M = mean distance between sun and Mercury
R_E = mean distance between sun and earth

In terms of distances in astronomical units, the ratio of illuminance on Mercury as compared to the earth is 6.68 to 1.

$$\frac{I_M}{I_E} = \frac{(1 \text{ A.U.})^2}{(0.387 \text{ A.U.})^2} = \frac{1}{0.1498} = 6.68$$

The average intensity of the sunlight on Mercury is almost seven times that reaching the outer atmosphere of the earth. Furthermore, the eccentricity of Mercury's orbit produces an even greater contrast. With an eccentricity of 0.20562, Mercury's displacement from the sun varies from 79.4 percent of the mean value when the planet is at perihelion to 120.6 percent of the mean value when it is at aphelion. Consequently, the ratio of illuminances at perihelion to aphelion is $(1.206)^2/(0.794)^2 = 2.30$, giving Mercury more than twice the intensity of sunlight when at perihelion than when it is at aphelion.

The extremes of temperature found on the front and back of Mercury are greatly increased by the fact that the planet has no surrounding atmosphere to help distribute the heat. Mercury cannot hold an atmosphere. Its surface gravity is only 38 percent of that at the surface of the earth and the escape velocity from its surface is only 2.6 miles per second. Hence, the molecules of any gas which might reach the surface of Mercury, whether rising from within the planet or from the surrounding space, would achieve velocities greater than the escape velocity, because of the high temperature on the solar side, and depart into interplanetary space.

Mercury's albedo may be even a little lower than the 0.07 indicated in Table 8.1. The surface is dark in color and is an extremely good absorber of sunlight. Over 93 percent of the light falling upon the surface is absorbed; less than 7 percent is reflected. It is postulated that Mercury is composed of materials rich in iron. This is supported by the average density of the planetary material as well as by the low albedo.

Venus Of all the planets Venus has most nearly the same size and mass as the earth. Venus also has an atmosphere but not like that of the earth. Its surface is obscured by a dense layer of clouds. Spectral absorption lines indicate the presence of carbon dioxide in concentrations more than 250 times that found in the earth's atmosphere. Water and oxygen have not been detected. Some scientists describe the atmosphere of Venus as dense smog, suggesting that the surface might have petroleumlike materials in abundance.

The rate of rotation of Venus is not known exactly. The lack of Doppler shift in spectral studies of Venus has been used to postulate a rotation period much less than that of the earth. Other factors suggest a rotation period of about a month.

Because the mean displacement of Venus from the sun is 0.723 A.U., its illuminance is 1.91 times that of the earth.

$$\frac{I_V}{I_E} = \frac{R_E^2}{R_V^2} = \frac{1}{(0.723)^2} = \frac{1}{0.523} = 1.91$$
$$I_V = 1.91\, I_E$$

The light intensity on the atmosphere of Venus is nearly twice the intensity on the atmosphere of the earth. With appropriate energy conversion into heat, this amount of light might produce at the surface of Venus a temperature equal to the boiling point of water.

The orbit of Venus is the most nearly circular of all the planets. The greatest elongation is about 46°. At its brightest, Venus can be seen with the unaided eye in broad daylight and at night it reflects enough light to the earth to cast shadows.

The nature of the materials in the solid surface of Venus is unknown. The clouds obscure the surface at all times. However, the mass and average density relationships indicate a material not too much different from the materials found in the other terrestrial planets including the earth.

Earth We shall devote several chapters to the earth and its materials and processes. Mention here is only to place the earth correctly into the solar system as a planet related to all of the other planets. The earth has the distinction of being the planet closest to the sun to have a satellite. Our moon is larger in comparison to its planet than any other in the solar system. Pictures of the earth-moon system taken from points in outer space will very soon be commonplace. The first men who have traveled into outer space have described the earth as having a beautiful bluish tint, as was expected for the same reason that our sky is blue. The moon is described as appearing yellowish in color.

Density relationships indicate that the materials making up the greater portions of the inner planets are probably similar. Therefore, our later inquiries into earth materials will shed light upon the make-up of the other planets as well. These similarities also have a bearing upon hypotheses of the probable origin of the solar system.

Mars Mars is the outermost of the terrestrial planets and is the most favorably placed of all the planets for observation from the earth. The average distance from the earth to Mars at opposition is about 48 million miles (0.52 A.U.). However, the eccentricity of the orbit of Mars is 0.09333; hence, the displacement of Mars from the sun varies from (0.90667 × 1.52 A.U.) 1.42 A.U. to (1.09333 × 1.52 A.U.) 1.66 A.U. Therefore, if opposition occurs when Mars is in perihelion and the earth is near aphelion, the distance between the planets is reduced to about 35 million miles. These most favorable oppositions occur at

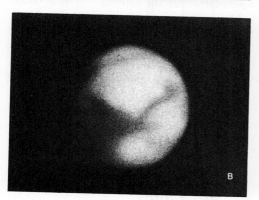

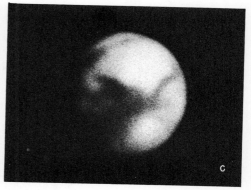

Three views of Mars showing rotation. [*Courtesy of the Mount Wilson and Palomar Observatories.*]

intervals of approximately 15 or 17 years.

The escape velocity from the surface of Mars is 3.1 miles per second as compared to 6.9 miles per second from the surface of the earth. Mars at 1.52 A.U. average displacement from the sun has a much lower intensity of solar radiation than the earth. Even when at perihelion Mars is 1.42 A.U. from the sun and hence has an illuminance only 0.4961 times that on the earth.

$$\frac{I_M}{I_E} = \frac{R_E^2}{R_M^2} = \frac{1}{(1.42)^2} = \frac{1}{2.016} = 0.4961$$

$$I_M = 0.4961 \, I_E$$

Therefore, it should not be surprising to find that Mars does have an observable atmosphere, although not nearly as dense as the earth's. Spectroscopic studies show that Mars has about 5 percent as much water in its atmosphere, volume for volume, as the earth has. Similar studies have indicated various values for oxygen content. The most optimistic determinations place the oxygen content at 15 percent that of the earth's atmosphere, others report a much lower value than this. Compared to the earth, therefore, Mars must be classified as an arid desert without enough oxygen in the atmosphere to support animal life as we know it.

The most conspicuous features of telescopic observations of Mars are the ever-changing polar white caps which appear and disappear with the seasons. When Mars is near aphelion a combined effect of orbital eccentricity and the planet's inclination to the plane of the orbit is the extension of the polar cap to greater area, particularly at the south pole. The pattern of advancing and receding polar caps in step with decreasing and increasing periods of sunlight suggests snowfall. However, in view of the limited water content in the atmosphere, the caps of Mars may be more in the nature of heavy white frost rather than the snow caps of the earth.

Mars has two tiny satellites, Phobos and Deimas. Phobos has a diameter of 10 miles and revolves on an orbit about 3700 miles above the surface of Mars. Its period of revolution is 7 hours, 39 minutes. Phobos makes more than three revolutions during each Martian day, and because it revolves counterclockwise from the surface of Mars, it rises in the west and sets in the east.

Deimas has a diameter of 5 miles and an orbit 12,500 miles above the surface of Mars. The sidereal period of Deimas is 30 hours, 18 minutes. Because the axial rotation of Mars is 24 hours, 37 minutes, Deimas moves slowly westward in the Martian sky.. An observer on the surface of Mars would see Deimas go through its whole cycle of moon phases during the time of its rising in the east and setting in the west.

THE ASTEROIDS

The region of the solar system between the orbits of Mars and Jupiter is subjected to periodic search for the small, planetlike objects called asteroids. Like the planets, the asteroids, have individual orbits of revolution about the sun. Actually, thousands of these miniature planets exist in this region. Hundreds of them have been discovered and catalogued.

Almost all the asteroids have average displacements from the sun ranging between 2.0 and 3.5 A.U. However, the average values range from 10.6 A.U. for asteroid 1927BD to 0.65 A.U. for asteroid 1932HA. The orbits of several asteroids are so eccentric that they pass inside the earth's orbit and at least one passes inside the orbit of Mercury.

The asteroids discovered before 1925 were given names. Eros, mentioned earlier in this chapter, was one of these. Since that time a new method of cataloguing has been used. Each month of the year was allotted two letters of the alphabet, one for each half of the month. The letters I and Z were omitted. Following these letters the alphabet was used a second time omitting I. Thus, 1927BD was the fourth asteroid discovered after Jan. 15 in 1927 and 1932HA was the first asteroid discovered after Apr. 1 in 1932.

If the materials contained in the thousand largest asteroids were combined, the total mass would be less than 0.03 percent of the earth's mass. It is not likely that the materials in all the asteroids put together would amount to as much as 1 percent of the earth's mass. Speculation as to the source of asteroids range from postulating an explosion of a planet to postulating that the materials represent a planet nucleus which never became or-

ganized to form a completed planet. Some astronomers think that meteors are tiny asteroids. If this is so, then asteroids contain much the same type of materials as the earth.

THE MAJOR PLANETS

The major planets—Jupiter, Saturn, Uranus, Neptune, and Pluto—can be generally characterized by great displacements from the sun, great volumes and masses, great numbers of satellites, and great angular momenta (the momentum which maintains the spinning motion). The short periods of rotation for these planets combined with their great masses produce angular momenta that proportionally are much greater than those of the terrestrial planets and proportionally much greater than the angular momentum of the sun. The combined mass of the major planets is more than 1000 times greater than the combined mass of the terrestrial planets; however, their average densities are less than those of the terrestrial planets. The

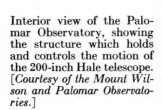

Interior view of the Palomar Observatory, showing the structure which holds and controls the motion of the 200-inch Hale telescope. [*Courtesy of the Mount Wilson and Palomar Observatories.*]

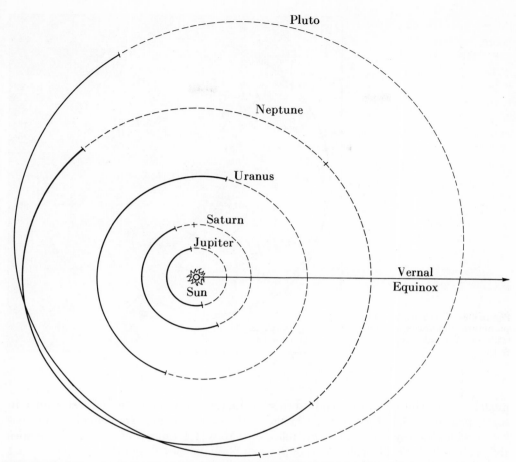

Figure 8.8 The orbits of the major planets. The portions of the orbits shown in dotted lines are below the plane of the earth's orbit. The cross line is the point of perihelion.

farthest member, Pluto, revolves around the sun at such a great distance that its illuminance is but 0.00064 that of the earth. These great contrasts must be considered when theoretical explanations of the evolution of the solar system are proposed.

Fig. 8.8 represents the orbits of the major planets. The plane of the page is again the plane of the ecliptic and the portions of the orbits above and below the ecliptic plane are indicated. To provide perspective of comparable distances in the solar system, Fig. 8.9 illustrates the orbits set to the same scale (12.2 map scale miles = 1 A.U.) used in Fig. 8.7. (But note the difference in map scales!) A large balloon, 600 ft in diameter, placed above the Los Angeles Sports Arena would represent the sun in this scale

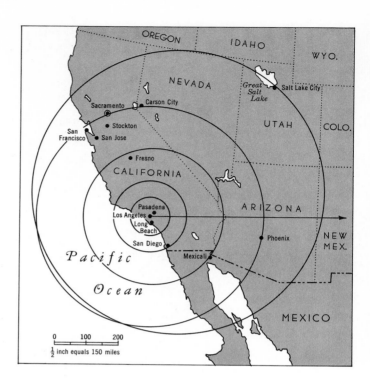

Figure 8.9 Comparison of planetary distances to the scale of 12.2 miles equals 1 A.U.

0   100   200
½ inch equals 150 miles

model. The orbit of Pluto would, to this scale, pass over Salt Lake City. Table 8.4 provides information concerning relative scale values for this scale model of the major planets. You will notice the orbits to this scale touch upon eight of the western states as well as two provinces of Mexico.

TABLE 8.4 Relative planetary values. Scale: 12.2 miles = 1 A.U.

Planet	Diameter to scale	Radius of orbit in A.U.	to scale
Jupiter	60 ft	5.203	63.5 miles
Saturn	50 ft	9.539	116.4 miles
Uranus	22 ft	19.182	224.0 miles
Neptune	21 ft	30.058	366.7 miles
Pluto	4 ft	39.518	482.1 miles

Jupiter Jupiter is the largest planet in the solar system. Its volume is approximately 1.4 times the combined volumes of all the other planets; its mass is 2.4 times the combined masses of the other planets. Because of its rapid rotation Jupiter bulges markedly at the equator. The equatorial diameter is 88,700 miles compared to 82,700 miles at the poles. Points along Jupiter's equator have a speed of more than 28,000 miles per hour. This is considerably greater than the escape velocity at the surface of the earth.

Although Jupiter dwarfs all of the other planets in size and mass, the presence of a deep atmosphere reduces its average density to less than one-fourth that of the earth. To account for the relationships of size, shape, and mass for Jupiter, an assumption is often used which divides

Jupiter, the largest planet in the solar system. (a) Shadow of satellite seen on disk; (b) both satellite and shadow seen, taken about 50 minutes after (a). [Courtesy of the Mount Wilson and Palomar Observatories.]

Jupiter into three general layers of material. A rocky, metallic central core is postulated having a radius of 18,500 miles and an average density of about 6 grams per cubic centimeter (six times the density of water). Over the central core the middle layer is of ice about 17,000 miles thick and compressed to an average density of 1.5 grams per cubic centimeter. Over the ice an atmosphere of hydrogen, methane, and ammonia has a height of 8000 miles. The tremendous pressure of this atmosphere would compress the lower portions of it almost to the liquid state. In fact, some authorities believe that the atmosphere may blend imperceptibly from gaseous, through a slushy solid, into the solid ice layers postulated for the planet. The surface observed is the top of the atmosphere and the dimension given in Table 8.4 is for this outer reflecting surface.

A dozen satellites have been discovered revolving around Jupiter. Four of these were discovered by Galileo in 1610. The two largest satellites, Callisto and Sanymede, have diameters of 3218 miles and 3200 miles, respectively, making them comparable in size to the planet Mercury. The five satellites nearest to Jupiter have nearly circular orbits which pass through the shadow of the planet at each revolution. The successive passages of one of these satellites through the shadow led to the first measured value of the speed of light. In 1666 Olaf Roemer reported to the French Academy the results obtained from observing the motions of Jupiter's satellites. He had observed that a greater time elapsed between successive passages of a given satellite when the earth was receding from Jupiter than when the earth was approaching. Roemer's calculations led him to conclude that light required about 22 minutes to travel the distance of the diameter of the earth's orbit. This gave a value of about 227,000 kilometers per second as the velocity of light, a value much too low when compared to the present-day measurement of 299,793 kilometers per second. It was, however, a value too great to be accepted readily by Roemer's contemporaries. Confirmation of the speed of light by other means was not achieved until 1728, 18 years after Roemer's death.

The four outermost satellites of Jupiter are so far distant from the planet that conceivably they might at some time be removed from their orbits around Jupiter by the sun's attractive force and take up separate orbits around the sun. These satellites also have another, more obvious distinction. They revolve around Jupiter in a clockwise direction in complete contradiction to the counterclockwise motions most generally observed in the solar system. Their discovery upset the regularity of planetary motion which formed the basis for several hypotheses concerning the formation of the solar system.

Saturn Saturn is the most remote of the "naked-eye" planets and, therefore, of all the bright planets moves the most slowly in its apparent wanderings among the stars. The planet itself resembles Jupiter except it is smaller in every detail. Some astronomers think it also to be similar in structure because, to account for its

Saturn and its system of rings. The outside ring has a diameter of about 171,000 miles. [*Courtesy of the Mount Wilson and Palomar Observatories.*]

known density characteristics, Saturn should have a solid rocky core 10,000 miles in radius surrounded by ice 15,000 miles in thickness and a 12,000-mile-deep atmosphere of hydrogen, methane, and ammonia. Spectral evidence indicates more methane and less ammonia in the atmosphere of Saturn than in that of Jupiter. The lower ammonia content could be expected because at the extremely low temperature of −243°F much of the ammonia would be frozen out of the atmosphere.

The most astonishing thing about Saturn is its system of rings. There are three thin, flat rings at the plane of Saturn's equator. The innermost ring begins at about 7000 miles above the planet's surface and extends outward to about 18,000 miles above the surface. The second and brightest ring begins at about 19,000 miles and extends to about 34,000 miles. The outer ring begins at about 36,500 miles and extends to about 46,500 miles. The outside diameter of the outer ring is about 171,000 miles, giving this broad view of Saturn almost twice the diameter of Jupiter. The rings are extremely thin; so thin in fact that they disappear from sight even in large telescopes when viewed edgewise.

Spectroscopic studies show a faster rotation for the inner edges of the rings than for the outer edges. Therefore the rings must be composed of small particles of solid materials, each particle revolving in its own individual orbit around the central mass of Saturn. Study of the light reflected from the rings suggests that they are composed largely of ice particles.

Speculation concerning the origin of Saturn's rings usually involves a study made by E. A. Roche, which indicates that if a satellite composed of materials having low tensile strength were to approach within 2.44 times a planet's radius (the *Roche limit*) from the center of mass, the resulting tidal forces would break up the intruder and distribute the pieces around the planet. The outer edge of Saturn's rings is at a distance of 2.30 radii from the planet's center. The nearest satellite approaches to 3.11 radii. Many astronomers interpret the rings as the remnants of one or more satellites whose orbits brought them too close to the planet. Others use the Roche limit as evidence for assuming that the tidal forces would prevent the particles of the rings from coalescing into satellites in a manner attributed to the formation of the more remote satellites out of protosatellite particles.

Saturn is known to have nine satellites. The largest, Titan, has about twice the volume of our moon, and is the only satellite in the solar system which is known definitely to have an atmosphere. Like the outermost satellites of Jupiter, the outermost satellite of Saturn, Phoebe, revolves in a clockwise direction opposite to most other members of the solar system. It has been suggested that these retrograde satellites may have been asteroids which were later captured by these large planets.

Uranus Uranus was the first planet to be discovered. Sir William Herschel made the discovery in March, 1781, while he was observing individually the stars in the constellation Gemini with his famous 7-inch reflecting telescope. Herschel named the planet "Georgium Sidus" in honor of George the Third of England, but the name was not generally accepted. Up until about 100 years ago, most astronomers preferred to call the planet Herschel in honor of the discoverer.

However, because all of the other planets had been named for mythical gods, the name Uranus, God of the Heavens, was suggested by Bode, Director of the Berlin Observatory, and is the one that is now used.

The temperature on Uranus is about −300°F. Since ammonia solidifies at −98°F, very little of this compound would remain as a gas in the atmosphere of Uranus. Methane freezes at about −302°F; thus much of this compound could remain gaseous. Hydrogen gas has been discovered by spectroscopic study of the infrared spectral absorption bands in the light from Uranus. Therefore, as would be expected, the atmospheres of the major planets are composed largely of hydrogen with smaller amounts of methane and ammonia; the amounts of ammonia become progressively less as the temperature is depressed below the freezing point of ammonia. As with Jupiter and Saturn, many astronomers assume that Uranus should have a small dense core of rocky materials, then a thick layer of ice, and a very deep atmosphere.

The rotation of Uranus is unique in one respect; its equator is inclined 98° to the plane of its orbit and consequently its rotation is clockwise as seen from the usual vantage point on the north side of the ecliptic. Hence, at the Uranian poles the midnight sun lasts for 42 earth years and is followed by a 42-year period of arctic night.

Five satellites have been discovered revolving around Uranus. Their orbits are precisely in the equatorial plane of the planet. Therefore when the planet's poles are turned toward the earth, the satellites are seen to follow almost circular paths. When the planet's equator is turned toward the earth, the satellites are seen to move up and down almost per-

The Palomar Observatory dome which houses the 200-inch Hale telescope. [*Courtesy of the Mount Wilson and Palomar Observatories.*]

pendicular to the plane of the planet's orbit.

Neptune Neptune was "discovered" on the pages of the calculation sheets of two mathematicians who were not aware that each was searching for the same result as the other. John Couch Adams, an undergraduate at Cambridge, became interested in the problem of the discrepancies which had developed between actual and predicted orbital positions for Uranus. In 1841, he set about calculating the probable position of an unknown planet which would account for the actual motions of Uranus. Adams presented the results of his calculations to Sir George Airy, the British Astronomer Royal. Airy postponed any serious attempt at searching for the supposed planet.

At about the same time, a young French astronomer, Urbain Leverrier, independently attacked the same problem in a general re-working of questions involving discrepancies in predicted planetary orbits. In 1845, Leverrier presented his results to the Paris Observatory but the calculations were returned to him unused. He then informed Johann Galle of the Berlin Observatory of the predicted location. Within a half hour after the astronomers at the Berlin Observatory began their search, the new planet had been located and confirmed to be within 1° of the positions calculated by both Leverrier and Adams.

In many ways Neptune is almost an identical twin of Uranus. Its size and mass are close to those of Uranus. Its atmosphere contains hydrogen, methane, and ammonia but because of the extreme cold, −330°F, much of the methane and ammonia undoubtedly has been solidified.

Two satellites have been discovered revolving around Neptune. Triton, the larger one, is somewhat larger than our moon and has an almost perfectly circular orbit. Triton revolves in the retrograde, clockwise direction. In contrast, Nereid, the smaller satellite, has the largest eccentricity of all known satellites, 0.76. Its distance from Neptune varies from 825,000 miles to 6,055,000 miles.

As you have perhaps observed in Fig. 8.8, Pluto's orbit cuts inside the orbit of Neptune. Several arguments point to the possibility that Pluto once may have been a satellite of Neptune, but the evidence is not conclusive.

Pluto The ninth planet was named Pluto, the god of the lower world, because its orbit, at an average displacement of 39.52 A.U. from the sun, exists perpetu-

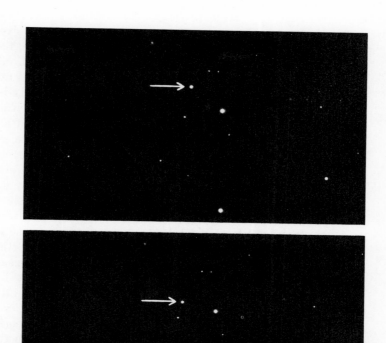

Two photographs showing the motion of the planet Pluto in 24 hours. [*Courtesy of the Mount Wilson and Palomar Observatories.*]

ally at the rim of "outer darkness." The discovery of Pluto in many ways resembled the discovery of Neptune. Small irregularities in Neptune's orbital motion bordered upon possible disturbances by a distant unknown planet. A number of astronomers tried to duplicate the work of Adams and Leverrier by calculating the position of the supposed planet. One of these was Percival Lowell, the founder of Lowell Observatory near Flagstaff, Arizona. In 1930, 14 years after Lowell's death, Clyde Tombaugh, using special equipment designed for the purpose at Lowell Observatory, discovered a planet moving slowly through the region which was substantially in agreement with Lowell's calculations. The name Pluto for the planet was also appropriate because the first two letters of the name were Lowell's initials, P. L.

Precise measurements of Pluto's dimensions are impossible because of distance. Many observers suggest a size smaller and less massive for Pluto than for Earth. If this is true, then Pluto differs greatly from the other four planets beyond the asteroid belt.

Pluto is unique in many ways. Its orbit has the greatest eccentricity of all the planetary orbits. The plane of its orbit has the greatest inclination to the plane of the ecliptic. Because of the eccentricity, Pluto at perihelion is 63 million miles inside of Neptune's orbit. But because of the inclination of the orbits, the closest approach of the two planets is about 240 million miles; there is therefore no danger of planetary collision. At the present time Pluto is moving toward perihelion which will be reached in 1989. Pluto has moved through only a small segment of its orbit since discovery in 1930. Pluto was then near its ascending node. Early in 1979 the planet Pluto will cross inside the orbit of Neptune; then, for a period of about 20 years, Pluto will be the eighth planet in terms of distance from the sun and Neptune will be the outermost planet in the solar system.

As was suggested in our discussion of Neptune's satellites, Pluto, in theory, could once have been a satellite of Neptune. Many of the above-mentioned characteristics of Pluto support this theory. Surely, when compared to its neighbors in space, Pluto is more moonlike than planetlike. Its orbit cuts inside of Neptune's orbit, and its orbital inclination to the ecliptic varies greatly from the other planetary orbits. These factors are difficult to explain using current theories of the genesis of the solar system, without including the satellite theory for Pluto. However, again the arguments are not conclusive. The problem of determining Pluto's origin, like so many other problems of science, must await further observation, speculation, and interpretation.

THE ORIGIN OF THE SOLAR SYSTEM

Our inquiry up until now has brought to light many of the facts and some of the implications concerning the materials and processes involved in the solar system. On the whole, the facts show an impressive degree of orderliness. For instance, all the planets revolve around the sun in a counterclockwise direction; the sun and most of the planets also rotate in this direction; and the satellites, with but a few exceptions, revolve around the planets in a counterclockwise direction. This orderliness is not thought to be a haphazard occurrence, but is used to support the hypothesis that the solar system evolved as a whole and as a result of a great cosmic action which is still in process in our portion of the galaxy. Evidence also suggests a similar action may be in process in other portions of our galaxy and in other nearby galaxies of the universe.

Several theories have been proposed down through the ages to interpret and explain the known facts about the solar system. But as new evidence was discovered, the older theories had to be modified drastically or abandoned because quantitative analysis proved the theories impossible. Undoubtedly, present-day theories will share this fate as more facts and better interpretations become known. But it would be folly to delay our inquiry by waiting for these developments, when experiences of the past indicate the inevitability of continued change. We must inquire into the meanings of present-day theories, otherwise we should have no basis upon which to compare the changing patterns of interpretation.

The protoplanet theory Evidence indicates that the planets were not formed from materials ejected or pulled out from the sun, as was once widely believed. It would now seem certain, for example, that at least two elements found in the earth's materials would not have been present had the original materials of the earth taken part in a thermonuclear reaction such as occurs in the sun. Deuterium and lithium, which are found intermixed in the materials of the earth and in meteorites reaching the earth from surrounding space, are known to be among the first materials consumed in a thermonuclear reaction and, hence, have not been detected in the solar spectrum. The sun and the planets are thought to have a common origin and to have evolved simultaneously from essentially the same store of cosmic materials, but the various bodies evolved in a process which led to the present distribution of materials, energies, and momenta.

One of a group of somewhat similar theories, sometimes referred to as the "dust cloud" theories, is the protoplanet theory. This has been most fully developed by Gerald P. Kuiper of Yerkes Observatory, the University of Chicago. According to Kuiper's hypothesis, the solar system evolved as a result of processes which developed within a huge contracting protostar. In the initial phases the slowly rotating protostar consisted of a very sparse cloud of dust particles and gas several million times the volume of the present sun. As the protostar began to contract under its own gravitational effects, increased rotation of the cloud set up inertial reactions in the materials which reduced the effect of the gravitational force. This reaction would have been most prominent in the materials near the equator of the spinning cloud and therefore a portion of the cloud flattened out into a wheeling disk extending outward from the protostar equator. This supposed disk is often referred to as a rotating "solar nebula."

The idea of a solar nebula is not new. In 1796 the French astronomer and mathematician, Simon de Laplace, published his nebular hypothesis for the formation of the solar system. As a descriptive representation, the Laplacian theory met very little opposition. The theory held sway for over a century. But from the standpoint of quantitative evidence it could not be defended. The major discrepancies in the Laplacian theory involved accounting for the measured angular momenta of the various spinning bodies in the solar system.

In order to make meaningful comparisons we need to understand better the nature of rotational motion.

Extending the laws of motion Our experiences with volleyballs and other objects which we have made contact with for the purpose of changing motion help us to understand that the linear motion of objects can be changed only by application of an outside force. Similarly, our experiences with hula hoops and bicycle wheels help us to understand that the rotational motion of objects can be changed only by application of a cranking action such as is applied through the bicycle pedals. The term *torque* is used to designate the effort represented by the cranking action. We shall find that the idea of torque is related to rotational motion in the same manner as the idea of force is related to linear motion.

In Chapter 6, Newton's laws of motion were introduced in explanation of linear motion. The laws of motion apply also to the angular motion of objects rotating about an axis. We shall state again the laws of linear motion and include as counterparts a statement in terms of rotational motion.

The First Law: Every material object persists in a state of rest or of uniform straight-line motion unless it is compelled to change that state by a force impressed upon it.

Also: Every material object persists in a state of rest or of uniform rotational motion about a fixed axis unless it is compelled to change that state by a torque impressed upon it.

The Second Law: An unbalanced force acting on a material object produces an acceleration which is proportional to the force and takes place in the direction of the unbalanced force.

Also: An unbalanced torque acting on a material object produces an angular acceleration which is proportional to the torque and takes place in the direction of the unbalanced torque.

The Third Law: To every action there is always opposed a reaction; or the mutual actions of two bodies upon each other are always equal and directed to contrary parts.

Also: The above statement applies to rotational motion.

With reference to the first law, the conditions of rotational motion which tend to be conserved are the direction of the axis of rotation and the time rate of rotation. Conventionally the vector direction of rotational motion is determined by the right-hand rule: *When the fingers of the right hand are curved about the axis of rotation in the direction of the rotation the thumb is pointing in the direction of the angular momentum.* Rotation, when viewed along the direction of the axis, is described as clockwise or counterclockwise. When the rotation is viewed in the direction of the vector, the rotation is clockwise about the axis. (See Fig. 8.10.) Commonly the time rate of rotation is

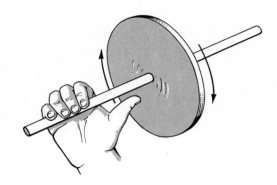

Figure 8.10 Right-hand rule. The thumb of the right hand points in the direction of the vector of rotation if the fingers are placed in the direction of the rotation.

measured in terms of the number of rotations per minute (rpm). But because a point on a rotating object travels a distance of one circular circumference ($2\pi R$) during each rotation, it is more convenient to record the rate of rotation in terms of radians. Motion in an arc of a circle equal in length to its radius is called a *radian.* There are, therefore, 2π radians in each rotation of the object. Consequently, the time rate of rotation most often used in scientific formulas is the angular speed in terms of the number of radians of rotation per second. The term *angular velocity* combines the ideas of rate of rotation and the direction of rotation. In terms of angular motion the counterpart of Eq. (6.4) is:

$$(8.1) \qquad \omega = \frac{\theta}{t}$$

where ω (Greek *omega*) = average angular velocity in radians per second
θ (Greek *theta*) = radians of rotation
t = time in seconds

For example, if a spinning top rotates

clockwise 700 rotations in 2 sec, the average angular velocity would be about 2200 radians per second directed vertically downward.

$$\omega = \frac{700 \text{ rotations}}{2 \text{ sec}} \times \frac{2\pi \text{ radians}}{\text{rotation}}$$

$$= 700\pi \text{ radians/sec}$$

With regard to the second law, torque, like angular velocity, is directed in a clockwise or in a counterclockwise manner as viewed along the axis of rotation. The amount of torque is determined by multiplying the tangential force by its radius of action. For example, if at a given instant a force of 10 newtons is applied to a point 20 cm removed from the axis of rotation and is directed such that the force is at right angles to the radius of rotation (see Fig. 8.11), the torque would be 2 newton-meters in a counterclockwise direction.

$$\tau = FR = 10 \text{ newtons} \times 0.2 \text{ meter}$$
$$= 2 \text{ newton-meters}$$
where τ (Greek *tau*) = torque
F = tangential component of force
R = radius of rotation

When more than one torque is acting on a body, the total unbalanced torque equals the sum of the individual torques. Since counterclockwise torques oppose the clockwise torques, the greater of the two prevails; subtracting the smaller from the greater determines the unbalanced torque.

Angular acceleration is the time rate of change in angular velocity. In terms of angular motion the counterpart of Eq. (6.5) is:

(8.2) $$\alpha = \frac{\omega_2 - \omega_1}{t}$$

where α (Greek *alpha*) = angular acceleration in radians per second[2]
ω_2 = angular velocity in radians per second at the end of the time period
ω_1 = angular velocity in radians per second at the beginning of the time period
t = time period in seconds

The counterpart of Eq. (6.6) is:

(8.3) $$\frac{\tau_1}{\alpha_1} = \frac{\tau_2}{\alpha_2} = \frac{\tau_3}{\alpha_3} = I$$

The constant indicated by the symbol I for the given object rotating about a given axis is the measure of the object's resistance to change in its state of rotation; it is called the *moment of inertia*. The moment of inertia depends upon the shape of an object and its symmetry with respect to its axis of rotation. For instance, the moment of inertia of a homogeneous sphere with the axis through its center is

$$I = \tfrac{2}{5}mR^2$$

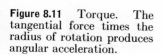

Figure 8.11 Torque. The tangential force times the radius of rotation produces angular acceleration.

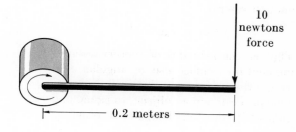

10 newtons force

0.2 meters

where I = moment of inertia of the sphere

m = mass of the sphere

R = radius of the sphere

The moment of inertia of a homogeneous disk with the axis perpendicular to the surface at its center is

$$I = \tfrac{1}{2}mR^2$$

Observe in these formulas that the moment of inertia varies in amount for the differently shaped bodies but the calculation in both instances is made in terms of the object's mass and the square of its radius. These formulas have far-reaching implications for bodies which may contract or expand as the result of self-contained energies.

Solving Eq. (8.3) for torque, we get $\tau = I\alpha$ and therefore

$$\alpha = \frac{\tau}{I}$$

Angular acceleration, like angular momentum, is a vector quantity. Therefore the acceleration can change the amount of angular momentum and/or the direction of the axis of rotation. An example of the second type is the precession of the earth's axis because the unbalanced torques produced by the gravitational attractions of the sun and moon for the earth's equatorial bulge produce changes in the direction of the axis of rotation.

According to the third law:

$$\tau_1 - \tau_2 = 0$$

and, therefore

$$I_1\alpha_1 - I_2\alpha_2 = 0$$

That is, the principle of conservation of momentum applies also to angular motion. Hence, when a change in angular velocity occurs in an object, an equal and oppositely directed change must occur in the objects that have effected this change in motion.

The conservation principle also applies when changes occur in the dimensions or the shape of rotating bodies. For instance, if a homogeneous sphere of radius 0.3 meter and 10 kg mass is accelerated to an angular velocity of 20 radians per second, the angular momentum would be 7.2 kg-meters² radians per second.

$$I_1\omega_1 = 2/5\ mR_1^2\omega_1$$

$$= \frac{2}{\cancel{5}} \times \cancel{10}^{\,2}\,\text{kg} \times 0.09\ \text{meter}^2$$

$$\times \frac{20\ \text{radians}}{\text{sec}} = 7.2\ \text{kg-meters}^2$$

$$\times\ \text{radians/sec}$$

If internal forces then caused the sphere to contract into a more dense sphere of radius 0.2 meter, the conservation principle would apply and the angular velocity would be increased from 20 to 45 radians per second.

$$\omega_2 = \frac{7.2\ \cancel{\text{kg}}\text{-meters}^2\ \text{radians}}{\text{sec}} \times \frac{\cancel{5}}{2} \times \frac{1}{\underset{2}{\cancel{10}\ \cancel{\text{kg}}}}$$

Figure 8.12 A device for experiencing conservation of angular momentum.

$$\times \frac{1}{0.04 \text{ meters}^2} = 45 \text{ radians/sec}$$

The angular velocity would be changed in proportion to:

$$\frac{\omega_2}{\omega_1} = \frac{R_1^2}{R_2^2}$$

Consequently

$$\omega_2 = \frac{\omega_1 R_1^2}{R_2^2} = \frac{20 \text{ radians} \times .09 \text{ meter}^2}{\text{sec} \times .04 \text{ meter}^2}$$

$$= 45 \text{ radians/sec}$$

Fig. 8.12 illustrates a device with which you can experience the surprising effects of the conservation of angular momentum. The weights in the hands of the subject constitute concentrations of mass which are rotating about an axis at the center of the device. If now the arms are lowered, the radius of rotation becomes shorter and the angular velocity increases accordingly. Lifting the arms to the original location slows the velocity to its former value less the attenuation due to friction.

Rotating objects within a rotating solar system The conservation of angular momentum is a crucial test for any hypothesis concerning the origin of the solar system. The nebular hypothesis of Laplace contained a number of irreparable flaws. First, in terms of the specified amounts and types of material and motion, it became impossible to conceive of a gaseous mass sloughing off rings or that such rotating rings would later condense into planets. Second, because the angular momentum would be conserved within the system, the larger part of the original momentum would be concentrated in the central sun. Actually only about 2 percent of the total angular momentum in the solar system is presently found in the sun.

However, speculation has returned to a modified form of the nebular hypothesis. Taking into account the possible interactions within the known materials in our own and nearby galaxies where stellar formation could now be in process and the explanation of the facts available from studies of the solar system and other star systems, present-day speculations suggest that the formation of planets was an incidental but not an unusual process accompanying the formation of the sun. In the protoplanet theory the origin of the solar system began with a contraction, under the effects of its own gravitation, of the cosmic dust and gas which constituted the original materials of a protostar. Because of an inherent but minor rotational motion within the materials of the protostar, the angular velocities would become enormous if a contraction in the ratio of a million to one were completed. In order to assimilate the large angular momentum of the system, the ultimate result of a protostar is usually not a single star but a double, triple, or a multiple star system. Thus, in the solar system, the instability produced as the protostar began to contract first produced a flattened bulge near the equator which served as the solar nebula (Fig. 8.13); then the solar nebula broke up into smaller concentrations of materials which Kuiper called protoplanets. Later, as the protoplanets had proceeded with their own contractions, the more massive protoplanets produced equatorial nebulae of their own out of which the protosatellites were formed.

In the early stages of the process, the protoplanets had essentially the same composition of materials as the sun. The amount of materials in each of the proto-

Figure 8.13 Contraction and rotation of the materials in a protostar.

planets was a natural outgrowth of the various distributions of materials within the solar nebula. Our earlier inquiry in this chapter showed that the planets differ greatly in the relative amounts of material components and that none have anywhere near the same ratio of components as the sun. Kuiper's explanation provides a means by which the protoplanets could lose the least massive elements of which the planets now are deficient when compared to the sun. As the concentration of the protoplanets took place, energy transformations accompanying the internal friction within the bodies and the tidal effects of the sun probably slowed the rotation of the protoplanets to a period of rotation equal to the period of revolution for each of the preplanetary orbits which were of smaller average diameter than the later planetary orbits. The conservation of energy and of angular momentum was achieved by transformation of binding energy between the protostar and the protoplanet in doing the work of reducing the rotational energy. The resulting increase of displacement between the bodies also achieved a transfer of angular momentum from the reduced rotation of the protoplanets to an increased angular momentum in the orbital rotation of a planetary system having a greater radius and hence a greater moment of inertia. This type of action would also explain the transfer of angular momentum from the sun to the revolving planetary system. The agglomeration and sedimentation of the heavier materials within the protoplanet would tend to concentrate the heavier materials at the center of the protoplanet leaving the lighter materials near the surface.

When the central sun had contracted to a point where energies reached thermonuclear reaction levels and solar radiation began, the radiation absorbed by the surface gases of the protoplanets increased the particle velocities there to energy levels of escape velocity. This would occur most often in the lighter materials such as hydrogen and helium which consequently returned to intergalactic space. The amount of material removed from a protoplanet in this manner would depend upon its nearness to the sun and upon the massiveness of the protoplanet. The more massive the body and the farther it was from the sun, the less material would have been removed in this continuing action. Therefore, Kuiper suggests that the protoearth probably had a mass about 1000 times the earth's present mass; the major planets, being more massive and farther removed from the sun, were formed from original masses 10 to 100 times their present masses.

Serious problems still exist in explaining the relatively small angular momentum of the sun as compared to the angular momenta of the planets and their satellites. Other problems exist in explaining the relationships between the composition of the planets and their positions in the solar system. The problem involving the unique characteristics of Pluto has been discussed earlier. A great mass of evidence is accumulating as a result of space probes and preparation for further space flights. Undoubtedly many new clues for speculation and explanation will be available for more adequate hypotheses.

SUMMARY

Knowledge of a planet's mean displacement from the sun, the eccentricity of its orbit, the inclination to the ecliptic, the longitude of the ascending node, and the longitude of the perihelion fixes the size, shape, and position of the planetary orbit in space with respect to the sun and the plane of the earth's orbit. The sun, nine known planets, their satellites, and a large number of asteroids, comets, and meteors comprise the solar system. The inner planets, Mercury, Venus, Earth, and Mars, have greater densities than the outer planets and, because of their nearness to the sun, they have relatively high average surface temperatures. The major planets, Jupiter, Saturn, Uranus, Neptune, and Pluto, have, except for Pluto, great volumes and masses, great numbers of satellites, and great angular momenta as compared to the inner planets.

Accuracy in measuring astronomical distances depends upon the accurate measurement of the astronomical unit, which is the mean distance from the earth to the sun. Values of the astronomical unit in the order of 9.29×10^7 miles have been determined by observations regarding asteroids, radar reflections from Venus, and signals from space vehicles.

The distribution and composition of planetary materials, the relative positions of the planets, and the distribution of angular momenta throughout the solar system are essential features of the protoplanet theory of the origin of the solar system. Serious problems still remain in explaining the relatively small angular momentum of the sun as compared to the planets. The unique characteristics of the orbit and size of Pluto are also a problem. Many new clues for speculation and interpretation will become available in the evidence measured as the result of space probes. Man is no longer tied to the earth—space exploration has begun.

PROBLEMS

1 Construct an eccentric ellipse to represent an orbit of a hypothetical asteroid. See Fig. 6.2. (a) Determine its eccentricity. (b) Place the sun

at the right-hand focus and label the points of perihelion and aphelion. (c) Indicate the direction of the vernal equinox such that the longitude of the perihelion is 120°. (d) Place the line of the node such that the longitude of the ascending node is 40°. Indicate with a dashed line the portion of the orbit which is below the ecliptic.

2 In Problem 1, had the eccentricity been 0.7 and the mean distance to the sun 3 A.U., what would be the distance to the sun at perihelion and aphelion in astronomical units and in miles to three significant numbers? The orbits of what planets would be encompassed by this hypothetical orbit?

3 In terms of Kepler's third law and knowledge of the earth's sidereal period and mean distance from the sun, compute the sidereal period in years of the hypothetical asteroid described in Problem 2.

4 On a road map of your locality, draw a model of the inner planetary orbits to scale similar to Fig. 8.7, using the location of your home or college as the sun's location.

5 From your personal observations describe examples illustrating the angular motion aspects of the three laws of motion.

6 In Fig. 8.12, the angular momentum which remains constant for the masses held by the participant might be expressed as follows: $mR_1^2\omega_1 = mR_2^2\omega_2$. When the arms were outstretched to a radius of 3 ft, an angular velocity of 10 radians per second was given to the participant. What would be the angular velocity needed to preserve the momentum when the masses were brought into a radius of 1 ft, assuming no losses to other bodies? How many rotations per second do these angular velocities represent?

9

WORK OF THE ATMOSPHERE

Since the days of the clipper ships perhaps nothing has aroused more thoughts of adventure than the dream of matching wits against the wind and weather while beneath the spread of sails.   In many minds, sea lore is still synonymous with adventure.   Terms such as the *trade winds*, the *westerlies*, the *roaring forties*, the *doldrums*, and the *horse latitudes* were a part of the descriptive language handed down from the early "windjammers" who sailed the seven seas.   Men have known for a long time that certain regions of the earth particularly over the seas were characterized by somewhat constant atmospheric conditions.   Vast quantities of data have accumulated regarding wind and weather conditions, but successful explanations for the over-all mechanics of the atmosphere have been lacking.   Sometimes it seems that the phenomena with which men have become most familiar are, upon closer scrutiny, the most complex and difficult to understand. This has been the situation in studies of the atmosphere.

Until comparatively recent times very little was done relative to fitting parts into a whole or testing whether the implied conservation principles of energy and momentum were actually being met. A part of the program achieved during the International Geophysical Year (1957–1958) was a simultaneous gathering of atmospheric data throughout the world. Many new insights will accrue from interpretations of the IGY studies.

At present, the scientific principles of cause and effect are used only superficially in explanations of atmospheric phenomena because the problems of obtaining quantitative measurements have not been solved. But enough is known about the lower portions of the atmosphere to erect a few models for theoretical consideration.

CHARTING THE COURSE

The atmosphere is a deep ocean of gases which stretches out toward interplanetary space. It is a part of the planet earth in the same sense as are the land and the seas; but it is different from these because being a gas the air can move independently of the solid portions of the earth. When materials exhibit changes in motion, we attribute this to unbalanced forces. When a force displaces material objects, we attribute this to energy doing work. These concepts have been at the core of our inquiries thus far. Can they help us to interpret the work of the atmosphere?

Preliminary evidence of work Before attacking a problem it is well to first de-

termine whether the problem really exists. Our statement that the atmosphere performs work does not make it so. We need evidence, and granted that we can feel the air moving as wind and that winds are seen to carry objects from one place to another, a localized wind is not the atmosphere. To think so is similar to saying that because Sam Smith consistently gets top scores in his spelling tests, the whole class is therefore making satisfactory progress in spelling. Each part may show evidence of an action of the whole, but not necessarily so. We need evidence concerning the atmosphere as a whole or at least as an integral part of the whole. Consequently, we shall concentrate our attention upon the broad air current systems, ignoring the localized details except when they are directly concerned with the mechanics of the whole.

The connotation of broad air currents is somewhat misleading since it suggests a steady flow of air from one region to another. This is not true. In data concerning the atmosphere taken over broad areas of time or space, the most simple characteristics extracted from the multitude of individual observations are *averages*. That a steady state is not present is evidenced by the *mean deviation* (fluctuation) about the average value. A comparison between average values of temperature gives us the evidence we seek to confirm our problem.

Although, exclusive of cloud cover, all regions of the earth have the same number of hours of sunlight each year, the polar regions have continuous sunlight for 6 months followed by 6 months without the sun. The rest of the earth has varying diurnal and continuous time distributions of the sunlight hours. If the energy absorbed by direct surface exposure to sunlight were the only source of heat in the polar regions, the temperature depression after several months without sunlight surely would reach levels comparable to outer space. The temperature on the dark side of the moon is about −240°F after only a few days without sunlight. Compared to this the temperatures in the arctic regions are high. The coldest average temperatures for the month of January are about −40°F for portions of Greenland and −50°F for portions of Siberia. Cold as these temperatures must seem to the inhabitants of these regions, they are considerably warmer than would be expected were it not for heat transport from the warmer regions of the earth to the polar regions. That this transport is of atmospheric size is emphasized by the fact that temperatures in the equatorial tropics are lower than might be expected. Other evidences, such as upper air motions away from the equator toward the poles and periodic movements of cold fronts near the surface toward the equator from the poles, also point to an atmosphere doing work.

Thus, in addition to validating our inquiry we have further limited our study to the broad, global aspects of atmospheric circulation.

General structure of the atmosphere

Nobody knows the height of the atmosphere. Like the speculations concerning the solar atmosphere, we can say that the earth's atmosphere ends at the level where its density reaches that of the surrounding space. Various theoretical considerations involving escape velocity and surface velocity due to the earth's rotation place the outer limit of the atmosphere at about 20,000 miles. Very little

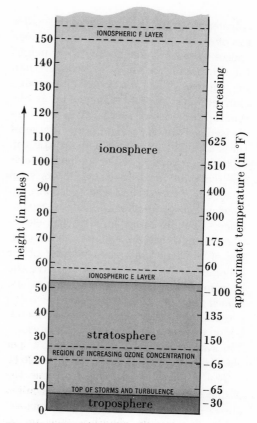

Figure 9.1 The layers of the atmosphere. The troposphere is the region of major energy exchanges.

is known about regions beyond a level of 500 miles above the earth's surface.

Fig. 9.1 indicates the approximate depth of the major layers of the atmosphere and the approximate temperature variation within them. The atmosphere may be divided into three major strata: the *troposphere*, the *stratosphere*, and the *ionosphere*.

The *troposphere* extends up to about 11 miles above the equator and drops to a height of about 5 miles above the poles. The difference in heights is largely caused by the variation in density between the warmer air over the tropics and the colder air over the poles. This variation also causes a seasonal change to greater height for the middle latitudes in summer than in winter. The major distinguishing characteristic of the troposphere is the gradual decrease of temperature with increased elevation. Minimum temperatures of $-70°F$ to $-80°F$ mark the top of the troposphere. The troposphere is the realm of most weather factors such as clouds, storms, and the thermal convection currents which produce turbulence. The air thins rapidly with elevation through the troposphere. The number of molecules per unit volume of air becomes fewer and fewer as we leave the bottom where greatest compression exists. The change in temperature with elevation is continuous and varies at a rate depending on the amount of water vapor present. The rate in moist air is about $3.2°F$ per 1000 ft, in dry air, about $5.5°F$ per 1000 ft.

The *stratosphere* extends from the top of the troposphere out to about 50 miles above the earth's surface. The stratosphere is virtually cloudless, has an almost constant level of humidity, and is free of storms. The lower stratosphere, up to heights of about 20 miles, has an almost constant temperature. Then the temperature begins to rise with further elevation, reaching about $150°F$ at 30 miles. Within this region of rising temperature, at heights of 20 to 25 miles, the presence of ozone is marked. Ozone is an extremely active form of oxygen. The ozone molecule is composed of three atoms of oxygen in contrast to the usual oxygen molecule of two atoms. Ozone is produced and dissociated at this level of the atmosphere when a photon of ultraviolet radiation of short wavelength (1600 A to 1800 A) is absorbed by an oxygen molecule, causing it to dissociate into

two oxygen atoms. The oxygen atoms immediately combine with oxygen molecules to form ozone molecules. Later the ozone absorbs a photon of ultraviolet radiation of longer wavelength (2400 A to 3000 A) and dissociates into an oxygen molecule and an oxygen atom. This process removes nearly all the high-energy ultraviolet radiation from the sunlight before it reaches the earth's surface.

Above 30 miles height the temperature again lowers gradually with increased elevation to $-100°F$ at about 50 miles.

As the name implies, the *ionosphere* is characterized by a high percentage of ionized particles. An ion is the electrically charged particle produced when an atom or a molecule gains or loses one or more electrons. The presence of the ionosphere first became known after the invention of radio when it was found that radio waves are reflected by ionized layers at great heights. The energy required for ionization comes largely from absorbing the extremely high-energy photons of X-ray radiation emitted by the sun. The temperature scale in Fig. 9.1 indicates a steady increase in temperature at elevations above 50 miles. Space flights have recorded air temperatures of over $1700°F$ at 250 miles above the earth and indications are that the temperature continues to increase at greater heights.

The Aurora Borealis (Northern Lights) in the north and the Aurora Australis in the south are electrical phenomena associated with the ionosphere particularly in the regions above the earth's magnetic poles.

Very little data has yet been accumulated concerning the stratosphere and the ionosphere. The greatest accumulation of data concerns only the troposphere. The work of the atmosphere, which we have singled out for our inquiry, is accomplished by the regions of turbulence found in this lowest strata of atmosphere. Consequently, we shall center our inquiry upon the energy relationships found in the troposphere.

Source and distribution of energy The earth including its atmosphere acts as an energy converter. The earth receives comparatively short-wavelength photons of energy from the sun and transforms them to long-wavelength photons (infrared) that ultimately are radiated into outer space. Of the initial energy reaching the earth, 29 percent is immediately reflected into space. (The earth's albedo is 0.29.) The remaining energy is absorbed by the materials of the earth and its atmosphere. Of interest in Chapter 4 was the phenomenon of scattering which explains the blue light reaching us from the sky.

The atmosphere acts as a powerful and discriminating screen for both incoming and outgoing radiation. It absorbs or reflects the potentially harmful high-frequency, high-energy, X-ray and ultra-violet photons, but transmits the vital middle-frequency visible light and the near-visible frequencies of infrared and ultraviolet radiation. The energy absorbed by the earth's surface is converted into heat, raising the temperature of these materials so that the earth itself becomes an effective radiating body. But because of the relatively low temperature, the photons emitted predominantly by the earth materials are the low-frequency, long-wavelength infrared radiation. The constituents of the troposphere, water vapor in particular, cause it to act like a greenhouse letting in the visible and near-visible frequency photons, but absorbing the low-frequency photons that are emitted by the earth materials.

The amount of energy received during a particular day at any given location on the earth's surface is limited by:

1. the *solar constant*
2. the screening action of the atmosphere
3. the time period of sunlight
4. the directness with which the sun's rays meet the earth

The Aurora Borealis taken at Oslo, Norway. The Aurora Borealis in the north and the Aurora Australis in the south are electrical phenomena associated with the ionosphere. [*Courtesy of Professor Carl Stormer.*]

The first factor is of least importance. In Chapter 7 we intimated that the sun's energy output was somewhat constant when measured at distances of the earth's orbit. The energy intercepted by each square centimeter of area set at right angles to the sun's rays and located just outside the earth's atmosphere is about 8.12 joules per minute. Converted to heat at 4.186 joules per calorie, this becomes 1.94 calories per minute per square centimeter.

$$\frac{8.12 \text{ joules/min}}{\text{cm}^2} \times \frac{1 \text{ cal}}{4.186 \text{ joules}}$$
$$= 1.94 \text{ cal/min/cm}^2$$

This is, of course, an average value. The solar constant fluctuates between extremes of 7.87 joules and 8.41 joules, or 1.88 calories and 2.01 calories, per minute per square centimeter. The fluctuations result from changes in the sun's rate of energy transformation and from orbital variations in the earth's displacement from the sun. The variations in solar constant do not have a very noticeable effect upon the work of the atmosphere.

The screening effect of the atmosphere is a more noticeable factor controlling the amount of energy reaching the various locations on the earth. As is apparent in Fig. 9.2, the screening effect is a function of latitude. Locations at the higher latitudes are shielded by a thicker layer of reflecting and absorbing atmosphere than the equatorial locations. In this regard, the variation is greatest when the earth is near the winter and summer solstices and the sun's rays are vertical at the Tropic of Capricorn and Tropic of Cancer, respectively, while alternately the opposite polar region is in total darkness. Cloud cover, humidity, and dust also affect the shielding action of the atmosphere.

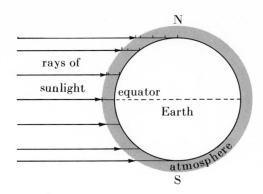

Figure 9.2 The screening effect of the atmosphere. Greater absorbing thickness screens the light reaching the polar regions.

The daily time periods of sunlight vary with latitude and season. The longer the period of sunlight, the greater is the possible energy absorption at a given location. At the poles the sunlight periods last for 6 months followed by 6 months without the sun's direct rays. At the equator the day and night are always equal. This effect is the combined result of the earth's rate of rotation, the inclination of the earth's axis to the ecliptic plane, and the earth's revolution in its orbit. The amount of energy absorbed per unit area per unit of time depends to

Figure 9.3 Direct and oblique rays. Light spreads over greater areas when it reaches the surface at oblique angles.

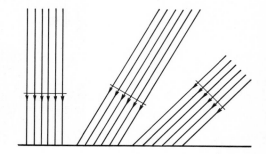

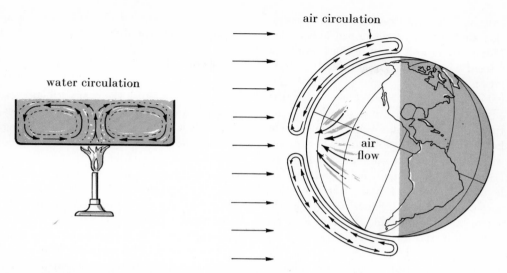

Figure 9.4 Air circulation on a non-spinning earth model. Circulation would be similar to that in a saucepan heated near its center.

a large extent upon the fact that oblique rays coming from a low-angle sun spread over a greater area of the surface than do the more vertical rays from a high-angle sun. (See Fig. 9.3.) This applies not only to the angle of the ecliptic to the celestial meridian at a given location, but also to the sun angle during the apparent daily motion of the sun across the sky. Consequently, the long periods of sunlight in the polar regions are largely offset by the low-angle sun throughout these periods.

From this discussion we should expect to find greatest energy absorption from the solar sources at the equator and a predictable decrease toward the poles. The evidence shows an annual reception of approximately two and one-half times as much energy from the sun at the equator as compared to the poles. But whereas we should expect a symmetrical distribution of energy about the equator based

strictly upon latitude, the actual distribution departs somewhat from this. The discrepancy can be explained by the predominance of land areas away from the equator and a greater prevalence of cloudiness near the equator. The mean temperatures in continental regions exceed those over the oceans at a given latitude and the tropical temperatures in the Southern Hemisphere are slightly cooler on the average than those of the Northern Hemisphere. Consequently, the mean annual temperatures are not distributed symmetrically about the equator but are distributed about 5° N latitude, which is called the "heat equator."

Major physical principles involved The general nature of the work of the atmosphere is clear. Unequal energy absorption between the equatorial regions and the polar regions makes possible the tropospheric transportation of energy-rich air from the topics toward the poles. If the earth did not rotate there would be a fixed wind pattern much like the circulation observed in a pan of water which is being heated at a point near its center (Fig. 9.4). In this hypothetical situation, surface winds would flow to the hottest part of the globe and when heated would rise because the air density decreases by the expansion produced by heat conducted to the air from the warm earth. The work done in lifting the warm air against the force of gravity would cool the air as the needed energy was transformed from heat to potential energy. In the upper troposphere the air would flow out in all directions toward the cold portions of the globe. Radiation from the molecules of warm air would cool the air and it would become more dense until the upper flow would begin to sink under the influence of the potential energy due to gravity. Upon reaching the surface, the flow process would be repeated. The facts, however, remain that the earth rotates on its axis and its constituent parts have an angular momentum proportional to the square of each radius of rotation. In the troposphere, the radius of rotation at each latitude varies from zero at the poles to about 3963 miles at the equator. The radius at any latitude is approximately 3963 miles times the cosine of the degrees of latitude. For example, the radius at 34° N latitude is about 3285 miles.

$$3963 \text{ miles} \times \cos 34° = 3963 \text{ miles} \\ \times 0.8290 = 3285 \text{ miles}$$

Using the relationships expressed for a contracting protostar, $\omega_2 = \omega_1 R_1^2 / R_2^2$, we can predict that if air moves poleward from the equator to the 34° latitude and conserves its absolute angular momen-tum, the angular velocity increases by a factor of approximately 1.45.

$$\omega_2 = \frac{\omega_1 R_1^2}{R_2^2} = \frac{3963^2}{3285^2} \times \omega_1 = 1.45 \, \omega_1$$

This would increase the eastward component of wind velocity to about 390 miles per hour which represents the resulting increase in air velocity over the surface velocity at this latitude. Hence, the air would need to be accelerated as it moves poleward, and an appropriate unbalanced force must be demonstrated in order to satisfy the fundamental laws of motion.

Conservation of energy and conformity to the fundamental laws of linear and angular motion must be satisfied in all models of atmospheric circulation.

Prelude to theory As has become customary in the preceding chapters, we are about to erect theoretical models to aid us in further inquiry. The announced purpose is an inquiry into the work of the atmosphere. Preliminary evidence indicates the troposphere exhibits broad air flow systems which somehow transport energy from the tropics to the polar regions. Sunlight transformed to heat at the earth's surface constitutes the primary energy source for the work. The "greenhouse" effect concentrates this energy in the troposphere for the time period needed to accomplish the work. Variables inherent in the rotation and inclination of the earth and in the thickness and obliqueness of ray paths relative to the earth's surface are factors that explain why the energy unbalance exists. The principles around which interpretation will take place have been limited to the conservation of energy and conformity to the laws of motion.

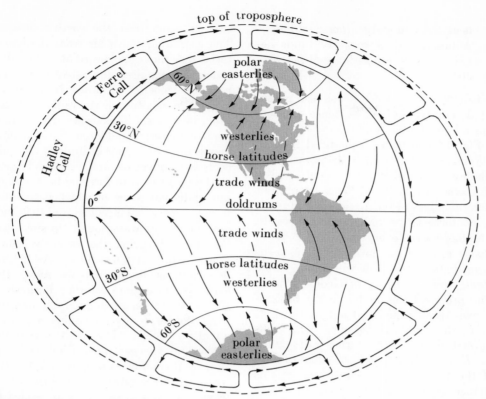

Figure 9.5 Classical model of tropospheric circulation. The average surface winds were the basis for the cell structures.

CLASSICAL MODEL OF TROPOSPHERIC CIRCULATION

The first useful model of atmospheric circulation was proposed in 1735 by George Hadley. The famous English meteorologist, with admirable simplicity, made the atmosphere into a machine for air circulation. As such, it became a heat engine which permitted a transformation of heat energy into the mechanical energy of winds. The laws of motion were satisfied by means of an assumed conservation of absolute angular momentum by the air currents involved.

Structure of the classical model   In most atlases, the flow patterns of the prevailing winds are shown on the maps of the world. The presence of these winds was known by all seafaring peoples. The detailed features around many of the land areas are complicated but the broad averages are, for the most part, clear and direct. The essential features of the patterns of average flow are:

1. A broad belt of easterly winds (blowing from east to west) between latitudes 30° N and 30° S. The flow is weaker at the equator (*doldrums*) and

near the boundaries (*horse latitudes*).

2. A broad belt of westerly winds between 30° N and 60° N and between 30° S and 60° S.

A belt of polar easterlies was also postulated; however, direct evidence of them was a long time in doubt.

Fig. 9.5 illustrates a modified form of the original circulation model proposed by Hadley. Essentially the model consists of a system of vertical loops set upright along the lines of the meridians and made to conform to prevailing surface winds. The loops were everywhere symmetrical along any given latitude. The cells formed above the trade winds were called *Hadley cells* in honor of George Hadley who proposed the model on the basis of known trade winds and antitrade winds over the tropical oceans. The cells formed above the westerlies were called the *Ferrel cells* in honor of William Ferrel of the United States who proposed this change in the model during the early 1800's.

Theoretical explanations The original proposals of the 1700's suggested the following explanations for the general atmospheric circulation. Air motion is started in the equatorial regions by solar heating of earth surface materials which warms the lower air causing it to rise by convection. The cooler air from the higher latitudes flows along the earth's surface toward the equator to replace the warmed air. This flow acquires a westward component of velocity in order to conserve angular momentum. That is, when moving from a smaller to a larger radius of rotation, the air attains a reduced angular velocity; consequently, it moves more slowly than the surface over which it flows. The result is an apparent

easterly wind near the earth's surface. The ascending warm air from the equatorial zone moves poleward at higher altitudes and acquires an eastward component of velocity in order to conserve angular momentum as the radius of rotation decreases. This eastward component increases rapidly as the air flow moves into the higher latitudes. The air cools as it moves toward the poles largely as the result of transforming heat energy into radiation, some of which penetrates to outer space. The colder and therefore more dense air was thought to sink near the poles, bringing the westerly winds down to the earth's surface. As the air flow returns to the tropics along the earth's surface, the westerlies diminish as the conservation of angular momentum from shorter to longer radius decreases angular velocity. This in effect puts the brakes on the eastward wind velocity, slowing them down until, eventually, the westward acceleration changes the winds from westerlies to easterlies as needed to explain the trade winds. The process is then repeated.

The original suggestions were modified to some extent to account for observed characteristics. Hadley introduced a partial descent of the upper poleward current along the horse latitudes in order to account for the dry desert regions found along this zone. The restraining effect of friction between the air currents and the earth was introduced to account for the fact that winds at ground level do not acquire the high speeds required by virtue of conservation of angular momentum. Evidence seemed to point to the required high-velocity current at higher elevations, especially in the middle latitudes. The addition of the Ferrel cell somewhat upset the simplicity of the original proposal by breaking up the continuous upper-level poleward flow and substituting an upper-level flow toward the equator above the regions of the westerlies.

Except for these alterations, the classical model was regarded as a satisfactory explanation of tropospheric circulation until the 1920's. Two basic assumptions remained unchallenged. First, the circulation could be regarded as symmetric in each cell from latitude to latitude. That is, the altitude, average speed, and direction of flow are everywhere equal for the currents crossing any given latitude. Second, the circulation could be explained on the basis of huge vertical loops or cells which provide the necessary transformation of energy and a hypothetical compliance with the laws of motion.

Challenging the basic assumptions Inevitably, when theory is based more upon speculation than upon measured observation, alternate theories become possible.

Air pressure patterns on a weather map. The solid lines connect stations of equal air pressure. The map shows several centers of high and low pressure systems and the intensely rapid change of pressure surrounding a hurricane. [*Courtesy of the U.S. Dept. of Commerce, Weather Bureau.*]

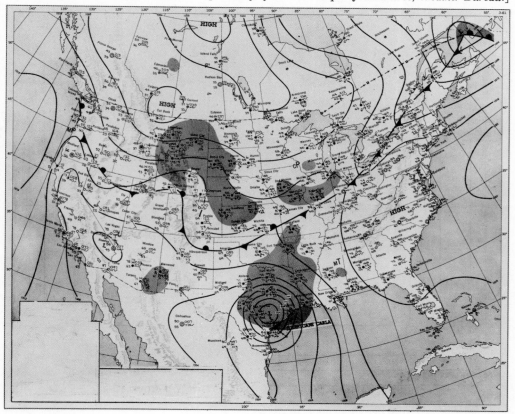

Then crucial issues of disagreement can be resolved only after critical data are available.

The classical model completely ignored the atmospheric disturbances which bring the day-to-day changes in weather. These disturbances are the circular, eddy-like, air flow patterns which lie horizontal rather than vertical to the earth's surface. The terms *high* and *low* are used to designate these patterns on weather maps. A low, sometimes called a *cyclone*, is a wide area of lower than average air pressure. A high, sometimes called an *anticyclone*, is a wide area of higher than average air pressure. Although the air disturbances surrounding these areas were used to explain local and temporary changes in wind directions, they were considered of no consequence in the large-scale energy transport required of the general atmospheric circulation. The first major challenge of the basic assumptions came in 1921 when A. Defant showed theoretically that horizontal disturbances having circular flow patterns of about 600 miles diameter could accomplish the work of heat transport in the atmosphere. Since 600 miles is the approximate diameter of the flow patterns around the highs and lows found on the daily weather maps, the question arose as to whether these *horizontal eddies* might be doing much of the work attributed to the vertical cells.

Shortly thereafter, in 1925, F. M. Exner questioned the basic assumption that stipulated symmetric cells of air flowing great distances across the lines of latitude. In the early 1930's, V. Bjerknes proposed an explanation in which large masses of air could be moved over large intervals of latitude if the symmetry of the conventional cells were disregarded and vortical air structures placed at intervals along the horse latitudes. Comparison of the daily and average pressure maps showing lines of equal pressure at the earth's surface and also at higher elevations proves the existence of these air

The development of a tornado. Tornados are severe but localized storms and should not be confused with the large weather systems called cyclones which have flow patterns of about 600 miles in diameter.

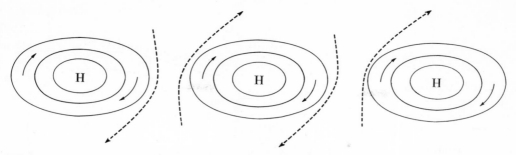

Figure 9.6 Vortexes of the subtropical high belt. Spinning air columns produce constant pressure channels for air movement north and south.

structures. The major advantage of this explanation is its elimination of high wind speeds. The formation of the vortexes is explained in the following manner. Several air masses of limited width and situated near a given latitude begin to move in opposite directions alternately north and south across the circle of latitude. As explained previously, an air mass moving poleward is deflected toward the east. If at the same time an air mass spaced further to the east began moving equatorward it would be deflected to the west. Consequently, the air between the two masses would be compressed, forming a region of high pressure, and also the moving masses would apply the torque needed to achieve rotation of the intervening air mass. Fig. 9.6 illustrates the resulting air motion. In the figure the solid lines mark points of equal pressure, the greatest pressure occurring near the center of each vortex. The broken lines show air currents. The air currents can travel long distances poleward or equatorward along the edges of these vortexes without a change in speed because the constant pressure relationship makes acceleration of speed impossible. These air motions are in accord with observation.

The absolute angular momentum of air masses transported in this manner is obviously not conserved. Other explanations of momentum exchange are needed because the total angular momentum of the earth-atmosphere system must remain constant.

Proposals and counterproposals continued to mount as more detailed data concerning the actual structure of the atmosphere were measured. Enough data have now been validated to indicate that the classical assumption of conservation of the absolute angular momentum of each individual mass of air is not supported by the observed facts. In other important features as well, the classic model seems beyond repair. More recently proposed models, although not complete, are generally more realistic in view of modern interpretations of data.

MODERN MODEL OF ATMOSPHERIC CIRCULATION

The general nature of the work of the atmosphere is clear. Unequal heating of the earth's surface makes possible the transportation of warm air from the

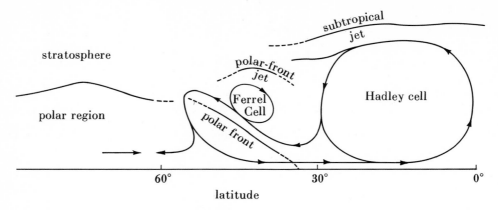

Figure 9.7 The Palmen model of tropospheric circulation. The dynamic model has indicated many details of known air circulation phenomena.

regions of energy abundance to the regions of scarcity. The transported heat reduces the temperatures in the tropics below what might be expected and increases the temperatures in the polar regions far above what might be expected. To accomplish this work air must be interchanged between the tropics and the polar regions. This is the only means of energy transportation which could act fast enough to maintain the observed long-term energy balance in these various regions. The processes of transportation are still somewhat in doubt. It may be, for instance, that the stratosphere plays a more important role in this regard than has yet been attributed to it. Also, the ocean currents take part. But the major scheme must be attributed to the general circulation of the troposphere. It will be instructive to inquire how a more modern model fits into the patterns of data now becoming available.

Structure of the Palmen model The Finnish meteorologist E. Palmen proposed a model of atmospheric circulation in the early 1950's which has received increasing support. He retains the Hadley or tropical cell, and places a remnant of the Ferrel cell over a polar front which slants toward the polar region. The polar cell has been removed and in its place is proposed a region dominated by horizontal eddies. The central portion of the model is extremely mobile. The polar fronts advance and recede; the polar-front jet stream moves forward and back and appears and disappears over the various regions along the middle latitudes; and the high-pressure vortexes of the horse latitudes appear and disappear from these regions. Fig. 9.7 illustrates a vertical cross section of the air flow systems proposed for the troposphere. Two gaps are shown along the top level of the troposphere. One is associated with the *polar-front jet* and the other with the *subtropical jet*. On the basis of ozone concentrations in the higher latitudes of the troposphere and the descent to the higher latitudes of radioactive dust particles originally forced into the stratosphere by hydrogen bomb explosions from locations in the low latitudes, it is argued that air passes from the stratosphere to the troposphere, and in the reverse, through these gaps, but the mechanism is not understood. The origin of the jet streams also is not yet fully explained.

The general surface flow patterns associated with the model are indicated in Fig. 9.8. Note that the *intertropical front* conforms somewhat to the heat equator. The horse latitudes are dominated by *subtropical highs*. The *polar fronts* are very irregular, suggesting a constant turbulence associated with frequent advances and recedings of the polar front activities into the various regions of the middle latitudes.

Further explanations and supporting evidence can best be sorted out in terms of the stipulated principles of interpretation—conservation of energy and the laws of motion as exampled by the conservation of angular momentum.

Conservation of energy   There are three principal mechanisms by which warm air, or the energy to heat it, can be transported across lines of latitude on its journey from the equatorial regions to the polar regions.

1. The vertical loops or cells, such as the Hadley cells, displace the colder air equatorward and the "warmer" air with greater potential energy poleward.

2. The larger horizontal eddies, or vortexes, operate an energy shuttle service; the air moving poleward is warmed before rotating to higher latitudes where it radiates more energy to the cooler surrounding air than it absorbs in return. The cooler air rotating equatorward radiates less because of its lower temperature and is warmed by contact with the earth's surface or by compression to provide the higher temperature for its return poleward.

3. The horizontal eddies moving bodily poleward transport their masses of warm air toward the polar regions. Similarly the eddies moving equatorward transport their masses of colder air toward the tropical regions.

Each mechanism does not operate with equal efficiency at all latitudes, nor do they all operate significantly in every region of the earth. The means by which the controlling mechanism is sorted out is significant. The regulating factors seem to be a natural selection in terms of most efficient energy transformation. Under a given set of circumstances, the most efficient mechanism develops to major proportions while the less efficient mechanisms contribute less or disappear entirely.

To understand the process of energy transformation in the earth's atmosphere, remember that on an average the earth must lose energy by radiation into space at almost exactly the same rate as it gains energy by absorption of sunlight. The earth's average temperature has not changed appreciably during the past 25,000 years. The absorption takes place primarily in the top layers of the ground and the ocean. Hence, most of the heat that comes into the atmosphere does so

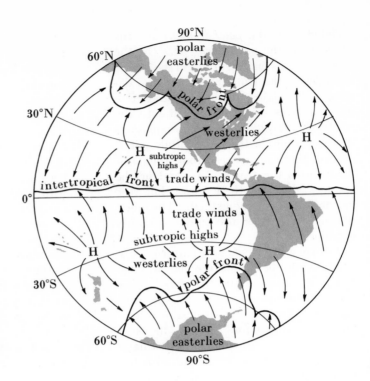

Figure 9.8 General patterns of surface air flow. A dynamic model produces irregularities in the indicated patterns from day to day.

by conduction through its surfaces of contact with the land and sea. Because the atmosphere screens out the low-frequency infrared photons, primarily because of the water molecules present in the lower troposphere, the ultimate radiation layer lies some distance above the ground at a level where the moisture level has been reduced below a certain critical limit. The amount of water vapor that the air can contain depends on its temperature. Consequently, the radiation layer remains at an almost constant temperature throughout the earth. The amount of energy radiated by a given substance depends on its temperature. Thus, the radiation from the earth into space is about equal at every latitude. The net result is that the balance between absorption and radiation shows a net loss in the higher

latitudes and a compensating net gain in the lower latitudes. The zone of change-over occurs at the horse latitudes.

In maintaining the balance the transport mechanisms must perform two tasks. First, heat must be delivered in large quantities from the earth's surface to the middle of the troposphere. Second, the excess heat in the lower latitudes must be delivered to the higher latitudes.

The Hadley cells of the Palmen model indicate well-developed vertical loops of air currents connecting the equatorial regions and the horse latitudes. The transport of heated air upward near the equator is accomplished because the heated air expands enough to float up through the cooler, more dense air to develop convection currents. This development is not quite as simple as it sounds. Because the atmosphere thins

Cumulonimbus calvus cloud formations. Many localized disturbances of this sort may result from energy transformations in a single cyclonic weather system. [*Courtesy of the U.S. Dept. of Commerce, Weather Bureau.*]

out rapidly with increased elevation, the actual density of the air is always less at higher elevations than at lower elevations. In order to compare densities for purposes of convection, we must compare air only when compressed to the same pressure. When a given mass of air is lifted upward against the force of gravity, work is done in lifting the mass and also in expanding the gas to greater volume. In the process, energy is transformed from heat to potential energy with the result of lowering the temperature. If in the surrounding air through which the moving mass is lifted, the temperature lowers with increasing elevation at a faster rate than the temperature of the flowing air, energy transport is possible; the flowing air continues to rise until a balance is reached where the only energy transformation possible is the absorption and radiation of photons. Additional transformation to potential energy is achieved by the convection currents near the equator because the air flowing equatorward near the surface crosses large areas of water. Here, great amounts of water are evaporated with a resulting increase of internal molecular energy without an increase in air temperature. When this moisture-mixed air is lifted and cooled by expansion, the moisture condenses into tropical rains, accompanied by the transformation of its internal energy into heat. The additional energy enables the elevation of the tropical convection currents to levels near the top of the troposphere. Consequently, the poleward upper-level air current is at a much higher *equal-pressure* temperature than the moist lower-level air current flowing equatorward. Thus under the circumstances, the Hadley cell is the most efficient system for transporting energy both upward and across lines of latitude poleward.

In the regions of the Ferrel cells where the directions of circulation are reversed this scheme is not applicable and more efficient mechanisms predominate. Between 30° and 60° latitude in both the Northern and Southern Hemispheres, temperatures recorded at various altitudes bear out the fact that large-scale convection could not take place because the average rate of temperature change with increasing elevation is less than required for convection. Localized convection does take place within small regions of the weather system eddies.

The energy shuttle system of the subtropical highs has been explained previously. The resulting radiation and the highly efficient transport of air currents across lines of latitude at the edges of equal-pressure streamlines in the vortexes dissipate very little heat while in transit poleward. The energy for the rotation of the vortexes and for maintaining the high-pressure columns is supplied largely by the compressional effects of the potential energy transported poleward by the Hadley cells.

In the middle latitudes, the transport of heat upward is accomplished in two important ways by the weather system eddies. First, the horizontal eddies tend to move heat upward by localized convection systems if the eddy moves great distances poleward. In the equatorward portion of the vortex, the air at high elevation remains cold in comparison to the lower air which is heated by conduction. Under these conditions, localized convection systems are prevalent as witnessed by the local showers and thunderstorms which characterize these cyclone regions. Second, cyclones move upward along the slanting polar fronts where a slight unbalance toward energy conversion to potential energy exists for poleward-moving eddies.

Near the 60° latitudes the Ferrel cell transports heat upward in much the same manner as the Hadley cell but with a reversed cellular air flow.

Beyond the polar front, transfer of energy is dominated almost entirely by horizontal mixing between horizontal eddies. The transport of energy upward by the Ferrel cell and the weather eddies moving over the polar fronts evidently is sufficient to keep the upper levels of the troposphere at polar latitudes always at comparatively higher equal-pressure temperatures than the air near the surface.

Conservation of angular momentum E. Palmen and M. A. Alaka computed for a given month (January) the angular momentum exchanged between all mechanisms operating in the regions between 20°N and 30°N latitudes. The results showed a small overbalance in the upper layers compared to the lower layers of the troposphere. Actually, however, the unaccounted-for residual was equal to the estimated needs for exchanges between the upper and lower layers by turbulence. The success of this endeavor covering a limited zone gave impetus to the development of measurements which may eventually lead to detailed computations on a world-wide scale. The reported computations involved the many facets of air movement in the vertical cells as well as the air movements in horizontal eddies. It is of special interest that nearly 90 percent of the net exchange of momentum across latitude 30° was found to be by horizontal eddies.

There are no simple and direct means for accounting for the momentum-exchange mechanisms but careful observations give clues to probable actions. For example, the trade winds flowing equatorward achieve a pronounced westward component so that those winds flowing south move from northeast to southwest and those flowing north move from southeast to northwest. In terms of angular momentum, the air flowing in the trade winds has less than average angular momentum. From the standpoint of air velocity with respect to the earth's surface velocity, the westward components in the trade winds oppose the earth's surface velocity. Forces of friction between the earth and the winds slow the wind velocity. The forces increase until a balance is reached between the forces accelerating the winds westward and the forces of friction. The amounts of these forces are difficult to estimate especially where mountain barriers exist. Principles of fluid dynamics indicate that when normal momentum relationships are restricted in a moving fluid by a surface stress, the effect is transmitted to adjoining layers of the fluid in such a manner as to counteract the action. In other words, when in the trade winds the normal decrease of angular momentum is restricted by the forces of friction, the effect is transmitted deep into the adjoining layers of air, setting up a poleward flow of air which exactly counteracts any change of angular momentum. This, of course, is exactly the motion present in the Hadley cells.

The action of the frictional forces upon the rotating earth, however, is a torque opposing the eastward rotation. Since it is unlikely that this opposing torque causes any net change in the rate of the earth's rotation, an equal torque of opposite sense must be acting elsewhere. At first thought, the westerlies of the middle latitudes seem to be the answer. However, because of the shorter radii of action at the middle latitudes, equal forces of friction cannot produce the equal torques necessary to counteract those produced by the equal forces but longer radii of rotation at the lower latitudes. The remaining torque must be found in the actions of the horizontal eddies.

With regard to the eddies, the principles of fluid dynamics indicate air flows that would develop into a low-pressure cyclone must have a rotation in the same direction as the earth's surface rotation around a vertical axis at the location (in the same sense we discovered for the Foucault pendulum). The rotation of air about a high-pressure anticyclone must oppose the surface rotation. Consequently, the cyclonic eddies (lows) are spinning faster than the earth and the anticyclonic eddies (highs) are spinning slower than the earth. The frequent disturbances caused by the polar fronts produce a preponderance of cyclonic eddies in the middle latitudes. These are thought to apply the necessary positive torque for balance.

With respect to angular momentum changes in the atmosphere, the transport of angular momentum by the horizontal eddies is concentrated near the top of the troposphere where the winds are strongest. Spinning vortexes have much the same action as spinning solids; vector relationships oppose a change in the direction of the spin axis. Here, also, if the normal momentum relationships are restricted, the effect is transmitted to adjoining layers in such a manner as to counteract the action. Consequently, appropriate poleward or equatorward flow of air is produced. In the regions where the angular momentum is being increased at the top, an equatorward flow of air is produced to counteract the action. This is evident in the Ferrel cells. In the regions where the angular momentum is being decreased at the top, a poleward flow of air is produced to counteract the action.

No attempt has been made here to minimize the complexity of the problems associated with the momentum relationships of atmospheric circulation. The average person has little concept of the problems behind the simple three-sentence weather forecasts in his newspaper, to say nothing about general circulation problems as a whole. The problems of meteorology which require precise answers, such as long-range weather forecasts or charting efficient long-distance operation of aircraft, require not only precise measurements but also a consistent theory with which to interpret their meanings. Only by the combination of the two can science distinguish between truth and superficial assumptions.

SUMMARY

The major strata of the atmosphere are the troposphere, stratosphere, and ionosphere. The atmosphere acts as a powerful and discriminating filter for both incoming and outgoing radiation. The most influential climatic and weather-producing energy conversions take place in the troposphere. Constituents such as water vapor cause the troposphere to act like a greenhouse, letting in visible and near-visible frequencies but absorbing the low-frequency photons emitted from the earth's surface.

The troposphere exhibits broad air flow systems which transport energy from the tropics to the polar regions. Principles of conservation of energy and angular momentum must be satisfied in accounting for these systems. Several types of transport are in operation. The predominating system in a given region is regulated by a natural selection of the most efficient energy conversion under the circumstances involved. Transport between the equatorial regions and the horse latitudes is accomplished largely by vertical loops of air currents called the Hadley cells. Between the 30°-to-60° latitude regions, the highly efficient shuttle system of the subtropical high vortexes and the horizontal eddies predominate. Near the 60° latitudes a small vertical loop called a Ferrel cell operates. Beyond the polar fronts, the energy transport is dominated by horizontal mixing between horizontal eddies.

Localized verification of regional energy and angular momentum exchange points the way to possible confirmation of theoretical predictions on a larger scale. Highly complex problems of interpretation and verification remain to be solved in the field of global meteorology, but greatly improved models and broader systems for simultaneous observation and measurement are bringing consistent meanings into explaining the work of the atmosphere.

PROBLEMS

1 What evidence supports the idea that energy is being transported to the polar regions of the earth from the equatorial regions?

2 Why is radiation from the earth into space about equal at all latitudes?

3 Compute the surface speed of the earth in miles per hour at your latitude. (Use three significant digits.) How might this speed be related to the direction and speed of the prevailing winds at your latitude?

4 Summarize the basic features of the classical model of the troposphere. In general, how does the structure of the Palmen model differ from the classical one?

5 The weight density of air under standard conditions is about 12.7 newtons per cubic meter. How much energy in joules is required to lift the amount of air in a room 4 meters × 5 meters × 2.5 meters against the force of gravity to a height of 1 kilometer?

6 Assuming that the same amount of frictional force is applied to the surfaces involved, what is the ratio between the torque produced by the trade winds at the 15° latitude and the torque produced by the westerlies at the 45° latitude? How is this unbalance overcome in the atmospheric circulation?

7 What evidence indicates why the Hadley cell is the most efficient system for transporting energy in the regions where it predominates?

10

WORK OF THE HYDROSPHERE

The oceans cover 70.8 percent of the earth's surface. The earth is a spheroid and because water flows freely to alleviate stress, the oceans accentuate the earth's bulge at the equator. The spherically shaped earth is an impression easily acquired at sea. In fact, observation of ships' masts disappearing beyond the horizon was one of the first arguments used in support of a spherically shaped earth.

People of all lands and all ages have been fascinated by the sea. How delightful it is to sit and watch the waves splash ashore! And yet we know that the waves are not always gentle. Some have learned this directly, having been pummeled by the rolling surf. Others have witnessed the terrifying and destructive pounding of a stormy sea. Since energy is defined as the ability to do work, it is not difficult to endow the ocean with plentiful energy.

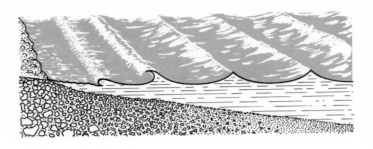

Figure 10.1 An immature beach. The beach materials are sorted out in the order of sizes and shapes of the particles.

The action of the sea most often visualized by the "landlubber" is the rolling surf. In the surf the ocean waves "break" and the energy transmitted by wave motion is transformed into the kinetic energy of flowing water. These wave-induced water flows are called *waves of translation*. They are not true waves but are masses of flowing water. During storms or high surf, these high-energy water flows strike objects along the shore like battering rams. Even in relatively calm seas the pulsating impact of tons of water against the shore performs visible amounts of work. The child's castle of sand is demolished by a very few "waves."

Nothing seems permanent in the path of such energy. Erosion wears away the most rugged coast lines. Incessantly the waves cut away the shores and transport the debris onto the beach where further actions take place. (See Fig. 10.1.) When the resulting terraces are broad, the energy is expended in moving the loose materials forth and back upon the beach. The grinding action of pebbles sliding across pebbles reduces the particles to ever smaller sizes and more spherical shapes. The smaller and rounder particles can be carried further seaward by the returning undertow. Consequently, the beach materials become sorted out according to size and shape. From the outer edges of the shoreline to deeper water are found, respectively, the coarse and less spherical pebbles, sand arranged from coarse grain to fine grain, and finally muds containing particles of various degrees of fineness. This story can be read on almost any beach. The evidence is qualitative and at times deceptive. How do waves get this energy?

THE CHALLENGE

Preliminary evidence The actions of the sea are not imaginary. The results are measurable. At Cape Cod and the islands nearby, each year 1 to 6 ft of shore are claimed by the sea. The cliffs near Dover on the English Channel are receding at the rate of 15 ft a year. The breakwater at Long Beach, California, had withstood the surf for years and then in 1930 a short segment of it was wrecked suddenly by the waves from a moderate storm. The breakwater was repaired but in 1939 a similar storm produced waves which breached it again. In a small way man attempts to control the sea. But the sea like all inanimate objects in nature is a system whose processes are controlled purely by natural law. The sea yields to man only insofar as he understands its processes.

Wave disturbances Since most of us have been introduced to the hydrosphere by observing water waves, let us first consider the processes of wave motions. A review of portions of Chapter 2 will be helpful to the reader. Recall that only the wave forms proceed continuously outward; the particles of the medium remain relatively stationary. Fundamentally, the function of waves is transmitting energy from one place to another without the necessity of the source accompanying the energy.

The speed of wave propagation is the time rate with which the individual waves advance in the medium. It might seem logical that the energy is transmitted at the same speed as the individual waves,

but this is not true in all types of waves. It is not true in water waves. This is a fact observed but not always understood by surf riders. When an experienced rider stands in the water planning to ride a roller into shore, he keeps his eyes on the rising swell out at some distance from the shore rather than watching each wave crest which moves towards him. To the uninitiated the surf can be most disappointing. By keeping his eye on each wave crest which approaches, too often he will prepare to ride a promising-looking crest only to find that it dwindles to nothing by the time it reaches his feet. If he attempted to ride this crest he might find himself lying prone on the bottom and pummeled beneath the true roller when it finally arrives. Rising to the surface he finds that the experienced riders are enjoying a swift ride to the shore while he is left

A section of sea beach. The erosional action of waves cuts away the shore and transports debris onto the beach. [*Courtesy of L. W. Brownell.*]

behind digging the sand out of his ears. The experienced riders may not know it but in watching the more slowly moving swell they are following the advancing energy fronts which result from complicated interference patterns of multiple waves.

The reason for the chain of events at the beach becomes partially apparent in the model shown in Fig. 10.2 of an advancing train of water waves. It is based upon the theory which was experimentally confirmed just prior to 1825 by Ernst and Wilhelm Weber of Germany. For waves moving along the surface of deep water, the particles at the surface were observed to move in circular orbits having diameters equal to the wave heights. The orbits of the particles beneath the surface reduced rapidly to insignificance. In shallow water the orbits became increasingly elliptical as the depth decreased.

With regard to the model, notice that as the particles proceed through one cycle the crest at A disappears and the crest at D is generated to replace it. This is the action which occurred for the would-be surf rider. During the passage of one wavelength through the initial location, the indicated water particle revolves once around its circular orbit. The

Figure 10.2 One cycle of wave motion. The wave crest at B advances one wavelength while the crest at A disappears and a trough develops carrying the energy forward one-half wavelength.

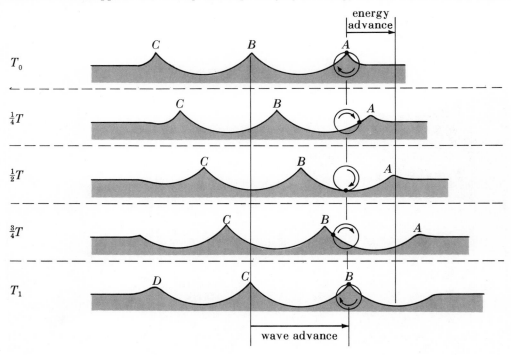

energy components advance one-half wavelength. Thus the energy potential advances at half the speed of the wave propagation. This will be developed in greater detail later.

The conditions at the beach are greatly complicated by the fact that usually there are several trains of waves having different wavelengths and different velocities arriving simultaneously. The idea that each seventh wave will be more energetic than the rest is but one of the many myths of the sea. The swell merely indicates where the apparent combined energy of the waves are at a maximum in the particular interference pattern of the advancing waves at that particular time. When a great swell "breaks" a wave of translation is generated from the combined potential energies which were in phase at that point.

Thus far we have been concerned only with the receiving end of the energy transmission. The source mechanism producing the waves is more obscure. The wind obviously is involved somehow in raising waves, but investigation of how energy is transferred from wind to wave has been conducted only recently.

CONNECTING HYDROSPHERE TO ATMOSPHERE

The hydrosphere does more than one type of work. Closely allied with wave production are the conditions which produce ocean currents. An inquiry into one of these involves the other as well. Contrary to the expectations of seafarers who live and work at sea but who have not measured its subtleties, the ripples found upon a calm sea are very important in explaining the energy conversions involved.

Energy from wind to wave The force of friction between gusts of wind and a calm sea produces ripples. The frictional forces also drag some of the water along the surface in the direction of the wind, but at the moment we are more interested in the undulating ripples. Because the water molecules stick to each other within the liquid and even more so at the surface "skin layer" than elsewhere, the water tends to be contained within the surface layer, forming oscillating motions within the limits of the forces involved. The frictional drag tends to pile the water momentarily into rounded crests separated by depressions. At the crest the action is carried forward and at the depression the action is in the reverse direction. If the wind continues to blow, the steep side of each wavelet acts like a sail against which the wind can produce forces in the direction of the action at the crest. The greater the outside force and the longer it acts upon the water, the higher the crest becomes until the forces break the "skin layer." This breaking occurs when the wave height is about one-seventh of the wavelength. Consequently, the longer the wavelength the higher the wave rises before it breaks.

Because the winds are gusty and turbulent, the original wavelets have a variety of wavelengths and directions of propagation. If the winds increase in strength and follow a given direction for longer periods of time, the shorter waves rise to the breaking point forming white caps. These are the waves of translation on the surface of the sea. The energies of the breaking waves are largely accumulated by the waves of longer wavelength which can grow to tremendous proportions. In those areas of the sea where strong, steady winds can add energy to waves for great distances, long waves of great height are often formed. Waves of heights ranging from 45 ft to over 100 ft have been recorded.

When the waves move beyond the influences of the winds that produced them, they tend to flatten out. The crests become lower and the wave forms become more symmetrical from wave to wave. The resulting series of wave trains move outward from the scene of disturbances in a number of directions and may travel thousands of miles. Since the individual wave trains can overlap without losing their identities, they form interference patterns which often appear as a diamond-shaped, short-crested swell of various sizes. These characterize the appearance of the open sea as observed from an aircraft.

Each wave moves forward with a velocity that increases with greater wavelength. An analysis of the particle motions in Fig. 10.2 indicates the waves at the front of a train of waves lose energy to those behind. During each cycle a wave crest disappears from the front and a new wave crest appears at the rear of the group. Hence, as was indicated, the energy of the group has a velocity only half that of the individual waves.

Because the velocity increases with wavelength there is no simple relationship between period, velocity, and wavelength of ocean waves. In the open sea, where the water is deeper than half the wavelength, waves in a swell have a period in seconds approximately equal to 0.442 times the square root of the wavelength in feet. The waves move at a speed in miles per hour approximately equal to 3.5 times the period in seconds. The average period of the swell reaching the shores of the United States is about 10 sec.

When the waves approach the shal-lower waters near the shore or where underwater obstacles reduce the depth of the water, their velocities are controlled by the depth of the water. Where the water is shallower than one-half wavelength, the velocity of the wave may be expressed by the equation $v = \sqrt{gh}$, where g is the acceleration of gravity and h is the depth of the water. When the waves enter the regions of rapidly changing velocities, only the periods of the waves remain unchanged. Thus, when speed is reduced the wavelength is correspondingly shortened. In order to transport equal amounts of energy the shortened wavelength must have increased wave heights.

When the period no longer depends upon the wavelength, refraction occurs. Because the velocities are related to water depth, the wave fronts are refracted to conform to the shape of the underwater contours. Hence, the waves reaching the beach have been refracted so that they approach almost parallel to the beach regardless of the direction of the incoming swell. The damage to the Long Beach breakwater, referred to earlier, was traced to an underwater mound about seven miles out at sea. The mound was shaped in such a way that refraction took place toward its center, producing waves of unusual height when waves crossed the mound from the south southeast. The mound acted like a lens focusing the waves onto the breakwater whenever a south-southeast swell occurred.

In terms of the wave model, when waves in shallow water increase in height, the particles no longer can complete their circular orbits. At first elliptical orbits are formed. But when the average water depth is reduced to about 1.3 times the resulting wave height, a breaker forms.

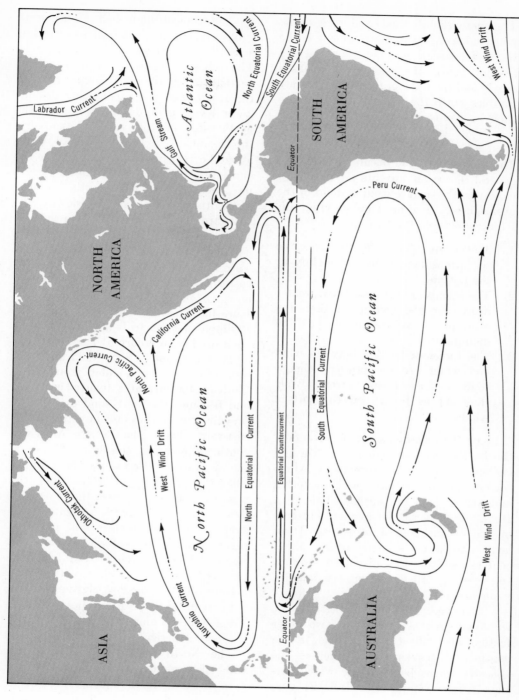

Figure 10.3 The major ocean currents. The ocean currents are closely related to patterns of average surface winds.

The more rapidly the swell releases its potential energy, the more violent is the wave of translation. On a long, gently sloping beach the energy is released slowly and the wave of translation merely tumbles down the front of the breaking wave as it moves shoreward.

The atmosphere and ocean currents In general the ocean currents are patterned closely to the surface wind systems of the atmosphere. The most outstanding differences between the two are:

1. The ocean is heated at the top while the atmosphere is heated mainly at the bottom.
2. The oceans are contained to a greater degree by the continents than the atmosphere is contained by the mountains.
3. The forces of friction between wind and water are the primary energy sources of the ocean currents while they act as brakes on the surface winds.

Using the recorded average currents of the Pacific Ocean as our model, we find currents flowing in directions which correspond to the prevailing easterlies and westerlies of the surface winds (Fig. 10.3). In general the average currents of the oceans consist of *gyres*. These large circulation systems rotate about centers which are displaced toward the west in order to conserve angular momentum.

The currents are kept in motion by the frictional drag of winds, but two other factors also affect them. One is the continental barriers; the other is the cohesive forces between the water particles. For example, the clockwise gyre of the North Pacific Ocean rotates about

the subtropical high belt. The north equatorial current is driven westward as a result of the stress of the trade winds. The cohesive forces between the water particles tend to slow this current with the result that a compensating flow at lower levels piles up the water on the north edge of the wind. Essentially, this results in a broad ridge of water about 3 or 4 ft high along this edge of the current. When the water flows by gravity back toward the south, angular momentum is conserved by slowing the eastward angular velocity; this results in an apparent westward surface velocity. The Asian continent interrupts the westward flow. The water piles up along the eastern coasts of Asia. This potential energy of the raised water level drives the Kurashio current northward from the Philippine Islands to Japan and starts the equatorial countercurrent back eastward along the regions of the doldrums. In order to conserve angular momentum, the Kurashio current is diverted eastward and becomes the west wind drift. The prevailing westerlies add impetus to this eastward flow. The North American continent interrupts this flow. However, the eastward rotation of the earth diminishes the piling up of water along the western coast. Because the eastward flow of water represents a greater than average angular momentum for this region, the cohesive forces within the water, which counteract the frictional forces of the winds, produce a stress that is transmitted to the lower layers of water with resulting deep water flows eastward. These well up along the western coasts of North America.

The North Pacific current and the Okhotsk current form a counterclockwise gyre in the North Pacific Ocean. A similar gyre does not exist in the South

Pacific Ocean. The continents of the Southern Hemisphere are everywhere displaced northward from the Antarctic continent at the south pole. In this region of open sea which circles the Antarctic continent the Antarctic current flows unobstructed towards the east completely around the earth at that latitude. The westerlies of this region accelerate the surface waters until the cohesive forces between water particles become equal to the wind stress. This stress must set up a circulation which reaches the bottom and any poleward motion is cancelled by the friction against the submerged hills and mountains.

Do the oceans exhibit counterparts of vertical cells such as the Hadley cell and vortexes such as the weather system eddies? The answer in both instances is yes. More detailed studies of day-to-day variations in oceanic characteristics have revealed these counterparts. However, much more data need to be gathered before they can be explained completely.

Evidence of the vertical cell is most marked in the Atlantic Ocean. It encompasses the whole of the North and South Atlantic Ocean crossing the equator both at the surface northward and at some depth southward. Because the current in this cell is very slow it has not been measured directly, but other factors mark its existence. Under the dry belts of the atmosphere, the ocean's surface waters become more salty (saline) because evaporation is greater than rainfall. Waters of a given degree of salinity are easily traced. A south-to-north general drift of warm saline water is superimposed on the gyres of the North Atlantic Ocean. The water sinks in the northern part of the ocean in the latitude of Iceland and is found drifting southward at depths of greater than a mile. The waters rise again somewhere near the Antarctic current and flow northward on the surface to complete the cell. It is estimated that this vertical cell may transport as much heat to the northern regions of the Atlantic as does the Gulf Stream.

It was pointed out in Chapter 9 that principles of fluid dynamics indicate anticyclonic eddies spinning slower than the earth's surface would develop from fluid stresses which oppose the surface rotation. In effect this produces a building up of potential energy within the eddy. In the atmosphere this resulted in regions of higher than average air pressure. In sea water it sets up a depression in which the warmer saline surface water is forced down against the buoyant forces of gravity from the more dense water displaced. In either situation potential energy is stored. By some random process not yet fully understood, the potential energy thus stored produces turbulence in the surrounding fluids wherein the potential energy is converted to kinetic energy of eddies similar to the weather system eddies of the atmosphere. The Gulf Stream gyre of the Atlantic sets up circulations which force warm surface water down thousands of feet within the gyre. These developments are a matter of record. Within the past 15 years data secured by the U. S. Navy Hydrographic Office has shown evidence of independent eddies within the Gulf Stream. One such eddy detected in 1950 was estimated to have transported 10 million million (10^{13}) tons of water from the Arctic region into the subtropical region of the Atlantic.

Thus we learn how the ocean waters are mixed and maintained at an almost constant salinity, heat is stored and transported great distances to temper the climates of the world, and potential energy is transported by waves across thousands of miles of ocean surface. Man's curiosity about the sea has only begun to bear fruit. As scientists more reliably comprehend the nature of the sea, its energies and its materials, we shall discover that new sources of raw materials, energy, food, and water have been made available to help solve the future problems of an expanding population. Here, again, we shall be made aware of the long-term value of efforts to expand the frontiers of knowledge. Science is opening an increasing number of new frontiers. However, the advancing growth of reliable knowledge will not be won if our society learns only to distrust scientists. Our people must somehow comprehend the importance of gaining knowledge for knowledge's sake, of maintaining the freedom to follow curiosities, to question ideas, to seek and share answers without fear of public ridicule or fanatic distrust. We can each act to insure this freedom by practicing its credo. We can allow our own curiosities to grow and encourage others to do the same. We can allow our own inquiries to range beyond the needs of the moment and to partake of the adventure of learning to gain better understanding of the world around us.

SUMMARY

The work of the hydrosphere is accomplished largely by systems involving breakers, waves, ocean currents, and eddies. The energy of the breakers in a rolling surf represents kinetic energy gained from the energy transmitted to the shore by wave motion. The breakers, called waves of translation, are not true waves but are masses of flowing water. Wave disturbances are described by their wavelength, frequency, period, and speed of propagation. Water waves are generated by the action of frictional forces between winds and the calm sea. The resulting ripples grow into waves as the windward side of the wavelets become sail-like surfaces against which the winds can act. White caps form when the stress of high waves breaks the "skin effect" of cohering water molecules at the water surface.

The energy of the wave is propagated at half the speed of the wave components. The speed of propagation in deep water increases with increased wavelengths. In shallow water the speed is proportional to water depth. This produces a refraction of wave fronts, turning the waves toward the regions of shallowest water.

Ocean currents are driven largely by the frictional forces between wind and water. Hence, they correspond in direction to those of the prevailing winds. A slowly flowing vertical cell is found to comprise the entire length of the North and South Atlantic Ocean. Conservation of angular momentum and principles of fluid dynamics combine in setting up independent recurring eddies within the oceans.

Only recently have verification activities begun in confirming the predictions of theories of ocean circulation. Yet to be gained are most of the fundamental data and interpretations needed to advance knowledge concerning the materials and processes of the hydrosphere.

PROBLEMS

1 Estimate the wavelength of waves that break at heights of 35 ft. What is the estimated speed of these waves in deep water?

2 Sea water has a weight density of 64 lb per cubic foot. How much potential energy does a cubic foot of sea water have by virtue of being at the surface of an 8-ft high breaker?

3 How many cubic miles of sea water were contained in the Gulf Stream eddy of 1950 which was estimated to have transported 10^{13} tons of sea water from the arctic to the subtropical region?

4 Show how the principle of conservation of angular momentum and the varying radii at the various latitudes help to explain the ocean currents in the Pacific region.

5 Explain how the principle of buoyancy is used to account for the building up of stores of potential energy in depressions of bodies of warmer water forced downward into the cooler and more dense water of an ocean.

11

MATERIALS AND
GENERAL STRUCTURE
OF THE EARTH'S CRUST

We need not move far to start our inquiry. The materials are close at hand. Mixtures of earth materials are available in your garden, on the beach, beside the road, or in a flower pot. Our inquiry into the earth's crust may start by examining a handful of soil.

There are those who would dismiss inquiry by saying, "The source of soil is crumbling rock," but this is typically oversimplified and quite meaningless. The questions of import are: "What is soil, what is rock, and how are they related?"

It is true that bedrock underlies all parts of the land surfaces and the oceans. Drilling operations for water and oil give evidences of this. And whenever bedrock is exposed, as in a cliff, the rock is obviously crumbling. Loose blocks and chips of rock form the rubble at the foot of the cliff. We can detach pieces of the cliff, often with very little effort, and many of them are so soft that they crumble to soil-like consistency between our fingers. But not all the chips are so easily crumbled; and if we scrape the surface materials from a portion of the cliff, we usually find the rock beneath is different from that at the surface, different in color, hardness, and texture. If the source of soil is crumbling rock then something happens to the rock before it crumbles.

INVITATION TO INVESTIGATE

As usual, when we look beneath the bare surface of things, we find curious discrepancies which beg for explanation. But lest our search is to resemble the aimless ramblings of children, we should show our increasing maturity in at least two ways: first, from time to time we should assess our progress toward a goal or purpose; second, before becoming overly enthused by our observations we should determine whether the assumed relationships between observations and purpose have any basis in theory or fact.

With regard to purposes and goals, we may find that as an investigation proceeds the character of the goal or purpose changes. This is as it should be. If the evidence warrants changes in purpose, they should be recognized. At times, changes in purpose occur so subtly that the investigator is hardly aware of them until he begins to evaluate the direction of his progress. Therefore, stating an unconditional purpose is rarely of interest to a scientist. A general purpose, such as "determining truth" or "discovering laws of nature," is more to his liking. This does not mean that scientists work without goal or plan. It merely reflects a recognition of the transitory nature of

most goals. Things are rarely the way we expect them to be. The findings of inquiry may change our expectations.

We should also recognize that advancement in knowledge is not caused merely by an accumulation of perceptual experiences or an awareness of more and more factors. These elements by themselves are like building blocks without a builder. Speculative thought sparked by venturesome and unusual ideas is our only means for creatively interpreting nature. The only restrictions in this regard are theories or other systematic plans for organizing our thoughts and experiences so that interpretations may represent a growing sense of reality rather than pure conjecture. What is venturesome and unusual depends upon the individual. You should be elated when ideas are used which to you seem unusual, because in them may lie a key to rapid advancement in understanding.

Preliminary evidence of relationships Is there evidence in soils of the assumed rock materials? A statement made without evidence to back it up would not warrant further inquiry. Let us therefore take a handful of soil and spread it out for preliminary examination.

Examination of a sample of soil, especially with a magnifying glass, reveals that soil contains materials other than rock debris—plant roots, plant stems, insect skeletons, seeds, and partially decomposed leaves may be present. This, of course, is not surprising; we are accustomed to seeing plants grow in soils. It follows though that soils are composed of many materials that do not faintly resemble rocks. However, we often may find grains of sand which are definitely rocklike. Also present are other flecks

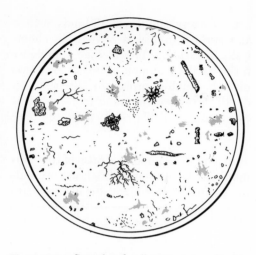

Figure 11.1 Sample of soil materials. Under a magnifying glass, soil is seen to be composed of a variety of materials.

of materials which look sufficiently like finely crushed rocks to warrant an inquiry into the relationship of soils to rocks.

However, before we investigate further, let us set the record straight: the term *soil* properly applies to disintegrated rock and organic (having once been alive) materials which have been so thoroughly decomposed, mixed, and modified that they support rooted plants.

Words that describe Our observations obviously show that the rock materials in the soil have been changed as compared to the rock materials in the cliff. There is also evidence indicating that changes have occurred in the surface materials of the rocks as compared to the materials within the rocks. Changes in materials are common events. We are aware of changes taking place around us every day. Water freezes (becomes a solid) in the refrigerator. Ice melts (becomes a liquid) in a glass of drinking water.

Water evaporates (becomes a gas) from our bathing suits. Charcoal burns, leaving but a small amount of ash. Iron rusts, sugar dissolves, cement hardens, dishes break, colors fade, and so on and on. Clearly, there are similarities and differences among these countless changes; understanding depends upon an awareness of the properties that distinguish them. A first step toward understanding is usually to agree upon some refinement of word usage.

The materials under consideration may be wholly of one specific kind or they may be a mixture of several different kinds in terms of composition. The kind of material having a singular homogeneous composition we shall refer to as a *substance*. When substances are mixed but each specific substance can be identified we shall refer to the whole as a *mixture*.

Every substance has at least one characteristic which is unique to it. It has other characteristics identical to those of other substances. The characteristics in common may aid us in classifying substances into similar groups; however, care must be used in identifying a specific substance in each group.

Because our purpose is to identify changes that occur in soil and rock materials, the characteristics we shall emphasize are those related to these materials. The key word is composition. A substance consisting of atoms having identical chemical properties is a *chemical element*. For example, pure aluminum is composed of aluminum atoms only and hence is classified as a chemical element. A substance that consists of two or more different chemical elements combined in a fixed proportion is a *compound*. For example, pure water is a compound composed of the chemical elements hydrogen and oxygen in the fixed proportion by weight of 1.008 to 8, respectively. The term *molecule* shall be used to identify the smallest particle of a substance which under ordinary conditions can exhibit the chemical properties of the substance. Under this system of classifying materials there can be two major types of changes in materials: chemical changes and physical changes.

In the process of a *chemical change* one or more substances lose their chemical identity and one or more entirely different substances are produced. For example, the chemical element carbon, which is the major substance of charcoal, and the chemical element oxygen, one of the major substances in air, may react to form the compound carbon dioxide. This specific process is called combustion or burning. There are many other chemical processes.

A *physical change* takes place in a process in which the composition of the molecules remains unchanged although other characteristics such as physical form, temperature, density, volume, shape, and/or visible particle size may be changed. For example, water can exist in different physical forms as gas, liquid, and solid. Whatever the form, the chemical composition of the water molecules remains unchanged. The processes involved in each change is one of the following: crystallization, sublimation, solution, vaporization, or melting.

From the standpoint of composition, the simplest substance is a chemical element. All other materials, whether compounds or mixtures, are composed of two or more chemical elements. One might ask, therefore, what chemical elements constitute the substances found in the surface materials of the earth?

Collected from all parts of the world,

a great many samples of all kinds of rock and surface materials have been chemically analyzed. The average abundance ratios of the common chemical elements in the earth's crust, at least to a depth of several thousand feet, are well-established. Table 11.1 lists the ele-

TABLE 11.1 Abundance ratio of the common elements of the earth's crust (excluding the hydrosphere and the atmosphere)

Chemical element	Chemical symbol	Percent by weight
Oxygen	O_2	46.6
Silicon	Si	27.7
Aluminum	Al	8.1
Iron	Fe	5.0
Calcium	Ca	3.6
Sodium	Na	2.8
Potassium	K	2.6
Magnesium	Mg	2.1
		98.5
All others	(81 elements)	1.5

ments having an abundance of more than 1 percent by weight; there are only eight of these. The elements oxygen and silicon constitute 74 percent of the materials. There were 103 elements discovered before the end of 1961. Several of these are known only from being produced in the laboratory by nuclear reactions. Eighty-nine of the elements have been found in the materials of the earth's crust.

With the exception of oxygen and silicon, the elements listed in Table 11.1 are true metals. All seven of the solid elements form compounds with oxygen, the gaseous element. This suggests strongly, in view of the abundance of oxygen, that the fundamental class of materials in the earth's crust is the *oxide* (the general name given to compounds of oxygen).

SPECULATION ABOUT PROCESS

Atoms are almost infinitesimally small, far beyond "common-sense" comparison. For example, if a five-cent coin of mass 5 grams were made of pure nickel it would contain 5.13×10^{22} atoms. This is over 50,000 billion billion atoms. Numbers of this magnitude are almost beyond comprehension. Contemplate the following comparison: The earth is thought to be about 6 billion years old. This amounts to about 1.9×10^{17} seconds— not even a billion billion.

Each individual atom is composed of smaller "particles"—electrons, protons, and neutrons. For example, the most abundant form of nickel is composed of 28 electrons, 28 protons, and 30 neutrons. The atomic particles may have electrical properties and are arranged in groups within the atom. The positively charged protons and the neutrons which have no electrical charge are grouped together in a compact but massive atomic nucleus. The negatively charged electrons are grouped into major energy levels surrounding the nucleus. To be more specific, nickel under normal conditions is pictured having electrons grouped within four major energy levels containing, respectively, from the inner to outer levels, 2, 8, 16, and 2 electrons per level.

In view of these facts, you must know that individual atoms and their structures cannot be seen in the ordinary sense of the word. For that matter, we are equally unable to taste, touch, smell, or feel the weight of an atom. It follows that we have not become aware of the individual atom by means of any of our senses; we have used speculative means. And still, these facts concerning atoms need not be accepted on faith. In this and later chapters we shall meet substantial evidence to verify these statements.

Intrinsic properties of atoms Energy is involved in every atomic reaction. When the nucleus is not solely involved, the electrons surrounding the nucleus are the systems of the atom most generally involved in transforming energy. In recalling the explanation developed in Chapter 3 for the photoelectric effect, we know that the conventional ideas of continuous energy transformation cannot be used successfully for most atomic systems. At atomic levels, energy transformed in units of quanta takes on basic significance. Under these conditions one quantum of energy, specific in amount, is the smallest change which may occur. This explains the grouping of electrons of an atom around discrete energy levels. For a given element, these levels represent the only available quantum changes of energy to bind the electrons into the atomic system under normal conditions. This does not mean that electrons are held physically to rigid orbits. Electron energies may take several forms. Only the total energies of exchange have discrete values. The electrons are merely the expressed carriers of these energies within the atomic systems.

The chemical properties of an atom or a group of atoms are closely related to the electronic structure of the outermost available energy level of the molecule. The available energy levels are determined in part by environmental factors such as temperature, pressure, and the proximity of other molecules as well as the inherent factors of stability found in the individual atoms involved. Atoms tend to assume the arrangement achieving the *lowest state of potential energy* which is available and suitable to achieve

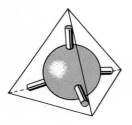

Figure 11.2 Solid surface and electron cloud models of atoms. Emphasis is placed upon relative sizes and the levels of the surface electrons.

stability under a given set of conditions.

A clue to stability of electron structure is found in a group of elements which do not react chemically. Because of their unreactive nature these elements are called *inert gases*. They comprise helium, neon, argon, krypton, xenon, and radon. Without at this time going into the system used by scientists to account for electron grouping, we shall reveal the clue and proceed to make use of it. With the exception of helium which has a total of only two electrons, the remaining inert gases each have the characteristic number of 8 electrons in the outermost energy level. This configuration of 8 electrons is referred to as a *completed outer shell*. It apparently represents a very stable and symmetrical arrangement of electrical charges because the inert gas

elements have unusually low potential energies. Two important properties of atoms in general can be traced to a completed outer shell. First, the state of lowest potential energy for an atom is attained when it has a completed outer shell rather than when it is electrically neutral. Second, whenever atoms react chemically with each other the tendency is toward attaining a completed outer shell.

Now, let us inquire as to the electron configuration of the eight elements listed in Table 11.1:

Oxygen has grouped in two levels: 2 and 6 electrons.
Sodium has grouped in three levels: 2, 8, and 1 electrons.
Magnesium has grouped in three levels: 2, 8, and 2 electrons.
Aluminum has grouped in three levels: 2, 8, and 3 electrons.
Silicon has grouped in three levels: 2, 8, and 4 electrons.
Potassium has grouped in four levels: 2, 8, 8, and 1 electrons.
Calcium has grouped in four levels: 2, 8, 8, and 2 electrons.
Iron has grouped in four levels: 2, 8, 14, and 2 electrons.

With the exception of iron it is quite apparent how the *completed outer shell* might be attained. In some manner oxygen can be completed by accepting 2 electrons, sodium by donating 1 electron, magnesium by donating 2 electrons, aluminum by donating 3 electrons, silicon by either accepting 4 or donating 4 electrons, potassium by donating 1 electron, calcium by donating 2 electrons. Iron, the exception, for some reason achieves stability by either donating 2 or 3 electrons depending upon the circumstances at the time of reaction.

From a standpoint of model building there are only two ways in which an atom may accept or donate electrons. One is by complete transfer of electrons from one atom to another. The other is by jointly sharing electrons with other atoms.

When electrons are transferred away from or into an atom or molecule, the process is called *ionization*. The resulting particles are called *ions* or, more specifically, according to apparent charge, *positive ions* (*cations*) and *negative ions* (*anions*). Symbols for ions show both the chemical symbol of the element and the charge. For example, the ion of aluminum is expressed Al^{+3}, indicating a loss of 3 electrons. Iron has 2 ionic forms, Fe^{+2} and Fe^{+3}. Oxygen gains 2 electrons and becomes O^{-2}. The plus and minus signs indicate positive and negative charges, not addition and subtraction in the usual sense. The tendency is to attain a completed outer shell; however, for atoms of any given element in the presence of other elements the symmetry of electrical forces and its relationship to the available levels of binding energy are factors determining the extent of ionization. Hence, we should not generalize too broadly with regard to ionization of elements as a total group. Each element and ion must be known by its own verifiable properties.

Most of the substances of the earth show evidence of both ionic electron transfer and cooperate sharing of electrons in each of the substances involved. A constant shift from one mode of electron control to the other is taking place in most of these substances in order to satisfy the quantum energy requirements that exist. The over-all energy status, however, remains a measurable quantity under each given situation.

Binding energy—the atomic glue In a manner somewhat similar to the concept of binding energy with which we explained the stability between the planets and the sun in the solar system, the stability of atomic systems also can be explored from the standpoint of binding energy. The transformation of energy into forms such as heat and electricity is often more easily detected and measured than other changes that may occur in atomic processes. Therefore, an energy audit may be a first step toward a more complete explanation of atomic processes.

For our purposes let us define binding energy as the amount of work (energy) required to dissociate the constituents involved in a particular atomic system into a state where they are independent of the system. An increase in binding energy involves a decrease in potential energy, and vice versa.

The forces involved in atomic systems are largely electrical. The term *electrical charge* expresses the fact of electric force in much the same manner as the term gravitational mass expresses the fact of gravitational force. Furthermore, in order to express the fact that electrical forces can produce repulsion as well as attraction the terms positive charge and negative charge are used. Bodies having like charges repel each other; those having unlike charges attract each other.

When an electrically charged body is forced to move against the action of electrical forces, work is done which becomes electrical potential energy of the system. If the electrical potential energy becomes greater than the smallest quantum of binding energy between charged particles in a system, the particle with lowest binding energy will dissociate. Electrical potential energy is expressed in terms of the energy transformed per unit of charge *multiplied* by the number of charge units moved in a given situation. The energy transformed per unit of charge is most often expressed in terms of the *volt*. When electrons are the charged bodies being moved it is most convenient to use the *elementary charge* (*e*) of the electron (and proton) as the units of charge. The energy is then expressed in terms of *electron volts* (ev) or multiples of this small quantity such as million electron volts (mev) and billion electron volts (bev). An electron volt is equivalent to 1.602×10^{-19} joules or, stated conversely, 6.24×10^{18} electron volts equals 1 joule. The large numbers merely express again the fact that we are dealing with almost infinitesimal units at the atomic level.

In atomic systems there are a number of moving electrons which are attracted to the positively charged protons in the nucleus and which are repelled by each other with similar forces. The resulting force acting on a given electron is very complex and continuously varying. The problem of predicting force relationships in such a system is greatly simplified by measuring the work required to dissociate an electron from the atomic system. The binding energy of an electron in an outermost energy level is a measure of how effectively the charges in the nucleus extend their combined forces to and beyond this level. The greater the binding energy, the more tightly is the outer electron bound to the system and the less effective have been the repelling forces of electrons at the inner energy levels in overcoming the attraction between the outer electron and the nucleus. The opposite situation of low binding energy indicates a more efficient opposition by the electrons at the inner levels.

Table 11.2 indicates the potential

TABLE 11.2 First-electron binding energy of gaseous atoms

Chemical element	Approximate binding energy in electron volts
Oxygen	13.6
Silicon	8.1
Iron	7.9
Magnesium	7.6
Calcium	6.1
Aluminum	6.0
Sodium	5.1
Potassium	4.3

electrical energy needed to remove the first electron from the atoms of the common elements while in the gaseous state. The different values are a measure of the extent to which an atom tends to attract electrons from other atoms. The greater the binding energy, the stronger are the forces from the nucleus in attracting electrons from other atoms. The less the binding energy, the more easily the outer electrons can be attracted away from the atom. The relative position of oxygen in Table 11.2 makes it apparent how oxygen will tend to ionize the other elements or tend to share their electrons in a chemical bonding. Thus we have gained measured evidence to explain the fact that the most prevalent substances in the earth's crust are the oxides.

From the standpoint of defining energy changes electrical forces are no different than gravitational forces. The relationship to work units is the same. We expressed quantitatively the gravitational force by Eq. (6.3): $F_g = Gm_1m_2/R^2$; we can express the electric force by the formula:

$$F_e = Cq_1q_2/R^2$$

where F_e = force in newtons

if C = a constant (9×10^9 newton-meters^2/coulombs^2)

q_1 and q_2 = electrical charge units in coulombs (the elementary charge $e = 1.602 \times 10^{-19}$ coulombs)

R = displacement between charges in meters

The important consideration at the moment is that the electric force is inversely proportional to the square of the displacement. In other words, a change in displacement is proportionately of greater influence than a similar change in electrical charge. Because of the extremely small displacements involved, the effective radius of an atom or ion has a great influence upon the attractive forces exerted by the nucleus on the outermost electrons or on other charged bodies nearby.

Consider the values shown in Fig. 11.3. Obviously, a factor involved in the active electron control by oxygen is its small atomic radius when compared to the radii of other atoms. Here also we are reminded of the diminutive size of atoms. The atomic-sized units of displacement like the energy units are much reduced. The *angstrom unit* (A) used is equal to 10^{-8} cm. In Chapter 3 we computed the wavelength of orange light to be 0.00006 cm/wavelength. Expressed in angstrom units this is 6000 A. Is it any wonder that atoms cannot be seen? They are in the order of a thousandth of the size of the wavelength of visible light. Their small size, however, has far-reaching effects when the ratios of sizes involved in energy relationships are brought to mind. Not only are individual electrons involved in binding energies but also atomic aggregates are involved if the displacements between these units can be reduced to atomic proportions.

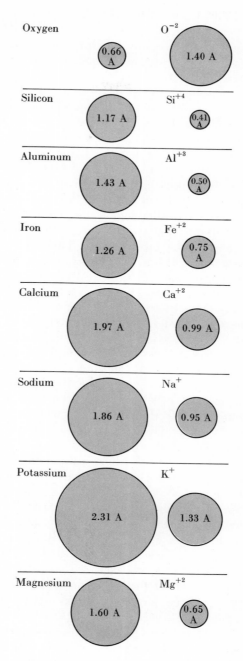

Figure 11.3 Relative sizes of atoms and ions. The values are of radii and are given in Angstrom units (1 A = 10^{-8} cm).

ESTIMATING PROGRESS

Supposedly we are inquiring into the meaning of the materials and the general structure of the earth's crust and, more specifically, into the relationship of soils to rocks. Preliminary evidence indicated rocklike materials are present in soils. In search of characteristics which might aid in understanding the nature of the changes in materials and possibly explain the differences in soil materials as compared to rock materials, we selected descriptive terms having meanings useful in classifying materials before and after changes have taken place. This led to recognizing two major types of change— chemical and physical. Although undoubtedly many physical changes must take place before rocks become soil, we have selected chemical composition as the key to classifying materials and processes. A review of composition divided materials into substances and mixtures with a further subdivision of substances into chemical elements and compounds. Making use of chemically analyzed abundance ratios of the common materials of the earth's crust, we find very few elements which are present in large abundance and a suggestion that these may occur fundamentally as oxides. Speculation as to processes brought to the foreground the electrical and spatial properties of atomic systems within the framework of energy considerations which seem basic at these levels. The speculation uncovered further evidence in support of the suggested importance of oxides.

You may now be wondering if we are progressing toward our original goal; whether a new goal has emerged; or, perhaps, we have just emerged from a blind alley ready to start out again from the beginning. These possibilities are always present in a scientist's work. In truth, we seem to be no nearer our original goal because the actual materials have not been examined and discussed, but at the same time there seems to be no new purpose in sight. We might ask what we have been doing. We have not been accumulating perceptual experiences with regard to the materials under inquiry; but by speculation we have been made aware of more and more factors with which we might possibly identify and interpret evidences of change and meaningful properties of the materials. To insure progress the next step would seem to be a discussion of the actual materials found in rocks and soils.

REPRESENTATIVE ROCK MATERIALS

Rocks and soils are complex mixtures of substances. Rarely have the results of earth processes made the work of the geologist simple. Most geologists use a lifetime of studying one geographic region, one particular earth process, or the products of an earth process in order to advance the understanding of energy and material relationships which occur naturally in the earth. Geology is a highly fertile field of science. Our inquiry must of necessity be selective and in no way comprehensive. Our purpose is to gain meanings and appreciations, but not to grasp a thorough explanation. Consequently, representative substances and mixtures will comprise our objects of inquiry concerning actual earth materials.

Silicon dioxide Because silicon and oxygen together comprise 74 percent of the

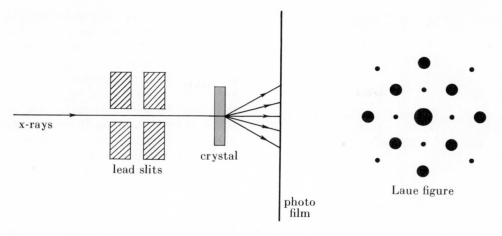

x-rays

lead slits

crystal

photo
film

Laue figure

Figure 11.4 Diffraction of X-rays by the atomic particles and a crystalline solid. The Laue figures are the evidence used to interpret crystal structures.

earth's crust, we could expect to find a great amount of silicon dioxide by virtue of the fact that silicon can donate four electrons, two electrons to each of two oxygen atoms. Silicon dioxide, SiO_2, is a very common mineral found in rocks such as sandstone and granite and is the major constituent in most types of sand. But the abundance is comparatively low. Silicon dioxide as a mineral comprises about 12 percent of the crustal materials.

A clue to the lack of abundance of pure silicon dioxide comes from X-ray analyses of its crystal structure. (See Fig. 11.4.) Wavelengths of visible light would not likely reflect or diffract appreciably from atoms because of their minute size. However, X-ray photons have wavelengths in the range of 0.01 A to 100 A; therefore, X-ray reflection and diffraction occur from atomic-sized particles. These reflection and diffraction patterns are recorded on photographic films and the patterns analyzed. X-ray analyses in-

Quartz crystals. Pure silicon dioxide has a network arrangement of linked tetrahedra. When a crystal forms, it becomes a macromolecule. No individual molecules exist in its structure.

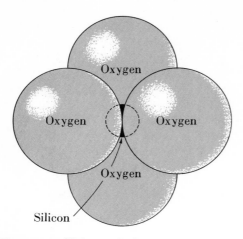

Figure 11.5 Unit tetrahedron structure of silicon dioxide. Oxygen ions are shared in common by adjacent units.

dicate that silicon dioxide consists of a silicon ion occupying the center of a tetrahedron of oxygen ions. (See Fig. 11.5.) Each tetrahedral unit is composed of a central silicon ion surrounded by four oxygen ions each sharing one electron with the silicon. The oxygen ions forming the "corners" of each tetrahedral unit are always shared by two of these units such that each oxygen ion shares two electrons—one from each of the silicon ions in the two units. Therefore, all structures of pure silicon dioxide have a network arrangement of linked tetrahedra and there are no individual SiO_2 molecules. Once formed this network is very durable because of moderately high binding energy at ordinary temperatures. It should also be noticed that since the energy bonds are all of like kind there is no difference between the binding energy of a unit or a group of units. When a crystal forms it becomes a macromolecule; no individual molecules exist in its structure.

Silicates The crystalline materials of the earth's crust in most cases have been formed deep in the crust under conditions of high temperature and high pressure. For example, it is improbable that any granite has been formed at depths less than 2000 ft below the earth's surface. Under these diverse conditions, crystals of widely different compositions can be formed out of the mixture of substances present at the time. The solid substances which form naturally during these situations are called *minerals*. Minerals have a distinguishing set of physical properties and a composition expressible by a chemical formula. However, most minerals have a variable composition. This variability is often traced to the tetrahedral structure of the SiO_4^{-4} unit.

Hundreds of different minerals involve SiO_4 tetrahedra. These minerals as a group are called *silica*. When elements other than silicon and oxygen are also involved, the minerals are called *silicates*. In terms of structural linkages the silicates may be divided into four major groups: discrete radical minerals, fibrous minerals, sheet minerals, and network minerals.

The discrete radical minerals are formed when single tetrahedra are linked to other ions so that the oxygen ions are

Feldspar crystal, a representative of minerals having structural linkages of the network type.

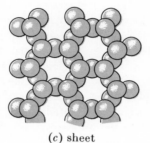

(a) discrete radical

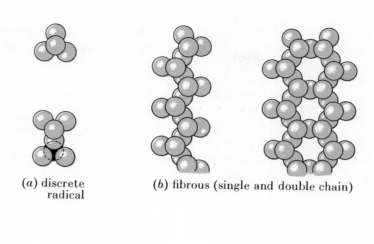

(b) fibrous (single and double chain)

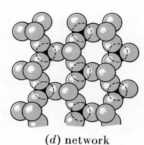

Figure 11.6 Basic structures of the silicates. Only the oxygen ions are shown.

(c) sheet

(d) network

linked only to a single tetrahedron (Fig. 11.6(a)). These minerals would most likely form when the ratio of iron, magnesium, aluminum, and calcium are high so that frequent linkages to these ions could take place. An example is the commonly found mineral *olivine* which has magnesium and iron dispersed between the tetrahedra. The formula $(Mg_1Fe)_2(SiO_4)$ for olivine merely shows the possibility of two Mg^{+2} ions, or two Fe^{+2} ions, or one of each to be linked to the SiO_4^{-4} ion, forming a single unit of neutral charge. Expressly the name olivine refers to the mineral having the ratio of 63 percent magnesium ions to 37 percent iron ions. Other forms of discrete radical minerals have groups of

two, three, or six tetrahedra so linked to peripheral positive ions as to form separate units neutral in charge.

The fibrous minerals are formed by endless chains of tetrahedra giving the crystals a threadlike consistency. (See Fig. 11.6(b).) Often when the fibrous pieces are pulled apart, the mass of fibers can be matted together like felt. Asbestos is a mixture of fibrous minerals having the complex formulas

$$Ca_2Mg_5(Si_4O_{11})_2(OH)_2$$

and

$$Mg_6(Si_4O_{11})(OH)_6 \cdot H_2O$$

The sheet minerals consist of layers of silicate tetrahedra in which the oxygen ions often share linkages with ions other than silicon but the continuity of the tetrahedra is maintained within thin sheets or layers. (See Fig. 11.6(*c*).) If the surfaces of the layers are uniformly neutral in charge, the layers may slide readily over each other. This explains the slippery feeling of the flakes of talc in face powders. Conversely, if the surfaces appear negatively charged as found in muscovite (mica) it is because Al^{+3} replaces Si^{+4} in the center of some of the tetrahedra and these units seem to be negatively charged. This charge is neutralized by distributing positive ions of potassium within the structure. The strong electric forces between the potassium ions and the negatively charged surfaces make it more difficult to slide mica surfaces over each other.

The network minerals provide a three-dimensional extension of the tetrahedral linkages forming a rigid boxlike structure. (See Fig. 11.6(*d*).) These minerals usually have a given proportion of the silicon tetrahedra (SiO_4) replaced by aluminum tetrahedra (AlO_4) which, as was indicated above, leaves the network negatively charged at these points. An appropriate number of positive ions of proper charge, size, and binding energy are fitted into the framework and linked to oxygen ions so that the total framework is electrically neutral. The proportion of aluminum and silicon tetrahedra are often indicated by the way these elements are grouped in the chemical formula. For example, the group of minerals called the feldspars have proportion groupings as follows: $(AlSi_3O_8)^{-1}$ and $(Al_2Si_2O_8)^{-2}$. The monoclinic feldspar called *orthoclase* has the formula $K(AlSi_3O_8)$. The plagioclase feldspar called *anorthite* has the formula $Ca(Al_2Si_2O_8)$.

We hope that no one has felt compelled to memorize the chemical formulas used here. The purposes for including them were to show that complicated structures are often formed from rather simple units and to indicate why such a wide variety of minerals are possible. The over-all structure of the earth's crust has been very aptly described as consisting of layers upon layers of spherical oxygen ions having a few ions of other substances fitted into the spaces between the spheres.

The question, of course, still remains: Why do these more complex minerals form rather than the simple oxides? The answer lies in consideration of binding energies and the environment of formation. We must turn to the laboratories of various scientists for the answers. First, let us turn to chemistry laboratories.

Chemists very often determine the binding energies of various compounds by measuring the heat absorbed or liberated during a chemical process. The nearest whole number proportions by weight of the various reacting elements are determined and recorded in terms of *gram formula weight*; that is, the mass in grams numerically equal to the sum of the atomic weights shown in the formula. Thus corresponding proportion units for each element are used in all records. Energy is measured in kilocalories (Cal— with a capital *C*; this is equal to 1000 calories with a small *c*). A calcium aluminum silicate similar to some found in nature has been produced in the laboratory. The formula in terms of the mineral oxides is as follows:

Calcium aluminum silicate
$$3CaO \cdot Al_2O_3 \cdot 2SiO_2$$

The total heat liberated during the formation of a gram formula weight of this compound is 1486.3 kilocalories (Cal). In the formation of the individual oxides the following energies are liberated per gram formula weight:

Calcium oxide (CaO)
    151.7 Cal $\therefore$ 3 CaO   = 455.1 Cal

Aluminum oxide (Al_2O_3)
    389.5 Cal $\therefore$ Al_2O_3 = 389.5 Cal

Silicon dioxide (SiO_2)
    201.3 Cal $\therefore$ 2 SiO_2 = 402.6 Cal
                    Total   1247.2 Cal

It becomes obvious that a considerable amount of chemical potential energy exists in the oxides which under proper circumstances can be reduced when they combine to form calcium aluminum silicate. Since atoms tend to assume the arrangement achieving the lowest state of potential energy, the calcium aluminum silicate forms whenever possible.

Next, let us turn to the geology laboratories. A large amount of information useful to geologists is gathered by cutting paper-thin cross sections of rocks and studying them under the microscope. Specially designed lighting sources and

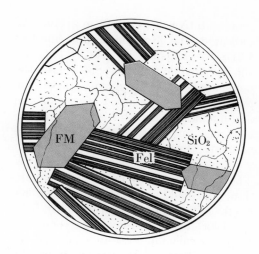

Figure 11.7 A composite thin section of granite. The completed crystal faces indicate the order of final crystal formation.

microscopes are used. Fig. 11.7 is a simplified diagram of a thin section of granite as it would appear under the microscope. Rarely would all of these crystals show up in a single viewing area. The diagram is a composite of many areas. The purpose here is to illustrate a sequence of crystal formation. Three

Blocks of exfoliating granite. The blocks have been fractured and transported by the action of frost and water. New areas of the rock are exposed to weathering.

representative types of minerals are indicated: the ferromagnesians (marked FM), the feldspars (marked Fel), and silicon dioxide (marked SiO_2). As the name implies, the ferromagnesians are the mineral species composed largely of iron and magnesium silicates. They are usually dark in color because of the iron content. In the diagram they are shown with all crystal faces fully developed. The feldspars are by far the most abundant rock-making minerals in the earth's crust. These minerals are usually light in color because they are composed largely of calcium, potassium, and sodium alumino-silicates. In the diagram the feldspars are shown with most of their crystal faces developed, but locally the crystals grew around the ferromagnesian crystals which had developed earlier. The silicon dioxide is shown without well-developed crystal faces, indicating that this mineral essentially filled in the spaces between the crystals formed earlier.

Granite is thought to form when the materials of a hot molten mixture of substances cool slowly enough to permit separation of the substances by crystallization into minerals of a fixed composition which solidify at different conditions of temperature and pressure. With reference to the diagram, the ferromagnesians are seen to develop at highest temperatures. The feldspars crystallize later and at lower temperatures, and finally the remaining silicon dioxide is solidified at the lowest temperature of the group. It should be evident that were there not an excess of silicon dioxide in the earth's crust, there would be little likelihood that this mineral would appear in large quantities.

With regard to the environment of formation, we have already referred to the high temperature and high pressure. Another factor of importance is that under these conditions certain of the materials in the molten mixture can exist only in the gaseous state. Of greatest importance among these materials is gaseous water. Small amounts of carbon dioxide, sulfur, and traces of other substances also remain gaseous. As gases these substances are too energetic to combine in important amounts in the minerals being formed. Therefore, the possibility exists that these substances might alter the composition of the minerals in environments having lower temperatures and lower pressures.

REPRESENTATIVE SOIL MATERIALS

We began our inquiry by examining a handful of soil. We found indications there of chemical and physical changes which must have taken place during soil formation. Also included in the soil were materials of plant and animal origin. These indications are undoubtedly interrelated. The chief agent which makes this interrelationship possible is the earth's atmosphere. The atmosphere is responsible for immense changes in the earth's crust. By transporting moisture evaporated from land and sea to higher ground and precipitating it as rain and snow, the atmosphere does work which is converted to potential energy. Streams and glaciers use this energy to grind up rocks and to transport the debris to lower elevations.

The gaseous substances of the atmosphere can penetrate deeply into the crevices of the earth's surface. This brings the chemically active substances in contact with bedrock as well as with the exposed surfaces. Because of weather relationships, the chemical and physical changes produced by the atmosphere are called *weathering*. The energy for the atmospheric work can be traced to sunlight.

Factors of change other than the atmosphere are also involved. Plants and animals help to break up rock materials physically and also produce substances which attack the minerals chemically. After it is precipitated, water continues to be an active agent in changing the minerals both physically and chemically. Temperature variations play a significant role. High temperatures tend to speed up chemical reactions and low temperatures in conjunction with water cause disruption by freezing.

The results of weathering are varied. We shall examine two common constituents of soil, clay and sand.

Clay

Clay More than 55 percent of the earth's crust consists of feldspars. When these minerals are weathered, the chief mineral product is clay, which is a major constituent in most soil mixtures. The chemical weathering of feldspar is the combined effect of the reactions with water and carbon dioxide. The following reaction is typical:

$$K(AlSi_3O_8) + H_2O + CO_2 \rightarrow$$

orthoclase   water   carbon dioxide

$$Al_2Si_2O_5(OH)_4 + SiO_2 + K_2CO_3$$

Kaolinate (a clay)   "sand"   potassium carbonate

Comparatively warm surface temperature and considerable rainfall or heavy dew promote this reaction. The interrelatedness of plants to weathering is evident: carbon dioxide in sufficient amounts for extensive reactions comes chiefly from decaying vegetation; potassium carbonate is an important plant food.

The products yielded by this reaction are not soil. In desert regions the parent rock crumbles into large fragments as this reaction slowly breaks up the feldspar crystals. Near granite cliffs large pieces of feldspar are mixed together with angular chunks of silicon dioxide and other minerals, producing a deep bed of materials at the bottom of which smaller particles of the clay minerals are found. Development of a good soil is an extremely slow process. In regions having considerable rainfall, the action of flowing water grinds the particles to smaller size while the chemical actions continue and humus from vegetation is added to the mixture. The vegetation not only adds materials to the process but the roots tend to hold the resulting mixture together, preventing erosion.

Sand

Sand The term "sand" refers only to particle size and not to composition. Sand has grain sizes ranging from diameters of 2 millimeters (mm) down to 0.05 mm. Particles with diameters greater than 2 mm are called pebbles or gravel. Silt particles range from 0.05 mm to about 0.004 mm. Clay sizes range below 0.004 mm. The average size of particles in beach sands is about 0.15 mm.

The most common constituent of sand is the mineral quartz, a form of silicon dioxide. Its great hardness and chemical inactivity at ordinary temperatures give quartz its durability. Correctly called quartz sand, this substance is what most people refer to when they speak of sand. However, in many soils, sand particles of feldspar, limestone, and quartz may be present.

We shall find that many rocks are formed from the fine-grained soil materials that have been transported and deposited by wind and water. The materials of the earth's crust are always in transition. The soil materials are but a stage in the ever-continuing cycle of building up of rocks from the surface sediments and breaking down of rocks by environmental factors at the earth's surface.

INTERPRETING PHYSICAL PROPERTIES OF MINERALS

Many methods have been devised for classifying minerals according to physical properties. Tentative identifications can often be made on the basis of a very few characteristics. Positive identification may involve both chemical and physical analyses by experts. However, much pleasure and greater depth of meaning can accrue for the individual who is curious enough to pick up a few rock samples and try to interpret what he sees.

Interpretations on the basis of light We noted earlier that when light strikes a given material it may be reflected, absorbed, or transmitted. All three results are present to some degree in every contact. Let us use each to investigate mineral properties.

The general outward appearance of the mineral is determined by reflected light. The general appearance of a fresh surface of a mineral in reflected light is called *luster*. Clues to internal structure can often be ascertained by observing luster. A good technique is to rotate the sample slowly around each of several axes and to sense the display of slightly different conditions in the crystal faces as they pass. An iridescent play of colors may be caused by thin sheet structures giving reflection from several surfaces within the mineral. Milky or pearly reflections from the interior may also be caused by sheet structure, although of deeper layers. A silky sheen may indicate a fibrous structure, particularly if it appears more strongly about a given axis of rotation than about others. A velvet look may be caused by reflections from myriads of discrete radical mineral composites. A reflection as from glass or porcelain is usually a result of a network structure.

Mineral colors result from selective absorption and reflection of light. When viewed in white light, the reflected colors represent the frequencies that are not absorbed. The colors are often clues to the chemical elements and ions involved, especially if they are viewed in a streak of the powdered mineral. The *streak test* is usually made by rubbing the mineral across a piece of unglazed porcelain. The presence of iron, for instance, is usually identified with a yellowish or red-brown streak.

Transmitted light is usually refracted. As a rule, the heavier the ions and the more compactly they are spaced, the greater is the change in the speed of the transmitted light and the greater the index of refraction. In some mineral crystals the arrangement of ions is such that photons having waves oriented in a given direction of oscillation pass through more swiftly than those having waves oriented in other modes. Thus, the photons having different orientations are separated and the transmitted light becomes polarized. The separated rays of light are refracted by different amounts so that doubling of images may be seen when viewed through the mineral. Iceland spar, a calcite mineral, shows this *double refraction* to a marked degree.

Interpretations based on manner of breaking The type of surface and the orientations of the surfaces when minerals are broken up give excellent clues of internal structure. When the forces between atoms or ions are about equal in all directions, the breaks usually occur around a flaw in the crystal. Since flaws are unpredictable features, the break may occur at any point of the specimen and the surfaces of the break are irregular. This manner of breaking is called *fracture*. Fibrous or splintery fractures generally denote a mixture of minerals having fibrous structure, as found in asbestos, for example. Conchoidal (shell-like) fractures often occur in specimens of rocks which were solidified too rapidly from the molten state for crystals of any size to grow. Generally this sets up internal stresses at various points in the glassy rock materials; these stresses are released when the specimen breaks. Quartz (silicon dioxide) also has a tendency to fracture in this manner.

When minerals break so that smooth plane surfaces are produced, they are said to have *cleavage*. This occurs most often in minerals having a sheet or a network structure. The forces between sheets are generally much less than the forces between the linkages of the layers; hence, cleavage in one direction or surface plane occurs which is repeated throughout the sample. Network minerals often have repeated at regular intervals in their linkage framework a positive ion having lower binding energy or lower force relationships in a given direction.

Recurring patterns of these result in planes of weak linkages, and cleavages on breaking. Since these planes occur periodically, the characteristic cleavage directions serve to identify the mineral.

Interpretations based on tests of hardness The relative hardness of a mineral can be determined by comparing it to materials in a standard scale. Moh's scale of hardness is given in Table 11.3. Min-

TABLE 11.3 Moh's scale of hardness

1	Talc	6	Orthoclase
2	Gypsum		6+ Steel file
	2+ Fingernail	7	Quartz
3	Calcite	8	Topaz
	3+ Copper coin	9	Corundum
4	Fluorite	10	Diamond
5	Apatite		
	5+ Knife blade		
	5++ Window glass		

erals of the same hardness may either scratch each other or not. The hardness of a mineral is usually indicated by recording the Moh's scale numbers between which the specimen's hardness falls.

It is often assumed—and with some justification—that relative hardness predicts the strength of forces binding the ions of a mineral. Generally the greater the number of shared electrons per unit volume, the greater is the hardness of the mineral. Hardness tests should be made on a fresh surface because of the changes which may occur upon contact with moisture and other chemical agents in the atmosphere.

Interpretation based on density Density has been defined as mass per unit volume. Two atomic factors affect density: the relative weights of the atoms, and the packing of atoms. The relative weights of atoms of the various elements are indicated as *atomic weight*. This is the ratio of an element's mass compared to carbon, which was given the standard atomic weight 12 in order that hydrogen, the least massive element, would have an atomic weight near unity (1.008). (The gram formula weight we referred to previously is the mass in grams that is numerically equal to the sum of the atomic weights of the atoms shown in the formula.) Table 11.4 lists the most com-

TABLE 11.4 Atomic weights of earth elements

Element	Atomic weight
Oxygen	16.01
Sodium	22.99
Magnesium	24.31
Aluminum	26.98
Silicon	28.09
Potassium	39.10
Calcium	40.08
Iron	55.85

mon mineral elements in order of their atomic weights. Note that minerals having a higher ratio of iron, calcium, and potassium would have greater density than those having a higher ratio of aluminum, magnesium, and sodium, if the two types had equal packing of atoms. It is interesting to notice that since iron generally imparts a dark color to its minerals, the dark-colored minerals—particularly those producing dark streaks—should be predictably more dense than the lighter-colored minerals. This is confirmed by the following examples: the light-colored feldspar *albite*, $Na(AlSi_3O_8)$, density 2.6 grams per cm^3; the darker-colored mineral *olivine*, $(Mg, Fe)_2(SiO_4)$, density between 3.3 and 3.4 grams per cm^3; the red-brown mineral *hematite*, Fe_2O_3, density about 5.3 grams per cm^3.

SELF-EVALUATION

Between initial curiosity and intelligent interpretations is a time period filled with recurring oscillations between observations, speculative search activities, predictions, and verifications—not necessarily in that order or any order. These are important stages on the way to reliable explanations. Even very careful reading and thinking about the contents of this chapter cannot fulfill these requirements. To gain first-hand experiences you must inspect actual samples of earth materials and seek out clues leading to interpretive predictions and verifications in your contacts with nature. This is a rewarding activity and is even richer when enjoyed with the assistance of persons who can help each other to fuller understanding.

SUMMARY

Rocks and soils are complex mixtures of substances. A substance is a kind of material with singular homogeneous composition. A substance consisting of atoms having identical chemical properties is a chemical element. A substance consisting of two or more different chemical elements chemically combined in a fixed proportion is a compound. A molecule identifies the smallest particle of a substance which under ordinary conditions can exhibit the chemical properties of the substance.

In producing soil, both physical and chemical changes take place. The the term *soil* goes beyond altered forms of rocks to include also organic materials in its mixtures. The soils reflect the type of rocks that have contributed materials to the mixtures.

Only 8 of the 89 known elements in the earth's crust exist in an abundance of greater than 1 percent by weight. Oxygen and silicon make up almost three-quarters of the crust. Electronic structure, atomic size, and the binding energies of the electrons in atomic and molecular structures explain the types and particle arrangements in minerals produced in nature under specified conditions. Electrical forces between positive and negative charges account for the energies involved.

The silicates are the most abundant mineral forms in the materials of the earth's crust. In terms of structural linkages, the silicates may be classified as discrete radical minerals, fibrous minerals, sheet minerals, or network minerals.

The representative mineral groups found in granite rocks can be classified as feldspars, ferromagnesians, or silicon dioxides. The feldspars are estimated to form more than 55 percent of the earth's crustal materials. Minerals formed in one type of environment are often weathered more easily when brought into a different environment.

When feldspar minerals are weathered, the chief mineral substance produced is clay. Clay is a prominent constituent of most soil mixtures. The most durable of the minerals found in rocks is silicon dioxide. Although changed physically into grains of small size, the most common constituent of sand is the mineral quartz which is a form of silicon dioxide. Most soil mixtures include sand.

The physical properties of minerals give valuable clues to the identity and structural characteristics of mineral samples. Gaining further experiences in interpreting these clues is a rewarding means of identifying oneself with a very fertile field of scientific endeavor.

PROBLEMS

1 From your own experience make a list of 10 or more specific natural events in which you have observed changes taking place in materials. Indicate which materials were changed, what changes took place, and whether the changes were physical or chemical.

2 Distinguish the meanings of the following terms: substance, mixture, element, and compound.

3 Indicate several distinguishing characteristics between soil and clay.

4 What is the difference between binding energy and potential energy, as applied to molecular structure?

5 Why are silicates more likely to form in the earth's crust than mixtures of silicon dioxide and the oxides of the other elements?

6 What structural differences distinguish discrete radical, fibrous, sheet, and network minerals?

7 Express sand grain sizes in terms of Angstrom units.

8 We buy electricity in units of the kilowatt-hour. One kilowatt-hour equals 3.6×10^6 joules. Express this energy in billion electron volts.

9 A mass of any element in grams equal numerically to its atomic weight contains 6.02×10^{23} atoms (*Avogadro's number*). The atomic weight of nickel is 58.71. Check the statement in the text that 5 grams of nickel contains 5.13×10^{22} atoms.

12

STATES OF MATTER

ON A WORLD-WIDE SCALE

The word *earth* brings to mind different meanings to different people. It may mean soil to a farmer, polishing agents to a cabinetmaker, clay to a potter, and the planet to an astronomer.   When we speak of *the* earth we may also conjure up various images.   Many people think of the earth as their living space from horizon to horizon as seen from their home.   Others may include all areas of the earth that they have visited.   To still others, it may mean the globe or maps in the den or living room.   For those who have been following the inquiries in this book the spinning earth has been placed out in interplanetary space and bound to the sun by tremendous energies as one of the nine known planets in the solar system.   Man's current efforts at space travel point up the loneliness of the planets in space.   But by the powers of human imagination the loneliness fades.   Even the immense reaches of space take on meaning because out of this space—10 million times the size of our present sun—is thought to have come the materials of the solar system including the earth. Consequently, the earth takes on dynamic meaning in terms of space, consolidation, and evolution. Only the human mind can encompass meanings as extensive as these. Only you as a human can become filled with curiosity about the world about you, can mentally transport yourself into the near-infinite regions of space and into the near-infinitesimal regions of atoms, and can devise tests to check upon the reality of your images. To become inquisitive and to inquire is to fulfill a human trait—that of wanting to know simply because we have the capacity to understand. We need no other motive nor purpose to begin an inquiry.

ORIGIN OF THE EARTH

The sun and the planets are thought to have a common origin derived from essentially the same store of cosmic materials in a single continuing process. Serious problems still exist in explaining various aspects of the probable formation process of the solar system. However, many good arguments have been brought forth in explanation of known relationships found within the solar system and nearby stars. Some of these explanations give continuity to inquiries and speculation concerning the states of matter on a world-wide scale. The major theses of these problems and arguments were set forth in Chapter 8. We shall inquire more specifically here with regard to the planet earth.

The protoearth Sharing in the over-all process in which the sun and the planets were formed, the materials of the protoearth were essentially the same as those of the sun. The solar composition is essentially the same as the other stars within our region of the galaxy and the interstellar materials are also of this composition. Hence, the solar system is not unusual and it is in no way unreasonable to assume an identical composition for the protosun and each of the protoplanets. Thus we can speculate that the protoearth was formed as a disk-shaped cloud of extremely cold materials, largely gaseous, and about 1000 times as massive as the present earth.

In view of the composition of the sun and the major planets, which retained more of their original materials, it is reasonable to include the following materials for the protoearth: (1) hydrogen in major abundance and helium; (2) other gases including neon, methane, ammonia, and water vapor (much of the ammonia and water, because of the low temperature, may have been snowlike condensation); and (3) the other substances which became the present earth in the form of fine dust consisting principally of silicates and iron or iron oxide. It is conceivable to envision this cloud as a gigantic snowstorm of interplanetary proportions. The initial aggregations of material have been described as fine dust dispersed in the gases. Some scientists propose that because of ammonia-snow, water-snow and perhaps also methane changed to a sticky oil-like condensate; the dust began sticking together forming larger grains which then began falling or spiraling in toward the center of the protoplanet under the influence of gravitation. Out of this loosely-held aggregation which accumulated near the center of the protoplanet, the earth formed. Nearby, a secondary aggregation developed, similar to a double star in stellar formation, which formed the moon. During this period of condensation the sun remained comparatively dark; the sun's present thermonuclear process had not yet developed.

From protoearth to earth   About 99 percent of stellar and interstellar materials consist of the two gases hydrogen and helium, with hydrogen in greater abundance. Since these elements are in very low abundance in the earth, a process must be postulated whereby they could escape from the earth. It is known that hydrogen and helium do achieve escape velocities in the outer portions of our atmosphere and thus are continually being lost from the earth. But the heavier gases of the atmosphere are not so affected. The ratios of the inert gases in our present atmosphere indicate that perhaps less than 0.1 percent of the present atmosphere consists of the gases of the protoearth. The remaining 99.9 percent must have originated in the materials of the solid aggregate. Consequently, we must postulate a process not now operating in the earth for the removal of the original gases.

A clue is found in the formation of comet tails. The comets are thought to be miniature aggregations of materials such as existed in the protoearth. The comet tails develop only when comets move close to the sun. The tail always points away from the sun. (See Fig. 12.1.) Apparently the energetic ultraviolet and X-ray radiations and the jets of particles emitted from the sun ionize and sweep out the gases and dust particles which form within the envelope of the loosely held materials of the comets. In a similar way, when the sun's com-

Halley's Comet. Comets are thought to be miniature aggregations of materials such as existed in the protoearth. The comet tails provide clues as to the processes which removed the original gases from the protoearth.

pressionally released energies reached levels where thermonuclear reactions began, the increased radiation and particle emission began to ionize and sweep out the nearby gases and dust particles of interplanetary space. It is possible that the interplanetary gases near the earth were cleared out by a combination of infall to the sun and by ionization and repulsion from solar emissions. You will recall that explanation of solar atmosphere phenomena might include ideas of the infall theory.

Some scientists argue that initially the sun became unusually bright and energetic as the more highly reactive nuclei of deuterium (heavy hydrogen) and lithium were consumed. This sudden flare-up would have swept away completely the gas envelopes which surrounded the inner protoplanets. It is argued that such an event would be necessary to account for the sparsity·of the heavy inert gases krypton and xenon in the earth's atmosphere.

Other scientists believe that the sun has maintained very nearly its present activity from the beginning of nuclear transformations. In this event the lighter gases could have escaped very efficiently from the atmosphere of a less compact protoearth. It is also argued that if the protoearth were in rapid rotation such that the lens-shaped gaseous envelope above the equator were moving at almost the velocity needed to achieve orbital equilibrium of force and inertial reaction, this portion of the original gas envelope could not have slowed enough to contract with the lower atmosphere but would

have remained in orbit. The lighter gases in this orbiting envelope could in time have escaped by achieving escape velocities, and the heavier gases could have been ionized by solar radiations and removed by bombardment of electrically charged solar particles. The small amount of remaining atmosphere near the protoearth also could have been removed by ionization and bombardment from the sun before a new atmosphere became stabilized.

In either event, the original gases escaped into space; with them were lost a great deal of the original supply of methane and ammonia as well as most of the inert gases of the protoearth.

From the time of formation, the aggregations of materials that coalesced near the center of the original protoplanet continued compaction under the influence of their gravitational effects. The work of compaction converted gravitational potential energy into heat so that these bodies began to warm up gradually toward the melting point. After a considerable amount of consolidation, the materials developed heat-insulating qualities so that heat was conserved. At this point the temperature increase was materially aided by the presence of radioactive elements in abundance over 15 times that in the present earth's crust. Geological evidence has been interpreted to indicate that the earth became hot enough to melt as a whole only once during geological time. In earlier theories the melting was interpreted as evidence of the earth's formation from condensation of hot solar materials pulled or ejected from the sun. But, as was indicated in Chapter 8, the presence of deuterium and lithium in the earth is proof that the earth materials never took part in the thermonuclear processes of the sun. Consequently the

Figure 12.1 Comet and tail. Solar radiation sweeps out the gas and dust particles from the coma into the tail.

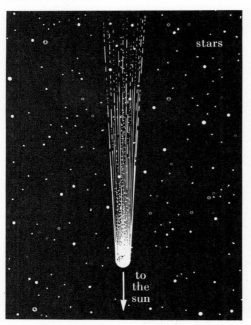

formation of the planets and the sun from the extremely low-temperature materials of interstellar space becomes a likely alternative. The more massive sun converted energy by compaction to the degree needed to start its thermonuclear processes which have consumed the deuterium and lithium in the early stages of reaction. The less massive earth converted only enough energy to melt or at least make plastic all of its original solid components.

Another question presents itself: Assuming that the lighter-weight elements were evaporated from the protoearth, is there evidence to indicate that the remaining materials have composition ratios of elements similar to their ratios in the sun and other stars?

As usual, the answers come from many sources. First, with regard to the earth, density and angular momentum relationships can be explained if the earth is divided into several concentric zones of different density. The gross model consists of a central core, composed mostly of iron, surrounded by a mantle of dense rock upon which a relatively thin crust of the less dense surface rocks were formed. This arrangement would require that the earth materials consist of about 30 percent by weight of iron, 40 percent largely consisting of silicon and magnesium, and 30 percent oxygen—the major constituents of dense minerals.

Second, analyses of meteorites which have reached the earth indicate that they are fundamentally of two types: stones and irons. The most abundant meteorites found are the stone variety. In most cases these are chondrites which contain grains of various minerals, largely silicates similar to those found in dense rocks, and flecks of iron-nickel alloys. The iron meteorites contain regular patterns of crystallized iron and nickel in abundance ratios of either about 6 percent or about 15 percent nickel. Meteorites are thought to be debris left over from earlier aggregations which formed during the protoplanet processes.

Third, with regard to the minute composition ratio of these materials in stars, analyses of spectral lines indicate a ratio of iron to silicon and magnesium which is reasonably within approximations of the three-to-four ratio required for an earth structured as indicated above. Thus, in a general way, the question of composition is answered satisfactorily.

Since we are dealing with origins, the next inquiry might concern the formation of the iron core. We have indicated that the earth once was molten. During this stage it is reasonable to believe that a process similar to that found in a smelter furnace could have taken place. In the furnace, when ore is smelted the metal settles to the bottom under gravitational effects, the less dense oxides and sulfides are buoyed up to settle out in a layer above the metal, and finally at the top is found the least dense slag composed of molten or near molten rock (Fig. 12.2). On a large scale, a similar gravitational separation of molten iron and molten silicates becomes possible. There is evidence also that some of the continental materials may have been partially differentiated during the later stages of this development.

Undoubtedly, if this early differentiation of core and mantle materials took place, the conversion of gravitational potential energy as the more dense iron moved inward added large amounts of heat to the molten core. Being surrounded by thick layers of mantle materials, the core is thought to have remained molten to this day. It is also likely that

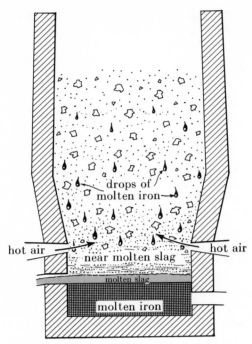

hot air →   ← hot air

Figure 12.2 Smelter furnace. The less dense materials are buoyed up to settle out above the molten metal.

is proportional to the mass times the square of the radius, the shortening of the radius produces a correspondingly greater increase in ratio of rotation in order to conserve angular momentum. However, too rapid rotation would have prevented consolidation. The development of the moon-earth system, therefore, provided a multi-bodied system rotating about a common center as well as two bodies rotating individually about their axes to conserve the total angular momentum. As noted earlier, the rapid rotation of the protoearth is a possible means of accounting for the loss of the heavier gases of the protoplanet. These molecules of gas would also have carried away their portion of angular momentum. The tidal effects between the sun and the protoearth are thought by many scientists to have resulted in slowing the rotation of the protoearth to a period equal to its period of revolution around the sun. The work of slowing the earth's rotation came at the expense of converting binding energy between the sun and earth by increasing the displacement. This also transferred angular momentum to the earth-sun system as the radius of revolution increased.

The formation of a more dense core in the earth would have shortened correspondingly the radius of rotation of this massive material and increased the angular velocity of the earth. Much of this increase has been counteracted by the tides of the moon. Actually, calculations involving eclipses which occurred thousands of years ago indicate that the earth's rotational period has been decreased by about two thousandths of a second per century. The moon has been slowed to a rotation period equal to its period of revolution about the earth. The moon, consequently, has moved fur-

the gravitational separation of iron is still taking place in the mantle and that the core continues to receive further amounts of dense molten materials and accompanying energy.

In our earlier inquiries we have emphasized the need for interpretations in terms of the principles of conservation of energy and momentum. We cannot disregard either of these. Hence, we must inquire somewhat into momentum relationships.

A slight rotation of the initial protoearth materials would lead to a very rapid rotation by the time they contracted to a thousandth of the initial radius. You will recall that angular momentum is equal to the moment of inertia of a system times the angular velocity. Since the moment of inertia of a disk or a sphere ther away from the earth to provide energy and transfer of angular momentum. However, careful calculations show that the moon has moved further than needed to account for the earth's change in rotation during this time. Hence, we can postulate a continuing inflow of materials from the mantle to the core.

Before leaving the subject of the iron core we must take notice of laboratory experiments involving the changing characteristics of minerals placed under high pressures and high temperatures. The results indicate that when such minerals as the olivines are placed under sufficiently high pressures, they might be forced into a metallic phase having properties of density and electrical conductivity similar to iron under similar pressures. A theory involving a single material in different phases has useful implications also in explaining why smaller planets such as Mars and Mercury do not have cores similar to the earth's.

Taking bearings We set out to gain continuity for our inquiry into states of matter on a world-wide scale. In a sense we have constructed bridges of contact with inquiries we have started previously. In Chapter 8 when we were inquiring into the characteristics of planets we indicated that our later inquiries into earth materials would shed light on the make-up of the planets, as well as on the hypotheses of the origin of the solar system. A review of Chapter 8 at this point would establish the continuity.

The protoplanet theory postulates a sun and planets each evolved from the materials of a single protostar. The variety of individual characteristics resulting from the processes of formation points to relationships which need to be understood in explaining the variety. The earth, of all the planets, lends itself best to an inquiry concerning materials. Our short concern with origins should at least give rise to the idea that although the protoplanet theory makes possible the explanation of similarities among stars and the probability of millions of solar systems similar to ours, each planet including the earth is unique because it formed at a particular position within the solar system. It is the author's opinion that the location of the earth and of the other planets was not a matter of chance; processes were functioning which located the earth as a natural outgrowth of the operation of natural laws.

Having bridged contacts to other inquiries let us focus upon observable evidence of world-wide processes in the earth.

CONCEPTS CONCERNING PROCESSES

There is perhaps no more awe-inspiring sight than a volcano erupting. In the aftermath, men can do little except get out of the way, if possible, and watch the fiery spectacle from a distance. Great destruction may ensue. Cities have been inundated by volcanic ash such as preserved the treasures of Herculaneum and Pompeii. Outbursts of volcanic gases have completely annihilated populations, such as the 26,000 or more persons at St. Pierre on the island of Martinique in 1902. The whole island of Krakatoa in the East Indies was virtually blown from the map in 1883 with world-wide effects upon the climates of the earth. Great mountain peaks have been spewed out of the earth; during the first 10 days of action, in February, 1943, Paricutin in

Paricutin, a newly formed volcano in central Mexico. During its first ten days of action, February, 1943, Paricutin grew to a height of 722 feet. [*Courtesy of Ewing Galloway*.]

central Mexico grew to a height of 722 ft.

In contrast to these spectacular eruptions other volcanoes such as Mauna Loa in the State of Hawaii produce great flows of lava from fissures along its flanks. Without explosions or great outbursts of vapor and ash, Mauna Loa's lavas flow quietly downward toward the sea building an island from the sea floor.

What are the reasons for the various volcanic effects—inundation, annihilation, explosion, rapid growth, and quiet flow? The inquiry concerning actual earth materials made it clear that natural laws of energy exchange provide clues as to which types of materials and processes are likely to predominate under given conditions. The prevailing characteristics of the elements are influenced by conditions of heat, pressure, and associated materials. We concerned ourselves primarily with chemical changes of molecules in Chapter 11; here let us also include physical changes.

Physical differences The city of Herculaneum was inundated by a *mudflow* from the sides of Mount Vesuvius in the year 79 A.D. This flow resulted when deep accumulations of dust and ash which had settled out from the explosive eruption of the volcano became saturated with water from rain and slid off the flanks of the mountain and engulfed the city. The mixture hardened like concrete and the city of Herculaneum was completely forgotten until by accident it was discovered in 1738. No hot liquid lava was involved in this disaster.

Nor was lava involved in the St. Pierre annihilation of 1902. Mount Pelée on the island of Martinique in the West Indies had been inactive for over a half century. Then, after a few mild warnings of impending action, on the morning of May 8th, an enormous explosion occurred which blew out horizontally from the flank of the mountain. A dense cloud of superheated steam and bits of extremely hot gas-charged lava was created which swept down the mountainside to the sea. St. Pierre, only 5 miles distant from the blast's origin, was in the path of the cloud. Within 5 minutes after the explosion the whole city and its population was instantaneously destroyed as the cloud swept through its streets.

Less spectacular but equally important are the quiet volcanic flows of Hawaii. The islands are of volcanic origin. These volcanoes can be pictured as the highest in the world. They reach to about 30,000 ft above the floor of the ocean. Mauna Loa reaches 13,680 ft above sea level. The almost constant outflow of very fluid lavas from Mauna Loa has produced a broadly based mountain which is the island of Hawaii. It is the largest active volcano of the present age.

As these accounts emphasize, solids, liquids, and gases are among the ingredients which issue from all volcanoes. The explosive power of volcanic materials depends primarily on how much gas is stored in the deep-seated mixture before eruption. If the gas can escape easily, it does not accumulate and the explosive power is lost. Accumulation of gases depends primarily on two factors. The first is the tendency for lava to solidify and seal off the volcanic vents. The second is the viscosity (stickiness) of the liquid which tends to prevent the flow of gas bubbles through the mixture and so the gas accumulates in large amounts within the liquid. But these facts lead only to further questions: Why do some materials solidify while others remain liquid? Why are some liquids more viscous than others? And why do gases provide explosive power in the first place?

Mechanical and thermal properties of matter Ice cubes and bubbles in a glass of soda pop demonstrate that solids, liquids, and gases can exist together in the same mixture. The explosive power of accumulated gases is demonstrated when a small boy shakes a bottle of pop and the contents squirt all over the place. After the cap is removed and the shaking occurs, the boy can no longer readily control the action which takes place. Why?

After the pop has been drunk our experience with the ice left in the bottom of the glass gives evidence that solids melt to liquids, and as long as any ice remains in the water the mixture stays ice cold. Also, very often moisture collects on the outside of the glass giving evidence of water vapor condensing to liquid on objects at low temperatures. We know that the ice was frozen from water in the low-temperature freezing compartment of a refrigerator. Thus it is clear that temperature is one factor that determines the predominating state of matter. It is not the only factor. In Chapter 7 temperature was described as a measure of the relative tendency for heat to flow from a given region to regions in contact with it. The temperature of an ideal gas was defined as proportional to the average kinetic energy of the molecules. In Chapter 2 molecular motions in a gas were described as almost free of attractive forces with other molecules, and molecules were found to move in all directions in a random manner and at a variety of speeds. The suggestion was made that the concept of molecular motion was a useful descriptive idea for materials other than gases. It is time we considered these suggested descriptions more intensively.

Properties of gases From a purely mechanical standpoint the molecules of a gas can be imagined as solid spheres in constant motion, directed randomly in space, moving at high speeds, and having frequent collisions with other gas molecules and the walls of the container, with each collision conserving both the momentum and the kinetic energy of the colliding bodies. The last-named condition must be preserved, at least on the average, if the gas is to remain in the gaseous phase of molecular aggregation. The term *molecule*, you will recall, is used to designate any aggregation of one or more atoms which can exhibit the chemical properties of a substance. Therefore, aggregations of a substance may change in size and number of atoms; but if the chemical properties are not changed, the molecule concept applies to all of the changing entities involved.

The constituent atoms are composed of a positively charged nucleus containing protons and neutrons and negatively charged electrons which surround the nucleus and move in orbits having energy levels which satisfy quantum requirements. Electrical forces are primarily responsible for holding the electrons in

their orbits as well as providing the potential energy relationships for operation of the principle of binding energy in atomic aggregations. Repulsion between electrons and their freedom to move to other energy levels make it unlikely that physical contact ever takes place in molecular "collisions." Consequently, the solid spheres of our mechanical model gives way to an elastic cloud model which helps to explain the observed properties of substances in their various states of existence.

We have established that forces originating in the positive nucleus may extend outward beyond the electron levels of a molecule. When forces react, the inverse square law, $F_e = Cq_1q_2/R^2$, describes the action of repulsion between like charges and attraction between unlike charges. The distribution of electrons about the nucleus sets up distance relationships between charged particles such that molecules exert slight forces of attraction on each other while they are some distance apart. If the molecules approach too closely, the force changes to repulsion. In the situation of attraction the positively charged protons concentrated in the nucleus produce a greater attraction upon the nearby electrons of other molecules than the forces of repulsion of the negative electrons which are on the average further apart. However, when the molecules approach more closely, the electrons at the approaching surfaces are repelled to available energy levels that allow them to move apart, thus increasing their potential energies. The reduction in distance between the positive charges in the massive nucleus increase the repulsion which stops and repels the molecules away from each other. Because of the quantum energy requirements and the large number of particles and charges involved, the actual operation of these force relationships are much more complicated than this account reveals. But the essential mechanical features of the elastic cloud model apply qualitatively as outlined.

Because of these force relationships, gas molecules are not moving with complete freedom from the attractions and repulsions for each other. But the kinetic energy of gas molecules is greater than the binding energy that might be produced between molecules by their attractive forces. It is possible, however, that while two molecules are in the proper displacement to each other a series of collisions with other molecules might reduce the energy of the two molecules so that a temporary attachment might be achieved. Larger aggregations of atoms are thus built up. But within a short time other molecular collisions would overcome the binding energy holding the parts together and the aggregation would revert to its original size. If the total energy of the gas is reduced, however, the chances are that more of these large aggregations would build up within the gas.

The spaces between molecules in a gas are most extensive. It is difficult to visualize the suggested relationships, however, because of the minuteness of molecules. A short exercise in arithmetic might help. We shall use monoatomic molecules of helium. The diameter of the helium molecule is given as 0.93 A or 9.3×10^{-9} cm. Assuming the molecule is spherical its volume would be 4.2×10^{-25} cm³.

$$\frac{\pi D^3}{6}$$

$$= \frac{3.14 \times 9.3 \times 9.3 \times 9.3 \times 10^{-27}}{6} \text{ cm}^3$$

$$= 4.2 \times 10^{-25} \text{ cm}^3$$

One gram atomic weight of any substance contains 6.02×10^{23} molecules. If the substance is a gas at standard conditions of temperature and pressure (0°C and 1 atmosphere), the gram atomic weight of gas would have a volume of 22.4 liters or about 2.24×10^4 cm³. Of the total volume the molecules would account for 0.25 cm³; the rest of the volume would be open space.

$$6.02 \times 10^{23} \text{ molecules} \times \frac{4.2 \times 10^{-25} \text{ cm}^3}{\text{molecule}}$$

$$= 0.25 \text{ cm}^3$$

The ratio of molecular volume to total volume would be about 1 to 90,000. To visualize the facts better let us figuratively expand the size of the molecules to that of golf balls, or about $2\frac{1}{2}$ in.³. The ratio of 1 to 90,000 would be equivalent to 1 golf ball per 130 ft³.

$$2.5 \text{ in.}^3 \times 9 \times 10^4 \times \frac{1 \text{ ft}^3}{1728 \text{ in.}^3} = 130 \text{ ft}^3$$

At this rate there would be about six golf balls flying around in an ordinary 10 ft by 10 ft dining room. Even at that, you would not venture into the room because the molecules move with average speeds equal to the speed of sound and collisions are frequent. Remember, however, that molecules are not solid as are golf balls; the analogy was between volume relationship only.

The gas molecules are much too small to be seen by even the most powerful microscopes. Yet, proof of molecular motion and their collisions can be observed. The phenomenon which makes this possible is called *Brownian motion*. A dust- or smoke-laden gas is introduced into the viewing chamber and illuminated by an intense beam of light. (Fig. 12.3). The space inside the chamber is viewed through a microscope. When magnified, the dust particles show up as points of bright light. These particles are seen to move about in a sharply shifting, zigzagged pattern as each particle is struck first by one molecule and then another while under observation.

Molecules not only collide with each other, they also collide with the walls of the container that confines the gas. In order to confine the gas the molecules of the container wall must rebound the gas molecules into the space of the container. Of course the container wall must be made of molecules held together by molecular forces, but for our present purposes we can simply think of these molecules as a continuous surface which the gas molecules bombard. Each molecule which strikes the surface will have its linear momentum changed because its velocity direction changes. Change of momentum requires equal and opposite forces involving the surface and the molecule. Although the force per molecule is small, it is estimated that in the order of 6×10^{22} molecules, under normal condi-

tions, strike each square inch of the surface every second. That is 60,000 billion billion molecules per second. Very few of these molecules would strike the surface perpendicularly; but because gas molecules move directionally at random, as many molecules would strike the surface from one angle as any other. Hence the total effect is a force exerted normal (perpendicular) to the surface. Because large and irregular surfaces are often involved it is more useful to speak in terms of pressure, the force per unit area, than of total force.

Properties of liquids and solids An ever-changing variety of gas molecule aggregations is indicated because of energy relationships attending the natural attractions between molecules. Two conditions may increase the trend toward larger aggregations. First, as was pointed out, decreasing the energy of the gas by cooling would prevent the breaking up of all the larger aggregations being produced. Second, increasing the pressure would increase the likelihood of the collisions necessary to induce molecular attachments among the molecules.

If large amounts of heat are removed from a given region, the molecules tend to aggregate into the long-range, orderly linkages characteristic of solids. Depending on the strength and arrangement of the linkages, the solid phase may exhibit a variety of molecular and intermolecular motions. We shall not attempt to describe them. Because of the nearness of adjacent particles and the variety of force and energy relationships made possible by the differences in particle sizes, the number and distribution of charges, and the quantum restrictions which can occur, it would be futile to

Figure 12.3 Observing Brownian motion. Smoke particles exhibit the random motion of molecules in the gas.

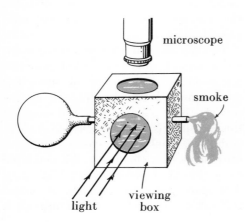

microscope

smoke

light

viewing box

begin discussing specific, individual particle motions. Not enough is known as yet about the interactions which occur when large numbers of particles are involved in simultaneous action. However, measurement of the energy changes indicate a very low state of potential energy for the particles of a solid, meaning that as a whole the binding energy between the particles is high. Almost all movement of the particles from one location to another within the solid is curtailed; some movement does occur. Oscillation and rotation of single particles or groups of particles are possible but energy changes in these motions are governed largely by quantum relationships. Only discrete units of energy exchange are possible. The total picture indicates that a high degree of order prevails in placement of particles and the degree of directional randomness is controlled by the positions of the surrounding particles. In solids the freedom of molecular motion has reached its lowest state.

If smaller amounts of heat are removed from a region, the gas molecules tend to form short-range linkages producing loosely structured aggregates having many holes within the structure. These holes allow molecules to move about within the structure and account for the fluid characteristics of liquids. Molecules can move into the spaces, leaving behind other holes for molecules to enter. The linkages between molecules are, therefore, in a state of constant change as molecules break loose and move to other positions and the molecular structure collapses and rebuilds as energy requirements are met. Molecular motions within the aggregates are restricted to oscillation and rotation as governed by quantum relationships. The freedom of molecular motion in liquids is a great deal more restricted and orderly than in gases but somewhat less restricted and orderly than in solids.

The prevailing phase of matter—gas, liquid, or solid—is thus related to the types of molecular arrangements and these in turn are related to the loss or gain of potential energy in the systems which binds certain aggregates of particles together rather than others. When binding energy is achieved, the molecules become restricted to certain characteristic motions which increase the amount of order in the aggregations.

Changing the states of matter Since each phase of matter is marked by binding energy producing a different degree of order in molecular motions, it is not surprising to find large-scale transitions from one phase to another taking place at definite conditions of temperature and pressure. We shall illustrate using the familiar materials ice, water, and steam. In Fig. 12.4, the graph outlines the energy requirements for changing ice to steam under conditions of constant pressure. The graph is for 1 gram of ice which was initially at −50°C. You will notice the temperature of ice rises rapidly from −50°C to 0°C. Approximately 22 calories of energy were required to produce this change in temperature. The average *heat capacity* of ice within this range of temperature is, therefore, 0.44 calories per gram degree centigrade.

$$C = \frac{Q}{m\Delta t} = \frac{22 \text{ calories}}{1 \text{ gram} \times 50°C}$$

$$= \frac{0.44 \text{ calorie}}{\text{gram}°C}$$

where C = heat capacity
Q = amount of heat used

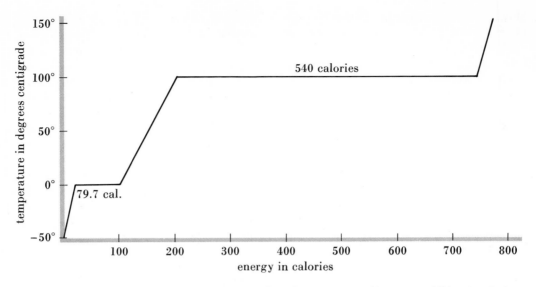

Figure 12.4 Change of state. The heat required to change 1 gram of ice at −50°C is 766 calories.

m = mass of the body
Δt = change in temperature

The temperature remains constant at 0°C while the addition of heat is overcoming the binding energy of the particles in the solid. The melting of 1 gram of ice requires 79.7 calories of heat. Had we used more ice, a greater amount of energy would have been required. The term *heat of fusion* is used to designate the amount of energy used per unit of mass melted. Hence the heat of fusion for ice is 79.7 calories per gram.

The heat capacity of water averages to 1 calorie per gram degree centigrade for the range of temperature between 0°C to 100°C. This average heat capacity of water was used to define the *calorie* as an energy unit. Specifically defined, 1 calorie equals one-hundredth of the energy needed to change the temperature of 1 gram of water from 0°C to 100°C under 1 atmosphere of pressure. Accord-

ingly, the graph indicates that 100 calories were required to change the temperature of 1 gram of water from 0°C to 100°C.

Water boils at 100°C and 1 atmosphere of pressure. The temperature again remains constant at 100°C until the water is completely vaporized. To vaporize 1 gram of water requires 540 calories of heat. The term *heat of vaporization* is used to designate the amount of energy used per unit of mass vaporized. Hence the heat of vaporization of water is 540 calories per gram.

The heat capacity of steam for the range of temperature 100°C to 150°C is 0.48 calorie per gram degree centigrade. Hence, the graph shows the conversion of ·24 calories to change the temperature of 1 gram of steam from 100°C to 150°C.

$$Q = mc\Delta t = 1 \text{ gram} \times \frac{0.48 \text{ cal}}{\text{gram}°\text{C}} \times 50°\text{C}$$
$$= 24 \text{ cal}$$

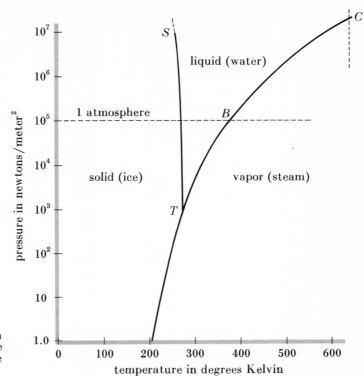

Figure 12.5 Phase diagram for water. Both pressure and temperature affect the state of matter.

Repeatedly we have implied that pressure also has an important role in phase relationships. To get a unified view of the pressure and temperature relationship to changes in phase, let us investigate a graph of saturated vapor pressure versus temperature, using water as an example. Interpreting the graph correctly depends upon an understanding of *Dalton's law of partial pressures*. This very significant generalization was expressed by John Dalton in 1807 and can be stated as follows: In a mixture of gases, the pressure exerted by each substance is equal to the pressure it would exert if it were alone in a volume equal to that of the mixture and at the same temperature as that of the mixture. Two inferences may be drawn from this. First, the total pressure of a gaseous mixture is equal to the sum of the partial pressures of the component gases. Second, the total volume of a gaseous mixture, when all measurements are made at constant pressures and temperatures, is equal to the sum of the volumes of the component gases. The term *saturated vapor pressure* designates the maximum amount of vapor pressure which can be exerted by a substance under stable conditions at a given temperature.

The phase diagram for water (Fig. 12.5) is based on a graph of saturated vapor pressures at the various temperatures. Note that the vertical scale of vapor pressure increases by powers of ten rather than a linear scale in order that the diagram can be compressed into a usable size. The value of 1 atmosphere of pressure is indicated for comparison purposes. We have selected a few crucial points of temperature and pressure for interpreting the general meaning of this type of graph.

1. Point *T* is called the *triple point*. At this combined condition of temperature and pressure, the substance can exist as a solid, liquid, and vapor without increasing the number of molecules exchanged to any one of the three phases. Molecules are exchanged freely from one to the other phases but as many molecules are absorbed as are released in each phase. A significant characteristic of water is indicated in the diagram. The line *TS*, which for most substances slants toward the right, slants to the left for water, indicating that water expands when it freezes. Indicated also is the fact that if the temperature is held constant and the surrounding pressure is increased, the phase balance is tipped toward the liquid phase. This would be expected on the basis of our discussion of aggregate formation because of molecular collisions. The higher pressure indicates more frequent collisions and increases the probability of conditions where molecules combine into more organized states. The graph shows too that decreasing the pressure increases the probability of free motion among the molecules. It must be pointed out, however, that the pressure can be decreased only by constant removal of molecules from the container, because at the given temperature the vapor pressure within the container would adjust almost immediately to the triple point value. An increase in pressure can be accomplished by introducing other gases such as air into the container. This increases the number of collisions and the liquid phase increases while the vapor is replenished at the expense of the solid phase which disappears. Hence, it becomes apparent that the triple point temperature (+0.01°C) is slightly above the freezing point of water measured at 1 atmosphere of pressure.

2. Point *B* is called the *boiling point*. This is the temperature at which the vapor pressure reaches standard atmospheric pressure. If the water is in an open container exposed to air pressure, point *B* marks the temperature at which a change of state from liquid to vapor takes place. If the container is vented so that air cannot enter, the resulting vapor can be kept at atmospheric pressure and the vapor can be increased in temperature to form superheated steam. It is left to the reader to ponder over the effects of lowering or increasing the pressure at point *B* temperatures. Might this explain the use of pressure cookers? What about the effect of decreasing pressures in mountain elevations upon boiling temperatures?

3. Point *C* is called the *critical point*. The line *TC* does not continue beyond this point. At a given temperature, which is a characteristic for each substance having a critical point, the curve ends. The temperature at this point is called the *critical temperature* of the substance. For water it is 374°C. Below the critical temperature, application of sufficient pressure will cause the vapor to condense. However, at the critical temperature or above, no amount of pressure can cause a change to the liquid phase. It is customary to reserve the term *gas* for substances which are above their critical temperatures and to use the term *vapor* when they are below the critical temperature. It now becomes evident

why the materials of the sun remain gaseous even though the density of the mixture near its center is estimated to be almost five times as dense as lead.

EVIDENCES OF VOLCANISM

The great geological processes which involve changes of phase are in their broadest sense classified under the heading of *volcanism*. At first thought, volcanism is apt to be associated with erupting volcanoes. There is, however, ample evidence showing that changes of phase have taken place within the earth which did not result in external eruptions of any kind. Erosion has exposed to view many types of rocks which have been solidified from a liquid phase under deep-seated conditions where slow rates of cooling produced large-sized crystals in the solid.

The products of volcanism, therefore, are of two types. Materials which were ejected or poured out on the surface of the earth are classified as *extrusions*. Materials produced from processes confined to deep-seated environments are classified as *intrusions*.

Extrusions Among the most abundant products of volcanism are gases and vapors. Two of these, water vapor and carbon dioxide, are of major importance. In our discussion of origins we indicated that about 99.9 percent of the present atmosphere developed after the proto-earth gases had been dissipated into space. The exhalations which formed the new atmosphere are assumed to have been of similar composition to those now brought to the surface. We find that ammonia, water vapor, and hydrocarbons such as methane are decomposed at various levels of our atmosphere when irradiated by the high-energy photons of solar ultraviolet radiation. Water molecules are composed of hydrogen and oxygen. Ammonia molecules are composed of hy-

Mount Rainier, a familiar peak of the Cascade Range which was once an active volcano. [*Courtesy of John Kabel.*]

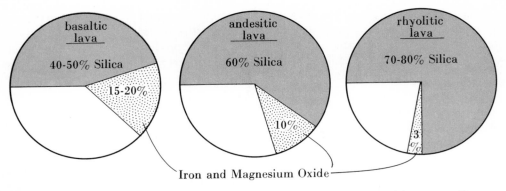

Figure 12.6 Approximate composition of lavas. Greater viscosity goes with greater silica content.

drogen and nitrogen. When these molecules are decomposed, some of the resulting hydrogen escapes into space after achieving escape velocity. The oxygen and nitrogen is added to the atmosphere. The hydrocarbons are changed to water vapor and carbon dioxide and other carbon compounds. The decomposition was perhaps much more extensive before the amount of free oxygen became very high. Much of the ultraviolet radiation is now absorbed by the oxygen and ozone in the ionosphere. Thus, it is probable that some of the most important products of extrusion are the gases and vapors of the present atmosphere and the abundance of water in the hydrosphere.

The liquid extrusions of volcanism are called *lava*. The molten rock materials, including the content of dissolved gases before reaching the surface, are called *magma*. We most generally associate lava extrusion with volcanic peaks, but other extensive extrusions are evident. Many of the familiar peaks, such as Mauna Loa in Hawaii and Baker, Rainier, Adams, Hood, Shasta, and Lassen of the Cascade Range in the Northwestern states are volcanoes, although only the

first- and last-named peaks have been recently active. However, at intervals in the past lava has poured forth from great fissures on a gigantic scale, flooding vast areas of the world. For example, the Columbia Plateau of Washington, Oregon, and Idaho is an immense lava field 200,000 square miles in area and reaching depths of as much as 4000 ft. A similar plateau, the Deccan trap in western India, covered about 250,000 square miles. These great horizontal sheets of lava rock give evidence of the extreme fluidity of the lava which flowed for miles from the issuing fissures before it congealed and ceased flowing.

The lava that has formed the peaks and plateaus is thought to be generated by a partial melting or a differentiation of melted minerals within the earth's mantle. The magma then rises into the earth's crust. Evidence gained by measurements of tiltmeters and frequent surveying of positions on the sides and tops of volcanoes indicate that the volcanoes swell and shrink during the periods of volcanic activity. This is interpreted to mean that subterranean chambers not too far from the surface are inflated by the magma before eruption and that deflation takes place during the eruption. The chambers are pictured as temporary storage systems which feed the volcanoes during their periods of eruption.

We have referred to a relationship between the viscosity (opposite to fluidity) and the accumulation of volcanic gases. An explanation may be found by relating mineral structure to the minerals found in the major types of lava. Types of lava are often named with respect to the type of rocks they produce. (See Fig. 12.6.)

The highly fluid lavas of the Hawaiian volcanoes and those that produced the rocks of the Columbia Plateau are called *basaltic* lavas. The basalt rocks are dark in color because of a high ratio of ferromagnesian minerals and a low silica content. Viscosity depends upon silica content. The low viscosity of basaltic lavas is due to its low, 40 to 50 percent of silica which is interspersed with a high, 15 to 20 percent of iron and magnesium oxides.

Most of the world's active volcanoes emit an intermediate form of somewhat viscose lavas called *andesitic* lavas. The andesite rocks have a lighter shade of colors and contain about 60 percent of silica and about 10 percent of iron and magnesium oxides.

Highly explosive volcanoes usually emit lavas of high viscosity called *rhyolitic* lavas. The rhyolite rocks are very light colored because of their high, 70 to 80 percent of silica and about 3 percent of iron and magnesium oxides.

The structural linkages in the various silicates were divided into four major types. The ferromagnesians are formed when the ratios of iron and magnesium are high and produce discrete radical structures such as found in the olivines. The other mineral groups form extensive linkage chains or networks. The higher

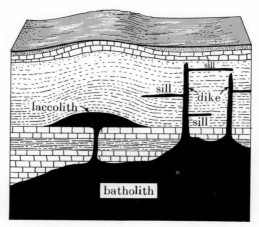

Figure 12.7 Magmatic intrusions.

the percentage of SiO_4 tetrahedra, the greater is the probability of network structures. It is not difficult to imagine, therefore, that as temperatures are reduced, extensive aggregations of partially formed networks could be set up in a lava having a high silica content. The resulting structure would become largely immobile. Now, if discrete radical structures were present, their short-range structures would interfere with extensive network formation and, hence, their liquids would have abundant molecular groups free to move about in the open spaces characteristic of liquids. These lavas rich in ferromagnesians would remain fluid over a wide range of temperatures.

It is evident that two conditions affect the viscosity of lavas. Increased viscosity results from high silica content and from reduction in temperature.

We shall discuss rocks more specifically in Chapter 14. However, two types of rock formed from gas-rich lavas are most logically mentioned here. The upper portions of a lava flow may contain so many gas bubbles that it becomes a froth. When the viscosity is high, the bubbles remain very small and the froth takes on an almost white color. When this small-bubble froth hardens, it is known as *pumice*. In the more fluid lavas of basalt, the bubbles, often called vesicles, consolidate into larger sizes and the cavities twist into highly irregular shapes. In rocks formed from this froth and when the cavities occupy almost as much space as the minerals, the rocks are said to be *scoriaceous*. Loose chunks of such rock are called *scoriae*.

Intrusions Magmatic intrusions are principally of five kinds: batholiths, laccoliths, sills, dikes, and volcanic necks. (See Fig. 12.7.) In Chapter 13 we shall find that the most important feature of large-scale intrusion is associated with the formation of mountains. In many mountain-building situations the overlying rock layers may be arched up and weakened by many fractures, forming fissures through which magma can flow easily. The magma may be injected through the fissures and forced between rock layers, extending the intrusion to great distances from the point of formation. The initial pool of magma may have formed the core of an entire mountain range. These large-scale crystalline mountain cores which appear to extend downward indefinitely into the earth's crust are called *batholiths*.

When erosion removes some of the overlying layers the batholith is exposed for observation. The batholith of the Sierra Nevada Range has been extensively uncovered. Mount Whitney, the highest point in the United States outside of Alaska, is a bold reminder of what was once molten magma thousands of cubic miles in volume. The greatest batholith in the world is the Coast Range batholith which extends southward from Alaska to beyond the 49th parallel. It extends for about 1250 miles and has an area of about 100,000 square miles. When we discuss the changing patterns of continents in Chapter 14 we shall find that the above-named batholiths are examples of comparatively recent intrusions, geologically speaking.

A laccolith can be likened to a blister in the layers of surface rocks. Magma was injected between layered rocks which formed enormous rounded domes storing a lens-shaped mass of magma which later solidified. The Henry Mountains of southern Utah are outstanding examples. The overlying rocks are arched up but the horizontal strata underneath are undisturbed.

If the injected magma penetrates between rock layers so that a somewhat parallel layer of magmatic rock is formed, the intrusion is called a *sill*. If the injection filled a fissure which cut across existing layers, the intrusion is called a *dike*. Sills vary in thickness from less than a foot to several thousand feet. The Palisade sill seen along the west side of the Hudson River in New York City is one of the most famous sill intrusions in America. Dikes are often formed with valuable ores in the mixture. Many dikes in the Colorado mountains contained rich veins of gold. Dikes often have a radial alignment extending outward from the magma source. Shiprock, near Farmington, New Mexico, is an exposed volcanic neck from which radial dikes can be seen to extend in many directions.

As the name implies, the *volcanic neck* is formed when, after a volcano becomes extinct, its supply pipe becomes filled with solidified magma. After the materials of the volcanic peak have been eroded away, the harder, more durable rock of the neck is all that remains to show where a volcano once formed.

PROCESSES OF VOLCANISM

The earth's crust is a thin shell about 10 to 35 miles deep beneath continental regions, and in places less than 2 miles deep beneath the oceans. Immediately below the crust lies a much deeper shell, the mantle, which reaches to 1800 miles. The discovery of evidence of the earth's crustal layer was first made in 1909 by A. Mohorovicic following a Balkan earthquake. Hence the name "Mohole" for the operations to drill a deep hole through the crust and into the mantle. Evidence from earthquake tremors tends to support

The Palisades sill along the Hudson River. One of the most famous sill intrusions in America. [*Courtesy of Ewing Galloway.*]

the belief that magmas originate at various depths of the mantle. However, a great deal more evidence is needed before this can be stated as a fact. Without direct access to the materials and measurement of pressures and temperatures at these levels, environmental factors must be estimated from evidence from indirect contacts with these regions.

Sources of energy The origin of energy for volcanism must be closely related to the energy of the earth as a whole. It is well known that the ground temperature rises as vertical descents are made into deep mines. The rate of increase varies from one mine to another. The average temperature increases about 30°C per mile of descent or about 1°C per 176 ft. Others would place the average increase per depth in the solid crust at about 1°C per 100 ft of depth. In either event, should this rate continue far into the mantle, the materials would change phase. But the mantle is rigid. Therefore, various estimates have been made of the temperature of the lower mantle based upon known factors and probabilities of materials. R. Verhoogen of California has estimated a rapid rise of temperature would take place until a 1500°C temperature is reached at a depth of about 120 miles. At this level the temperature would be very near the estimated melting point of materials of that region. The estimated rate of increase then drops off, and Verhoogen's reports place the temperature of the earth's center at not less than 2000°C.

The transformation of energy for the earth as a whole is most generally traced to the decrease in gravitational potential energy during the compression of the original protoearth materials. Some of this is still going on. To a lesser extent, energy of radioactivity is transformed to heat. Other lesser sources are liberation of heats of crystallization during the solidification of magma, and chemical reactions within the crust and within the lavas reaching ground levels. The lesser sources cannot be held important to volcanism since they imply that change of phase has already occurred. It was once thought likely that regional concentrations of radioactive materials were responsible for volcanism. There is no direct evidence to substantiate this. Recent measurements of radioactive emissions from volcanic gases and lava flows do not reveal increased radioactivity in the products of volcanoes. Therefore, at present there are no direct evidences on which to base a statement concerning the energy source for volcanism. However, volcanoes continue to erupt. Magmas are formed. These are facts for which verifiable explanations are still being sought.

Sources of materials In our discussion of the order of crystallization of minerals as indicated by evidences from thin sections, we supported the idea that ferromagnesians crystallize at the higher temperatures followed at lower temperatures by the feldspars and then silicon dioxide. A further application of this sequence would be the separation of materials within magmas. The application could be made in two ways: incomplete melting and settling out of crystals. In either way it is possible to theorize a common source of supply for all types of magmas and lavas. In fact, the lack of direct evidence of mantle composition would not make it impossible that the mixtures of various composition ratios of silicon dioxide, feldspars, and ferromagnesians could be originated as magmas within a mantle composed of uniform materials similar to the olivines. The order of melting would be in reverse of that in crystallization. Hence, temperature variations of several degrees and heat sources of limited power would produce different magmas, particularly if they are transported from their place of origin to a new environment where further mixing can take place and eventual ejection or solidification results.

Although there is nothing wrong with this sort of speculation, based as it is upon a good deal of experimental facts, the ideas should be recognized as speculation. The geological evidences do not conclusively favor this hypothesis over others. Scientists suspend judgment until evidence clearly justifies a conclusion. In volcanology, as in all sciences, there is no lack of basic areas needing imaginative research.

SUMMARY

The constituent materials of the earth are differentiated into three major layers: the central core, the mantle, and the crust.

The earth's present atmosphere is thought to have evolved from the gaseous volcanic extrusions rather than to be gases of the original protoearth. The theoretical ratio of earth materials are in agreement with the somewhat uniform ratios found in interstellar space, meteorites, the sun, and the nearby stars of our galaxy. The hypothesis of a common origin of materials is, therefore, strongly supported.

The kinetic molecular theory of gases, liquids, and solids is strongly supported by the observed mechanical and thermal properties of matter in the three states. Energy relationships that describe the changes in states of matter are expressed in units of the calorie. The average heat capacity of water is used to define the calorie. The term *heat of fusion* designates the amount of energy converted per unit mass in melting a substance. *Heat of vaporization* designates the amount of energy converted per unit mass in vaporizing a substance.

The observed products of volcanism are classified as extrusions or intrusions, depending upon whether the molten materials solidified after reaching the earth's surface or while beneath the surface. The liquid extrusions are called *lava*. The volcanic mixtures found beneath the earth's surface are called *magmas*. Lavas are classified in general as basaltic, andesitic, or rhyolitic, on the basis of silica content. The structural linkages of the various silicates found in the lavas account for the fluidity and gas content observed in characteristic volcanic eruptions.

Volcanic peaks and lava plateaus are the major evidences of lava extrusions. Batholiths, laccoliths, sills, dikes, and volcanic necks are the major evidences of magmatic intrusions.

The energy sources for volcanism are not completely known. Evidence exists which may indicate that both materials and energy for volcanism originate, at least in part, deep within the mantle. The evidence for confirmation is not conclusive, hence the need for suspended judgment on these speculations.

PROBLEMS

1 What are the evidences to support the idea that the protoearth consisted of the same ratio of materials as found in the sun and in other stars of our galaxy?

2 Summarize the speculations regarding how angular momentum was conserved in the protoearth during its supposed contraction to a thousandth of its initial radius.

3 What are the energy and motion characteristics of molecules used to distinguish between gases, liquids, and solids?

4 On the basis of the phase diagram for water, explain the action of pressure cookers and the depressed boiling points at higher elevations.

5 Explain the probable relationships of the structural linkages of silicates and the characteristic viscosities of lavas.

6 If the rock of the lava field of the Columbia Plateau has a weight density of 180 lb per ft³, what would be the weight of the field if its average depth were 1000 ft?

7 What is the heat capacity of a material when 15 grams of it requires 33 calories to change its temperature from 20°C to 30°C?

8 In the analogy of helium gas molecules to golf balls, if the size analogy were changed to that of one helium gas molecule equals one baseball of volume 15 in.³, how many baseballs would be found in an auditorium 60 ft × 100 ft × 15 ft?

13

EFFECTS OF FORCES

IN THE EARTH'S CRUST

The materials of the earth's crust have less weight per unit volume, are more easily distorted and broken, and have greater variety of properties than do the materials in the rest of the earth. There is very little agreement as to how the crust has come about or why uniformity should not be more prevalent. But the evidence is conclusive; the earth's crust is remarkably variable. It lies deeper under the continents than beneath the oceans. Its thickness varies greatly from place to place beneath these regions as well. The crustal materials vary suddenly from one place to the next. Curiosity-stirring clues are everywhere around us, but their meaning is more obscure. Because it is impossible to measure directly the properties of the materials and processes which occur beneath the earth's surface, the evidence used for interpretations must be largely speculative. To be conclusive, therefore, the interpretations must be compared to others generated by evidences from collateral sources. In this realm the fluctuations in the recorded measures that were previously thought to be only of nuisance value now have great meaning. The sensitivity of measuring instruments is being increased constantly in order to distinguish pertinent differences. Sensitivity is dictated by needs. Instruments sensitive to one part per million, for instance, would be absurd if your only concern were a weekly check upon loss or gain in personal weight. But if you were concerned with whether the earth were shrinking or expanding, such accuracy might be of utmost importance.

Instruments for measuring crucial properties are devised by ingenious methods. Success in measuring unusual characteristics usually leads to new discoveries. New discoveries lead to new speculations and new hypotheses to guide research. Imagination, skill, and ready knowledge are the ingredients most needed for these activities, whether the purpose is devising new means of measurement or interpreting the measured values. These attributes are prized highly in the sciences; they are at least as valuable in all the activities of life. They are the requisite ingredients for decision-making and progress. Our task of the moment is to nourish our zeal for progress by actively participating in our own gathering of insights into problems and answers concerning the planet on which we live.

MEASURING THE EARTH

It took men a long time to reach the conclusion that the earth was round. Not many people, even today, can give conclusive reasons for this belief. You might search out your own. But men had hardly accepted the idea of roundness before it had to be modified in many respects. The earth is not perfectly spherical. We are not now speaking of the minor surface irregularities such as mountains and ocean depths. These are no greater than the wrinkles on the surface of an orange. The earth is actually an irregular ellipsoid. Measurably not spherical, it is flattened at the poles and bulging at its middle. But it is bulging less at the equatorial regions than would be expected from the average properties attributed to the earth.

Vital statistics Table 13.1 presents some well-established values of the general characteristics of the earth. Two facts stand out forcefully. First, the earth bulges at the equator by an increased radius of over 7000 meters greater than the spherical value, but it is flattened at the poles by over 14,000 meters less than the spherical value. Second, the average density of the earth is more than twice the average density of the continental surface rocks.

TABLE 13.1   General characteristics of the earth

Equatorial radius	6,378,388 meters
Polar radius	6,356,912 meters
Ellipticity	1/297
Radius of sphere of equal volume	6,371,221 meters
Mass	5.976×10^{24} kg
Average density	5.517 grams/cm³
Average density of continental rocks	2.67 grams/cm³
Mean linear speed of rotation at equator	465 meters/sec

The fact that the earth has flattened more than it has bulged may come as a surprise unless you realize that the mean linear speed due to rotation reduces gradually for locations considerably removed from the equator. If measured on a true sphere, the linear speed at latitudes 10°N and 10°S would be 458 meters per second. At 20°N and 20°S the speed would be 437 meters per second. The inertial reaction to rotational acceleration would be reduced by only about 12 percent at the speed of the 20th parallel. Hence, the inertial reaction of the materials in rotation would be considerable throughout a broad range of latitudes, and the materials for the broad bulge would be pulled away from the polar regions.

We have intimated that the actual bulge is less than would be expected from the average properties attributed to the earth. At first thought, perhaps, the explanation for this statement might seem to lie in the fact that the inertial reaction for the less dense continental rock is less than half that which would obtain were the surface rocks of average earth density. The reaction, for instance, of 1 cubic meter of surface rock at the equator is about 90 newtons.

ratio does apply and as was indicated in Chapter 6 the equal reaction-action ratio for both instances is less than 3.5 parts per thousand. However, we are not speaking in the present investigation about isolated chunks of rock but of world-wide and hundreds-of-miles deep layers of rock which form the earth's crust and interior. We are speaking of forces of gravity and their relationship to the concentrations of mass and the displacements between these mass concentrations which describe gravitational effects. By definition an unbalanced force is measured in terms of the acceleration it produces in known quantities of mass. You will recall that 9.8 meters per second *per second* is the value most often used to indicate the acceleration of gravity. More precisely the value computed for locations at sea level over the equator is 9.780 meters/sec² and at the poles it is 9.832 meters/sec².

If the earth were of uniform density throughout, the acceleration computed for an object as it fell through a hypothetical hole into the earth would diminish as the object moved downward to the center. This would occur because the portion of the earth's mass above the

$$F_e = \frac{mv^2}{R} = \frac{2.67 \times 10^2 \, \text{kg} \times 465 \, \text{meters/sec} \times 465 \, \text{meters/sec}}{6.38 \times 10^6 \, \text{meters}} \times \frac{1 \, \text{newton-sec}^2}{\text{kg-meter}}$$

$$= 90.5 \, \text{newtons}$$

Had the surface rock the average density of the earth, the reaction would be about 187 newtons, a value more than twice as great.

But, you might ask, does not the gravitational effect of 9.8 newtons per kilogram apply in both situations, so that the action-reaction ratio remains constant? The question is valid. The constant

object would attract the object upward, thus reducing the unbalanced force. At the earth's center the object would have zero acceleration. But the earth is not of uniform density. In the actual earth, the calculated acceleration does not diminish immediately upon going below the surface but increases slightly with increased depth until the "falling body"

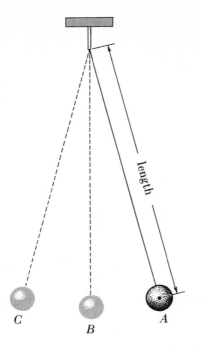

Figure 13.1 Simple pendulum. One cycle is the motion from A to C and back to A.

any given location. Ingeniously devised instruments have been produced, having sensitivity as high as one part in 50 million, for the purpose of detecting small changes in gravity throughout the continental surface and beneath the sea. High standards of accuracy are achieved by timing several million swings of a pendulum of accurately known length characteristics. The world's standard for comparing all gravity measures is kept at the Helmert Tower in Potsdam, Germany. The acceleration of gravity at Potsdam is 9.81274 meters per second per second.

You too can make an estimate of the acceleration of gravity at your locality by using a simple pendulum of known length. (See Fig. 13.1.) If the amplitude of swing is held to 7° or less, the following formula gives a close approximation of the period per cycle of a simple pendulum. The *smallest* error would be about one part per thousand.

$$(13.1) \qquad T = 2\pi \sqrt{\frac{l}{g}}$$

where T = period of a simple pendulum in seconds

l = length of the pendulum in meters

g = acceleration due to gravity in meters/sec²

Solving for acceleration of gravity:

$$g = \frac{4\pi^2 l}{T^2}$$

This is an indirect measure of the acceleration due to gravity in terms of measured values of pendulum length and period per cycle. For example, a simple pendulum exactly 1.45 meters long was timed carefully for 100 cycles. The time for 100 cycles was 4 minutes, 1.7 seconds (241.7 seconds). The acceleration of gravity

reaches the edge of the core. This calculated increase results from the concentration of dense materials in the core and mantle of the earth. The estimated acceleration at the edge of the core is about 10.2 meters per second per second. From that point on the acceleration would decrease rapidly and become zero at the earth's center. In terms of probable effects upon earth materials, this concentration of forces within the earth tends to compress more greatly the materials throughout the mantle and the core than if the density were uniform. Thus, the extent of the bulge is reduced.

Is there any direct evidence that this force anomaly actually occurs? Measuring the force of gravity has been found to be a good indicator of the density of materials beneath the earth's surface at was computed to be 9.799 meters per second per second.

$$g = \frac{4\pi^2 l}{T^2} = \frac{4 \times 9.8696 \times 1.450 \text{ meters}}{2.417 \text{ sec} \times 2.417 \text{ sec}}$$

$$= 9.799 \text{ meters/sec}^2$$

You will recall that the force of gravity is directly proportional to the product of the masses of the bodies involved and is inversely proportional to the square of the displacement between their centers of mass (Eq. 6.3). It would be expected, therefore, that gravity would diminish as one moved away from the earth's center in climbing a mountain. Measured results show conclusively that the force of gravity does decline upon climbing a mountain but *at a faster rate* than can be explained by the change in displacement. This fact was first discovered by the mathematician Pierre Bouguer while he was accompanying the French expedition of 1738 to Peru for the purpose of measuring the length of a meridian arc. Upon climbing the mountain Chimborazo in the High Andes the expected plumb line deflection, which had been carefully computed to allow for the supposed effect of the mountain, did not materialize. No adequate explanation was available at that time. This and similar irregularities in gravitation are now explained by postulating an extension of the low-density rock of the mountain to deep levels beneath the mountains, thereby decreasing the force of gravity. The speed with which earthquake waves travel through these regions confirms the existence of the postulated mountain "roots." The important conclusion at this point is the measured effect upon gravity. Were this low-density rock distributed throughout the earth's crust in depths equal to that found beneath mountains, the force of gravity would everywhere be of this lower value rather than those now generally obtained.

Revelations of earthquakes Important clues concerning the crustal and internal structure of the earth are revealed by recording the periods and amplitudes of seismic waves produced by earthquakes. Most major earthquakes occur when the forces acting upon the elastic materials of the earth's crust exceed the limits of elasticity, and the materials break or yield in forming fractures or by sudden displacements along the surfaces of existing faults. In terms of wave motion there are four fundamentally different seismic disturbances.

1. *Primary waves (P waves)* are compressional waves similar to sound waves. These waves travel fastest and arrive first at distant stations, hence, the name primary wave. The motion is longitudinal and is parallel to the direction of propagation.

2. *Secondary waves (S waves)* are shear waves. The motion is transverse and is at right angles to the direction of propagation. P and S waves are called *body waves* because they travel through the earth's interior to reach the points of detection. The shear waves cannot be transmitted by liquids. Therefore, important measures with regard to magma pockets and the earth's core are interpreted from secondary wave shadows.

3. *Love waves*, named for A. E. H. Love who discovered them, are horizontally polarized transverse waves that vibrate the earth's surface horizontally at right angles to the direction of propagation.

4. *Rayleigh waves*, named for Lord Rayleigh who first described them, are

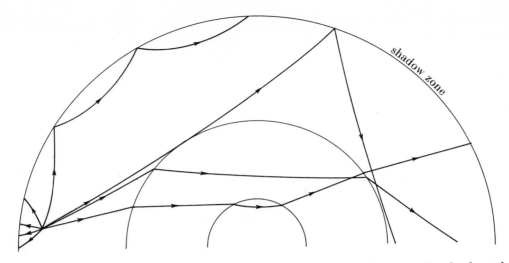

Figure 13.2 Ray diagram of earthquake waves. The primary waves are reflected and refracted as they travel through the materials of the earth.

waves similar in some respects to motions of water waves in shallow water. When this wave passes a point on the earth's surface, the point moves around an elliptical path in a direction opposite that in a water wave. The point moves in the direction of propagation in the troughs and in opposite direction in the crests of the waves. Love and Rayleigh waves are called *surface waves* because they travel along the surface. They are also referred to as *long waves* because of their long periods per cycle of vibration.

The speed of propagation of the primary wave in a given material measures the incompressibility of the material; that is, its resistance to further compaction under increased pressure. The secondary wave reveals the rigidity of the material, that is, its resistance to a shearing stress. A solid material resists both compaction and shearing in characteristic ways. A liquid material has a characteristic resist-

ance to further compaction but its rigidity approaches zero.

Both primary and secondary waves can be traced by using the ray concept introduced in Chapter 3 for tracing light (Fig. 13.2). As was true in situations involving light, if the medium is homogeneous the rays of seismic waves travel in straight lines from a point source to the points of detection. The seismic wave fronts are spherical for P and S waves. In actual measurement the rays are usually refracted upward, indicating that the speed of transmission increases with increased depth toward the earth's center. Take a moment to bring the concept of speed ratio to refraction angles clearly to mind.

The interpretation given to this increased speed at greater depth is that the compression of the lower materials by the force of gravity upon the outer levels has increased the rigidity and the incompressibility of the materials at greater depth. The pressure at the bottom of the mantle is about 1.3 million atmospheres. Pressures of over 100,000 atmospheres have been attained in research laboratories. At high pressures considerable compaction and other changes take place in some of the characteristic properties of rock materials.

When seismic waves reach depths of about 1800 miles, the recorded characteristics of the body waves change abruptly. The speed of the primary waves decrease by almost 40 percent and the secondary waves either disappear or become very faint. The abrupt decrease in speed produces a marked refraction of the primary ray toward the normal when entering the core and away from the normal when leaving the core. Evidence for this is a region known as the "shadow zone" where these waves are absent from records in surface stations and reappear at stations having a greater angular displacement. The definite size and shape of the shadow zone establishes the size of the core and also the ratio of speeds that produce the observed refraction. The sharp reduction of the shear waves is interpreted to mean that the core is liquid or almost so.

The surface waves also contribute significant data. Detection of significant properties in the group profiles and group velocities of the Rayleigh waves and use of high-speed computers to analyze the recorded values have greatly increased the clues related to the materials and processes of the earth's crust and upper mantle. Use of controlled explosions rather than exclusive dependence on earthquake shocks has made possible the placement of detection centers into patterns giving maximum effectiveness. The earth's crust has become a scientific laboratory for controlled experiments. Important tests of hypotheses regarding the crustal structure are now being planned and performed. The results

may have far-reaching implications. A side issue concerning the feasibility of detecting underground atomic explosions relates to a low-velocity seismic zone in the upper mantle which might produce shadow zones for detection stations.

OBSERVABLE FEATURES OF THE EARTH'S CRUST

The idea that the earth has a "crust" was assumed because it was reasonable to believe that materials below a certain depth would be deformed by the high temperatures and pressures postulated for these regions. The assumed crustal layer is no longer in doubt. Seismic measurements reveal a definite demarcation between surface materials and mantle materials. Many questions remain to be answered with regard to the substances and environmental conditions found within the various layers, but the fact of crustal demarcation cannot be questioned. The *Mohorovicic discontinuity* marks the level at which sudden velocity changes and wave reflections take place. They mark the bottom of the earth's crust.

When enough of the crust is uncovered in mountains and canyons, a diversity of materials and clues to crustal activities can be observed. The apparent folding and fracturing of crustal materials indicate that the crust has taken part in dynamic activities in the earth. Our purpose in briefly outlining the interior regions was that the energy for many of the surface activities must come from powerful changes taking place within the earth. Let us inquire into the evidence suggesting certain crustal activities.

Different kinds of rock In terms of apparent crystalline structure there are three principal classes of rocks: volcanic, sedimentary, and plutonic. *Volcanic rocks* were discussed in Chapter 12. Included are those rocks which are known to have flowed as liquid magma or lava along fractures and fissures in the preexisting rocks. *Sedimentary rocks* are formed when the sediments of erosion are deposited in the sea and are subsequently cemented and hardened in layers. *Plutonic rocks* are coarsely crystalline rocks which have formed at depth within the crust. Some of these result from extremely slow cooling of magmas so that large crystals of each mineral are formed. Others are formed by recrystallization of volcanic or sedimentary rocks under high temperatures and pressures.

Often the name *igneous* is used to designate all rocks—whether volcanic or plutonic—which have been molten. The name *metamorphic* is often used to designate the recrystallized rocks. The inferences involved in these names have led to many misunderstandings. And identical rocks can be traced to both processes. These names are now being replaced by the more specific classes referred to above. Further references to the characteristics of the various kinds of rocks will occur in Chapter 14.

Deformation and movement All deformations and movements of sections of the crust which result in relative vertical or horizontal changes in the positions of components are generally referred to as *diastrophism*. Abrupt movements of the crust are felt directly as earthquakes. These dramatic and often destructive events fill us with wonder at the unleashing of the tremendous energies stored in rocks which are under stress. Equally wonderful are the evidences of deforma-

tion and movements where broad areas of rock layers have yielded slowly but permanently to the crustal stresses acting over long periods of time.

Because they are formed in horizontal layers, the sedimentary rocks yield particularly useful clues of diastrophism. Evidences in the sedimentary layers often show that deep layers of rock have been *warped* into large-scale domes or depressions. For example, the Colorado Plateau of Arizona and Utah has been warped upward until sedimentary rocks which were once below sea level are now thousands of feet above sea level. The Grand Canyon of the Colorado River and other less-publicized canyons have cut through the layers while they were being lifted and have exposed the arched layers to view.

In many areas of the earth the sedimentary layers have been buckled into more or less regular *folds* as if a number of thick blankets had been shoved from the edges by forces acting toward the center of the region. Most of these folded fields of rock are on such a large scale that studies extending over miles of terrain are needed to distinguish the nature of the folded arcs. Folds are distinguished from warps by the structuring of the folded rock layers into successions of up-

Figure 13.3 Anticlines (A) and synclines (S). Rock layers have been folded into ridges and valleys.

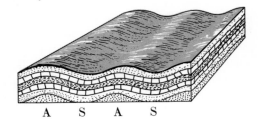

A   S   A   S

folds and downfolds called, respectively, *anticlines* and *synclines* (Fig. 13.3). Initially anticlines form ridges and synclines form valleys, but present surface configuration might be far different. Erosion may produce cuts across the folds. It is not uncommon to find a reversal of features so that rock synclines are exposed on ridges and anticlines have been replaced by valleys. Careful observation of the rock layers at many locations is required to reconstruct the patterns of the original folds.

The tremendous forces which produced the warps and folds acted through long periods of time so the rocks would yield slowly without fracturing. We must also keep in mind when we view these folds that the layers of rock now exposed were deformed while deep in the crust where the pressure exerted by overlying layers effectively reduced the possibility of large-scale fracturing.

Not many of the earth's deformations have proceeded without fractures. More often than not, evidences of folding and fracturing are found hand in hand. Distinguishing features of fractures also yield clues to the processes which took place. Special names are given to some of these features. A *joint*, for example, is a fracture on which there is very little evidence of displacement parallel to the surfaces of the break. Had displacement taken place so that corresponding features of rock were offset on the fracture surfaces, the name *fault* would apply. If a space were opened up between the surfaces of the break, the term *fissure* would apply. The extrusion of lava through fissures was mentioned in Chapter 12. Some fissures remain open and others are filled with mineral deposits.

Earthquakes are associated with active faults. About 95 percent of the recorded earthquakes in the continental United States have occurred along the active faults of California and Nevada, marking this region possibly as a portion of the great circum-Pacific seismic belt which extends around the perimeter of the Pacific Ocean. The greatest active fault in the California region is the San Andreas fault which extends from Pt. Arena southward for 650 miles to the Salton Sea. Displacements recorded in a single series of earth shocks give an indication of the extraordinary forces and energies involved. The most publicized of recent quakes, the San Francisco earthquake of 1906, resulted in a horizontal displacement along the San Andreas fault. The eastern block moved southward a maximum of 21 ft just south of Tomales Bay. The greatest displacement ever recorded in the California-Nevada region occurred in the Owens Valley earthquake of 1872. Displacements were recorded from Haiwee to Bishop along one of the Sierra Nevada faults. Near the town of Lone Pine east of Mount Whitney the displacement had a vertical component of 23 ft and a horizontal component of about 20 ft. The exposed fault *scarp* is still visible after nearly 100 years of erosion. (See Fig. 13.4.)

Motion involving great distances of a fault has also been recorded. The Fort Tejon earthquake of 1857 produced dis-

Figure 13.4 Normal fault and scarp.

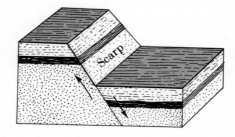

placement along 225 miles of the San Andreas fault from the Cholume Valley to San Bernardino. The effects of this quake were felt from Sacramento to Fort Yuma, a distance of over 550 miles.

Not all earthquakes are centered within the earth's crust. Earthquake foci have been recorded to a maximum depth of about 450 miles. These would be far into the mantle. Other foci at 27 to 150 miles deep would be located in the upper portion of the mantle. The shallow foci occurring above 27 miles are attributed to crustal displacements. All the destructive quakes have come from centers relatively close to the surface. The wide range of focal point depths again illustrate the fact that energy for surface deformation often originates far below the earth's crust.

Mountain regions In Chapter 12 we delved into mountains and plateaus of volcanic origin. These are important manifestations of activities in the earth's crust and mantle which were undoubtedly linked to the energies resulting in localized crustal movements as well. The predominating form of mountain units now in existence have been produced directly or indirectly by localized crustal movements. Evidences observed in the existing mountains place into four classes the types of faults and crustal movements responsible.

In the later stages of development the Sierra Nevada Range of California produced evidences of being *fault-block mountains*. These result when large crustal blocks are lifted up between complex faults in the crust. The Sierra Nevada is tilted westward. Its eastern edge has been uplifted more than 10,000 ft more than the western edge. Consequently the eastern front forms a precipitous scarp which was, and still is, a formidable barrier for the westward traveler. By contrast the western edge descends on a long gentle slope toward the Great Valley of California. The tilting action may still be in progress.

In another class of mountains the localized warping which accompanied the formation of laccoliths produced *dome mountains*. We have indicated that the Henry Mountains of southeastern Utah are classic examples of laccolith formations. Other examples are the Black Hills region of South Dakota and the Moccasin Mountains of Montana. In the formation of the Moccasin Mountains the laccolith was ruptured in several places forming irregular uplifts of dome formations and localized volcanic flows.

Many mountain ranges give evidences of a complex mixture of faulting and folding. The Rocky Mountains, for instance, are a complex system of ranges extending from near the Mexican border northward across the United States and into western Canada. Important segments of these mountain ranges consist of deformed sedimentary rocks and plutonic rocks of sedimentary origin which show evidences of varying degrees of folding and thrust faults. Where evidences of folding are clearly dominant, the formation is called a *fold mountain*. Where evidences show a complex admixture of folding and fault movements, the formation is called a *complex mountain*.

Evidences of extremely energetic crustal movements are found in mountain features called *thrust faults* (Fig. 13.5). In these movements forces parallel to the earth's surface not only have folded surface structures but have also moved large segments of mountains horizontally across each other for considerable distances.

Gigantic rocks in the Garden of the Gods, Colorado Springs, Colorado. They were formed by wind and rain erosion of rocks at the edge of complex mountains which show evidences of folding and fault movements. [*Courtesy of the Colorado Springs Chamber of Commerce.*]

The intermediate structures were crushed and compressed into complicated deposits and the original layers become displaced in unusual ways. A classic example of thrust fault movement is the great Lewis thrust which is a tourist attraction in Glacier National Park. Reconstructing the probable development of this mountain indicates a horizontal compression took place which formed a large anticline. The compressional forces continued and a thrust fault formed along the leading edge of the fold. The energies being transformed carried the resulting block of mountain material across the land surface for distances estimated to be from 10 to 35 miles or more. Chief Mountain is an isolated peak which remains as a remnant of the material which once was part of the Lewis thrust.

The ocean floor The largest portion of the earth's crustal surface lies beneath the oceans. The topography of these vast areas has been almost completely

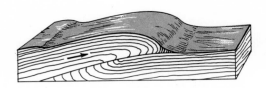

Figure 13.5 Thrust fault. A block of mountain rock has been folded, broken and thrust across the existing land surface.

shrouded in mystery until recent years. Submarine mountain ranges and great ocean trenches, both of unusual proportions, are the subject of much speculation in current studies of the earth's crust. We have implied that the crust thins out appreciably beneath the oceans. We have also indicated that the rocks making up the ocean basins are predominantly basaltic and hence of greater density than the surface rocks of the continents.

The discovery of submarine mountain ranges was not thought to be unusual, although recent profile studies suggest that rather unusual activities may be related to them. The discovery of ocean trenches was difficult to accept, however, because there are no similar developments in continents with which to make comparison. The trenches are found only in the Pacific Ocean. In size and shape these great troughs in the ocean basin are without parallel. Reaching to depths of 35,000 ft and extending for 2000 miles in length, these V-shaped chasms can be best described as "upside-down mountain ranges." Strung out like beads on a string, this group of steep depressions forms a ring which parallels the ring of active volcanoes and the intense, deep-seated earthquake zones which mark the perimeter of the Pacific Ocean. The fact that the trenches are near to the locations of earthquake foci having the deepest

centers ever recorded has suggested the possibility that the earth activities which are responsible for these chasms originate deep in the mantle.

Evidences gathered by numerous expeditions have produced somewhat detailed profiles of various cross sections of the ocean basins. Interest was aroused when in the late 1800's a raised section along the center of the Atlantic Ocean was discovered. No details were produced until a German expedition of 1925–27 discovered by means of echo-sounding apparatus that the mid-ocean rise is in reality a rugged mountain range which divides the Atlantic Ocean into two basins. Within a few years other expeditions to widely separated oceans of the earth found evidences of mountain ranges in the northern Indian Ocean and in the eastern Pacific Ocean. The Indian Ocean ridge is called the Carlsberg Ridge and the range in the Pacific is called the East Pacific Rise.

Seismic data showing earthquake foci beneath the oceans soon showed a pattern of centers along the known mid-ocean ridges and also extensions which indicate a continuous pattern of activity connecting the explored regions of mountain formations. Comparatively recent expeditions of the International Geophysical Year and its sequels have confirmed the existence of the continuous mid-ocean mountain range. Consequently the earth's crust takes on a fourth topographical feature. Along with the continents, the ocean basins, and the ocean trenches, the crust is marked by a submarine mountain range of great proportion. The mid-ocean range has been traced from the Arctic regions south through the mid-Atlantic Ocean, east around Africa to the Indian Ocean joining with the Carlsberg Ridge, then continuing eastward to the south of Australia and branching up into New Zealand, and north along the eastern Pacific Ocean to central Mexico. This is by far the longest mountain range in the earth. It forms a major seismically active fracture system in the earth's crust. The range is still largely unexplored. It holds many clues to the processes taking place in the earth's crust.

DYNAMIC FEATURES OF THE EARTH'S CRUST

In the first chapter our quest was unalterably tied to using observed properties as clues for discovering evidences of energy transformations which might outline the systems involved and the probable relationships of our observations. Ability to do work was the central definition of energy. The observed surface features of the earth's crust combined with the indirect measurements of depth and elastic properties of the crustal materials give evidences of many dynamic relationships in the earth. The long-term activities would be hardly noticeable during one lifetime of observation. But new experimental techniques, highly sensitive measuring instruments, and electronic data processing have confirmed of some of the assumed processes. Other proposed earth processes are still held to be highly speculative or have been disproved.

The energy transformations involved in earth processes are largely of three types: those related to changes in gravitational potential, those related to changes in tectonic deformations of materials, and those related to changes involving heat. Generally all types are involved in every process, but evidences of one type are more easily detected than the others in a given situation and consequently take on greater significance.

We must always be careful in our interpretations to distinguish between that which is confirmed by evidence and that which is highly speculative. Both of these facets are needed in science. But we must use them for what they are and not make speculative hypotheses appear as verified truths. The immature intellect, particularly in this day of pseudo-scientific advertisements and "thrilling science adventure" movies and TV programs, finds the careful cross-check system of scientific speculation and confirmation prosaic and unworthy of his attention. It may be fun to be fooled by a magician, but it becomes tragic when a person can no longer distinguish between truth and fantasy and accepts even poorly disguised "magician's tricks" as truth. It is a mark of prudence to ask what *understandable* relationships involving observed evidence are used to support an explanation. Let us now establish a few understandable relationships concerning processes in the earth's crust.

Isotasy The continents have been described as "rafts of rock" floating on a "sea of rock." This sentence may be merely a descriptive statement poetically describing the appearance of the continents as viewed on a relief map of the world. In this event we need no further explanation.

But then in light of the less dense rocks found in continents and the more dense rocks found in the ocean basins, the idea of "floating" might be meant literally. In this event the idea needs much further explanation.

The idea of floating involves gravitational displacement of one material by another until a balance of forces is achieved. The principle of buoyancy was first expressed and demonstrated by Archimedes, the Greek mathematician and inventor, who lived before 212 B.C. Archimedes' principle is stated as follows: *A body floating or submerged in a liquid is buoyed up by a force equal to the weight of the liquid displaced.* For example, if a wooden block weighing 55 grams is placed in water, it sinks into the water just far enough to displace 55 grams of water. (See Fig. 13.6.) Since water has a density of 1.00 grams/cm³, 55 cm³ of water is displaced before the block floats. If the volume of the block is 125 cm³, then 70 cm³ of the block would lie above the surface of the water and 55 cm³ below it. The force of buoyancy is equal to the weight of the liquid displaced. Consequently, by definition of weight, the mass of the floating object is equal to the mass of the liquid displaced.

If an object sinks completely it displaces its own volume of the liquid and is buoyed up by the weight of this volume of liquid. Hence, if the density of the liquid is known and a means of measuring

the apparent mass of the object when submerged can be devised, the density of the object can be computed. Density is defined as the mass per unit volume. For example, a milk-white pebble of quartz sinks in sea water. The density of sea water is known to be about 1.025 grams/cm³. The pebble is weighed and its mass recorded as 53 grams. Next the pebble is weighed while sunk in sea water and its apparent mass under sea water recorded as 32.5 grams. The difference between its mass in air and its apparent mass under water, 20.5 grams, is the mass of the sea water displaced by the submerged object. The volume of the sea water displaced is computed to be 20 cm³. This is also the volume of the pebble.

$$V_w = \frac{m_w}{D_w} = \frac{20.5 \text{ grams}}{1.025 \text{ grams/cm}^3} = 20 \text{ cm}^3$$

The density of the object—in this case, the pebble—is 2.65 grams/cm³.

$$D_o = \frac{m_o}{V_o} = \frac{53 \text{ grams}}{20 \text{ cm}^3} = 2.65 \text{ grams/cm}^3$$

The simplicity of Archimedes' principle should encourage its use in actually determining the density of objects so that the principle may be understood from direct experience as well as reading.

The essential feature of the floating block is that the portion of the block raised above the water does not create additional stress upon the molecules of the system. The weight of the water pushed aside sets up the buoyancy which balances the gravitational effect of the total block. The system is in balance. Were the liquid highly viscous, like cold tar, a considerable period of time would elapse before the liquid would flow aside in great enough volume to compensate for the weight of the block. During the

Figure 13.6 Wood floating in water. Fifty-six percent of the wood is above the water, buoyed up by the water displaced.

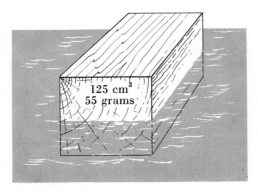

125 cm³
55 grams

An iceberg floating in sea water. A floating object is buoyed up by a force equal to the weight of the liquid displaced; only about one-eighth of the mass of the iceberg remains above the surface of the water. [*Courtesy of the U.S. Coast Guard.*]

interim the molecules of the liquid would be under stress.

Similarly, it was suggested that the less dense mountains could be held high by a buoyant force set up by displaced rock of greater density into which the mountains were floating. Gravity observations near mountains and the continents suggested an extension of the less dense continental rock to greater depths beneath many of the localized elevations. Seismic exploration has confirmed these extensions into the crust below the mountains. It was postulated that the maintenance of buoyancy was produced by a flow of the dense rock materials at great depth to compensate for the changing characteristics of the elevated regions. This process is called *isostasy*. Although impressive evidence was found to support the principle of isostasy, many localized discrepancies

seemed to stand in the way of full acceptance. For example, the tilt block feature of the Sierra Nevada Mountains is not correlated by a similar change of gravitational effects which would express a directly compensating extension of mountain materials into the crust beneath the higher eastern edge. In the Big Horn and Powder River basins of the Rocky Mountains, the opposite discrepancy prevails. The gravitational effect in these basins indicates a greater extension of low-density rock than necessary to compensate for the elevation. Clearly no single process can explain the localized effects.

Isostasy has been demonstrated on a regional and continental scale. Comparison of seismic wave velocities with laboratory measurements of rocks of similar type under controlled conditions of temperatures and pressures similar to those likely to occur at the various depths of the earth has increased the probability that the interpretations deduced from records of travel times in refracted seismic waves may be used with accuracy. The correlation of seismic wave records, including those for Rayleigh waves, to results of gravity measurements have conclusively demonstrated the feasibility of isostatic compensation on a continent-wide or regional basis. The energy transformed in producing isostatic flow is largely gravitational, showing its kinship to buoyancy. The elastic properties of the rocks tested under laboratory conditions indicate that the compressional wave velocities of 6.0 to 6.2 kilometers per second and shear velocities of 3.5 to 3.6 kilometers per second measured in the continental layer are consistent with that of granite which is composed of the less dense andesitic mineral mixture needed to explain the lower gravity measurements recorded on the continent. In the oceanic layer the compressional wave velocity of 6.5 to 7.0 kilometers per second is consistent with that of gabbro which is composed of the more dense basaltic mineral mixture. In the mantle beneath both the continents and oceans the compressional wave velocity of 8.0 to 8.2 kilometers per second is consistent with that of dunite which is composed of the very high ferromagnesian ratios found in the mineral mixtures of the dense olivines.

The density relationships between these materials show that forces on a continent-wide scale are essentially held in balance by isostasy. A concept of isostasy now showing promise involves the question of whether an intermediate basaltic layer occurs uniformly under all continental areas. Crustal thickening under regions of high land elevations might be produced by a thickening of the intermediate layer more generally than by a thickening of the outermost layer. Evidence in many situations favors this hypothesis.

Tectonic deformation The analysis of a vibrating system in Chapter 1 involved distorting an elastic system whereby energy was transformed to potential energy when the spring was flexed. This energy became transformed into kinetic energy of the inertial system during the portions of the cycle when forces were increasing the speed of the central mass. The potential energy in the flexed spring was a property of the molecular structure involved. Similarly, energy may be transformed to potential energy when an external force is applied to any solid material. Whenever a force is applied to a solid object, the material changes size or shape. Such changes are called *deformations* and are an indication that work has been done. If the material is elastic the energy can restore the object to its original size or shape; then the energy would be transformed to another form as a property of another system.

The relationships of the molecular structure of matter help to explain the observed facts of deformation. The action of the external forces is to move some of the surface structural particles in the solid slightly away from their usual equilibrium positions within the crystal structure. This change in position disturbs the neighboring particles, causing an adjustment of their positions in order to balance the new force patterns within the structure. If the adjustment sets up restoring forces which can return the displaced particles to their former structural positions, the material is elastic and as soon as the external force is released, the material tends to return to its former size and shape.

When the forces resulting in deformation of the structural systems in the earth's crust set up restoring forces in these materials, the available energy from these sources is called *tectonic energy*. The energy transformed in earthquakes is of tectonic origin. It is thought that deformation takes place in the rock materials on each side of the fracture zone. The energy builds up as the forces increase. When the materials along the fault reach their elastic limits and permanent displacement of particles takes place, the movement of the materials on each side of the fault surfaces is accomplished by transformation of tectonic energy.

Some of the unusual characteristics recorded in the vicinity of the deep ocean trenches of the Pacific may involve tectonic energy in large quantities. The intense earthquake activities near the zone of the trenches indicate rapid accumulations of tectonic energy. Measurements of gravitation near the trenches indicate a deficiency of gravity. This is surprising because seismic evidence shows that the crust is thin beneath the trenches and that there is a sharp downward fold of the Mohorovicic discontinuity at the seaward side of the trenches. The forces which pull the trenches downward into the crust must be acting in opposition to the buoyant forces of gravity. Clearly, isostatic balance does not exist in these zones. Perhaps the forces needed to maintain this state of unbalance also are responsible for the tectonic energy manifested in the earthquakes of this region.

Heat flow The flow of heat by conduction in crystalline materials is very slow because the particles tend to transfer their increased energy of vibration very slowly through the crystalline linkages. There are small amounts of heat conducted outward from the hot interior of the earth. Some convection may also be present in various regions of the earth. Measurable amounts of heat do reach the earth's surface from the interior. The amount is generally uniform throughout the surfaces of the continents and ocean floors. The average heat flow is about 0.011 calorie

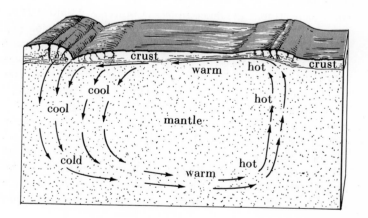

Figure 13.7 Heat transport in the mantle. It is proposed that convection currents in the mantle carry heat to the surface.

per square meter of surface per second. Highly sensitive instruments have detected deviations from the average in many areas of the earth's surface. For example, higher levels of heat flow have been recorded at the crest of the Mid-Atlantic Ridge and along the crest of the East Pacific Rise. The amount of heat reaching the surfaces in these regions is from two to eight times the average. Interesting too is the measurement which shows a lower than average heat flow in the Pacific trenches. Measurements made in the Acapulco-Guatemala Trench indicated an approximate 50 percent reduction from the average in the heat flow there.

The variations in heat flow are used as evidence to support the hypotheses of convection currents in the materials of the earth's mantle beneath these regions. (See Fig. 13.7.)

WORKING HYPOTHESES

Development of major scientific principles progresses by the contributions of numerous scientists in several associated fields. A hypothesis may become a step toward establishing a principle. But even before a hypothesis can emerge, a fund of pertinent evidence must be built up which requires explanation. As soon as hypotheses emerge they engender programs of crucial tests of the postulated relationships and this gives direction to research activities. When evidences from varied sources begin to support a given hypothesis, it becomes modified and enlarged so as to unify the reliable evidences from many fields. It may then achieve the status of a theory Several hypotheses concerning the processes of crustal activities have gained supporting evidence. We shall give short outlines of their major premises. Lack of agreement concerning important interpretations has made unification impossible and unwise. Research now in progress may uncover evidences which will disprove one or more of these hypotheses, or help create new ones. The history of scientific discovery has hardly begun.

Hypothesis of a shrinking earth The formation of thrust faults, and the evidence of folding and warping of vast surface areas of the earth are the evidences most generally used to support the hypothesis that the earth as a whole is shrinking. The shrinking is related to the contraction of materials upon cooling and, thus, the hypothesis assumes that the earth is cooling off. Estimates made from folds visible in the regions of the Appalachians indicate a decrease of 40 to 50 miles from the original width. Folds in the Alps indicate a possible shortening of as much as 200 miles for that region as a whole. Evidence of the required general reduction of temperature has not been found.

Hypothesis of convection currents The discovery of a well-defined rift valley down the center of much of the Mid-Atlantic Ridge is interpreted as showing expansion of the surface in these regions. This interpretation, coupled with the records of abnormally high heat flows along the Mid-Atlantic Ridge and the East Pacific Rise, has suggested that convection currents are present in the materials of the earth's mantle. According to this hypothesis hot materials rise in the mantle toward the earth's crust in regions where high heat flow is recorded and flow horizontally away from these regions to descend beneath the regions where the heat flow is lower than average. It is held that the thermal expansion of the mantle forms a series of tension fractures which aid the flow and that the convection current arches and thins the materials of the crust. The upward and lateral movement may produce a rift in the crustal formations which would be parallel to the rise. Further movement would pull the rift apart to form fissures through which materials would flow to the surface. The crust would thicken toward the outer edges of the lateral flow and this would produce the forces and energy transformation necessary to cause folding and thrust faults. Unusual depressions might result in the regions where the convection current sinks back into the mantle. The ocean trenches may be a feature of such a development. No conclusive evidences of large-scale convection currents within the earth have been obtained.

Hypothesis of continental drift One of the first hypotheses to explain the Mid-Atlantic Ridge and the continental outlines made the assumption that the continents were originally joined together, and that they broke up and slowly "floated" apart. The fact that the coastal outlines of Africa and South America seemed to fit together was used as supporting evidence. The Mid-Atlantic Ridge was postulated to be either a fragment left behind or evidence of debris which filled the opening gap between the receding continents. Dredging in the region has brought up samples of highly dense rocks usually associated with the earth's mantle. No evidence has been brought up of low-density continental rocks. Seismic studies also disprove the idea that the mid-ocean ridge was ever a part of the continents. However, records of the magnetic orientation of particles in both sedimentary and volcanic rocks have been interpreted as evidence supporting continental drift. On the basis of this interpretation the records would show Europe and North America have moved apart as much as 2000 miles since the rocks were formed.

Hypothesis of an expanding earth The apparent expansion which produced the rifts in portions of the Mid-Atlantic Ridge and the data from studies of magnetic orientation of rock particles have been combined to suggest a hypothesis of an expanding earth. The fact that the mid-ocean ridges extend to all sides of the continents would make expansion outward from these crustal faults satisfy the evidences of apparent magnetic displacement of continents and the present activity along the mid-ocean ridges. To explain the general expansion, however, would very likely require evidence supporting a postulated decrease in the constant of gravitation or a change in the density of materials comparable to a change in phase. These are not completely new ideas, nor can they be excluded from speculation, but measured evidences in their support have not yet materialized.

SUMMARY

The earth is shaped as an irregular ellipsoid. This fact is explained by means of the effects of rotation and distribution of the more massive materials in the earth. Evidence of the earth's inner structure must be achieved by indirect means. Extremely sensitive gravity measurements are a good indication of the varying density of the materials beneath the earth's surface from one location to another. The measured effects of naturally and artificially produced earth tremors give important clues concerning the crustal and internal structures of the earth. Evidence of vast regions of deformation caused by long periods of crustal stresses are found in the surface features of the earth's crust. Warps, folds, joints, faults, and fissures are evidences of these diastrophic events. Mountains are highly informative manifestations of crustal activities.

Mountains are often classified on the basis of the crustal activities responsible for their being. General classification is made under headings of fault-block mountains, dome mountains, fold mountains, and complex mountains.

The vast uncharted areas of ocean bottom are currently the subject of renewed exploration. Submarine mountain ranges and trenches of unusual dimensions have stirred extensive speculation concerning the past and present crustal activities in the earth. The longest mountain range on the earth is the mid-ocean range extending from the north Atlantic, south around Africa, and onto the western shores of Mexico. This range is still largely unexplored.

The energy transformations involved in these earth processes are largely of three types: those related to changes in gravitational potential, those related to changes in tectonic deformation of materials, and those related to changes involving heat.

Several working hypotheses exist in interpretations of the many forms of data available for today's earth scientists. These hypotheses are admittedly in need of unification, revision, or abandonment as crucial tests are made and new evidences uncovered. Man's study of the earth has hardly more than begun.

PROBLEMS

1 What evidences would you use as proof that the earth is approximately spherical?

2 What evidences indicate the existence of mountain "roots"?

3 What evidences indicate the existence of a liquid core in the earth's structure?

4 Describe an earth process which gives evidence of depending mainly on each of the following energy sources: gravitational potential, tectonic deformation, and heat.

5 What are the distinguishing characteristics of volcanic rock, sedimentary rock, and plutonic rock?

6 A simple pendulum 1.8 meters in length requires 4 minutes 29 seconds to complete 100 cycles of motion. Calculate the acceleration due to gravity at the location of the pendulum.

7 A sample of rock which weighs 23.8 grams in air has an apparent mass of 15.6 grams while submerged in water. What is the average density of the rock materials?

8 What evidences would be searched for in order to classify a mountain in each of the following classes: fault-block, dome, fold, and complex mountains?

9 Summarize the evidences which support each of the following: the shrinking earth hypothesis, the convection current hypothesis, the continental drift hypothesis, and the expanding earth hypothesis.

14

TIME AND THE CONTINENTS

The work of Charles Lyell marked a turning point toward a new mode of thinking about the apparent changes in the earth's crust. Sir Charles Lyell preceded Charles Darwin by a generation. He published the first volume of his *Principles of Geology* in 1830; Darwin's *Origin of Species* appeared in 1859. It has often been said that Lyell made Darwin's work possible by the gift of geologic time.

Before Charles Lyell's penetrating interpretations of the evidence in rock strata, men did not understand nor want to understand the real age of the earth. There had been a slowly increasing awareness of the succession of life forms in the strata of the earth, and it was seen that these extinct forms of life showed an increasing complexity as the strata approached present levels. But the new scientific evidence was observed and interpreted in the light of pre-existing mythological fantasy instead of as basic clues to an understanding of natural laws. The study of earth forms was considered a dangerous science. It was feared that men would be trapped into forming unorthodox interpretations which could not be supported by Scriptural documentation. In order to reconcile their observations with their dogmatic religious beliefs, the observed record of extinct life forms was interpreted as proof of sudden catastrophic events in the past. Mountain ranges were thought to have materialized overnight. Gigantic floods, convulsive quakes, and outpourings of lava were thought to mark the sudden end of the frequent periods of calm which had existed on the earth. In these catastrophes all existing life had vanished from the earth, only to be renewed by divine creation in advanced forms for each new age. Into this amalgam of ideas mixed of fact and the supernatural, Lyell forced a comprehensive re-examination of evidence in terms of the action of perfectly natural forces and processes which are now in action and can be studied. He and his followers felt that there must be a natural explanation for the succession of life forms as well as the geological changes. This hypothesis of slow progressions of natural changes called for a concept of limitless time during which all of the observed changes could take place.

It is difficult for us who have become imbued consciously or unconsciously with more modern thought patterns to realize that the idea of gradual change over what seemed to be unlimited time marked a revolution in men's thinking. Too often today the problem lies in a too-easy acceptance of ideas in the name of science without first insisting upon reasonable and proper evidence. We, too, must learn to interpret from an adequate knowledge of the facts, but for a different reason. Many persons today have placed science on a pedestal which is as far removed from their rational everyday thinking as were the superstitions which controlled men's decisions of old. Science has become the modern-day wizardry. Perhaps the dilemma of intellectual blindness has simply shifted horns. Surely, educated persons must learn to *use* evidence, not simply to *accept* conclusions without question.

MEASURING GEOLOGIC TIME

The concept of earth changes encompassing millions of years became established as an outgrowth of applying Lyell's principles of *uniformitarianism* to geologic changes and Darwin's principles of *natural selection* to organic evolution. Since the time dimension is a central concept to understanding earth processes, a grasp of the principles related to the measurement of age through isotopes is imperative. Basic nuclear characteristics are involved in the meaning of the term *isotope*.

The atomic nucleus In the general structural pattern attributed to atoms, the nucleus is the center containing the massive particles which describe the mass characteristics of the atom. For simplicity, we shall refer to a nucleus consisting of *protons* and *neutrons* which together are called *nucleons*. The number of nucleons in an atomic nucleus is the characteristic called *mass number*. For example, in uranium-235, or U-235, the 235 is the mass number.

The nucleus is also the center of electrical charges about which the electron motions take place. We have learned

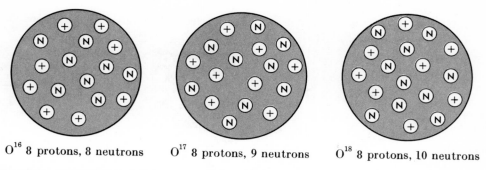

O^{16} 8 protons, 8 neutrons O^{17} 8 protons, 9 neutrons O^{18} 8 protons, 10 neutrons

Figure 14.1   Three isotopes of oxygen.   All have the same number of protons but different numbers of neutrons.

that the chemical characteristics of an element are determined by the force and energy relationships of the electron configuration of its atoms.   The positively charged protons of the nucleus are the center of electrical force activities, and the number of protons in the nucleus determines the number of electrons in the outer structure.   Hence, the number of protons in the nucleus is the characteristic called *atomic number*, which identifies an element.   For example, the element uranium has 92 protons in its nucleus. Therefore, atomic number 92 is uranium.

Many elements have atoms that vary in mass number, although, of course, the atomic number remains constant.   The number of protons remains constant but the number of neutrons varies.   The atoms having equal atomic numbers but varying mass numbers are called *isotopes* of the element.   For example, three physically different isotopes exist in elemental oxygen: oxygen-16, oxygen-17, and oxygen-18.   (See Fig. 14.1.)   The three different oxygen atoms differ only in their masses.   The mass numbers refer to the number of nucleons but they also are approximate atomic weights.   Actual atomic mass is measured in *atomic mass*

units (amu).   This system of units was developed on an equal ratio scale using the mass of oxygen-16, arbitrarily given the value of 16.0000 amu, as a point of comparison.   Carbon-12 has recently replaced oxygen as the standard for atomic weights.

Unstable nuclei   Not all combinations of protons and neutrons can exist together to form stable nuclei.   As a general rule the stable isotopes of the lighter-weight elements have about 1 neutron for every proton.   For example, oxygen-16 has 8 protons and 8 neutrons.   The nuclei of intermediate-weight elements have somewhat more neutrons than protons.   For example, silver-107 has 47 protons and 60 neutrons.   Of the heavier-weight isotopes, all nuclei of mass number greater than 209 are unstable.   These nuclei seem to be too large for natural stability.

In the elements whose isotopes are predominantly stable, if the number of neutrons in a given nucleus deviates too far from the average for nuclei of that element, the isotope is certain to be unstable and radioactive.   For example, three radioactive isotopes of oxygen have been

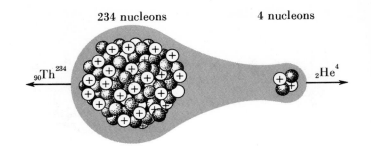

234 nucleons

4 nucleons

$_{90}Th^{234}$

$_2He^4$

Figure 14.2 Alpha decay. Uranium-238 emits an alpha particle and becomes thorium-234.

produced: oxygen-14 and oxygen-15 have fewer neutrons than average, and oxygen-19 has a greater than average number of neutrons for oxygen. These isotopes are not found in elemental oxygen but are short-lived products of nuclear reactions.

Just as the electrons of atoms can exist in any one of a number of quantized energy levels, so also a nucleus has a set of discrete, quantized nuclear energy levels in which it can exist. Only quantized energy changes occur in nuclear systems. Just as electron systems in atoms and molecules assume more stable configurations by converting discrete quanta of energy, so the unstable nuclei assume more stable forms by converting discrete quanta of energy. But whereas environmental factors (temperature and pressure) can be used to affect the rate and type of energy conversion in electron systems, similar changes have no effect on the rate and type of nuclear conversions. The spontaneous changes whereby unstable nuclei achieve stability are called *radioactive decay*. The law of radioactive decay is a probability-of-survival law. The probability that a given nucleus among a large number of unstable nuclei will survive after a given period of time depends on the relative activity of the decay processes.

Radioactive time-keeping The measurable results of radioactivity indicate that radioactive decay proceeds in four different ways: alpha decay, beta decay, orbital electron capture, and gamma decay. Alpha decay involves ejecting nucleons and electric charge as well as transforming energy. Beta decay involves ejecting electric charge and transforming energy. Orbital electron capture involves annihilating an electron from the innermost orbit and injecting the charge into the nucleus. Gamma decay does not involve ejection of charge or nucleons, but does involve transformation of energy. There are other conservation principles involved but we shall not be concerned with them at this time.

In *alpha decay* the particle emitted consists of 2 protons and 2 neutrons. The alpha particle is a helium-4 nucleus. The remaining nucleus is reduced by 2 protons in atomic number and by 4 nucleons in mass number, as compared with the parent nucleus. For instance, the atomic number of uranium is 92. When a uranium-238 nucleus emits an alpha particle, the remaining nucleus is atomic number 90, thorium, of mass number 234 (Fig. 14.2). The energy transformed in doing the work of ejecting and accelerating the particles is 4.21 million electron volts per action. The action may be represented by this equation:

$$_{92}U^{238} \rightarrow {}_{90}Th^{234} + {}_2He^4 + Q \text{ (4.21 mev)}$$

where ${}_{92}U^{238}$ = atomic number 92, uranium, of mass number 238

$\rightarrow$ is read as "yields"

${}_{90}Th^{234}$ = atomic number 90, thorium, of mass number 234

${}_2He^4$ = the alpha particle, atomic number 2, helium, of mass number 4

Q = the *disintegration energy* of the activity

The disintegration energy is shared by the two resulting particles.

In *beta decay* the process involves changing the charge of the nucleus without changing the number of nucleons. In other words, the atomic number is changed without changing the mass number. For example, the atomic number of thorium is 90. When thorium-234 emits a beta particle, the remaining nucleus is atomic number 91, protactinium, of mass number 234 (Fig. 14.3). One of the neutrons has become a proton. The equation is:

$$_{90}Th^{234} \rightarrow {}_{91}^*Pa^{234} + {}_{-1}e^0 + \nu + Q$$
$$\text{(0.13 mev)}$$

where ${}_{-1}e^0$ = the beta particle, which is an electron of negative charge the emission of which increases the atomic number by 1 without change in mass number

ν = a neutrino which is a particle needed to conserve energy and momentum requirements

Q = energy transformed in ejecting and accelerating the particles

and where the asterisk means that the resulting ${}_{91}Pa^{234}$ nucleus is in an excited quantum level from which it will be changed to an unexcited state by emitting a high-energy photon of gamma radiation. The disintegration energy of the activity is shared by the three resulting particles.

In *orbital electron capture* (often called *K capture*) a proton is changed into a neutron within the nucleus when an orbital electron combines with the nucleus. The negative charge of the electron neutralizes a positive charge of a proton. The electron is annihilated as an entity. The number of nucleons remains unchanged but the atomic number is decreased by 1. X-ray photons are emitted when electrons from outer energy levels replace the captured electron. An example of electron capture (Fig. 14.4) is indicated in the following equation for potassium-40 changing to argon-40:

$$_{19}K^{40} + {}_{-1}e^0 \rightarrow {}_{18}Ar^{40} + \nu + Q \text{ (1.5 mev)}$$

Potassium-40 also decays by beta emission to calcium-40:

$$_{19}K^{40} \rightarrow {}_{20}Ca^{40} + {}_{-1}e^0 + \nu + Q \text{ (1.4 mev)}$$

Argon-40 and calcium-40 are stable isotopes.

In *gamma decay* the process involves changing a nucleus from an *excited state* to an unexcited *ground state* by emitting a photon of gamma radiation. The gamma decay of excited protactinium may be represented.

$$_{91}^*Pa^{234} \rightarrow {}_{91}Pa^{234} + \gamma \text{ } (h\nu = 0.09 \text{ mev})$$

where γ = gamma radiation

$h\nu$ = photon energy in terms of Planck's constant times the frequency of the radiation

The rate of decay of unstable nuclei is independent of their present environmental condition and past history. Experi-

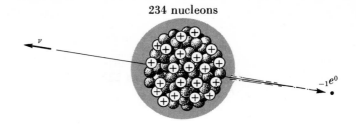

234 nucleons

$-_1e^0$

Figure 14.3 Beta decay. Thorium-234 emits a beta particle and becomes protactinium-234.

mental evidences show that, although we cannot say precisely when any single nucleus will decay, if we have measured a few important characteristics of a given decay process we can predict the statistical rate of decay for large numbers of identical nuclei. Very early in the observations on radioactivity it was discovered that the rate of activity of a radioactive material decreases with time, Thus, when the activity of a given sample decreased to half a former value it was postulated that only half of the former number of radioactive nuclei remained. The time ($T_{1/2}$) required for a sample of a radioactive isotope to lose 50 percent of its activity is called the *half-life* of that isotope. This is a most important characteristic for time studies. The rate of activity was found to be characteristic of the specific isotope under observation.

The number of nuclei of an isotope which decay in a given time interval is proportional to the total number of unstable nuclei present. Stated by equation:

$$\Delta N = -\lambda N \Delta t$$

where ΔN = the number of nuclei which decay

N = the total number of unstable nuclei present at the beginning of a comparatively short time period

Δt = the time period

λ = a constant of proportionality called the *decay constant*

The negative sign in the equation indicates that the process leads to a decrease in the number of unstable nuclei with time. The decay constant is actually the fraction of the unstable nuclei which decay per unit of time. It can be shown by means of the calculus that the half-life of an isotope is related statistically to its decay constant in the following proportion:

$$T_{1/2} = 0.693/\lambda$$

For example, experimental measurement of the activity of measured quantities of

Figure 14.4 K Capture. Potassium-40 nucleus captures an orbital electron and becomes argon-40.

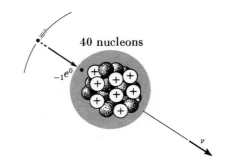

40 nucleons

$-_1e^0$

ν

uranium-238 indicates that about 1 nucleus from each 2.05×10^{17} nuclei present will decay during the time of 1 sec. This is a very slow decay process. At this rate about 1 nucleus per 6.49 billion nuclei will decay during the time of 1 year. The decay constant would be 1.54×10^{-10} per year.

$$\lambda = -\frac{\Delta N}{\Delta t N} = \frac{-1 \text{ nucleus}}{1 \text{ year} \times 6.49 \times 10^9 \text{ nuclei}}$$

$$= -1.54 \times 10^{-10}/\text{year}$$

The half-life of $_{92}U^{238}$ is computed to be -4.5×10^9 years.

$$T_{1/2} = \frac{0.693}{\lambda} = \frac{0.693}{-1.54 \times 10^{-10}/\text{year}}$$

$$= -4.5 \times 10^9 \text{ years}$$

Fig. 14.5 is a graph showing the decay of an unstable isotope in terms of the percentage of the initial nuclei (parent nuclei) which remain at the end of time periods plotted in terms of half-life. This curve is equally valid for half-life periods in millionths of a second or millions of years. It is a universal graph. In using the graph it becomes evident that if the decay constant of an isotope and the ratio of parent nuclei to stable decay nuclei can be reliably measured, the age of the decay process can be determined. For instance, the half-life of potassium-40 is

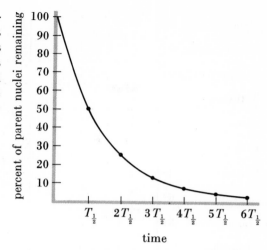

Figure 14.5 Decay of a radioactive substance. The number of radioactive parent atoms are reduced by one-half during each half-life period.

1.31×10^9 years. If the ratio of $_{19}K^{40}$ to $(_{18}Ar^{40} + _{20}Ca^{40})$ in a sample is found to be 1:3 then the ratio of $_{19}K^{40}$ remaining compared to the initial amount is 1:4 or 25 percent.

$$\frac{N_p \text{ (number of parent nuclei)}}{N_d \text{ (number of decayed nuclei)}} = \frac{1}{3}$$

$$\text{Percentage remaining} = \frac{N_p}{N_p + N_d}$$

$$\times 100\% = \frac{1}{1+3} \times 100\% = 25\%$$

TABLE 14.1   Isotopes used in measuring geologic time

Parent isotope	Half-life in years	Number of generations to a stable isotope
Uranium-238 ($_{92}U^{238}$)	4.51×10^9	14 generations to lead-206 ($_{82}Pb^{206}$)
Uranium-235 ($_{92}U^{235}$)	7.13×10^8	11 generations to lead-207 ($_{82}Pb^{207}$)
Thorium-232 ($_{90}Th^{232}$)	1.39×10^{10}	10 generations to lead-208 ($_{82}Pb^{208}$)
Rubidium-87 ($_{37}Rb^{87}$)	4.71×10^{10}	1 generation to strontium-87 ($_{38}Sr^{87}$)
Potassium-40 ($_{19}K^{40}$)	1.31×10^9	1 generation to argon-40 and calcium-40 ($_{18}Ar^{40}$) and ($_{20}Ca^{40}$)

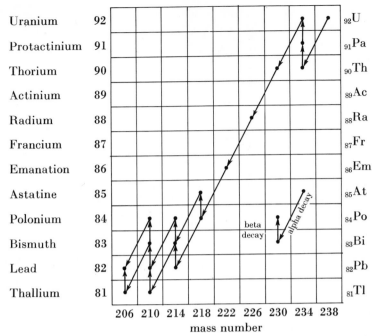

Figure 14.6(a) The 14 radioactive generations in the $_{92}U^{238}$ series. The rate of decay of succeeding generations is governed by the rate of formation; the half-life of uranium-238 controls the activity of the entire series.

From the graph, the age of the sample would be determined to be $2T_{1/2}$. Multiplying by the measured half-life gives the age of the sample as 2.62×10^9 years ($2 \times 1.31 \times 10^9$ years).

In practice, mathematical equations are used instead of the graph. Our purpose here was to give proof that age determinations can be made if reliable measurement values of decay constants and isotope ratios are available. Securing reliable data is the major problem in isotope age measurement.

Methods of geologic time measurement
The isotopes found to be most applicable to geologic time measurement are listed in Table 14.1. The decay products listed

for uranium-238, uranium-235, and thorium-232 are the stable nuclei which result after a series of unstable generations. Fig. 14.6(*b*) shows the complete decay scheme of the 14 radioactive generations in the uranium-238 series. Notice in Table 14.1 that each of the three series shown ends in a different stable isotope of lead. The ratio of the proper lead isotope to its parent isotope can be used in age determinations.

The half-life constants are known to within a probable error of 5 percent or less. The reliability of measurement of isotope ratios has been reported to be within 3 percent or less. Often replicate analyses of a given sample are made in several laboratories in order to insure accuracy.

Uranium-238 series

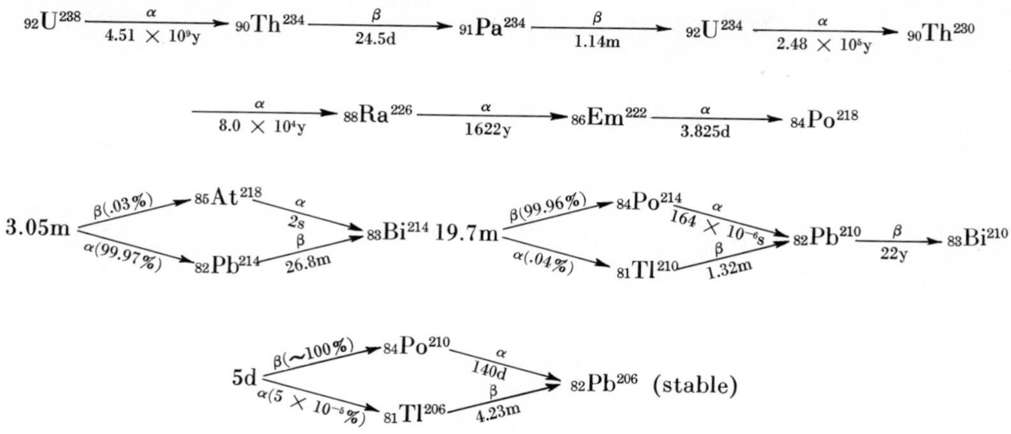

$$_{92}U^{238} \xrightarrow[4.51 \times 10^9 y]{\alpha} {}_{90}Th^{234} \xrightarrow[24.5d]{\beta} {}_{91}Pa^{234} \xrightarrow[1.14m]{\beta} {}_{92}U^{234} \xrightarrow[2.48 \times 10^5 y]{\alpha} {}_{90}Th^{230}$$

$$\xrightarrow[8.0 \times 10^4 y]{\alpha} {}_{88}Ra^{226} \xrightarrow[1622y]{\alpha} {}_{86}Em^{222} \xrightarrow[3.825d]{\alpha} {}_{84}Po^{218}$$

$3.05m$ — $\xrightarrow{\beta(.03\%)} {}_{85}At^{218} \xrightarrow[2s]{\alpha}$ — $\xrightarrow{\alpha(99.97\%)} {}_{82}Pb^{214} \xrightarrow[26.8m]{\beta}$ — ${}_{83}Bi^{214}$ $19.7m$

$\xrightarrow{\beta(99.96\%)} {}_{84}Po^{214} \xrightarrow[164 \times 10^{-6}s]{\alpha}$ — $\xrightarrow{\alpha(.04\%)} {}_{81}Tl^{210} \xrightarrow[1.32m]{\beta}$ — ${}_{82}Pb^{210} \xrightarrow[22y]{\beta} {}_{83}Bi^{210}$

$5d$ — $\xrightarrow{\beta(\sim100\%)} {}_{84}Po^{210} \xrightarrow[140d]{\alpha}$ — $\xrightarrow{\alpha(5 \times 10^{-8}\%)} {}_{81}Tl^{206} \xrightarrow[4.23m]{\beta}$ — ${}_{82}Pb^{206}$ (stable)

Figure 14.6(b)

The minerals listed for each isotope in Table 14.1 have proved to be capable of remaining as closed chemical systems under the specified geologic situations where they are used.

Analyses involving lead isotopes are referred to as the *lead method*. When the relative amounts of each lead isotope, each uranium isotope, and each thorium isotope have been accurately determined for a selected rock sample, four sets of ratios are available for age calculations: (1) U^{238}/Pb^{206}, (2) U^{235}/Pb^{207}, (3) Th^{232}/Pb^{208}, and (4) Pb^{207}/Pb^{206}. An analysis reported in 1956 for uraninite from rocks in the Black Hills, South Dakota, gave the following ages determined by each of the respective ratios. (1) 1.58×10^9 years, (2) 1.60×10^9 years, (3) 1.44×10^9 years, and (4) 1.63×10^9 years. These indicate close agreement in the results of the calculations based on the various ratios found in one sample. Interpreting Fig. 14.7 in the same manner as Fig. 14.5 was used in the example of the potas-

sium-40 sample, reveals how one of the age determinations could have been accomplished.

The *rubidium-strontium method* has the advantage of involving only one transformation. The isotopes are solids under normal conditions; consequently, leakage is not a problem. Where gaseous products are formed, such as the emanation isotopes in the uranium series and argon in the K^{40}-Ar^{40} decay, gas leakage must be accounted for by measurement. There has been some difficulty in determining a reliable value for the half-life of rubidium-87, but this seems to have been resolved recently. The age determinations by the Rb^{87}-Sr^{87} method are now in excellent agreement with determinations by other methods.

The *potassium-argon method* has the advantage of wide distribution of potassium minerals among the feldspars and micas in the earth's crust. It was discovered, however, that the potassium feldspars did not retain the argon gas as

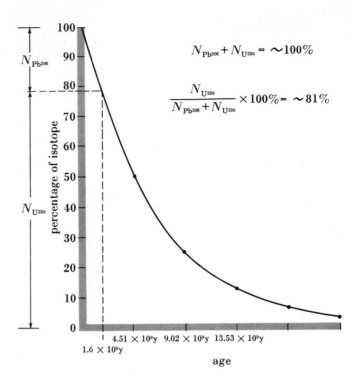

$$N_{Pb^{206}} + N_{U^{238}} = \sim 100\%$$

$$\frac{N_{U^{238}}}{N_{Pb^{206}} + N_{U^{238}}} \times 100\% = \sim 81\%$$

Figure 14.7 Age determination by ratio of isotopes. The ratio of parent isotope remaining establishes the age of the sample.

well as did the micas. Consequently, biotite from igneous rocks and a related mineral called glauconite found in sedimentary deposits were the minerals tested for this method in Table 14.1. The potassium-argon method has been developed to a high degree of sensitivity and is being used more generally than others in age dating of critical rock strata.

TIME AND THE EARTH'S CRUST

Any working hypothesis concerning how the continents have developed must be reasonably consistent with the crustal activities now discernible in the earth. This is Lyell's principle in action. An overwhelming amount of evidence shows that the continents have not existed in their present outlines during any but comparatively recent times. Changes are even now in progress. Just how and when the more permanent changes took place in the past is still largely a mystery, but the curtain is being lifted in many regions. Extensive studies are being reported on the rock systems of the western United States largely from California, Oregon, and Washington. These findings are being compared and correlated with European studies on rocks of the same geological epochs. The most compelling evidences are those gained by isotopic age measurement in some of the major rock systems of the North American continent.

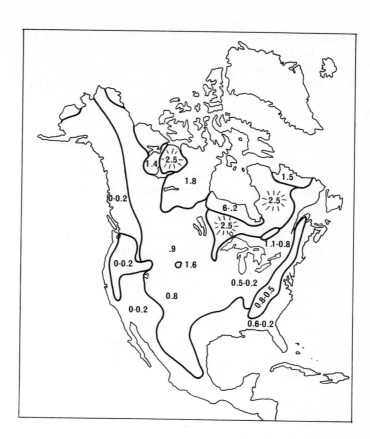

Figure 14.8 Ages of regional rocks in billions of years.

Age of rock layers Widespread analyses by isotopic age measurement reveal one or more continental focal regions in each continent (Fig. 14.8). These central regions were formed between two and three billion years ago and are surrounded by rock zones which become progressively younger toward present continental margins. This is not to infer that these regions were undiscovered before age measurement. Quite to the contrary— there was much evidence indicating the relative order with which the major rock layers were produced, but their actual ages were not known. Also, with more accurate knowledge of age many clues which previously had been disregarded have taken on new meaning.

How is each of the three general classes of rocks—sedimentary, plutonic, and volcanic—thought to be formed? The most prevalent class found on the continental surface of North America is the sedimentary. It is interesting that these are laid down predominantly in sea water. Throughout the central plains, sandstones, shales, and limestones lie in flat layers under the top soil. The deepest layers are found along the gulf coast of Texas and Louisiana. Here the sedimentary platform is more than 40,000 ft thick. It has been accumulating for about 100 million years. In the mountains the sedimentary layers may have been tilted, warped, folded, and broken into thrust blocks, but their presence indicates that these regions once were below sea level. Indeed, in many cases they formed deep folds called *geosynclines* into the earth's crust. Only age determination gives reliable clues as to the timing of the various events which have left records in layer upon layer of rocks.

Beneath the sedimentary rocks are found plutonic rocks of a much earlier age. The plutonic rocks, igneous and metamorphic, have been formed at depths within the crust and often when formed were not in contact with the present layers above them. Significantly, these rocks are formed predominantly from andesitic mineral mixtures. The continental focal regions are plutonic. The rocks are metamorphic gneisses, shists, and quartzite in most areas. This indicates that there were earlier rocks from which the sediments were formed.

There are three large areas of North America where the plutonic rocks form the surface of the continent. The oldest of these is the continental focus around the Hudson Bay in Canada. These rocks are estimated to be about 2.5 billion years old. The second great outcropping of plutonic rock lies along the Atlantic Coast extending from Newfoundland to the piedmont area of Alabama and Georgia. These rocks are not as old as the focus region. Their estimated ages are from 1.1 billion to 800 million years. The third area lies along the Pacific Coast extending from Alaska to the tip of Baja California. The rocks here are much more recent. The ages range from very recent up to a maximum age of about 200 million years. These are not the only places where plutonic rocks are exposed. Regions of limited range are found in northern Canada where the rocks are of ages similar to those of the Hudson Bay. Rocks from the Black Hills of South Dakota are about 1.6 billion years old and those from the Wichita Mountains of Oklahoma are about 550 million years old. Plutonic outcroppings are also found in widely scattered locations, in eastern Maine and Nova Scotia, Alabama and Tennessee, and Colorado and Utah.

The third general class of rocks exposed to the surface is of volcanic origin. These cover large areas in the northwestern states and were poured out upon older deposits. These mass eruptions took place about 17 to 18 million years ago.

Mountain belts Even if the complete history of the rocks found in one mountain range were available, it would be much too complex and lengthy for the purposes of this book. But at the same time, we must not make the mistake of making mountain formations appear to take place with great rapidity or with uniformity throughout any given range. The history of a mountain is very complex and the histories vary from one mountain range to the next. But perhaps more significant in developing a general hypothesis for continental growth is the relative fluctuation of mountain building cycles during the history of a continent. Only fragments of the early history are known, but some of the physical principles are fairly well established. For instance, the principle of isostatic equilibrium on a regional or continental basis requires that adjustments in surface elevations be considered from the vantage point of total regions because, undoubtedly, isostatic readjustments were involved. When we adopt this continent-wide view, some interesting speculations appear.

Starting with the fact that the focal regions of Canada have metamorphic rocks which show invasion of granites and volcanic rocks within their boundaries, the suggestion has been made that the whole North American continent may have begun as a single group of volcanic islands. These were the nucleus from which the sediments eroded to form the rocks which later were recrystallized to form the present Hudson Bay shield. From this nucleus continental additions have developed by a series of volcanic island belts which have appeared repeatedly at widening arcs off its borders. This is an intriguing idea—not very well substantiated by detailed evidence, but perhaps worthy of use as a speculative hypothesis if for no other reason than that it permits inclusion of present-day crustal hypothesis. Let us pursue the speculation further.

For the first billion or more years of continental development a great deal of volcanic activity took place which formed the plutonic rocks now underlying large areas of the continents at various depths. It is suggested that these rocks were formed from magmas which rose to the surface from deep within the mantle. Present-day disturbances along continental crustal fractures are often accompanied by earthquakes having deep foci at places extending to a maximum depth of about 450 miles into the mantle.

After the first continental nucleus had been formed, volcanic activity, erosion, sedimentation, and cycles of mountain building took place in succeeding arcs outward from the Canadian focal regions. The granite cores of the early mountain ranges are discernible particularly in the Great Lakes region. For instance, one of the somewhat offset mountain ranges, the old Killarney Range, was raised across the Great Lakes district for a distance of over 1000 miles in a general east-west direction slanted somewhat to the north. The vestiges of this range suggest that it was folded out of a geosyncline which had been filled with sediments from earlier mountain ranges. Two other geosynclines were being formed during this period and sediments were being carried into them. The Appalachian geosyncline was forming off to the east and southeast of the Killarney Range; and in the west and southwest the Cordilleran geosyncline was forming. At a later time these two great downfolds of deposition were to be partly upfolded to become, respectively, the Appalachian Mountains and the Rocky Mountains.

Within 200 to 250 million years after its rising, the Killarney Range had been completely eroded. Only the granite "roots" remained. Meanwhile, volcanic activity had resumed in central and eastern North America. A new arc of volcanic islands were forming. But the major factor in all this extensive activity was *time*. Continents develop slowly. Sediments from the Killarney Range and associated highlands produced rocks which have revealed ages less by about 1.5 billion years than the rocks at the continental focus. Since the time that these rocks were produced until now, only about 500 to 600 million years have passed. During the time of these early events three-fourths of the continental age to the present date had passed. However, the stage had been set for many later events.

The first 200 to 250 million years of the remaining time record was marked by extensive cycles of erosion and deposition.

Major deposits of sediments were occurring along the Appalachian geosyncline, the Cordilleran geosyncline particularly in the section now forming the southern Canadian Rockies, and the Ouachita geosyncline of the present states of southern Missouri, Arkansas, and eastern Oklahoma. Great layers of sandstone and limestone were formed in the seas which covered much of the area of present-day Minnesota, Iowa, Illinois, Indiana, and Ohio. These layers are now known by such familiar names as Shakapee dolomite, St. Peter sandstone, Platteville limestone, Galena dolomite, Beekmantown dolomite, Chazy limestone, Black River limestone, Trenton limestone, and Lorraine sandstone. The end of this long period of sedimentation was marked by small uplifts or warps occurring in the regions of the Ozarks, the Adirondacks, and the Cincinnati arch. The northern part of the Appalachian region also began to rise. In ash beds found in the Appalachian geosyncline from New York to Alabama volcanic activity was recorded for this period in volcanoes of northeastern Quebec and along the eastern United States, a region which then was an island arc.

About 260 to 270 million years ago the Ouachita geosyncline was folded. Soon after this the Appalachian geosyncline also passed out of existence and was folded, becoming the Appalachian Mountain range which closed the gap between the outer volcanic islands and the continent. A secondary mountain range was folded up on the continent side of the major uplift. The Valley and Ridge province of New York and Pennsylvania remains as evidence of this event.

Somewhat later—50 to 70 million years later—an elongated Pacific geosyncline developed near the present locations of the Cascade and Sierra Nevada ranges. Volcanic activity of major consequence was taking place in the southwestern region of Canada. Volcanic activity spread to the Pacific coastal region and continued in major cycles for about 100 million years. Mount Lassen is still slightly active.

About 125 to 150 million years ago the Pacific geosyncline was severely folded. The uplift may still be in progress. The earlier extrusive volcanism was followed by the intrusion of the great granite batholiths found along the west coast of Canada and in the Sierra Nevadas of California. For a time this Pacific region formed an extensive island arc.

At about this time the Appalachian Mountains, which had been eroded to almost a flat plain, were warped up again to heights of 2000 to 3000 ft. The present Appalachian ridge structure has resulted from erosion of this uplift.

Considering the Sierras and west coast ranges of Canada as primary mountains, the Rocky Mountain ranges extending from Alaska to Mexico are thought to be a secondary region of mountain folds. These are also on the continent side of the primary uplift. The deep deposits of sedimentary rocks in the Cordilleran geosyncline became the scene of mountain building in major proportions. Folding, thrust faults, and overthrusts shoving eastward over sedimentary strata marked the end of the Cordilleran geosyncline, starting some 100 million years ago.

The present-day grandeur of the Rockies came in part from a later uplift which took place about 20 to 25 million years ago. The Cascade range formed primarily of volcanoes began their activities also at this comparatively late age. The great basaltic lava flows of the Columbia Plateau took place in several cycles about 17 to 18 million years ago.

During the last 100 million years or more, regions of major deposition have been the Mississippi Valley and the gulf coast from Florida to northern Mexico. Volcanic activity has subsided along the Pacific coastal region but still persists. in central Mexico and in the island arc off the coast of Alaska.

This is a brief and partial outline of the cyclic growth of the continent of North America. The growth may still be in progress. Remember the speculative nature of this hypothesis, but remember also that there are many *substantiated* findings recorded by historical geology and paleontology. Speculation and evidence must complement each other. Isotopic age determination is doing much in this regard.

PRESENT-DAY EVIDENCES OF CYCLIC ACTIVITY

Lyell's principle that the effect of natural laws on the earth is constant is fundamental in our present inquiry. Knowledge of earth processes has expanded tremendously in the past few years. The expansion is certain to continue. It must be kept in mind that a scientifically acceptable hypothesis comes into being only after substantial amounts of evidence need explanation. The hypothesis must stand or fall on its value in reliably interpreting, uniting, and organizing the evidences that accumulate in all related fields. To be conscious of the clues and current interpretations while the working hypotheses are being developed and tested is like watching a mystery story unfolding before your eyes. The fun is in finding out the clues and in knowing what is taking place.

Stages of continental growth cycles The cyclic growth sequence we have outlined can be conveniently organized into five stages of development.

1. *Island arc stage* formed by volcanic activity and the warping or fault block elevation of sediments which have accumulated in an ocean trough.
2. *Geosyncline development stage* initiated when large deposits are accumulated on a comparatively broad area of downfold in the earth's crust.
3. *Mountain building stage* produced when comparatively rapid folding, block faulting, and thrust faulting raise the deposits of geosynclines to higher elevations. Usually two types of mountain ranges result: a primary range having extensive intrusions of igneous batholiths, and a secondary complex range on the continent side of the primary range.
4. *Inactive mountain stage* brought about when rapid erosion begins to make inroads in leveling the mountain range. This process of erosion has been operating from the time of the initial rise but the mountain growth rate has kept pace. Now that the growth cycles are completed, the mountain begins to disappear. The sediments produced fill the intervening areas between mountain ranges and may supply the sediments for new geosyncline deposits. The rate of erosion tapers off as the elevation is reduced.
5. *Continental provinces stage* is the scars of former activities now in final operations. Only the roots of former mountain ranges are evident. The erosion has become very gradual because of the general leveling of the terrain.

Examples in the present crustal processes

Let us initially add to the stages outlined above the processes involved in crustal fracture zones which extend into the mantle. These zones are located by mapping the foci of seismic disturbances, volcanic activities, and ocean trenches. There is much evidence to support the idea that two types of fracture zones exist in the earth's crust. The *mid-ocean* fracture zones are characterized by comparatively shallow earthquake foci which never exceed depths of more than 45 miles into the mantle and by volcanoes which issue basaltic type lavas. This type of fracture zone is associated with the mid-ocean ridges which extend throughout all of the oceans. The second or *continental* type of fracture zone is characterized by occasional deep earthquake foci which reach maximum depths of about 450 miles into the mantle and by volcanoes which issue predominantly andesitic or rhyolitic lavas. These fracture zones are associated with continental margins and deep ocean trenches. It is the second type of fracture zones that we shall incorporate into our outline of continental growth, although it may well be that both types ultimately will be involved in future theories.

The first stage, then, is the formation of a *continental fracture zone*. The deep ocean trenches off the coasts of the Aleutian Islands and Japan are typical examples. In previous chapters we have discussed how these trenches may represent regions of downflow in convection currents of the mantle. The fact that they are not in isostatic equilibrium has also been discussed. There is evidence to believe that if marine sediments flowing outward from distant continental surfaces and volcanoes increase beyond a certain volume level, the trenches

become filled and the resulting sedimentary rocks may be lifted as fault blocks forming an arc of sedimentary islands which replace the trenches. Examples of this type of island are Kodiak Island near Alaska and the islands of Tobago, Trinidad, and Barbados of the West Indies.

The *island arc stage* develops after the main arc of volcanoes reaches the surface on the continent side of the deep ocean troughs. These volcanoes issue andesitic lavas typical of continental volcanoes. Examples of this development are the larger islands of Japan, New Zealand, and New Guinea which have been building up for over 400 million years and which still have highly active volcanoes.

The *geosyncline stage* results when deposits of eroding volcanic islands and from the older continental highlands form deep layers of sediments in the comparatively shallow seas which separate the island arc from the continent. An example is the East China Sea which is being filled by debris from the nearby volcanic islands and from the outpourings of the Yangtze and Hwang-Ho Rivers.

The *mountain building stage* is perhaps best exemplified by the Sierra Nevada Range of California as a primary range and the Rocky Mountains as secondary ranges. It should be noted also that the outer trench pattern still is in evidence here. The Coast Range of California represents such an uplift of deep-sea sediments. In nearby situations the trench has remained open and deep, as in the Acapulco-Guatemala Trench off southwestern Mexico.

The *inactive mountain stage* is observed in the ridge structure of the Appalachian region. Much of the former mountain range now lies buried beneath the deposits which have built up on the edges both inland and along the eastern coast. Only low hills remain of the mountains which once stood high over central Newfoundland and the New England states. Sites of the ancient volcanoes can still be found in New Hampshire, Maine, and New Brunswick. Comparatively rapid erosion is still taking place in the regions of higher elevation along the Appalachian range and a system of dams has been erected to offset man's tampering with natural processes.

The *continental provinces stage* has been reached in the Canadian shield of the Hudson Bay area and south to the Great Lakes district. When isotopic age determination has been made of samples from more detailed boundaries of these older rock formations, a great deal more will be known concerning the early history of North America. It may well be that the working hypothesis we have been investigating will be strengthened or abandoned when this research is accomplished.

SUMMARY

Lyell's principle of uniformitarianism was predicated on the idea that given enough time, all observed geological changes could be explained on the basis of the natural processes which are now in progress and thus can be studied and better understood. Isotopic age measurement is being refined to give reliable age estimates of volcanic and plutonic rocks.

The unstable nuclei of radioactive isotopes achieve stability through radioactive decay. Each radioactive isotope is characterized by a uniquely different level of decay activity which can be expressed in terms of the half-life of the isotope. When the isotope ratio of the parent and stable decay nuclei in a sample and the half-life period of the parent isotope are known, the age of the sample can be computed.

Isotopic age analyses have revealed a progressive time development of continents, region by region, outward from one or more continental focal regions. Although not substantiated by detailed evidence, the island arc hypothesis of continent development presents a somewhat unified system of assumed cyclic crustal activities. If the hypothesis is verified, it could lead to better understanding of some of the long-term processes taking place in the earth's crustal regions.

PROBLEMS

1 Why is accurate age determination so important to modern explanations of continental development?

2 How many protons and how many neutrons are indicated for each of the

nuclei of the following isotopes: $_1H^2$, $_6C^{12}$, $_8O^{16}$, $_{20}Ca^{40}$, $_{37}Rb^{87}$, $_{82}Pb^{207}$, $_{90}Th^{232}$, $_{92}U^{235}$, $_{92}U^{238}$?

3 Describe the effect upon the parent nucleus of each of the following decay modes: alpha decay, beta decay, electron capture, and gamma decay.

4 The half-life of $_{37}Rb^{87}$ is 5×10^{10} years. What is its decay constant?

5 The rocks of the continental focus are estimated to be about 2.5 billion years old. If this age had been determined by the Rb-Sr method, estimate the ratio of rubidium to strontium measured in the samples. Use the graph in Fig. 14.5.

6 What evidences show that the regions of the continental focus are older than the present rocks found in these regions?

7 Summarize the evidences found in a presently occurring crustal process which support each of the five stages of growth outlined in the island arc hypothesis of continental growth.

15

DEVELOPING THE CONCEPT

OF ATOMS

The word *atom* has appeared on the front pages of our newspapers almost every day during the last decade. Everyone who reads has achieved meanings and connotations for the word—some truth, some nonsense—and a great amount of confusion. But, true, false, or confused, the individual's concept of the atom exists—and is called on for a variety of interpretations. These may involve radioactive fallout, or rocket propulsion, or anti-smog devices, or sea-water conversion projects, or the Van Allen radiation belt, and so forth. These meanings are not about a nebulous something called an atom but are concerned with a multiplicity of characteristics which define the elements, particles of compounds, the isotopes, ions, molecules, and the atomic particles—electrons, protons, neutrons, and how these definitions explain the processes involved. Our problem is not whether we have a concept of atoms; the problem lies in how valid and reliable our concepts are for correctly interpreting each situation which confronts us in reading, observing, listening, and deciding.

MEANINGS FROM CONTEXT

The frequent references to atoms in this book merely point out dependence upon concepts of atoms for adequate explanation of physical phenomena. Some acquaintanceship with ideas of atoms—however vague these ideas may have been—has been assumed. This acquaintanceship has served to help organize explanations of various energy transformations and the physical properties of the systems involved. Let us turn again to some of the patterns used in these explanations.

Molecular motion   Motion of molecules

first entered our discussions with regard to the propagation of sound. The interpretations used in Chapter 2 were hinged upon three postulated ideas. First, gases consist of molecules. Second, in gases molecules move with a variety of speeds in random directions and have frequent collisions with other molecules. Third, the absolute temperature of the gas is directly proportional to the average kinetic energy per molecule. These postulations were needed to explain, respectively, the following observed facts: (1) Compressional waves must travel through material media. The waves do not penetrate a vacuum. (2) Sound waves have spherical wave fronts. In a homogeneous medium, sound waves are propagated in all directions at equal speeds. (3) The speed of sound increases with increased temperature. When a group of molecules in a gas is given a slight change of speed in a certain direc-

Figure 15.1   Types of molecular motion. The diagrams depict diatomic molecules, and in the case of vibrational motion the atomic nuclei oscillate about an "imaginary" center of gravity.

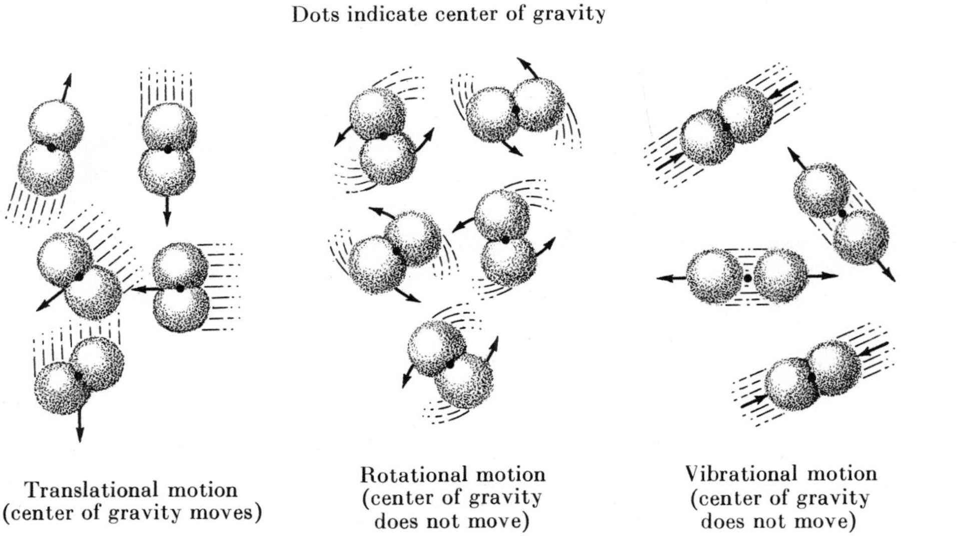

Dots indicate center of gravity

Translational motion
(center of gravity moves)

Rotational motion
(center of gravity
does not move)

Vibrational motion
(center of gravity
does not move)

tion, some of the molecules are already going in that direction and carry the energy forward. Therefore, the speed at which they travel to collide with other molecules and so to transmit the added energy to the new molecules is proportional to the molecular speeds. The average kinetic energy of the molecule also is proportional to the molecular speed ($KE = \frac{1}{2}mv^2$). Hence, the proportionality between temperature and the speed of sound.

It was suggested that the fact that compressional waves are transmitted through solids and liquids is also related to the molecular motions in these media. We found in later discussions that explanations of observed phenomena in gases, liquids, and solids often required molecules to have three types of motions (Fig. 15.1): translational (linear), rotational, and vibrational. Changes of velocity (acceleration) require the action of appropriate forces. The electrical forces between molecular particles include forces of both attraction and repulsion since both electrons and protons are involved.

With respect to surface features of molecules, the molecular model might appear as an elastic cloud of electrons (Fig. 15.2). The clouds repel each other. Consequently, these forces of repulsion greatly modify our usual idea of bodies in collision. Molecules in collision do not make material contact. The electron clouds are distorted by forces at a distance. But forces from the positively charged nucleus also extend beyond the molecular surface. Hence, attraction between the positively charged nucleus of one molecule and the negatively charged electrons of other molecules produces an apparent attraction between molecules that are not too closely spaced.

The action forces which do work upon

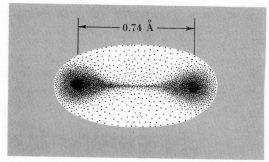

Figure 15.2 Electron cloud model. Cross-sectional diagram of the most probable electron distribution in the hydrogen molecule. Regions of highest electron density surround the atomic nuclei; electron density is relatively high in the region between the nuclei. The atomic nuclei continually oscillate, moving toward and then away from each other, the distance 0.74 A° being the most probable time-average distance between the nuclei.

molecular systems involve concepts of energy, and energy may have quantum limitations. Changes in rotational and vibrational motions take place only in allowable transitions between specific quantum states. Because of the nature of electrical forces and energy quanta, the mechanical view of molecules as solid spheres in collision and rebound motions does not adequately explain the observed facts except in a very general manner.

In gases molecular motion is primarily translational. Almost complete freedom of molecular motion is possible. Momentary restrictions may take place when two or more molecules lose their kinetic energy while under the influence of mutual forces of attraction. Aggregations of molecules may build up. These energy transformations may take place in the process of multiple collisions. For a time the binding energy between molecules, because of attraction, is greater than the kinetic energy of the respective molecules. In the resulting aggregates vibrational motions occur which represent specific quantum transitions within the systems. Rotational motion may also be present in multi-atomic aggregations. These also are restricted to specific quantum states.

In liquids the molecules are much more restricted than in gases. Short-range aggregates of molecules build up wherein vibrational motion is the principal mode of molecular motion. However, the aggregates are not permanent and translational motion of molecules between holes within the structure gives liquids their fluid nature.

The observation of Brownian movement in liquids and gases is offered as proof of molecular motion and of the directional randomness of the translational motions.

In solids the structural particles are restricted to vibrational motion. Long-range aggregations of molecules occur and their motions are highly ordered. Exchange of particles from one position to another may take place but this is infrequent.

In all states of matter—solid, liquid, and gas, the temperature is proportional to the average kinetic energy of the molecules. The kinetic energy of the molecules therefore determines to a large extent which state will predominate in a given substance. Pressure is the only other major factor involved.

Motion of molecules is closely allied with heat. Heat is associated with the kinetic and potential energies of molecules. Instead of attempting to designate the energy systems involved, it is common to speak of internal energy as the total energy of the molecular system. We made use of this concept in our discussion of the solar atmosphere. The concept was extended in terms of force and energy relationships of molecular particles taking part in processes of volcanism. It was found that all molecular motion associated with internal energy is related to heat phenomena. The transfer of heat by conduction is explained as the transfer of molecular kinetic energy from molecule to molecule. Consequently, the tendency for heat to flow can be predicted on the basis of temperature relationships. Heat can flow spontaneously only from a body of higher temperature to a body of lower temperature.

Spectral relationships and quanta Early in our inquiries the relationship of atomic theory to light was a basis of explanation. In order to explain the rainbow and other dispersion phenomena, the ideas of spectra from atoms and molecules were essential. The spectral clues to the nature of atomic origins of light were stressed. Continuous spectra were clues of mutual interference between closely packed atoms in solids and liquids and in gases under high pressure. Bright-line spectra from elements in the gaseous state reveal information of energy relationships in the electron systems and serve to identify each element. Each element has unique quantum relationships in its electron energy levels. Band spectra of molecules also identify the energy relationships present and give clues to identify the constituent elements.

The quantum nature of light was emphasized in Einstein's explanation of the photoelectric effect. The quantum of energy absorbed ($E = h\nu$) gives a measurement of the binding energy of the electrons of the element used. It serves also to confirm the quantum nature of all spectral phenomena.

The absorption and re-emission of photons by material particles were used to explain the phenomenon called scattering. The blue sky and "searchlight" beams were explained on the basis of scattering of light. The scattered light is plane polarized.

The relationship between temperature and the intensity and range of the spectral colors (frequencies) was emphasized in the interpretations given to spectral clues from various solar phenomena.

Electrical and magnetic forces The hypothetical interpretations of phenomena occurring in the solar atmosphere were given meaning in terms of the interacting electrical and magnetic forces. The clues provided by the Zeeman effect when bright-line spectra emitted by atoms placed in a magnetic field split into three or more lines having slightly different frequencies establish much more evidence with regard to solar events. They also indicate the interrelationship of magnetic forces to the possible electron energy levels of atoms.

Chemical properties of elements The explanation for mineral abundances in the earth's crust involved the chemical characteristics of the elements. The chemical properties of atoms and atomic aggregates are related to the electron structure of the outermost available energy levels of molecules. The basic principle used in explanations was that atoms tend to assume the electron structure arrangement which achieves the lowest state of potential energy available in a given situation. The concept of the completed outer shell as interpreted for the inert gases helped to organize conceptual models for chemical reactions.

The relationships of electrical forces to the sizes of atoms and to the measured binding energy of the first electron served as meaningful clues for explaining the observed mineral abundances in view of the abundances of the various elements in the earth's crust.

The structural linkage systems of the various silicates gave meaning for the complete molecular interrelationships involving electrical forces, binding energy, electron quantum energy levels, nuclear and molecular forces, and atomic motion as explanations of observed phenomena of the earth's crust.

Questioning validity Useful as these contextual meanings for atomic characteristics have been in our interpretations, no great attempt has been made to determine the validity of the assumed atomic relationships. The meanings have been purely speculative. It was mentioned that atomic characteristics have been brought into existence by speculative means rather than by sensory observation. But in science pure speculation is not enough. The meanings must be tested with reference to correspondence in natural events. Results must correspond with predictions. Therefore, our meanings also would suffer if we were to be cut off from the verification aspects of concept development. We should know something about the genesis of atomic ideas so that we can gain a perspective of the growth of some of the meanings we use.

THE ATOMIC HYPOTHESES

Let us for a moment go back to a world which was devoid of atoms, molecules, electrons, protons, and neutrons. Let us look at the world through the eyes of the informed citizens of the early 1700's. It was customary then to think that all things in the universe were seeking their ideal nature, that they were working toward a changeless universe. In the ideal state, all things would be in complete equilibrium. Nothing could change. The picture was of a universe now disorderly but seeking its order in an ideal hierarchy of things as they ought to be, and they ought to be changeless. Many natural objects were endowed with guiding spirits or souls which animated them. This was a passivist world, because as long as spirits were directing things and the ultimate directions had been preordained, man was a helpless pawn in the hands of capricious spirits.

But revolutions were in the making. A few men had discovered that they could reason out explanations which could be tested against the operations of a lawful universe. Mankind had discovered science. A new ideal of order had entered the thought arena.

Classifying substances Three hundred years ago the sort of things held to be acceptable by some men as *substances* worthy of study would be excluded today because our criteria are more meaningful. In those days airs, earths, metals, heat, light, fluids (including liquids and electric, caloric, and magnetic fluids), and spirits (including animal spirits, the human spirit, and alcoholic spirits) were among the entities thought by many to be the participating ingredients in natural phenomena. The development of useful standards for more critical classification was slow and sporadic.

The first useful classifications were developed by the trades and often were trade secrets. Metallurgy and pharmacy, particularly, developed broad classifications of their materials. Later these classifications became the nucleus for scientific work.

With regard to atomic concepts, the study of gases was destined to be most crucial. Van Helmont of the Netherlands, in the early 1600's, definitely established the fact that several kinds of gases existed. He was foolish enough, however, to maintain that he possessed the ability to transmute metals. By the late 1600's, Boyle of England successfully stressed the idea of obtaining pure substances for study. He introduced classification by element, compound, and mixture. But neither of these men actually succeeded in setting up criteria for distinguishing between the substances they were attempting to define. For example, they were satisfied to designate gases as modified forms of air.

As early as 1630 the Frenchman Jean

Figure 15.3 Lavoisier's apparatus for combining metals and oxygen. Mercury was introduced into the retort. A known volume of air was confined in the bell jar. The retort was heated. Red mercuric oxide formed in the retort. The volume of gas in the bell jar was reduced by one-fifth.

Rey had recognized that when lead or tin is heated in air, its weight is increased by a limited amount. But quantitative measurement of the changes was not accomplished.

In the early 1700's, Gabriel Fahrenheit of Germany produced quality instruments for measuring temperature. He also discovered that a pure liquid boils away at a constant temperature, and that the boiling temperature is altered by changes in atmospheric pressure.

The first gaseous element to be isolated was hydrogen. It was poorly defined. A description of the gas was given by Henry Cavendish of England in 1766, who called it "inflammable air."

The late 1700's brought forth a rash of discoveries. By 1771 the Swedish scientist Karl Scheele and Joseph Priestley of England had isolated oxygen. Priestley experimented extensively with this gas between 1771 and 1774. He found that it is necessary to animal life, is given off by plants, and increases the activity of burning. He called it "dephlogisticated air." Chlorine was discovered by Scheele in 1774. By 1784 Cavendish had described the properties of nitrogen, had determined the composition of the atmosphere, and had established the composition of water. The experiments on water were repeated by Antoine Lavoisier of France. He named the constituents of water—hydrogen and oxygen—and confirmed the respective proportions by weight to be one to eight.

Only with Lavoisier did these substances become distinct elements independent of spirits or influx of other supposed substances. Not only were oxides reduced to constituent metals and oxygen but the metals and oxygen were recombined to form the oxides again (Fig. 15.3). By means of a "balance sheet" indicating that the weights of the initial materials were equal to the weights of the products, Lavoisier accumulated experimental verification for his explanations of the reactions. The important contribution of Lavoisier to experimental study was the principle of insisting upon constant properties for substances worthy of explanation. Quantitative experimental verification of these properties is a prerequisite to further study. The application of this principle in searching for pure and unvarying substances led to the rapid increase in reliable descriptions of newly recognized elements which were discovered after Lavoisier's publications in the late 1700's.

Quantitative analysis A central idea in Lavoisier's methods was the criterion of accepting as substances only those ingredients which had, or could have,

Antoine Lavoisier. [*Courtesy of the Bettmann Archive.*]

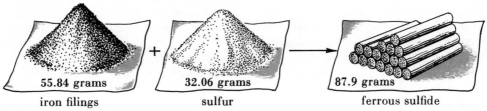

| 55.84 grams | 32.06 grams | 87.9 grams |
| iron filings | sulfur | ferrous sulfide |

Figure 15.4 Law of definite proportions. The same compound always contains the same elements in the same mass proportions.

measured masses. This eliminated speculation upon phenomena and interpretations which could not be readily verified. An early consequence of this approach was the discovery that when elements combine to form a new substance, the same ratio is always found between the masses of the substances involved. For example, when hydrogen and oxygen combine forming water, the ratio of masses is always 2.016 parts of hydrogen to 16.000 parts of oxygen. This fact is generalized in terms of the *Law of Definite Proportions: The same compound always contains the same elements in the same mass proportion.* (See Fig. 15.4.)

A standard laboratory demonstration of this fact is to mix 55.84 grams of iron filings and 32.06 grams of powdered sulfur in a test tube and heat the bottom of the tube until the ingredients at the bottom begin to glow. The reaction proceeds throughout the total mass without further heating, because of the energy released as the chemical reaction progresses. The resulting substance is the compound ferrous sulfide which has properties totally different from the constituent elements. For instance, the iron filings are attracted by a magnet, but the ferrous sulfide is not; the sulfur melts at a fairly low temperature, but the ferrous sulfide does not. It makes no

difference what ratio of weights of iron and sulfur are used; the amounts which combine are always in the exact ratio of 55.84 parts iron to 32.06 parts sulfur. The compound so formed must have a fixed and measured composition. The results are easily verified.

Another discovery concerning proportions of elements which combine to form different compounds was to have far-reaching implications. For example, under various but specific controlled

Figure 15.5 Demonstration of the Law of Definite Proportions. When iron filings and sulfur are mixed and heated to glowing at the bottom of the test tube, the reaction becomes self-sustaining.

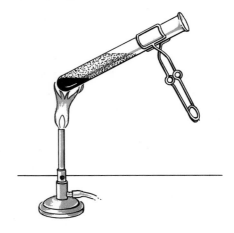

conditions, nitrogen forms several different compounds with oxygen. We mention three. *Nitrous oxide* is a colorless gas which supports combustion. *Nitric oxide* is a colorless gas which does not support combustion. *Nitrogen dioxide* is a reddish-brown gas. If a constant amount of nitrogen is combined in forming each of these compounds, the amounts of oxygen combined in the various compounds form ratios of simple whole numbers. For illustrations study the following list of combining weights (Fig. 15.6):

In nitrous oxide 14 grams of nitrogen combine with 8 grams of oxygen.

In nitric oxide 14 grams of nitrogen combine with 16 grams of oxygen.

In nitrogen dioxide 14 grams of nitrogen combine with 24 grams of oxygen.

The ratio of the various weights of oxygen are as the small whole numbers 1:2:3. Other examples of compounds of this sort are the two oxides of carbon and the two oxides of hydrogen:

In carbon monoxide 12 grams of carbon combine with 16 grams of oxygen.

In carbon dioxide 12 grams of carbon combine with 32 grams of oxygen.

In water 1 gram of hydrogen combines with 8 grams of oxygen.

In hydrogen peroxide 1 gram of hydrogen combines with 16 grams of oxygen.

The relationships shown in these examples are summarized in the *Law of Multiple Proportions: When the same two elements combine to form more than one compound, the different masses of one of the elements that combine with a constant mass of the other are in the ratio of small whole numbers.*

Logically the next question would be: Is there any relationship between the masses of the various elements which combine with one another in different compounds? For example, hydrogen combines with both oxygen and chlorine, and calcium does likewise. Are equivalent amounts of oxygen and chlorine involved when combined with hydrogen and with calcium? The answer is yes. Experiments show that 1.008 parts by weight of hydrogen combine with 8 parts of oxygen to form water. Also, 1.008 parts by weight of hydrogen combine with 35.5 parts of chlorine to form hydrogen chloride. We would expect to find, therefore, that 8 parts of oxygen are equivalent to 35.5 parts of chlorine in

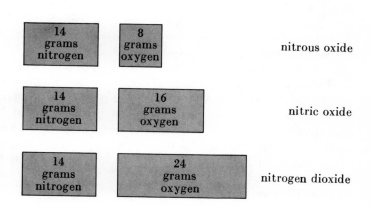

Figure 15.6 Law of multiple proportions. When the same two elements combine to form more than one compound, the different masses of one of the elements that combine with a constant mass of the other are in the ratio of small whole numbers.

nitrous oxide

nitric oxide

nitrogen dioxide

other compounds of these two elements.

Experimental results with calcium compounds show that 20.4 parts by weight of calcium combine with 8 parts of oxygen to form calcium oxide (unslaked lime), and that 20.4 parts by weight of calcium combine with 35.5 parts of chlorine to form calcium chloride. The expected ratio of equivalent weights is a measured fact. This relationship is expressed in the *Law of Combining Weights: To each element may be assigned a number called its combining weight which when multiplied by a small whole number expresses the mass of that element which combines with the combining weight of another element in forming a compound.*

The empirical laws (based only on observation) stated above merely describe the observed results. They do not explain the processes. Inasmuch as the observers cannot see how the elements unite, they must resort to speculations and hypotheses in attempts to explain the observed laws. The atomic theory was not devised specifically to explain these results, but its applications to this end were an important break-through in the search for useful explanations.

Atomic hypotheses The concept of atoms has been revived repeatedly since the time of the early Greek philosophers. The beginnings of atomic concepts are shrouded in the early Greek speculations regarding the nature of matter. There were two schools of thought. The first can be summarized by Aristotle's model of the universe. The universe was described as the central stationary earth surrounded by successive layers of earth, water, air, and fire. These were Aristotle's four changeable "elements." Beyond the moon lay the indestructible "quintessence" of the "superior" celestial world. The "elements" could be divided an infinite number of times. There were no fundamental particles.

The other school of thought was first enunciated by Democritus about 400 years before Christ. The atomists were convinced that all matter was indestructible and discontinuous. The indivisible particles of the ultimate division were called atoms and were of many kinds, weights, and sizes. The atoms were the fundamental particles.

The concepts of both schools were purely speculative and had no verification by experimental observations.

The atomic concepts met a similar fate to some conceptual models of the universe; the influence of Aristotle and the domination of the early Church discouraged useful revival until late in the 1500's. Giordano Bruno, who was burned at the stake for supporting the Copernican heliocentric scheme of the universe, also found it useful in his teachings to describe matter in terms of indivisible spherical units which were ordered by natural and unchangeable laws. Bruno, obviously, did not make friends by adhering to these concepts.

In the early 1600's, the Greek idea of indestructible atoms was revived by the Catholic priest Gassendi. The religious prejudice against the atomic concept was removed by Gassendi. He was convinced in his own mind and served to convince other leaders of Christianity that atoms were God's handiwork. Being indestructible, the atoms must have been created by God. The concept of atoms remained purely speculative, but it could now develop without fear of reprisals from the Church.

The first actual application of the concept of atoms to explain specific observations was published in 1789 by the English scientist William Higgins. He evidently failed to follow up on the idea by further applications to other observations. His name is all but lost in the flurry of activity which was prompted by the works of Priestley and Lavoisier at about the same time.

John Dalton, an English chemist-schoolmaster, is credited with the first clear statement of a general theory of atoms based upon observed relationships of elements particularly in his study of the atmosphere. The year was 1803. Dalton also announced his discovery of the law of multiple proportions in 1803. He applied the atomic theory in explaining this law. Dalton assumed that elements in some instances might combine by having one atom of one element combine with two or more atoms of another element. The basic assumptions of Dalton's theory of atoms were: (1) all matter is composed of tiny, discrete particles called atoms; (2) the atoms of different elements have different masses; (3) all atoms of the same element have the same mass; (4) atoms are indivisible. A comparison of these assumptions with present-day concepts will prove interesting!

Molecules and Avogadro's hypothesis

Dalton took a great step toward organizing theoretical chemistry by introducing the atomic hypothesis. He assumed that each element consisted of atoms and that compound substances consisted of combinations of a few atoms of different kinds. Dalton's theory, being an application of a speculative concept, had no need for explaining how many atoms of each element were combined in a particular compound. Quantitative data were not important to the originators of the atomic concept. Dalton tried to verify his previously stated theories by later experiments. In reference to the law of multiple proportions the results provided support for his ideas. For example, Dalton could make the simplest assumptions regarding the atomic constituents of water and hydrogen peroxide. He could assume that, since water consisted of 1 part by weight of hydrogen plus 8 parts of oxygen, then in forming water 1 atom of hydrogen combines with 1 atom of oxygen. And, since hydrogen peroxide consists of 1 part by weight of hydrogen plus 16 parts of oxygen, then in forming the hydrogen peroxide 1 atom of hydrogen combines with 2 atoms of oxygen. But these are ambiguous statements. The assumptions of Dalton's theory would not be violated if one were to assume that water consists of 2 atoms of hydrogen plus 1 atom of oxygen, or 1 atom of hydrogen plus 2 atoms of oxygen.

John Dalton. [*Courtesy of the Bettmann Archive.*]

With corresponding increases in mass, hydrogen peroxide could then consist, respectively, of 2 atoms of hydrogen plus 2 atoms of oxygen, or 1 atom of hydrogen plus 4 atoms of oxygen. Dalton's theories failed to provide unique ratios of atoms for particular compounds. The mass ratios did not provide clues as to the number of particles involved.

These problems of ambiguity were evident to other scientists almost immediately, but, unfortunately, Dalton was not easily convinced of the weaknesses of his hypotheses. He refused to accept the concept of molecules. As a result the acceptance of the idea of molecules was delayed for almost half a century.

Evidence to eliminate the ambiguity of the assumptions had been provided in 1808 by Gay-Lussac. The controversy was not cleared up until 1860. The evidence was contained in Gay-Lussac's measurements of the *volume* of gases involved in chemical reactions. The volume of all gases was measured at the same temperature and pressure. For instance, quantitative measurements of volumes show that, when water is decomposed into its constituent elements, exactly twice the volume of hydrogen is produced as the volume of oxygen. Furthermore, when water is formed by combination of the gases, the volume ratio is always two of hydrogen to one of oxygen. Reactions using other gases give similar whole-number ratios for the volumes of the gases involved. These results are generalized as *Gay-Lussac's Law: Whenever gases appear or disappear in a chemical reaction they do so in the ratio of small whole numbers of volume.*

In 1811, by introducing the idea of molecules, Amedeo Avogadro, an Italian scientist, reconciled the empirical law of Gay-Lussac with the atomic theory.

Amedeo Avogadro. [*Courtesy of the Bettmann Archive.*]

Avogadro proposed that a chemical reaction was a process whereby a group of atoms of one substance linked up with a group of atoms of another substance, forming into groups he called molecules. *Equal volumes of any gas measured under constant temperature and pressure would contain equal numbers of molecules.* Hence, when it became evident that two volumes of hydrogen plus one volume of oxygen produced two volumes of water vapor, the relationship could be explained by assuming that $2n$ molecules (each containing 2 atoms) of hydrogen combine with n molecules (each containing 2 atoms) of oxygen forming $2n$ molecules of water (each consisting of 2 hydrogen atoms linked with 1 oxygen atom). The factor n is the equal number of molecules per unit volume of any gas.

The usefulness of Avogadro's idea was not recognized immediately, perhaps, in part, because no means were then available whereby the number of molecules in a given volume of gas could be estimated. Between 1811 and 1860 confusion reigned with regard to the meaning of such terms as atoms, molecules, atomic weight, combining weight, and molecular weight. The terms were often used interchangeably to convey the same meanings. There was great need for clarification.

The Italian professor of chemistry, Stanislao Cannizzaro, successfully led the scientists of his time to consider more carefully the relationship between Avogadro's hypothesis of molecules and Dalton's hypothesis of atoms. Cannizzaro also was instrumental in fixing a reliable standard for determining relative molecular weights based upon ratios of density. He used hydrogen with an arbitrary molecular weight of 2 as the standard. This standard has since been changed. Because oxygen combines with more elements and is heavier than hydrogen, the ratios for oxygen are more easily measured with precision. The standard for determining molecular weights was therefore shifted to oxygen which was given an arbitrary molecular weight of 32. The standard is now carbon with a molecular weight of 12.

Slowly the atomic theory emerged as the organizational basis for experiments in widely diverse areas of investigation. With this recognition the atomic theory gained validity because of its successful representation of verifiable data. The theory has been changed constantly to improve its validity.

ELECTRICITY AND THE ATOMIC CONCEPTS

Recounting chronologically the development of the central ideas of physical science often presents what seems to be a discontinuous display of oscillations into history. The continuity is restored only after the several ideas merge in an inclusive theory which embodies the various meanings which have been developed. Thereafter, the ideas are associated in their newly found relationships and are seen from a unified perspective. Such is the situation with electricity and the elements of atomic theory.

Static electricity No word we have used so far throughout this book has the broad scope of meanings gained from experience as the word electricity. The technological applications of electricity are so wide that hardly a moment of our day can be singled out as being devoid of its influence. Many persons have come to look upon electricity as one of the principal sources of modern technical wizardry; very few bother to try to understand the nature of its applications. Because of the aura of enchantment associated with modern electrical appliances, the illustrations we shall use may seem quite trivial. In the sense of power and energy transformed, they are trivial. Yet, in the sense of understanding some of the fundamental characteristics of electricity, the effects are most significant.

The word *electricity* came indirectly from *elector*, an ancient Greek word for the *sun*. More directly the word came from *electron*, the Greek word for *amber* and for *gold*, perhaps because of their supposed association with the yellow brilliance of the sun. Amber when rubbed by wool or any other animal fiber has the property of attracting small bits of paper or other materials such as chaff or straw which were known to the ancients. The early Greek philosophers such as Thales of Miletus ascribed to amber and also to the lodestone (natural magnets), an immaterial spirit or soul which was roused in amber by the action of rubbing.

The effect can be demonstrated by simply combing hair and then noting the attraction of the comb for small bits of paper. Our explanation, of course, is that the plastic material of the comb has a higher affinity for electrons than the hair. Combing allows the electrons to move from the hair to the comb. The comb thereby acquires a negative charge and the hair is left with a positive charge. But we have jumped far ahead of our historical account.

At about the same time that Boyle was introducing ideas of classifying substances, Otto von Guericke of Germany was inventing an electric machine. It consisted of a large globe of sulfur mounted so that it could be rotated while a hand was placed on the surface, providing the required contact for charging the surface. Up until this time (late 1600's) it had been assumed that the electrical charge remained totally attached to the body on which it was generated. The fact that electricity could move from one place to another, except as the whole charged body was moved, was completely unknown. Von Guericke was the first man to record an observation of electrical conduction. He had observed that the electrical charge could be extended from the sulfur globe through a linen thread so that the thread would attract or be attracted by other bodies. He did not carry the experiment to any further application, nor did his account create any special interest elsewhere when it was published in 1672.

Not until 1732 was the study of electrical conduction to receive anything but casual attention. In that year Stephen Gray, an English scientist, announced the results of his experiments regarding conductors and insulators of electricity. Gray had succeeded in transmitting electrical effects over distances of .700 ft or more through pack thread. In the process of his experiments he had identified several good electrical insulators such as glass, silk, horsehair, and resin. He also had discovered that pack thread and brass wire, as well as other metallic objects, were conductors of electricity. Gray's experiments were given widespread publicity. Many scientists repeated Gray's experiments and extended the applications to other materials and phenomena.

It was natural that the development of the electric machine should have stimulated speculation concerning the similarities between lightning and the electric spark. One of the foremost experimenters in this regard was Benjamin Franklin. His famous kite and key demonstration of 1752 proved the electrical nature of lightning. His was a foolhardy operation; others have been killed in similar situations. A kite was raised into a storm cloud. As the kite string became wet and conducting, Franklin performed a few crucial tests. He was holding the kite by a string of dry silk while standing in a dry and sheltered position. Franklin was fully aware of the potential dangers involved. He brought his knuckle near to a key which was attached to the end of the wet string. A spark jumped from the key to his hand. The sound was that of known electric sparks produced in the laboratory.

Franklin then charged a Leyden jar by lowering the key to its surface. The test was completed. The sparks produced by electricity from the clouds were identical to the sparks produced by electric machines. Another natural phenomenon had become associated with the familiar events of the laboratory.

Franklin also is credited with naming the electrical charges. He proposed a one-fluid theory of electricity which was to be short-lived, but his charge designations were destined to continue. Franklin believed that electric charge was the result of a redistribution of electricity already in the materials involved. A lack of sufficient electric fluid produced a negative charge and an oversupply, a positive charge. He argued that if in the process of rubbing glass with silk the glass acquired a positive charge, the other material (the silk) must have lost that amount of charge and thus acquired an equal and opposite "negative" charge. We now know that the negative and positive charges are characteristics of atomic particles such as electrons and protons, respectively.

Current electricity Electricity and chemical reactions are closely related. Our everyday experiences with dry cells and automobile batteries attest to this. The first identification of circumstances producing current electricity was made in 1792 by a professor in the University of Bologna, Luigi Galvani. Galvani observed that the legs of frogs under dissection moved spasmodically when the dissecting hooks and the attached specimen were pressed against an iron plate or iron railing. Unfortunately, however, Galvani interpreted the effect in terms of an "animal electricity" and almost lost

his place of honor in the history of science. Galvani's interpretation aroused a considerable curiosity among the physicists, physiologists, and medical men of his time. Among the physicists was a fellow countryman of the University of Pavia, Alessandro Volta. Volta demonstrated conclusively that animal tissue was not a necessary ingredient in producing the electrical effect.

Volta's curiosity about current electricity did not stop with the demonstration of Galvani's error but extended into new discoveries. In a long series of experiments, Volta brought pairs of metals into contact with various moist surfaces and also into contact with each other. He was able to show that two dissimilar metals become oppositely charged when brought in contact with each other. For example, when a piece of zinc is placed in contact with a piece of copper, the zinc becomes positively charged and the copper negatively charged. By comparing the charges produced on numerous metal pairs, Volta constructed a list of metals such that when any two of them were brought into contact the metal higher in the list became positively charged and the lower metal negatively charged. The more widely separated the materials so listed, the more pronounced is the charge developed between them upon contact. Volta's list was as follows:

1. Zinc	5. Copper
2. Lead	6. Silver
3. Tin	7. Gold
4. Iron	8. Carbon

In 1800, in a letter to the Royal Society of London, Volta described a prototype of the modern *electrical battery*. Essentially, the battery consisted of a series of individual cells connected as in Fig. 15.7.

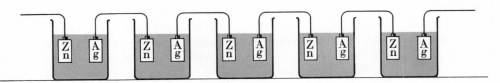

Figure 15.7 Volta's electrolytic battery. Each cup constitutes an electrolytic cell. Several cells hooked together become a battery.

Each cup was filled with brine and into the brine was placed a strip of zinc and a strip of silver. The strip of zinc in one cup was connected by solder to the strip of silver in an adjoining cup. The greater the number of cells, the greater is the electrical effect. Directing the electrical current into external circuits was achieved by connections to the unconnected strips of zinc and silver in the end cups.

Michael Faraday. [*Courtesy of the Bettmann Archive.*]

As soon as a reliable source of current electricity was made available, a great influx of electrical effects were discovered and described. In 1801, the heating effect of the electric current was demonstrated. In 1802, a crude form of carbon arc light was produced. Because these effects required such large series of voltaic cells for operation, they were considered only as scientific curiosities rather than as potentially useful. The first commercial application of electricity is said to be the ignition of blasting powder by electricity in 1808.

Electroplating with zinc was first recorded in 1802. The process, which became known as "galvanizing," later developed into an important industry.

In 1800, Nicholson and Carlisle observed that when an electric current flows between two metal strips dipped into water, hydrogen is produced at one strip and oxygen at the other. This was the first important observation of the electrical decomposition of water. Notice that discovery of the electrical effects in decomposing compounds preceded the introduction of atomic concepts. It was to take almost 30 years before the concepts of electricity and those of the atomic hypotheses were united.

Electrolysis The brilliant English scientist Michael Faraday, in the early 1830's,

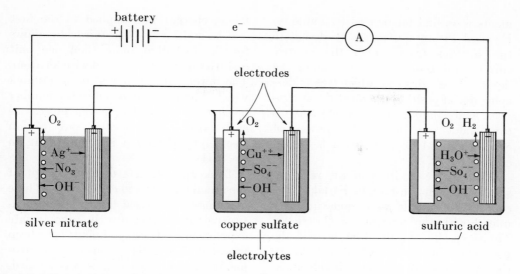

Figure 15.8 Faraday's laws of electrolysis. Twice as many silver (Ag^+) ions are liberated per unit time as copper (Cu^{++}) ions.

began a series of experiments prompted by certain unexplained aspects related to electroplating and to decomposition of water. Again, careful observation and quantitative measurements were to lead the way to better understanding. While experimenting with the conductivity of various water solutions, Faraday noticed that the electrical current halted abruptly when a thin film of ice formed on the metal electrodes he had inserted into the solution. Further experiments showed that the solid state of water was a non-conductor of electricity. Experiments on other substances showed that conduction and decomposition began after the substances were melted, but ceased again when they became solids. No water was involved. This showed that water was not an essential ingredient to electrolysis. Faraday also confirmed the fact that a compound decomposes electrolytically into its constituent elements

in the same mass ratio as they combine chemically to form the compound.

A summary of Faraday's experimental results was set forth in the three general laws of electrolysis which now bear his name (Fig. 15.8). Phrased in modern terms *Faraday's Laws of Electrolysis* are:

1. The mass of the substance deposited or liberated at either electrode from an electrolyte is proportional to the quantity of electricity driven through the solution.
2. The masses of the substances deposited or liberated from an electrolyte by a given quantity of electricity are proportional to their atomic weights.
3. The masses of the substances deposited or liberated from an electrolyte by a given quantity of electricity are inversely proportional to their respective valences.

Many of the terms used in these statements were first introduced by Faraday. He used the term *electrode* to designate the surfaces from which the electric current was brought into or out of the liquid. The substance which was undergoing decomposition he called the *electrolyte*. Only liquids that are electrolytes can conduct electricity. The process of electrochemical decomposition he called *electrolysis*.

With the recognition of the relationships stated in the laws of Faraday, the concepts of atoms were quantitatively united with the concepts of electricity. To be specific, in the first law, if the proportionality were extended down to the atomic-sized portions involved in electrolysis, it could be concluded that each atom of a given element has associated with it the *same* quantity of electricity. The second law expresses the idea that the same number of atoms of different elements are associated with a given quantity of electricity and, consequently, the *same* quantity of electricity is associated with every atom involved in the electrolysis, regardless of the substance involved. The third law modifies the meaning of the second law somewhat. A basic unit quantity of electricity (now known to be the electronic charge) was implied in the first and second laws. The third law allows for the fact that more than one unit quantity may be associated with an atom. The term *valence* refers to a number which is numerically equal to the number of *electrons* associated in the process as each atom is deposited out of an electrolyte or an ion is liberated at an electrode.

Thus was begun a unified concept of the atomic theory and electricity. These meanings were based firmly upon quantitative measurements in appropriate experiments. The experiments have been repeated thousands of times. The atomicity of electrical charges was implied, but it cannot be said that the relationships were understood, although Faraday spoke of his conviction regarding the idea that the same forces govern electrolysis as govern chemical attraction between elements.

The stage was set for the next phase of development in the atomic theory. Important associations had been made between ideas of electricity and atoms. It was to take another 60 years before the compelling evidences were to be discovered which would revolutionize man's concepts of matter and energy.

SUMMARY

The idea of atomicity of matter was first recorded in the teachings of Democritus about 400 B.C. The wide interest in chemical elements during the later part of the eighteenth century led to the discovery of several empirical laws describing the reactions between various elements:

The same compound always contains the same elements in the same mass proportions.

When the same two elements combine to form more than one compound, the different masses of one of the elements that combine with a constant mass of the other are in the ratio of small whole numbers.

To each element may be assigned a number called its combining weight which when multiplied by a small whole number expresses the mass of that element which combines with the combining weight of another element in forming a compound.

Dalton's application of the theory of atoms in explaining his law of multiple proportions brought useful insights into the interpretations of the above-stated laws. With the addition of Avogadro's hypothesis of molecules, the atomic theory emerged as a useful representation of verifiable data.

Since Volta's discovery of the voltaic cell using the energy potential between dissimilar metals, electricity has been closely associated with chemical elements. The uniting of concepts developed in interpretation of electrical events with concepts of atomic events took place in Faraday's laws of electrolysis. The implication of atomicity of electrical charges in connection with atomic events in electrolysis was based firmly upon quantitative measurements in appropriately controlled experiments. The relationships were not understood, but firm associations were established linking the theories of electricity to the atomic theory of matter.

PROBLEMS

1 What specific observations were generalized in the statements of the following laws: law of definite proportion, law of multiple proportions, law of combining weights, and Gay-Lussac's law?

2 Summarize the evidences requiring a specific atomic structure or atomic process to explain an observed natural event.

3 Compare the basic assumptions of Dalton's theory of atoms to those necessary for the concepts you have summarized in Problem 2.

4 What were the crucial tests whereby Franklin proved that lightning was electricity?

5 How does each of Faraday's laws of electrolysis quantitatively measure a relationship between electricity and the atomic theory?

6 If 100 grams of iron filings were mixed and heated with 40 grams of powdered sulfur, how much of each would be combined in the resulting ferrous sulfide?

7 Separate water solutions of each of the salts of cadmium (at. wt. 112.40), copper (at. wt. 63.54), silver (at. wt. 107.87), and zinc (at. wt. 65.37) are used as electrolytes in four cells arranged as in Fig. 15.7; 54 grams of silver are deposited by a current passing through the series of cells. How much cadmium, copper, and zinc would you predict would be deposited on the electrodes of their respective cells?

8   If 130.8 grams of zinc combine with 16 grams of oxygen to form zinc oxide, how many grams of chlorine would you predict would combine with 130.8 grams of zinc to form zinc chloride?

16

GENERATING

NEW ATOMIC MODELS

The tempo of scientific progress is set by the stimulating union of experimental observation and imaginative theoretical speculation. Advances in either aspect bring a need for unifying activity in the other. This activity results in an unending growth in man's understanding of natural processes. One's personal understanding of these processes also depends upon the union of knowledge generated by observation and theory. Advancement in atomic theory has become highly dependent upon observations of events interpreted by their relationships to electricity and magnetism.

Interaction between electricity and magnetism was discovered in 1819 by Hans Christian Oersted. A bar magnet is suspended above an electric wire, and the position of the wire is adjusted so that it is parallel to the length of the magnet. When an electric current flows through the wire, the magnet turns to a direction crosswise to the wire (Fig. 16.1). When the current is

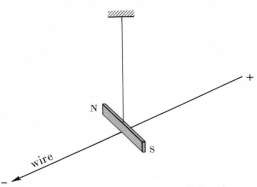

Figure 16.1 Oersted's magnet and electric current experiment. When electricity flows, the magnet turns crosswise to the wire.

shut off, the magnet returns to its parallel position. If then the direction of the electric current is reversed, the magnet turns crosswise again but with the poles reversed from their first positions. Also, in each situation if the wire were placed above the suspended magnet, the magnetic poles would be turned to the reversed positions from those produced when the wire is below the magnet (Fig. 16.2). We are led to conclude that the electric current produces a magnetic

force effect which (1) reverses directions when the current is reversed, and (2) is directed oppositely above and below the wire.

Furthermore, the directional quantities of the force between an electric current and a magnet are different from previously described forces. The forces of attraction or repulsion observed between two magnets or between two charged objects are directed along the lines which connect the two objects. But the forces observed between an electric current and a magnet are not directed along the connecting lines; they act in directions perpendicular to the connecting lines. Useful applications of this fact are found in the operation of electric motors and in the synchronizing of picture patterns in a television tube.

Stimulated by Oersted's discovery, Andre Marie Ampere made extensive investigations of the magnetic effects of electric currents. One of his early descriptions involved the relationship between the direction of the electric current and the direction taken by a compass needle placed near the electrical

Figure 16.2 Effects of current direction and location of magnet.

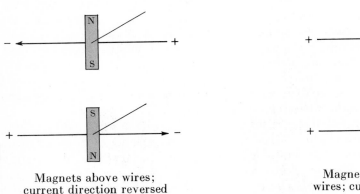

Magnets above wires;
current direction reversed

Magnets below and above
wires; current direction same

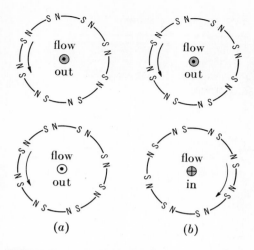

(a) (b)

Figure 16.3 Ampere's model of magnetic effect between current-carrying wires.

conductor. Most easily remembered as the *right-hand rule*, Ampere's description may be stated as follows: *Encircle the electrical conductor with the fingers of the right hand, thumb extended in the direction of current flow* (from positive to negative electrodes); *the fingers then point in the directions of deflection of a north pole placed at any point near the conductor.*

A very significant part of this description was Ampere's establishment of a *conventional direction* for the flow of electricity. This was done primarily to avoid having to qualify repeatedly the relationship of the conductor to the battery electrodes. In the early 1800's no one knew whether the current consisted of negative flow, positive flow, or both simultaneously. It was assumed that the description of external phenomena would be unaffected whichever choice of flow was used. Unfortunately, Ampere chose to describe the current direction as that from the positive electrode to the negative electrode of the battery. The electron flow which now

characterizes the electric current in solids is exactly opposite in direction. Therefore, when the electric current is described in terms of *electron flow* the *left hand* is substituted for the right hand in Ampere's conventional description.

Ampere also established a description for the force which exists between parallel currents. He observed that a force of attraction exists between currents flowing in the same direction, and a force of repulsion between currents flowing in opposite directions. The forces were accounted for by a model which figuratively pictured the magnetic effect of a current as a series of concentrically arranged tiny magnets surrounding the path of the current. Fig. 16.3 pictures the model. Recalling the force relationships of magnetic poles, the arrangement of magnets in the model explains imaginatively the forces existing between currents. The magnetic effect does not depend upon the type of conductor. The flow of electrical charges in any medium produces the same effects. The observations of magnetic effects of electrical currents have become an important tool for experiments which probe electrical and atomic phenomena.

Toward the end of the nineteenth century many experimenters in England and Germany became particularly interested in the spectacular displays produced from electrical discharges in gaseous media. When the pressure of the gas can be lowered and controlled at low pressures, an electrical discharge through the gas may produce beautiful and thought-provoking effects. The investigation and interpretation of these effects led to a revolution in men's mode of thinking. The immediate effect was to overthrow the ancient idea of indivisible atoms. The long-range effect

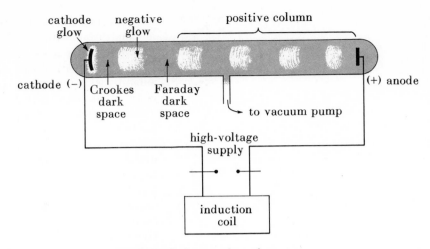

Figure 16.4 Apparatus for observing electrical discharges through gas.

ELECTRICAL DISCHARGE IN LOW PRESSURE GASES

The discoveries of electrons and of X-rays were two very important results of observation of electrical discharges through gases at low pressure. These discoveries took place between 1895 and 1900. The experimental techniques were an outgrowth of improved apparatus. The low gas pressures were made possible by new vacuum pump techniques invented by Heinrich Giessler of Bonn, Germany, in 1855. The discovery of electromagnetic induction by the American scientist Joseph Henry and by Michael Faraday made possible the designing of the high-voltage induction coils needed for producing the electrical discharges. New techniques in glass-blowing and of sealing metal electrodes into glass made possible

the building of apparatus never before available. The time was right for important new observations.

General observations A convenient arrangement of apparatus for observing electrical discharges through gas is shown in Fig. 16.4. If the tube is relatively long there is no discharge through the gas at atmospheric pressure. When the pressure is reduced to about one-tenth atmospheric pressure, the first observable discharge takes the form of a series of violet-colored threads of light extending

Figure 16.5 Cathode ray tube producing fluorescence and shadow.

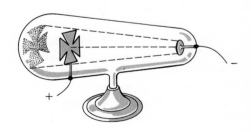

Figure 16.6 Cathode ray tube designed to demonstrate momentum.

from one electrode to the other. As the exhaustion of air continues, these thread-like streamers of light are replaced by a uniform soft pinkish glow which fills the tube. Continued reduction of air pressure produces a succession of changes in the appearance of the tube until at pressures between 0.001 and 0.002 atmosphere the discharge has the characteristics shown in Fig. 16.4. When the pressure is reduced to about 0.0000001 atmosphere the Crookes' dark space appears to fill the tube and the glass walls at the anode end of the tube fluoresce with a bright greenish light. When other gases are used in the tube instead of air a similar pattern of events takes place, but each gas produces its own characteristic glow colors. Lecture demonstrations of these gas tube properties attracted much attention and were very popular public performances in the latter part of the nineteenth century.

Cathode rays Not the first but surely one of the most productive experimenters with electrical discharges in evacuated tubes was Sir William Crookes. Much of his success is attributed to his assistant, G. C. Gimingham, who was a remarkable glass-blower. Many of the discharge tubes designed and built by Gimingham have never been improved upon.

Crookes was not the only experimenter in this field. The term "cathode ray" was introduced by Goldstein of Berlin. Goldstein proposed that the luminous "rays" given off at the cathode were a type of electromagnetic radiation similar to light. Crookes suggested the hypothesis that the cathode rays were "radiant matter."

Crookes was able to show that cathode rays produced fluorescence, moved in straight-line paths, were deflected by magnets, had properties of momentum, and transmitted energy. Crookes attributed these effects to corpuscles. In light of our inquiries in Chapters 2 and 3, you might evaluate Crookes' assumption.

The type of discharge tube shown in Fig. 16.5 demonstrates the production of fluorescence by cathode rays. The sharp shadows visible at the end of the tube show the straight-line propagation paths of the "rays." When the cross-shaped target is flipped down, the entire surface of the end of the tube is fluorescent.

Gimingham's device to demonstrate the momentum of the cathode rays is shown in Fig. 16.6. The paddle wheel at W has vanes of lightweight mica and rolls easily along the horizontal rails. In use, when the electrode at A is the cathode, the wheel rotates toward the right. When the cathode is reversed to B, the wheel rotates toward the left. Although the results seem to prove conclusively that the paddle wheel turns because of bombardment and transfer of momentum of the cathode particles, we must also take notice of J. J. Thomson's demonstration of a similar effect produced by heating the vanes with radiant energy.

The cathode ray tube shown in Fig. 16.7 demonstrates the transmission of energy by cathode rays. Use is made of the fact discovered by Goldstein that the "rays" given off by a cathode are propagated only in directions normal to the emitting surface. This is unlike emitters of radiant energy where propagation proceeds in all directions about equally. Thus, when a cathode is a portion of a sphere, the cathode rays focus at the point of the center of curvature. In Fig. 16.7 the point of focus is b in a

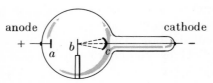

anode   cathode

Figure 16.7 Cathode ray tube designed to demonstrate kinetic energy.

platinum disk. When a discharge is produced the disk at b becomes white hot. If the cathode rays are deflected by a magnet to areas outside the disk, the heating effect does not take place. Again, we point out that *except for the deflection of the cathode ray by a magnet* all of the characteristics demonstrated by Crookes in support of "radiant matter" might also be explained by the characteristics of electromagnetic radiation.

Particles or electromagnetic radiation

The controversy over whether cathode rays are matter or electromagnetic radiation was to be solved very shortly by scientific analyses which involved measurement of the resulting effects. Two important experiments of this type were carried on by J. Perrin in France and J. J. Thomson in England. The results were published in 1895 and 1897, respectively.

Perrin's contribution was to establish that the cathode rays transport negative charges. The device he used is illustrated in Fig. 16.8. The insulated cylinder at C was placed inside a larger cylindrical anode which had but a small opening through which the "rays" could enter. The insulated cylinder was connected to an electroscope. When the discharge tube was in operation, the small pencil of rays which penetrated to C charged the electroscope negatively. If the discharge was deflected by a magnet so that the "rays" did not strike the anode opening, the electroscope failed to become charged. The charge would appear again when the magnet was removed. Thus the electric charge characteristic of the cathode ray was measured as a negative charge.

Thomson's experiments were more extensive and also more decisive. He

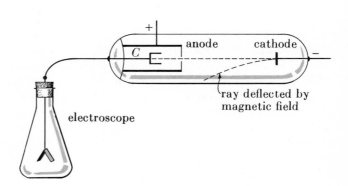

anode   cathode

ray deflected by magnetic field

electroscope

Figure 16.8 Perrin's tube. The cathode ray charges the electroscope with negative electricity.

Sir Joseph John Thomson. [*Courtesy of the Bettmann Archive.*]

proved the existence of electrostatic charge deflection of the cathode ray; and by a combination of measurable electrostatic deflection and magnetic deflection he was able to determine the mass-to-charge ratio of cathode rays. His experimental apparatus was a device by which he could balance the electrostatic deflection against the magnetic deflection; Fig. 16.9 shows the essential parts. Thomson could adjust the electrostatic charge at the deflecting plates and the magnetic force of the externally placed electromagnets. With proper adjustment the effect of the electric charges could be balanced by the magnetic effects. After measuring the conditions for balance, the deflection of the ray produced by each effect acting independently was measured. Computation involving measured values of the dimensions of the apparatus components and the quantity of charge and electromagnetic current revealed a surprising result for the ratio of mass-to-charge. It was about one-thousandth of the corresponding ratio found for the hydrogen ion in electrolysis.

By inserting cathodes made of several different materials, Thomson determined that the ratio was independent of the materials used for the electrodes. He also determined that the ratio was independent of the gas in which the discharge took place. The ratio of approximately 5.7×10^{-12} kilograms per coulomb is the

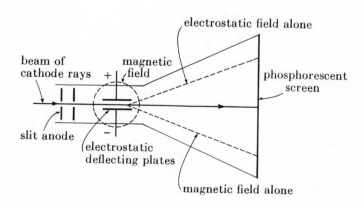

Figure 16.9 Thomson's apparatus. By adjusting the electrostatic and magnetic fields, a balance of forces is achieved.

mass-to-charge ratio of cathode ray particles.

Conclusions and their significance A few months before Thomson's surprising results with cathode rays, the Dutch theorist Hendrik Lorentz had reached a similar conclusion in explanation of the Zeeman effect. Zeeman had discovered that spectral lines were separated into several lines by placing the emitter in a strong magnetic field. In explaining the effect Lorentz assumed that vibration of ions or electrically charged particles in an atom produces light in the same manner as electrical oscillations in an antenna produce radio waves. Placing an atom in a strong magnetic field would subject the assumed vibrating particles to an electromagnetic force which produced a change in the frequency of the emitted light, as observed in the Zeeman effect. Using this hypothesis Lorentz was able to calculate the value of the required mass-to-charge ratio of particles within the atom which would produce the observed effect. His results, within the limits of experimental variation, were precisely the value obtained by Thomson for cathode rays. These results provided independent confirmations of the particle nature of the carriers of electric charges.

The year 1897 marked the end of the ancient concept of an indivisible atom. The Irish theorist G. F. Fitzgerald was perhaps the first to interpret the significant meaning of Thomson's results. Although he realized that the experimental results did not prove that atoms had been dissociated, Fitzgerald strongly suggested that such a hypothesis would have to be recognized as a possibility. He suggested too that cathode rays consisted of free "electrons." Lorentz had also used the term "electron" in describing his calculated expression of the Zeeman effect. The work of Lorentz also marked the electron as an important entity in explanation of light emission.

Within a few years experimental techniques were devised to measure the electronic charge. Before this was done no one could explain the small mass-to-charge ratio except to show that it might be produced by a small mass and constant charge unit for all such ratios, or it might be produced by a larger charge unit for the particles of the cathode ray than for the ion ratios previously obtained. R. A. Millikan at the University of Chicago achieved the most significant experimental determination of the electronic charge. The essential features of his experimental arrangement are shown in Fig. 16.10. Oil drops are sprayed from an atomizer and a few droplets fall through the small hole in the upper plate. These droplets generally become electrically charged. Entering the chamber the droplets come under intense illumination from a light at S and are clearly visible in the field of the viewing telescope. When the electric potential is applied to the upper and lower plates, some of the negatively charged droplets move upward. The observer selects one of these for measurement. The droplet is allowed to fall under the force of gravity only and its downward acceleration and speed is measured. Its upward acceleration and speed is measured when the droplet is placed under the net force of a known electric potential overcoming the force of gravity. After the viscosity of air, the acceleration due to gravity, and the electrical potential have been determined, the charge on the droplet can be calculated. Millikan and his students made thousands of observations and

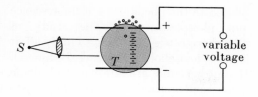

Figure 16.10 Millikan's oil drop apparatus. Electrically charged oil drops are observed through a telescope.

calculations. In every situation they found that the charge on the droplet was a certain multiple of an average constant value of 1.59×10^{-19} coulomb. The commonly used unit of electric current, the *ampere*, is a rate of flow of electric charge of 1 *coulomb* per second. At present the most probable value of the electronic charge e is 1.602×10^{-19} coulomb. An ampere of current represents the flow of 6.24 billion billion electrons (6.24×10^{18}) per second.

Substituting the numerical values of the mass-to-charge ratio and the electronic charge gives the mass of the cathode ray particle. The mass m of the electron is 9.108×10^{-31} kilograms. This is compared to 1.673×10^{-27} kilograms as the mass of the hydrogen atom. The hydrogen atom has a mass 1837 times that of the electron.

By the end of the nineteenth century, electrons were an established fact. It had been established without a doubt that electrons form a part of the *structure* of every atom. Atoms no longer were the indivisible building blocks of the universe. Two changes seemed imperative in all future models of atoms. First, as a result of Thomson's findings in cathode rays, atoms must have independent particles called electrons in their structure. Second, as the result of the Lorentz calculation of electron oscillation to

produce the Zeeman effect, the electrons must circulate in definite orbits within the atom.

There was no agreement at that time upon how many electrons an atom might contain or how the atom was structured. Several models were proposed; one of the more inclusive ones was J. J. Thomson's (Fig. 16.11). He pictured the atom as

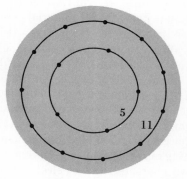

Figure 16.11 Thomson's atom model. Electrons were embedded in a fluid sphere.

consisting of electrons embedded in a sphere of positively charged, fluidlike material. The electrons were shown moving in orbits like planets, except that there were several electrons in each orbital ring. In an effort to explain the stability of atoms, Thomson found he needed to limit the number of electrons in each orbit. Therefore, as shown in Fig. 16.11, the model had a maximum of 5 electrons in the first orbit. The sixth electron started a new orbit. The second orbit showed a maximum of 11 electrons. The seventeenth electron would start the third orbit, and so on.

RADIOACTIVITY AND THE BIRTH OF THE NUCLEAR ATOM

On November 8, 1895, Wilhelm Roentgen discovered X-ray. Professor of physics at Wurzburg, Germany, Roentgen was investigating the effects produced by cathode rays in air and hydrogen when he observed fluorescence in materials too far removed from the apparatus to have been activated by cathode rays in air. Shifting his study to this newly observed effect, Roentgen within a few weeks had ascertained several characteristics of these new rays: (a) all materials are to a degree transparent to X-rays; (b) the rays affect photographic plates; (c) the rays are not deflected by magnets; (d) the rays produce fluorescence in materials even after passing through a considerable range of air; (e) air irradiated with X-rays becomes ionized and, therefore, can discharge electrified objects. These penetrating rays also displayed the commonly known characteristics of electromagnetic radiation such as reflection, refraction, and interference. Newspapers throughout the world gave wide coverage to the discovery during January of 1896. The fascinating stories of the development of X-rays to their present use make an interesting series of reading. Very few scientific announcements have so stirred the general public as did the discovery of X-rays.

The discovery of radioactivity Roentgen's discovery of X-rays was reported to the French Academy of Science on Jan. 20, 1896. A fallacious hypothesis was proposed to the effect that X-rays emanated from the part of the discharge tube glass which fluoresced most strongly. Consequently, X-rays were thought to be related to the phenomena of fluorescence and phosphorescence. The study of phosphorescence had been a family affair in the household of Henri Becquerel. His father and grandfather had made many contributions in this field. Becquerel possessed the training, the materials, and the apparatus necessary for an immediate test of the hypothesis of X-ray origin in fluorescence. His was not a haphazard discovery.

Becquerel set about the task of systematically checking the possibility of fluorescence as a source of X-ray. He wrapped a photographic plate in black paper of sufficient thickness to prevent photographic action when exposed to direct sunlight for a whole day. He then placed on the prepared plate an open vessel containing a phosphorescent substance and exposed the total package to direct sunlight for several hours. The plan was that if X-rays were produced by the resulting phosphorescence, the photographic plate would become exposed. After several substances had given negative results, Becquerel tested a compound of uranium and got positive results. The uranium salts were emitting radiations which penetrated the paper and activated the photographic materials. This result was reported on Feb. 24, 1896. Within one week, Becquerel had a more startling announcement to make. The uranium salt produced the same photographic effect without exposure to incident light; it was emitting the penetrating rays while kept in total darkness. The activity did not depend upon exposure to other sources of light. By Mar. 9, Becquerel had shown that the "Becquerel rays" from uranium were able to ionize air in the same manner as X-rays. Oddly enough, very few scientists and fewer persons in the general public paid any attention to Becquerel's momentous discovery of radioactivity.

Among the scientists who were interested were the young Polish physicist Marie Curie and her husband Pierre who were then working in Paris. The story of the discovery of polonium and radium has been widely publicized. The highly radioactive radium became an important source for further study.

The discovery of radium was reported in December of 1898. In 1899, Becquerel in France and Giesel in Germany reported that a part of the Becquerel rays emitted by radium was deflected by a magnetic field. The direction of deviation was the same as that of cathode rays.

Radioactive transformation Early in 1899, a young New Zealander, Ernest Rutherford, working at the University of Manchester, found that there were at least two distinct types of radiation present in the rays from uranium. The type which was easily absorbed he termed *alpha radiation* and the more penetrating ray, *beta radiation*. Later a very penetrating radiation was observed being emitted by radium. This was called *gamma radiation*. Any substance which spontaneously emits one or more of these rays is said to be *radioactive*.

In 1903, Rutherford increased the intensity of the electric and magnetic fields used to deflect the Becquerel rays and succeeded in deflecting the alpha ray as well as the beta ray. He postulated that the alpha ray consisted of high-speed helium ions each carrying two positive electronic charges. He gained support for this hypothesis by accounting for the measured heating effect of radium on the basis of the kinetic energy of the alpha particles which are emitted from a gram

of radium each second. Later that year, Rutherford and Frederick Soddy proposed a theory of radioactive transformation very similar to the one we used in Chapter 14.

The central theme of the Rutherford-Soddy theory is that the atoms of radioactive substances are naturally unstable and are transformed into other substances spontaneously. The complexity of radiations results when a series of transformations follow one another in a given family of active elements. In Chapter 14 we saw how, when an atom of uranium-238 emits an alpha particle of mass 4, the remaining atom is thorium-234, which also is radioactive. When the atom of thorium-234 emits a beta particle, the remaining atom is protactinium-234, also radioactive. The series proceeds through fourteen generations to the stable isotope, lead-206. The original Rutherford-Soddy theory of radioactive transformation has not been changed in any essential detail.

The spontaneous transformation of atoms of one element into atoms of other elements definitely established the fact of divisible atoms and of atoms containing particles of positive electrical charge as well as electrons.

Scattering of alpha particles by thin metal foils Only a very few scientists at the turn of the century were very interested in atomic models. The problem of studying atomic structure was held to be much too speculative and inaccessible to warrant serious concern. But to those who had been investigating the nature of radiation from radioactive substances, the question of how mass and charges were distributed within the structure of the atom was of primary interest. There were questions of whether beta particles produced gamma rays by bombardment similar to the production of X-ray. The investigation of atomic phenomena continued.

A variety of experiments had revealed the size of atoms to be in the order of 1 Angstrom unit (10^{-8} cm). We have emphasized that visible light has wavelengths which are thousands of times greater than the atomic size; hence, it is impossible to observe details of atomic structure by reflection or diffraction of light. Rutherford suggested to his students the use of the *scattering* of alpha particles as a possible means of indirect measurement of particle and charge distribution within the atom. Ernest Marsden and Hans Geiger working in Rutherford's laboratory performed most of the fundamental scattering experiments. The essential arrangement of components for these experiments is shown in Fig. 16.12. The method of scattering is based upon the strategy that if the alpha particles emerge in a forward direction with but a slight loss of speed, the particle has not encountered any atomic particles while in transit. A

slight deviation would indicate a near miss of a charged particle. If the alpha particle is strongly deflected from its original direction, it has been encountered by collision particles of substantial mass.

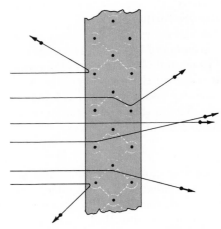

Figure 16.13 Foil particles. Alpha particles are deflected by the positive charges in each nucleus.

When a stream of alpha particles was directed at a thin metal foil of gold, most of the particles passed right through, a few were turned aside slightly and very few were deflected by large angles. Occasionally an alpha particle actually came back emerging from the foil on the same side it went in. The deflections were much greater than could be accounted for by the Thomson model of the atom or any other model then in use. In May 1911, Rutherford published an account of the scattering experiments completed until that time. The major assumption made in the report brought on the epoch of the nuclear atom. The hypothesis used to explain the scattering

Figure 16.12 Scattering of alpha particles. The entire positive charge of the atom is confined to a central sphere called the *nucleus*.

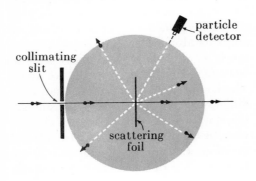

results pictured the atom as consisting of a central charge (called the nucleus in later papers by Rutherford) surrounded by a sphere of electrical charge equal but of opposite charge to the nucleus. Calculations showed that the observed scattering of alpha and beta particles by the thickness of foil used could be explained by assuming that the central charge was concentrated in a sphere of about 3×10^{-14} meters radius. The remainder of the atom consisted of electrical charges of opposite sign confined to a sphere of about 10^{-10} meters radius. In general these dimensions are those in use today. (See Fig. 16.14.)

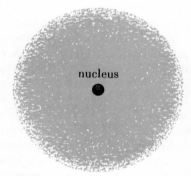

Figure 16.14 Rutherford model of the atom. The massive nucleus is located at the center of a sphere.

No attempt was made by Rutherford to assign electrons to definite orbits. The problem of having electrons accelerated in circular paths was that theoretically they should radiate continuously. This they obviously did not do. The loss of energy through radiation would collapse the atomic structure as each electron spiralled into the nucleus. Rutherford preferred to speak only of the

nucleus of which he had positive facts to report. He discovered that the magnitude of an atom's central charge was proportional to its atomic weight. In a book published in 1913, Rutherford did refer to electrons in describing the distribution of charges surrounding the nucleus. He also postulated special short-range forces to hold the component positive charges of the nucleus together. We might point out that nuclear forces still remain one of the most difficult problems in nuclear physics.

The successful explanation of the scattering experiments did not cause widespread scientific interest in atomic structure. Rutherford's publications were largely overlooked as items of little concern to the scientific world at that time. But it soon became clear that only men of daring imagination and unusual experimental techniques could improve upon the nuclear model of the atom as proposed by Ernest Rutherford.

HYDROGEN SPECTRUM AND BOHR'S THEORY OF THE ATOM

In the spring of 1912, Niels Bohr from Copenhagen, Denmark, spent several months working in Rutherford's laboratory at Manchester. He became convinced of the correctness of the nuclear model of the atom. As a result of calculations based upon this model, he concluded that hydrogen had a positive charge of 1 electronic unit in its nucleus. Helium was described as having a nucleus of 2 positive electronic units. Bohr firmly believed that the structure of atoms consisted of a positively charged nucleus surrounded by electrons. He soon began to speculate about electron structures which might explain the known

Neils Bohr. [*Courtesy of the Bettmann Archive.*]

spectral emissions of the hydrogen atom.

Spectrum of hydrogen atoms In Chapter 3 we introduced the idea of spectra in order to explain the dispersion of the various colors by prisms and by the raindrops which produce rainbows. It was explained further that each element emits light of characteristic frequencies which identified the elements found in the sources of light. The fact of identifying spectra was first discovered in 1859 by Kirchhoff and Bunsen. The fact that spectral lines of known elements matched the position of absorption lines discovered in the solar spectrum by Fraunhofer identifies the elements found in the solar atmosphere. Kirchhoff and Bunsen identified the absorption lines as those of sodium, calcium, iron, and other elements for which they had measured characteristic bright-line spectra. What they had accomplished was an indirect chemical analysis of the solar atmosphere. Since then analysis of observed emission and absorption spectra has served to identify the elements present in other stars and other material objects in the universe. Spectral analysis continues to be a very rewarding field for experimental study.

When an electric discharge is maintained in hydrogen, spectra of both hydrogen atoms and hydrogen molecules are observed. The bright-line spectrum of atomic origin is the most prominent. When dispersed, the light from hydrogen reveals four lines of the bright-line spectrum most clearly. These occur at wavelengths of about 6562.1 A, 4860.7 A, 4340.1 A, and 4101.2 A. Photographic investigation using long time exposures reveals a large number of lines of shorter wavelength than these four. These lines lie increasingly closer together as the wavelengths decrease, and reach a limiting frequency beyond which no visible lines are detected.

The analysis of atomic spectra was placed on a mathematical basis when in 1885 Johann J. Balmer succeeded in describing the spectral lines of hydrogen by a simple empirical formula:

(16.1) $\qquad \lambda = 3645.6 \text{ A } \dfrac{m^2}{m^2 - 4}$

where $m = 3, 4, 5, 6, \ldots$, successively. The first four wavelengths computed in this series are 6562.08 A, 4860.8 A, 4340 A, and 4101.3 A. The computed values are in good agreement with the measured ones.

A formula of broader application was devised by the Swedish spectroscopist J. R. Rydberg. The Rydberg formulas express the relationships for the reciprocals of the wavelengths. The reciprocal of Eq. (16.1) is:

$$\frac{1}{\lambda} = \frac{1}{3.6456 \times 10^{-5} \text{cm}} \times \frac{m^2 - 4}{m^2}$$

Multiplying both the numerator and denominator by 4:

$$\frac{1}{\lambda} = \frac{4}{3.6456 \times 10^{-5} \text{ cm}} \times \frac{m^2 - 4}{4m^2}$$

$$= 109720 \text{ cm}^{-1} \left(\frac{1}{4} - \frac{1}{m^2} \right)$$

The value 109720 cm^{-1} was known as the *Rydberg constant* and is given the symbol R. A later and more precise determination resulted in the value $R = 1.0967758 \times 10^5$ reciprocal centimeters. The Rydberg formula for the Balmer series is:

$$\frac{1}{\lambda} = R \left(\frac{1}{2^2} - \frac{1}{m^2} \right)$$

where $m = 3, 4, 5, 6, \ldots$, successively.

In 1906, T. Lyman discovered a similar series of emissions from hydrogen occurring in the ultraviolet frequencies. The Rydberg formula for the Lyman series is:

$$\frac{1}{\lambda} = R \left(\frac{1}{1^2} - \frac{1}{m^2} \right)$$

where $m = 2, 3, 4, 5, \ldots$, successively.

In 1908, F. Paschen discovered the first series of emissions from hydrogen occurring in the infrared frequencies. The Rydberg formula for the Paschen series is:

$$\frac{1}{\lambda} = R \left(\frac{1}{3^2} - \frac{1}{m^2} \right)$$

where $m = 4, 5, 6, 7, \ldots$, successively.

Several series have been discovered in the infrared range of the emissions from hydrogen, but none other than the Lyman series is found in the ultraviolet range. The explanation for this will be pointed out later in this chapter.

We emphasize that the Rydberg formulas are empirical equations which make possible the calculation and prediction of observed spectral lines. Devising an atomic theory which would explain these events in terms of the characteristics of atomic structure was a major contribution begun by Niels Bohr. The vital concept is that of quanta in energy transformation.

In order that we might interpret more meaningfully the proposed structure for various atomic models we need to review and extend our inquiry into the relationships involved in potential and kinetic energy as applied to charged particles.

Potential energy of electricity   A review of the inquiry made in Chapter 7 would aid in the interpretations we are about to make. In the example of the wheelbarrow on an incline, work was done in overcoming the earth's force of gravity as the wheelbarrow was rolled up the incline. The energy used was transformed into *gravitational potential energy* of the wheelbarrow. This potential energy could do useful work. If the wheelbarrow falls off the platform, the potential energy becomes transformed into kinetic

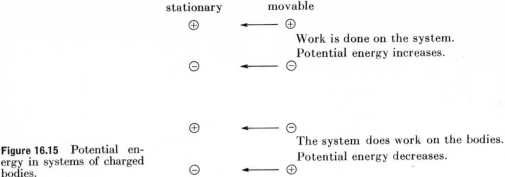

Figure 16.15 Potential energy in systems of charged bodies.

energy as the wheelbarrow falls. The quantity of energy transformed is measured in terms of the change in potential energy:

$$\Delta PE = mgh_2 - mgh_1$$

where m = mass of the falling object
g = acceleration due to gravity
h_1 = initial height of object
h_2 = height at time of measurement

Notice that since h_1 is greater than h_2, the change in potential energy will be negative for a falling object, thus correctly indicating a loss of potential energy. Also notice that since the change in potential energy is given in terms of the difference between two displacements, we could arbitrarily have designated any level as the zero level as long as the upward direction was designated as positive. For instance, we could have designated as the zero level the center of the earth, the top platform of the incline, the bottom of the incline, sea level, or any other useful arbitrary level. It was most convenient in the example of the wheelbarrow to use the bottom of the incline as the zero level.

Using the same general interpretation of the action of forces, when an electrically charged body is moved from one location to another *against* the existing electric force, work is done. The energy used is transformed into *electrical potential energy* of the charged body so moved. This potential energy also can do useful work. The charge can transform its potential energy if allowed to move under the influence of the electrical forces. *It is most convenient, therefore, to designate the points of zero force as the level of zero potential energy. The direction in which a positive test charge would tend to move is designated as the positive direction.* Thus, when a charge is brought toward a like charge, work is done against the force of repulsion. The potential energy of the charge is increased. However, when a charge is brought toward an unlike charge, the force of attraction aids in the work. The potential energy of the charge in this case, is decreased. (See Fig. 16.15.)

Coulomb's law of electrical force is expressed by an inverse square equation very similar to the expression of Newton's law of gravitation:

$$(16.2) \qquad F = \frac{kq_1q_2}{r^2}$$

where F = the coulomb force in newtons

if $k = 9 \times 10^9$ newton-meters² per coulomb²

q_1 = electrical charge in coulombs of first body

q_2 = electrical charge in coulombs of second body

r = displacement in meters between the charged bodies

The force between unlike charges is one of attraction; the force between like charges, one of repulsion. For example, the force between two electrons is one of repulsion between two negative charges. The force between two protons is one of repulsion between two positive charges. The force between a proton and an electron is one of attraction between a positive charge and a negative charge. The force of attraction between the proton and the electron in a hydrogen atom of radius 5.3×10^{-11} meters is 8.2×10^{-7} newtons.

$$k = \frac{9 \times 10^9 \text{ newton-meter}^2}{\text{coul}^2}$$

$$= \frac{9 \times 10^9 \text{ meter-volts}}{\text{coul}}$$

q = the electrical charge in coulombs

r = the displacement in meters between the acting charge and the position of measurement

A positive test charge is arbitrarily placed at the position of measurement to establish direction of forces. Therefore, if the charge producing the field is positive, the potential is positive; if the charge producing the field is negative, the potential is negative. Would potential energy of the test charge increase or decrease when being brought from a great distance to the position of measurement? For example, the electrical potential at the outer surface of a hydrogen atom with

$$F = \frac{kq_1q_2}{r^2} = \frac{9 \times 10^9 \text{ newton-meter}^2 \times 1.6 \times 10^{-19} \text{ coul} \times 1.6 \times 10^{-19} \text{ coul}}{\text{coul}^2 \times 5.3 \times 10^{-11} \text{ meter} \times 5.3 \times 10^{-11} \text{ meter}}$$

$$= 8.2 \times 10^{-7} \text{ newton}$$

Compare this value to the force between the sun and the earth in the solar system.

With further comparison to gravitation, you will recall that gravitational potential as expressed by Eq. (7.2), $P = \dfrac{Gm}{R}$, was joules per kilogram. An analogous expression for electrical potential with respect to a charged body is:

(16.3) $$V = \frac{kq}{r}$$

where V = the electric potential in volts (1 volt = 1 joule per coulomb)

respect to the positively charged nuclear proton is 27.2 volts.

$$V = \frac{ke}{r}$$

$$= \frac{9 \times 10^9 \text{ meter-volts} \times 1.6 \times 10^{-19} \text{ coul}}{\text{coul} \times 5.3 \times 10^{-11} \text{ meter}}$$

$$= 27.2 \text{ volts}$$

The potential is positive because the potential energy of the positive test charge would increase as work was done in overcoming the force of repulsion between two like charges moved toward each other.

Recall from the discussion in Chapter 11 of the binding energy of the first electron in the elements that the energy transformed by moving an elementary electronic charge e through a potential of 1 volt is expressed as 1 *electron volt* (ev). An electron volt is equal to 1.6×10^{-19} joule.

$$1 \text{ ev} = 1.6 \times 10^{-19} \text{ coul} \times 1 \text{ volt}$$

$$\times \frac{1 \text{ joule/coul}}{\text{volt}} = 1.6 \times 10^{-19} \text{ joule}$$

The potential energy of a charged body moved to the level of a given electrical potential is calculated in terms of the electrical potential multiplied by the charge carried by the body in question:

$$(16.4) \qquad PE = Vq$$

The potential energy of the charged body is expressed in joules if V is in joules per coulomb and q is in coulombs. The potential energy is expressed in electron volts if V is in volts and q is in elementary electronic charges. The potential energy of an electron at the surface of a hydrogen atom is -27.2 ev.

$$PE = Vq = 27.2 \text{ volts} \times (-e)$$

$$= -27.2 \text{ ev}$$

The minus sign expresses reduced potential energy in the atomic system. An electron which has a negative charge moves toward the nucleus under the influence of a force of attraction. This motion is similar to the action of a falling object. In both cases, potential energy is being transformed into other forms of energy. Because the level of zero potential energy is designated at the level of zero force, the reduction in potential energy of the electron is expressed as a minus quantity. Combining Eqs. (16.3) and (16.4) gives an expression for the potential energy of an electron in an orbit of a hydrogen atom.

$$(16.5) \qquad PE = \frac{-ke^2}{r}$$

where PE = potential energy in joules

if $\quad k = 9 \times 10^9 \dfrac{\text{newton-meters}^2}{\text{coul}^2}$

$\quad e = 1.602 \times 10^{-19}$ coulomb (the elementary electronic charge)

$\quad r$ = radius of the orbit in meters

Problems of the conventional Rutherford atom The Rutherford model of the hydrogen atom consisted of a positively charged nucleus around which an electron was revolving in a manner such as to apparently fulfill the volume characteristics of the atom. The simplest imaginable nuclear model fulfilling the requirements would be a miniature copy of the Copernican solar system. In the atomic planetary model of hydrogen, the proton, which is 1836 times more massive than the electron, would remain comparatively motionless at the center. The electron would be accelerated in a circular orbit by the coulomb force between unlike charges. Although gravitation exists between all masses, calculation reveals that for masses of a proton and electron at atomic distances, the coulomb force would be 10^{39} times as great as the force of gravity. Therefore, we can neglect the effects of gravitation between atomic particles.

But the inertial reactions of the masses cannot be overlooked. The laws of motion are not to be violated in atomic systems. For the electron being accelerated in a circular atomic orbit, the inertial reaction is expressed by Eq. (6.9):

$$(6.9) \qquad F = \frac{mv^2}{r}$$

The force producing the acceleration is expressed by Coulomb's law as follows:

$$F = \frac{ke^2}{r^2}$$

where $e =$ the elementary electronic charge.

Therefore

$$\frac{ke^2}{r^2} = \frac{mv^2}{r}$$

and

$$mv^2 = \frac{ke^2}{r}$$

This means that if the radius r is increased by an outside force doing work on the system, the total energy increases toward zero.

From a purely mechanical standpoint, the planetary atomic model indicates agreement with experimental facts. The hydrogen atom has a known radius of about 5.3×10^{-11} meters. The binding energy of the electron of hydrogen is known to be about 13.6 electron volts. Calculations involving Eq. (16.7) show an energy of -13.6 ev for the system.

$$E = -\frac{ke^2}{2r} = -\frac{9 \times 10^9 \text{ newton-meters}^2 \times 1.6 \times 10^{-19} \text{ coul} \times 1.6 \times 10^{-19} \text{ coul}}{\text{coul}^2 \times 2 \times 5.3 \times 10^{-11} \text{ meter}}$$

$$\times \frac{1 \text{ joule}}{\text{newton-meter}} \times \frac{1 \text{ ev}}{1.6 \times 10^{-19} \text{ joule}} = -13.6 \text{ ev}$$

This suggests that if both sides of the equation were divided by 2, we would have an expression of the kinetic energy of the electron in a circular orbit $(KE = 1/2\, mv^2)$.

$$(16.6) \qquad \frac{1}{2}\, mv^2 = \frac{1}{2} \frac{ke^2}{r}$$

The sum of the kinetic and potential energy of the electron in a circular orbit would be expressed by combining Eqs. (16.5) and (16.6).

$$E = KE + PE$$

$$(16.7) \quad E = \frac{1}{2} \frac{ke^2}{r} - \frac{ke^2}{r} = -\frac{ke^2}{2r}$$

In the same manner as in our inquiry of planetary motion in the solar system, Eq. (16.7) indicates that the kinetic energy of the electron is quantitatively equal to half the potential energy of the system. Eq. (16.7) also indicates that the total energy of the system is negative.

If 13.6 ev of work were done upon the electron, its energy would be increased to zero level, which is the level of zero force. Hence, the electron would no longer be bound to the system. This prediction has been confirmed repeatedly by experiments.

But the apparent stability of atoms is incongruous with electromagnetic theory of radiation. From the standpoint of classical theories of electromagnetic radiation, an accelerated electric charge will produce electromagnetic waves, as is demonstrated by radio transmission. The frequency of the waves thus produced should be equal to the orbital frequency of revolution for the orbiting electron. Therefore, according to this theory the atom described in the Rutherford model should radiate energy continuously. The radiated energy would be transformed from the electron's potential energy, thereby steadily reducing the orbital radius. The electron should spiral inward to the nucleus. *This does not occur.* Atoms are remarkably stable. When one contemplates the fact that molecules of gases remain stable even though each molecule collides with other molecules about 10 billion times per second and at speeds of over 1000 miles per hour, the older idea of solid, indestructible atoms seems more durable than the open-spaced planetary model.

But experimental facts can be interpreted only in terms of a nuclear model. The nuclear statistics of the Rutherford atom represent vital facts. Niels Bohr was convinced of its accuracy. He also was convinced of the accuracy of Planck's quantum hypothesis of the emission of light and of Einstein's extension of the quantum hypothesis in interpreting the photoelectric effect. He applied these ideas to the problem of explaining atomic stability.

The Bohr atom   To account for the magnetic effect upon light-emitting substances, the studies of Zeeman and Lorentz had associated the frequency of the emitted light with the motions of electrical charges within the emitting materials. Later, Balmer, Lyman, and Paschen had discovered the regularity in the series of spectral lines emitted from hydrogen. Niels Bohr was to propose a theory of the structure of hydrogen atoms which would account for these effects.

Bohr attacked the problem by accepting the verdict of experimental evidence. The evidence indicated that theories used formerly in explaining large-scale electrical processes do not apply in explaining atomic processes. He began searching for complementary principles which would enable him to account for planetary atoms which constitute non-continuous radiating systems and which preserve the validity of the successful interpretations formerly used for large-scale electrical phenomena. With rare insight, Bohr produced a solution for the problem with regard to atoms of hydrogen. Central features of the solution are two postulates.

In the *first postulate,* Bohr's atomic model specified that electronic orbits be restricted to those in which the *angular momentum* of the electron is equal to a whole-number multiple of Planck's constant divided by 2π. The complementary principles involved in this postulate are two relationships expressing frequency of oscillation and of energy quanta. In terms of electron speed and circular orbit, the period of revolution is:

$$T = \frac{2\pi r}{v}$$

But frequency equals the reciprocal of the period:

$$f = \frac{1}{T}$$

Hence,

$$f = \frac{v}{2\pi r}$$

In terms of energy quanta $(E = h\nu)$, the frequency

$$\nu = \frac{E}{h}$$

By Eqs. (16.6) and (16.7) the electron energy is:

$$E = \frac{-ke^2}{2r} = \frac{-mv^2}{2}$$

Quantitatively, therefore, the frequency associated with this energy would be:

$$\nu = \frac{mv^2}{2h}$$

Combining the two principles, and assuming that f equals ν:

$$\frac{mv^2}{2h} = \frac{v}{2\pi r}$$

and

$$mvr = \frac{2h}{2\pi}$$

where the right side of the equation involves constants. In order to provide for more than one orbit, the postulate uses the more general formula:

$$(16.8) \qquad mvr_n = \frac{nh}{2\pi}$$

where mvr = angular momentum of the orbiting electron

$n = 1, 2, 3, 4, \ldots$ successively

h = Planck's constant (6.625×10^{-34} joule-sec)

Dividing both sides of Eq. (16.8) by mv gives an expression for the length of the orbital radius.

$$(16.9) \qquad r_n = \frac{nh}{2\pi mv}$$

In order to calculate the orbital radius, we must solve for the velocity in terms of known constants. Multiplying the equation $mv^2 = ke^2/r$ by the radius·

$$mv^2 r = ke^2$$

Dividing this by Eq. (16.8), we solve for the velocity in terms of whole-number fractions of constants:

$$\frac{mv^2 r}{mvr} = \frac{ke^2}{nh/2\pi}$$

$$v = \frac{2\pi ke^2}{nh}$$

Substituting this expression of velocity into Eq. (16.9) gives:

$$(16.10) \qquad r_n = \frac{n^2 h^2}{4\pi^2 mke^2}$$

Using Eq. (16.10) in calculating the length of radius for the first allowable orbit ($n = 1$) of the hydrogen atom gives a value of 5.28×10^{-11} meters.

$$r_1 = \frac{n^2 h^2}{4\pi^2 mke^2}$$

$$= \frac{1 \times (6.625 \times 10^{-34})^2 \text{ joule}^2 \text{ sec}^2}{4\pi^2 \times 9.1 \times 10^{-31} \text{ kg} \times 9 \times 10^9 \text{ newton-meters}^2/\text{coul}^2 \times (1.6 \times 10^{-19})^2 \text{ coul}^2}$$

$$\times \frac{1 \text{ kg meter/sec}^2}{\text{newton}} \times \frac{1 \text{ newton}^2\text{-meter}^2}{\text{joule}^2} = \frac{4.39 \times 10^{-67} \text{ meter}}{8.25 \times 10^{-57}} = 5.28 \times 10^{-11} \text{ meters}$$

This value is in excellent agreement with experimental determinations of atomic size.

In the *second postulate*, Bohr's atomic model (Fig.16.16) specified that when an electron makes a transition from an outer orbit of electron energy E_2 to one of the inner orbits of electron energy E_1, the change in energy, $E_2 - E_1$, is transformed into a photon such that

$$h\nu = E_2 - E_1$$

Dividing both sides of the equation by Planck's constant, the frequency of the emitted radiation is expressed as:

$$\nu = \frac{E_2}{h} - \frac{E_1}{h}$$

But the energy of an electron in an orbit of radius r_1 was found to be

$$E_1 = \frac{-ke^2}{2r_1}$$

Substituting the expression of Eq. (16.10) for r_1 gives:

$$E_1 = \frac{-ke^2}{2} \times \frac{4\pi^2 mke^2}{n_1^2 h^2}$$

$$= -\frac{2\pi^2 k^2 e^4 m}{h^2} \times \frac{1}{n_1^2}$$

Therefore, if $n_1 = 1$,

(16.11) $\qquad \frac{2\pi^2 k^2 e^4 m}{h^2} = -E_1$

And for $n = 2, 3, 4, 5, \ldots$ successively

$$E_n = \frac{-E_1}{n^2}$$

Calculating the value of E_1 from Eq. (16.11) using present-day values for the constants gives an energy of -13.6 ev which is in excellent agreement with experimental results.

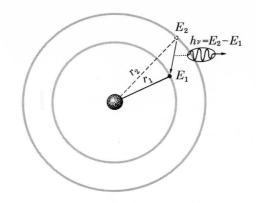

Figure 16.16 Bohr's second postulate. When an electron makes a transition from an outer orbit to an inner orbit, the difference in energy is transformed into radiation.

E_1

$$= \frac{-2\pi^2 \times (8.987 \times 10^9)^2 \text{ joules}^2\text{-meters}^2 \times (1.602 \times 10^{-19})^4 \text{ coul}^4 \times 9.108 \times 10^{-31} \text{ kg}}{\text{coul}^4 \times (6.625 \times 10^{-34})^2 \text{ joule}^2 \text{ sec}^2}$$

$$\times \frac{1 \text{ joule}}{\text{newton-meter}} \times \frac{1 \text{ newton}}{\text{kg-meter/sec}^2}$$

$$= \frac{-9.5636 \times 10^{-85}}{4.389 \times 10^{-67}} \text{ joule} = -2.179 \times 10^{-18} \text{ joule} \times \frac{1 \text{ ev}}{1.602 \times 10^{-19} \text{ joule}} = -13.6 \text{ ev}$$

The fact that the Rydberg constant can be derived from calculations involving the second postulate reveals the validity of predictions given by the Bohr atomic model of hydrogen. The frequency of radiation predicted by the energy transformation stipulated in the second postulate is:

$$\nu = \frac{E_2}{h} - \frac{E_1}{h} = \frac{1}{h}(E_2 - E_1)$$

Substituting values for E_n where $n = 2$ gives:

$$\nu = \frac{1}{h}\left(-\frac{E_1}{2^2} - [-E_1]\right)$$

$$= \frac{1}{h}\left(\frac{E_1}{1^2} - \frac{E_1}{2^2}\right) = \frac{E_1}{h}\left(\frac{1}{1^2} - \frac{1}{2^2}\right)$$

But the frequency of light is defined by the ratio of the speed of light divided by the wavelength $\left(\nu = \frac{c}{\lambda}\right)$. The Rydberg constant is found in the expression for the reciprocal of the wavelength and by the definition quoted above:

$$\frac{1}{\lambda} = \frac{\nu}{c}$$

Therefore,

$$(16.12) \qquad \frac{1}{\lambda} = \frac{E_1}{hc}\left(\frac{1}{1^2} - \frac{1}{2^2}\right)$$

The Rydberg formula for the Lyman series is:

$$\frac{1}{\lambda} = R\left(\frac{1}{1^2} - \frac{1}{n^2}\right)$$

where $n = 2, 3, 4, 5, \ldots$ successively

Eq. (16.12) predicts the reciprocal wavelength of the first line of the Lyman series ($n = 2$); hence, the value of E_1/hc should equal the Rydberg constant. Calculations show agreement between these values. The value quoted for the Rydberg constant earlier in this chapter is $R = 1.0967758 \times 10^5$ reciprocal centimeters. The calculated value of E_1/hc is 1.097×10^5 reciprocal centimeters.

A similarly expressed general formula in terms of the Rydberg constant would be:

$$(16.14) \qquad \frac{1}{\lambda} = R\left(\frac{1}{m^2} - \frac{1}{n^2}\right)$$

HYPOTHESES FOR ATOMIC STABILITY

The outstanding feature of the Bohr theory is the extension of Planck's quantum hypothesis to all atomic processes. Bohr had the ingenuity necessary to adopt the planetary atomic model and also to introduce into it the basic ideas of the quantum hypothesis. As a result, three basic assumptions have stimulated and guided the generation of the more recent models of atomic structure.

(1) A bound atomic system can exist only in certain stationary states without radiating. In its normal state the atomic system is in the lowest energy level. Radiation cannot be emitted until the

$$\frac{E_1}{hc} = \frac{2.179 \times 10^{-18} \text{ joules}}{6.625 \times 10^{-34} \text{ joules-sec} \times 2.998 \times 10^{10} \text{ cm/sec}} = 1.097 \times 10^5 \text{ cm}^{-1}$$

It follows, therefore, that Eq. (16.12) is identical to the Rydberg formula for the first spectral line of the Lyman series. The general formula expressing the various spectral series in terms of the Bohr atom is:

$$(16.13) \qquad \frac{1}{\lambda} = \frac{E_1}{hc}\left(\frac{1}{m^2} - \frac{1}{n^2}\right)$$

where for the Lyman series $m = 1$ and $n = 2, 3, 4, \ldots$
for the Balmer series $m = 2$ and $n = 3, 4, 5, \ldots$
for the Paschen series $m = 3$ and $n = 4, 5, 6, \ldots$

system's energy is increased to a higher level. Energy to bring about this increase might be transformed in atomic collisions due to high temperature, by impact of high-energy electrons, or by absorption of radiation. The amounts of energy transformed in each increase are limited to certain discrete values. The energy levels required to raise the atomic system to these higher energy states are called the *excitation potentials* of the atom. These are well-defined characteristics of given atomic systems. The Bohr model defines the total energy of the electron in orbit in the same

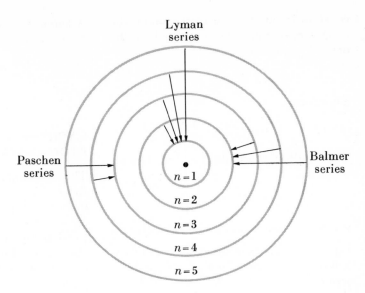

Lyman
series

Paschen
series

Balmer
series

$n=1$

$n=2$

$n=3$

$n=4$

$n=5$

Figure 16.17 Bohr's model of the hydrogen atom. Circular orbits represent the stationary energy states.

manner as the Rutherford model. To remove the electron from the system requires an energy numerically equal to this binding energy. The energy level required is called the *ionization potential* of the atom.

(2) The stationary states are those in which the orbital angular momentum *mvr* of the electron system is an integral multiple of Planck's constant divided by 2π. We shall discover in Chapter 17 that this postulate is a consequence of wave characteristics of electrons in orbital motion. At the time of Bohr's initial work, this property of electrons was unknown. Bohr arrived at the quantization of the angular momentum as a result of arbitrarily combining Planck's quantum theory and the frequency aspects of electron revolution predictable for certain orbits where calculations showed coincidence between electron frequency and those of energy quanta. The partial

success of this combination led to the discovery of electron waves at a later time.

(3) When an electron undergoes a transition from an upper energy state E_2 to a lower energy state E_1, the loss of energy is transformed into a photon of energy $h\nu$. If a photon is absorbed by an atomic system, an electron makes a transition from a lower to a higher energy state so that $E_2 = E_1 + h\nu$. According to the Bohr theory, differences between the various excitation potentials for a given atomic system should be equal to the differences in electron energy levels as determined from spectral emissions. Verification of all predictions of the Bohr theory with regard to hydrogen atoms was demonstrated in 1913 by Franck and Hertz. They bombarded the gas with electrons of controlled energies. Results showed that if an atom were struck by an electron having insufficient energy to

raise it to its first excited state, the electron did not lose energy in the collision. If the electron energies were great enough to excite the atom, the predicted emission of light resulted from the absorption of energy in the incident electrons.

SUMMARY

The modern concepts of electron structure in matter are an outgrowth of studies made on cathode rays by Crookes, Goldstein, Perrin, and Thomson. Perrin established that cathode rays transport negative charges. Thomson measured the mass-to-charge ratio of the cathode ray particles. Lorentz had reached a similar conclusion in calculations involving the Zeeman effect. In 1897 and thereafter, the cathode ray particle was called an electron. Fitzgerald suggested that the electrons resulted from atomic dissociation. Millikan determined the quantity of the unit electronic charge. The established charge of the electron is 1.602×10^{-19} coulomb, and its mass is 9.108×10^{-31} kg.

In 1895 Roentgen discovered X-ray. The fallacious hypothesis of X-ray origin in fluorescence led Becquerel to investigation of fluorescent substances and the discovery in 1896 of radioactivity in uranium salt. Radium was discovered by the Curies in 1898. The following year, Rutherford distinguished between alpha, beta, and gamma emissions from radium and its products.

The spontaneous radioactive transformation of atoms of one element into atoms of other elements definitely established the fact of divisible atoms and the presence of both positive and negative charges within the atom. Scattering of alpha particles in passing through thin foils established, in 1911, the nuclear atom.

Spectral analysis by means of dispersion and measurement of the spectral lines produced by known elements had been discovered in 1859 by Kirchhoff and Bunsen. Mathematical description of the spectral characteristics of hydrogen was begun in 1885 by Balmer, and was extended to ultraviolet emissions by Lyman in 1906, and to infrared frequencies by Paschen in 1908. The quantum explanation of the photoelectric effect was made by Einstein in 1905.

Combining the known descriptions of the nuclear atom, the spectral effects of hydrogen, and the quantum hypothesis, Bohr produced a workable model of the hydrogen atom. His model was based on two revolutionary postulates:

1. Electron orbits about the massive nucleus are restricted to those in which the angular momentum of the electron is equal to whole number multiples of $h/2\pi$.

2. When an electron undergoes a transition from an upper to a lower energy state, the change in energy is transformed into a photon of radiation.

Verification of predictions of the Bohr theory with regard to hydrogen atoms was demonstrated in 1913 by Franck and Hertz.

PROBLEMS

1 What evidences support the statement that the force between an electric current and a magnet is different from the forces described earlier?

2 Crookes attributed the cathode ray's effects to "radiant matter" (corpuscules). Evaluate the various evidences indicated in the various discharge tubes as conclusive or inconclusive in support of this assumption.

3 What evidences proved that the cathode ray consisted of electrons?

4 A 60-watt electric light bulb carries about 0.5 ampere of current. How many electrons per second flow through the light bulb? What mass of electrons flows each second?

5 What evidences proved that atoms possess nuclei?

6 Using the Balmer formula (Eq. 16.1), compute the wavelengths of the hydrogen lines where $m = 5, 6, 7,$ and 8.

7 What is the difference between gravitational potential and electrical potential?

8 Compare: the Thomson model of the atom to Dalton's model; Thomson's model to Rutherford's model; and Rutherford's model to Bohr's model.

9 How did the three basic assumptions of the Bohr atomic hypothesis overcome the weaknesses listed for the Rutherford atom?

10 Using the results calculated for E_1 by Eq. (16.11), compute the difference in energy between E_2 and E_3 ($n = 2$ and $n = 3$) in terms of Bohr's second postulate. What frequency is represented in the photon formed when this energy is transformed in the electron transition? What wavelength? Compare this to the first line of the Balmer series for hydrogen.

17

PERIODIC CHART OF
THE ELEMENTS

The atoms are basic physical systems. The properties we give to atoms provide the principal meanings around which we interpret all natural phenomena. Our acceptance of new ideas, our awareness of physical events, and our interpretations of these ideas and events depend upon applications of valid meanings, often based upon atomic hypotheses. But essentially we have more immediate reasons for wanting to know more about atoms. Our curiosity has been aroused. We have found that things are not as they seem to be and we are curious as to why and how this comes about.

With the concordance of the Bohr atom to quantitative measurements, the path was charted for orderly development of the essential atomic characteristics. The path was not clearly marked, although its early successes were impressive. But the success of Bohr's model depended upon an arbitrary union of Newton's laws of motion and Planck's quantum hypothesis. There was very little basis for this union. If it hadn't been for the fact that predicted outcomes with regard to the hydrogen atom actually occurred, there would have been very little else to recommend a continued pursuit of these ideas. But it is very difficult to argue against success, even only a partial one. The Bohr model predictions hold only for certain features of hydrogen and hydrogenlike atoms. It cannot explain the spectra of atoms having more than one electron. It also fails to explain the binding energies between the components of molecular groups in gases, liquids, and solids. The fundamental reason why the Bohr model is defective is that it is too closely aligned with the Newtonian cause-and-effect relationships. These require precisely defined displacements, speeds, and orbital frequencies for acceptable explanations. Atomic events cannot be so defined. Here again, observed relationships must be accepted without reservation. We must accept atomic and subatomic characteristics as they are and not try to picture them as we should like them to be. At the same time, however, we must reconcile the fact that the Newtonian relationships do explain admirably the events of the macroscopic world.

THE LANGUAGE OF SCIENCE

The words and symbols used to explain the relationships which interpret the natural processes scientists discovered rest upon both speculation and observed verification. The language and perceived meanings of science grow and change as the speculation and confirmation of ideas show these meanings to be true and helpful in interpreting natural processes.

In explaining atomic processes we are entering a phase of scientific description and explanation which defies the use of sensory models. There are no commonly observed or inventable machines or diagrams, no matter how idealistically devised, which can mimic the observed facts of atomic processes. We are therefore forced to rely solely upon the words and symbols of language to communicate the meanings of modern science. It is because we must rely upon experience-centered meanings that we return for some further analyses of experiences derived from our earlier inquiries.

Characteristics of planetary systems

The reader might find it highly useful at this time to re-establish the meanings derived during our inquiry into the characteristics of elliptical orbits which were encountered in Chapter 6, and the characteristics of rotational motion encountered during the latter part of Chapter 8. Unifying certain of the meanings related to rotating systems makes possible more precise descriptions of these processes.

(1) Let us inquire further with regard to the angular momentum of a planetary particle moving in an elliptical orbit around a fixed center of force at one of the foci. By definition the angular momentum is equal to the product of the moment of inertia I and the angular velocity ω,

$$p_\theta = I\omega$$

But for a particle of mass m displaced at a distance r from the axis of rotation, the moment of inertia can be shown to equal the product of the mass and the square of the displacement, $I = mr^2$. The angular velocity is equal to the quotient of the component of the linear velocity $v \cos \theta$

(see Fig. 17.1) that is directed at right angles to the radius, divided by the length of the radius. Thus, $\omega = v \cos\theta/r$, and the angular momentum of the particle at any position is:

$$p_\theta = mrv \cos\theta$$

Under the circumstances stated above, the particle would be accelerated linearly by the tangential component of the force, $F_t = F \sin\theta$ (see Fig. 6.11). The particle's linear momentum is being changed by the unbalanced force. We should question whether the angular momentum of the system also is being changed.

Angular acceleration is produced by an unbalanced torque as defined by $\tau = I\alpha$, where τ is the torque, I is the moment of inertia, and α is the angular acceleration. But, by definition, $\tau = Fr$, where τ is the torque, F is the net force equal to the component that is at right angles to the radius, and r is the length of the radius. Because the force between two particles is directed along the line connecting them, there can be no component of force directed at right angles to this line. Therefore, there can be no unbalanced torque. *The angular momentum of a particle in an elliptical orbit remains constant.* It now becomes evident why we indicated that the product of velocity

Figure 17.1 Angular momentum of bodies moving in eliptical orbits. Because there is no torque, the angular momentum remains constant.

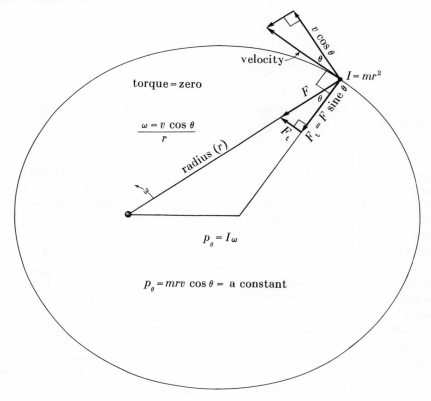

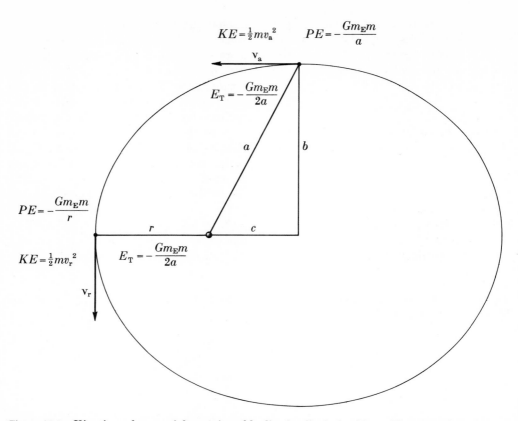

$$KE = \tfrac{1}{2}mv_\mathrm{a}^2 \qquad PE = -\frac{Gm_\mathrm{E}m}{a}$$

$$E_\mathrm{T} = -\frac{Gm_\mathrm{E}m}{2a}$$

$$PE = -\frac{Gm_\mathrm{E}m}{r}$$

$$KE = \tfrac{1}{2}mv_\mathrm{r}^2 \qquad E_\mathrm{T} = -\frac{Gm_\mathrm{E}m}{2a}$$

Figure 17.2 Kinetic and potential energies of bodies in eliptical orbits. The sum of the kinetic and potential energies remains constant.

and radius is *approximately* constant in planetary orbits. The more exact statement of Kepler's second law is that $rv \cos \theta = k$. For orbits having very small eccentricities, θ is approximately zero and the $\cos \theta \simeq 1$, allowing us to simplify the expression as $vr \simeq k$.

(2) In Chapter 7 our inquiry revealed that the total sum of potential and kinetic energies of a planetary particle in an elliptical orbit remains constant for all points of the orbit. We can designate any displacement level as an arbitrary level of zero potential energy. By choosing the displacement of the zero force

level as the level of zero potential energy, the total energy of the planetary particle at the point of average displacement for the force center is (see Fig. 17.2):

$$E_\mathrm{T} = \frac{-Gm_\mathrm{E}m}{a} + \frac{1}{2}\,mv_a^2$$

But the kinetic energy proved to be one-half the binding energy at that level, as was defined in Chapter 7:

$$\frac{1}{2}\,mv_a^2 = \frac{Gm_\mathrm{E}m}{2a}$$

Thus, the total sum of kinetic and potential energies at the point of average displacement is:

$$E_T = \frac{-Gm_Em}{a} + \frac{Gm_Em}{2a} = \frac{-Gm_Em}{2a}$$

For example, the total energy of the earth with respect to the sun is -2.652×10^{33} joules.

$$E_T = \frac{-Gm_sm_e}{2a} = \frac{-6.673 \times 10^{-11} \text{ newton-meter}^2 \times 1.986 \times 10^{30} \text{ kg} \times 5.983 \times 10^{24} \text{ kg}}{\text{kg}^2 \times 2 \times 1.495 \times 10^{11} \text{ meters}}$$

$$\times \frac{1 \text{ joule}}{\text{newton-meter}} = E_T = -2.652 \times 10^{33} \text{ joules}$$

At perihelion the potential energy is:

$$PE = \frac{-Gm_sm}{r}$$

and the kinetic energy is increased by the amount of change in potential energy between the displacement levels a and r. That is:

$$\Delta PE = \frac{-Gm_sm}{a} - \left(\frac{-Gm_sm}{r}\right)$$
$$= \frac{Gm_sm}{r} - \frac{Gm_sm}{a}$$

Therefore the total sum of kinetic and potential energy is

$$E_T = PE_r + (KE_a + \Delta PE)$$

$$E_T = \frac{-Gm_sm}{r}$$
$$+ \left(\frac{Gm_sm}{2a} + \frac{Gm_sm}{r} - \frac{Gm_sm}{a}\right)$$
$$= \frac{-Gm_sm}{2a}$$

Likewise, the total energy proves to remain constant at all points of the orbit.

Fig. 17.3 illustrates several elliptical orbits of varying eccentricities but of equal values for the major axis. A little thought makes it clear that regardless of eccentricity of orbit a planetary particle of constant mass would have the same total energy whatever orbit it was following. *The total energy of a planetary system is independent of the eccentricity; it depends only on the average displacement of the planetary particle from the center of force.*

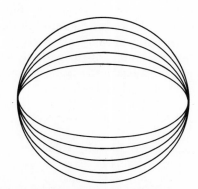

Figure 17.3 Elliptical orbits having equal major axes but varying eccentricities.

(3) In Chapter 5 our inquiry revealed that the proof of the earth's rotation lies in the fact that when a Foucault pendulum is allowed to swing freely in space, the earth rotates beneath it around a vertical axis passing through the pendulum's point of suspension. This rotation constitutes an angular velocity around the axis to this zenith, and this angular velocity ω_z is a component of the earth's angular velocity ω_θ around its axis of rotation. Fig. 17.4 is equivalent to Fig. 5.6. You will recall that the earth's angular velocity around its axis of rotation is 15° per sidereal hour. By

the right-hand rule for vector direction, the eastward rotation directs the vector toward the north celestial pole. We also computed the angular velocity about the vertical axis at Long Beach, California. It is $8\frac{1}{3}°$ per sidereal hour directed toward the zenith. As indicated in Fig. 17.4, the angular velocity ω_z is given by the formula: $\omega_z = \omega_\theta \cos\theta$, where angle θ equals 90° minus the degrees of latitude in the Northern Hemisphere.

We shall now apply this experience to the components of the angular momentum of a planetary system directed along any axis to a zenith in space. Using the right-hand rule we can picture the direction of the angular momentum vector, as well as compute its magnitude with respect to any axis in space. The computation involves the equation:

$$p_z = p_\theta \cos\theta$$

The angle θ can take any value measured with respect to the axis of p_θ. The importance of this relationship is the fact that p_z remains constant along any axis directed into space and has a value depending only upon the angular momentum p_θ and angle θ.

(4) The total angular momentum of a planetary system includes also the angular momentum of the rotation in each of the individual bodies involved. For instance, in the planetary system involving the sun and the earth, the total angular momentum is the *vector sum* of the angular momentum of the revolving earth, the angular momentum of the rotating earth, and the angular momentum of the rotating sun.

We shall find ample reference to these planetary characteristics when we inquire further into interpretations of atomic structure.

Distinguishing characteristics of particles and waves A flow of energy can take place from one location to another by means of a stream of particles or by means of wave motion. In this regard, we think of particles as compact bundles of energy traveling through space. When two particles collide, the principles of conservation of energy and conservation of momentum require a redistribution of energy and momentum such that the total energy and momentum remain unchanged.

Therefore, these distinguishing properties of particles can be determined, at least in principle, by measuring the changes in energy and momentum they produce when colliding with other particles.

Identification of wave motion is made primarily on the evidence of interference and diffraction patterns. Recall from Chapter 3 the conditions which yield these phenomena. Interference results when two waves are so directed as to intersect at the place of observation. The form and extent of the interference depends upon the frequency, amplitude, and phase of the waves. The net disturbance observed will be the sum of the disturbances of the separate waves. If the intersecting waves are in phase (crests and troughs coinciding with their counterparts), the result will be waves of increased amplitude equal to the sum of the individual amplitudes. If the intersecting waves are exactly opposite in phase (crests and troughs coinciding with their opposites), the result will be waves of reduced amplitude. If waves that are opposite in phase are of equal amplitude, the result is one of zero disturbance. Interference patterns are also the cause of diffraction. Because of diffraction patterns, the shadow of an object is

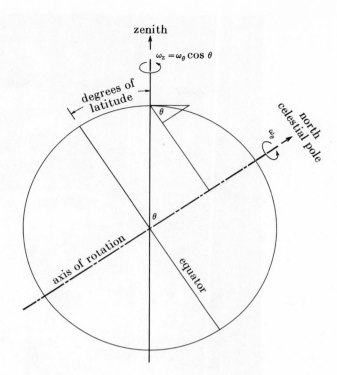

zenith

$\omega_z = \omega_\theta \cos \theta$

degrees of latitude

north celestial pole

ω_θ

θ

θ

axis of rotation

equator

Figure 17.4 Components of the angular velocity along any axis to a zenith in space.

always somewhat blurred at the edges. The smaller the object, the more clearly apparent are the alternate dark and bright fringes which constitute the diffraction pattern at the edges of the shadow.

Highly precise measurements of wavelengths of monochromatic light are accomplished by observing the interference patterns produced in the interferometers (see Chapter 4). Invisible radiation requires special means of detection. The wave nature of X-rays was first demonstrated by Von Laue in 1912. Laue's method involved diffraction of X-ray by the atomic particles which constitute the structure of crystalline solids. (See Fig. 17.6.) The Laue diffraction patterns made possible the

measurement of X-ray wavelengths. As a result of these measurements there is acceptance of the wave description of X-ray. The use of X-ray analysis in investigation of the distribution of atoms and ions in the structure of minerals was referred to in Chapter 11. Important information about the atomic structure of solids and liquids has been determined by X-ray diffraction analysis.

Although waves and particles have distinctly differentiating properties, both particles and waves have a way of exhibiting each other's characteristics. This may have been anticipated when we encountered the energy quanta of photons in explanation of the photoelectric effect. After this explanation, the discovery of particle qualities in X-ray photons may

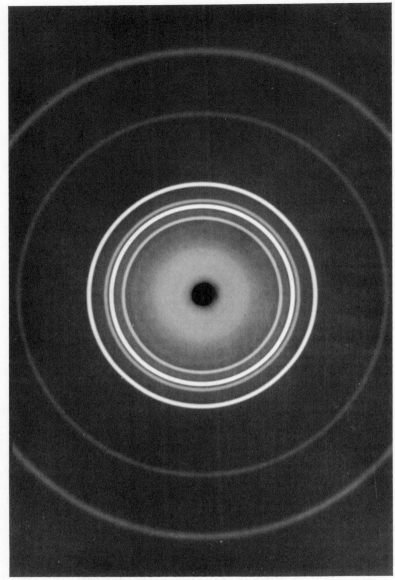

X-ray diffraction pattern of polycrystalline aluminum.   [*Courtesy of Bell Telephone Laboratories.*]

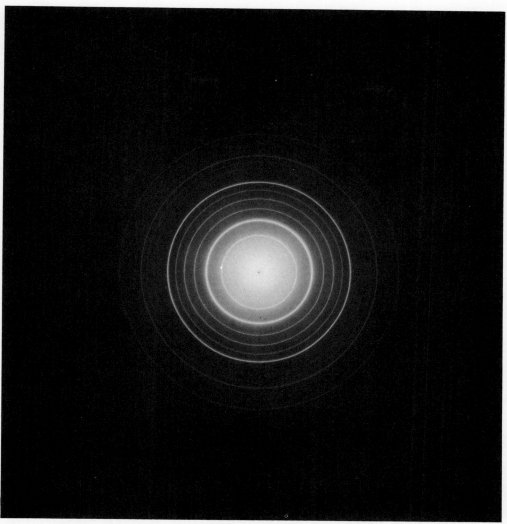

Electron-diffraction pattern of polycrystalline tellurium chloride.   [*Courtesy of the Radio Corpora-tion of America.*]

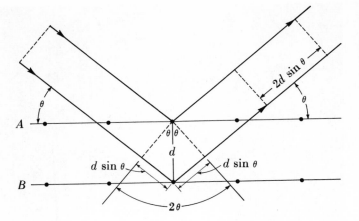

Figure 17.5 Reflection of X-rays from atomic planes in a crystal. The atoms in atomic planes A and B act as if they were half-silvered mirrors of an interferometer. When $2d \sin \theta$ equals a whole number of wave lengths, constructive interference takes place.

not be surprising. But electron waves are also observed which have X-ray wavelengths. The evidence supporting the particle nature of electrons was explained in Chapter 16. Observations made during the last 50 years have challenged both the wave description of X-rays and the particle description of electrons.

Interpretations of relativity We shall confine our inquiry to a comparison of meanings which have been altered by

Einstein's theory of special relativity. The origin of the need for change was introduced earlier. For example, in Chapter 4, our inquiry included a description of the Michelson-Morley experiments in which an attempt was made to detect the relative motions of a source of light, the observers, and the supposed medium through which light was thought to be propagated. The perplexing results of these experiments were resolved by Einstein in the theory of special relativity. The fundamental postulates of the theory have been outlined: first, the laws of

Figure 17.6 X-ray diffraction apparatus used by von Laue. The geometrical pattern of spots was that predicted by von Laue.

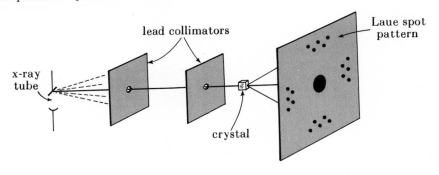

science are the same in all inertial systems; second, the speed of light in a vacuum is a constant which is independent of the inertial system, the source, and the observer. The postulates of relativity would be incompatible had not drastic changes been made in the usual Newtonian-inspired meanings of space, time, and mass in order that more valid descriptions be made of observed events.

First, with regard to space, the usual concepts would hold absolute the measured length of an object, regardless of the relative velocities of the object and the observers making the measurements. But if this concept were true the results of the Michelson-Morley experiments could not be explained. The relativity theory predicts a phenomenon known as *space contraction*. Let us suppose two observers A and B meet and select identical meter sticks of length L_0. Then, let us set observer A into motion at a high speed v relative to observer B. If B now compared the apparent length of the meter stick held by A to the length L_0 of his own, he would observe:

$$(17.1) \qquad L = L_0\sqrt{1 - v^2/c^2}$$

where $L =$ the apparent length of the stick in motion
$L_0 =$ the length of the meter stick of the observer
$v =$ the speed of the stick in motion with respect to observer B
$c =$ the speed of light in a vacuum

Observer B finds the length of the moving objects contracted in ratio of $\sqrt{1 - v^2/c^2}$. Observer A would likewise find a contraction of the same ratio in measuring moving objects with respect to the length L_0 of his meter stick. The contraction occurs *only* in the direction of motion.

No changes occur in lengths directed perpendicular to the direction of relative motion.

Second, with regard to time, the usual concepts would hold absolute the time measured for the interval of an event, T_0, by two clocks synchronized while at rest and later set into relative motion at high speed. But in this situation also, the usual concepts are not true. Each observer accompanying a given clock would observe his own clock running slower than the moving clock. The observed time of the moving clock as seen from the position of the fixed clock would be:

$$(17.2) \qquad T = \frac{T_0}{\sqrt{1 - v^2/c^2}}$$

where $T =$ the apparent time of an interval measured by the moving clock
$T_0 =$ the time of the interval measured by the fixed clock
$v =$ the speed of the moving clock with respect to the observer
$c =$ the speed of light in a vacuum

This relativistic phenomenon is known as *time dilatation*. For example, suppose the moving clock were moving at 0.866 the speed of light; the time measure of an interval as observed on the moving clock would be twice that of the fixed clock. The observers would find

$$T = \frac{T_0}{\sqrt{1 - v^2/c^2}} \qquad \frac{T_0}{\sqrt{1 - \left(\dfrac{0.866c}{c}\right)^2}}$$

$$= \frac{T_0}{\sqrt{0.25}} = 2\,T_0$$

The times measured in the system moving relative to himself expanded by a ratio of $1/\sqrt{1 - v^2/c^2}$ as compared to his fixed clock.

Third, with regard to mass, the usual concepts would describe mass as remaining absolute in quantity regardless of relative speeds of the mass and the observer. But, mass also exhibits relativistic changes with changes of speed. An object having a *rest mass* m_0 would exhibit a *relativistic mass*, when set in motion at high speed v, which is expressed as follows:

$$(17.3) \qquad m = \frac{m_0}{\sqrt{1 - v^2/c^2}}$$

Eq. (17.3) makes it obvious why no material object can attain the speed of light; if $v^2 = c^2$, the relativistic mass would become infinitely great.

A convincing array of evidence confirms the reliability of these relativistic meanings. However, we emphasize that Newton's laws have not been abandoned. The Newtonian concepts are valid and useful approximations of reality except when the ratio of v^2/c^2 becomes significantly large. Because the Newtonian expressions are usually less cumbersome than the relativistic ones, we shall continue using them in situations for which they remain valid. But we recognize that the basic explanations for the events have changed. The changing patterns of meaning have been a theme of this book. We have observed how science has grown, from Ptolemy to Copernicus, to Kepler, to Newton, and now to Einstein. The exciting part of the last step is that it is current history. But in our enthusiasm for the new, we do not abandon the valid in the old. Just as we still use some of the relationships expressed by the celestial sphere of the Ptolemaic system for time-keeping and navigation, when their use leads to valid results, so we continue to use the relationships based upon the Newtonian system

where these lead to valid results. In both instances, however, we acknowledge that the underlying assumptions of these relationships are in error. Utility does not confer accuracy of meaning to these ideas. Meaningful concepts extend beyond utility. Concepts have to do with explanation and understanding of the meaning of natural processes.

THE LOGIC OF SCIENCE

The purposes of scientific endeavors obviously are not to attain absolute answers because these are unattainable. They are directed, rather, toward discovering the problems which result from invalid interpretations, and toward discovering and testing the assumptions which form the bases for these interpretations. This quest is not without rules. Those unwilling to expose their predictions to the tests of confirmation in the observed events of natural processes do not take part in the scientific game. The meanings gained from speculations and experiences of the past become reliable interpretations only for as long as future experiences prove them accurate. No better illustration exists of the logic of science at work than the speculations and experimental confirmations which helped shape the growth of concepts of the atom.

Relativistic speculation The relativistic meanings for space, time, and mass have far-reaching effects upon our meanings for the basic principles of conservation of momentum and conservation of energy. The levels of mathematics involved are beyond those used in this book. But in inquiries of modern science the relativistic effects cannot be overlooked.

Relativistic momentum is defined in the usual manner as the product of mass and velocity but the mass is relativistic mass. Hence,

$$(17.4) \qquad p = mv = \frac{m_0 v}{\sqrt{1 - v^2/c^2}}$$

When we analyze the meaning of Eq. (17.4) it becomes evident that when an unbalanced force produces a change in momentum of an object, not only is velocity being changed per unit time, but also mass is being changed per unit time because of the velocity change. Newton's second law involves change in both mass and velocity.

Concepts of energy are more drastically changed. The relativistic kinetic energy is *not* defined in the usual manner as $\frac{1}{2} mv^2$. Mathematical analysis shows that an increase in energy of a system, whether it be potential energy, kinetic energy, heat, or any other form, produces a corresponding increase in the mass of the system. The relativistic kinetic energy corresponds to the product of increase in mass and c^2. In terms of rest mass and relativistic mass, kinetic energy is expressed:

$$(17.5) \quad KE = mc^2 - m_0 c^2 = (m - m_0)c^2$$

In situations where the potential energy remains constant, the kinetic energy represents the increase in the *total energy* of the object:

$$KE = E_T - E_0 = mc^2 - m_0 c^2$$

where KE = kinetic energy of the object
E_T = total energy of the object
E_0 = energy of the object while at rest

Therefore, it is most helpful to designate for an object of *rest mass* m_0 a *rest energy*:

$$(17.6) \qquad E_0 = m_0 c^2$$

The total energy of an object is given in terms of its relativistic mass:

$$(17.7) \quad E_T = mc^2 = \frac{m_0 c}{\sqrt{1 - v^2/c^2}}$$

The discovery of the equivalence of mass and energy is a most important insight. We shall recognize this fact, henceforth, by referring to the conservation principle as the *conservation of mass-energy*.

A further extension of the principle of conservation of mass-energy to situations involving the energy quanta of photons is that photons must exhibit mass effects. That is, the photon, which has zero rest mass, because of the energy relationship,

$$E_T = mc^2 = h\nu$$

has relativistic mass

$$m = \frac{h\nu}{c^2}$$

where m = relativistic mass
h = Planck's constant
ν = frequency of the radiation
c = speed of light in a vacuum

The principle of conservation of momentum requires a photon of mass m moving at speed c to have in the direction of motion a momentum of quantity equalling

$$(17.8) \quad p = mc = \left(\frac{h\nu}{c^2}\right)c = \frac{h\nu}{c} = \frac{h}{\lambda}$$

The Compton effect In 1922, Arthur H. Compton discovered a change in frequency of the X-rays which had been scattered by material objects. The frequency change denotes an energy change. Fig. 17.7 shows schematically how the Compton effect was measured. Compton showed that the effects of X-ray scatter-

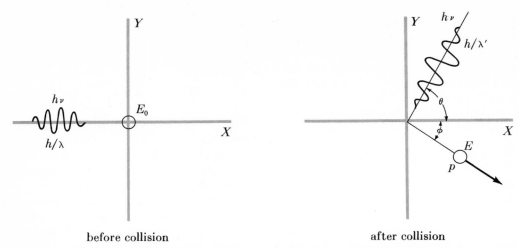

before collision   after collision

Figure 17.7   The Compton effect.   Scattering of X-rays is in accord with the speculative predictions for a relativistic photon.

ing were in accord with the speculative predictions for a relativistic photon. Conservation of energy is achieved when $h\nu + E_0 = h\nu' + E$, where $h\nu$ and $h\nu'$ are the energies of the incident and scattered photons, respectively, E_0 is the initial energy of the scattering particle, and E is the final energy of the scattering particle. If the scattering particle were initially at rest, its initial momentum would be zero; and the conservation of energy is achieved by showing:

$$\frac{h}{\lambda} = p \cos \theta + \frac{h}{\lambda'} \cos \phi$$

where $\dfrac{h}{\lambda} =$ the momentum of the incident photon

$\dfrac{h}{\lambda'} =$ the momentum of the scattered photon

$p =$ the final momentum of the scattering particle

It is important to notice that the photon momentums are discrete multiples of the Planck constant. Thus, light not only

has a corpuscular nature with regard to its energy quantization, also it produces particle effects when in collision with other particles of matter. The Compton effect shows measurably the particle-like aspects of photons of radiation. The photoelectric effect and the Compton effect are explained by the combined predictions of the quantum theory and the theory of relativity. The energy and the momentum quantities of electromagnetic radiation are revealed to be quantized as predicted by these theories.

The de Broglie waves   In 1924, Louis de Broglie revealed in his doctoral dissertation a startling prediction as a result of speculation involving the theory of relativity, Planck's quantum hypothesis, and the Compton effect. One of the insights produced by his argument is that the energy E of a physical system is related to a frequency ν by a quantized relationship $E = h\nu$ in much the same sense as the momentum p of a photon of radiation is related to a wavelength λ by the quantized relationship $p = h/\lambda$. Solving these quantized expressions for the constant h, we find:

$$h = \frac{E}{\nu} = p\lambda$$

and

$$\frac{E}{p} = \nu\lambda$$

You will recall that the relationship $\nu\lambda$ was used to define and measure the velocity of standing waves in a resonance tube. That is,

$$\nu\lambda = v'$$

where $\nu =$ the frequency of the wave phenomenon
$\lambda =$ the wavelength of the wave phenomenon
$v' =$ the velocity of the wave phenomenon

But, in terms of relativistic mass, the energy and momentum of a particle are, respectively, $E = mc^2$ and $p = mv$. Substituting these values for the combined expression above:

$$\frac{E}{p} = \nu\lambda = \frac{mc^2}{mv} = v'$$

and

$$c^2 = vv'$$

where $c =$ speed of light in a vacuum
$v =$ velocity of the particle
$v' =$ velocity of the associated wave phenomenon

Remembering that the energy can be expressed as $E = h\nu = mc^2$, and substituting the equal value vv' for c^2 in this expression, we get for the particle waves:

$$h\nu = mvv'$$

or

$$\frac{v'}{\nu} = \frac{h}{mv}$$

Recall that in wave phenomena the wavelength $\lambda = v'/\nu$; hence

$$(17.9) \qquad \lambda = \frac{h}{mv}$$

Eq. (17.9) is de Broglie's famous formula. It makes a prediction which seems very strange at first meeting: Any particle having relativistic mass m has associated with it a wave phenomenon of wavelength whose value is given by Eq. (17.9). You might ask why scientists were so long unaware of these waves.

Let us consider the predicted wavelength for a ball of mass 0.25 kg moving at a relative speed of 12 meters per second. The associated wavelength would be 2.21×10^{-34} meters. This is far too short for observation.

$$\lambda = \frac{h}{mv} = \frac{6.62 \times 10^{-36} \text{ joule-sec}}{0.25 \text{ kg} \times 12 \text{ meters/sec}}$$
$$= 2.21 \times 10^{-34} \text{ meters}$$

Observation of interference or diffraction of these short wavelengths would be hopeless because no slits of such small size exist. But the waves do exist. An electron, because of its small mass, exhibits measurable wavelengths. For example, an electron which has been accelerated from rest through a potential difference of 150 volts has a wavelength of 1 A. This is in the X-ray range. At the comparatively low velocities achieved at this energy, the kinetic energy of the electron can be expressed by $KE = \frac{1}{2}mv^2$. In terms of momentum $(p = mv)$, the kinetic energy can be expressed by $KE = p^2/2m$. But $p = h/\lambda$; hence, the kinetic energy, which is equal to the electron charge multiplied by electrical potential, is $KE = ev = h^2/2m\lambda^2$. Solving for wavelength: $\lambda = h/\sqrt{2mev}$

$$\lambda = \frac{h}{\sqrt{2mev}} = \frac{6.62 \times 10^{-34} \text{ joule-sec}}{\sqrt{2 \times 9.11 \times 10^{-31} \text{ kg} \times 1.60 \times 10^{-19} \text{ coul} \times 1.5 \times 10^{2} \text{ joules/coul}}}$$

$$\lambda = \frac{6.62 \times 10^{-34} \text{ kg-meter}^2/\text{sec}}{6.61 \times 10^{-24} \text{ kg-meter/sec}} = 1 \times 10^{-10} \text{ meter} = 1 \text{ A}$$

In 1927, C. S. Davisson and L. H. Germer of the Bell Telephone Company discovered that an electron beam reflected from a nickel crystal shows a diffraction pattern like that of X-ray and has the required wavelength predicted by the de Broglie formula. Thus was the existence of particle waves established by theoretical prediction confirmed by observation in natural events. Confirmations of wavelength have been observed not only for electrons but also for atoms, molecules, and neutrons. These entities can no longer be described completely in terms of particles or of waves. Again, we are reminded that our purposes cannot be to formulate *wishes* as to how these phenomena *should* be explained; our purpose can only be to *extend* our understanding of them.

The uncertainty principle The use of a beat frequency for measuring frequency in piano tuning was described in Chapter 4. A tuning fork of a standard pitch was used as one of two sources of frequency. The piano string was the other source, and it was tuned to a frequency which produces "zero beats" when sounded with the fork. The expression "zero beats" was placed in quotation marks because it expresses an approximation. To measure the frequency with no uncertainty would imply that we had waited for an *infinite time* period and had observed not a single beat. To imply such accuracy would be absurd. We must be satisfied when no beats are

produced during some finite time period Δt. Under these circumstances if longer time periods are contemplated, it is possible that beats will be heard. The beat frequency $\Delta \nu$ would be expressed by $\nu_1 - \nu_2 = \Delta \nu_1$, where ν_1 and ν_2 are the frequencies of the tuning fork and the string, respectively. The reciprocal of the beat frequency $1/\Delta \nu$ is the period of the beat in seconds. Therefore, we can establish that this beat period must be equal to or greater than the initial measuring period Δt. That is, $\Delta t \geq 1/\Delta \nu$ and

$$(17.10) \qquad \Delta t \Delta \nu \geq 1$$

If the initial measuring period is very short, the uncertainty of the frequency measurement is large. The greater the value of Δt, the less is the uncertainty of the frequency.

In a similar manner, the uncertainty in measurement of wavelength can be deduced. During a given time interval Δt, a wave will travel a distance $\Delta s = v \Delta t$, where v is the speed of the wave disturbance. Because $\Delta t \geq 1/\Delta \nu$, the change in displacement of the wave would be:

$$\Delta s \geq \frac{v}{\Delta \nu}$$

But the speed of a wave is measured by the product of the frequency and wavelength. That is $v = \nu \lambda$, so that $\nu = \frac{v}{\lambda}$. Therefore, the beat frequency

$$\Delta \nu = \nu_1 - \nu = \frac{v}{\lambda_1} - \frac{v}{\lambda_2} = v \left(\frac{\lambda_2 - \lambda_1}{\lambda_1 \lambda_2} \right)$$

But in situations where measurement of

uncertainty would have any consequence, $\Delta \nu$ would be very small so that the above relationship can be expressed as follows without loss of meaning:

$$\Delta \nu = \frac{v \Delta \lambda}{\lambda^2}$$

When this expression for $\Delta \nu$ is substituted into $\Delta s \geq \dfrac{v}{\Delta \lambda}$, we get:

$$\Delta s \geq \frac{v \lambda^2}{v \Delta \lambda} \geq \frac{\lambda^2}{\Delta \lambda}$$

and

(17.11) $\qquad \Delta s \Delta \lambda = \lambda^2$

Equations (17.10) and (17.11) imply that infinitely small uncertainties could be achieved if unlimited time and displacements were used in the measuring situations. The established principles involved in the Compton effect and in the de Broglie waves place the meanings of uncertainty in a new frame of reference. Infinitely small uncertainties are physically impossible.

First, with regard to the energy of a photon, frequency is expressed by $\nu = E/h$. Then any uncertainty in the frequency results in the following amount of uncertainty in the energy:

$$E_2 - E_1 = h\nu_2 - h\nu_1 = \Delta E = h \Delta \nu$$

and

$$\Delta \nu = \Delta E / h$$

Substituting in Eq. (17.10):

$$\Delta t \Delta \nu = \frac{\Delta E}{h} \Delta t \geq 1$$

and

(17.12) $\qquad \Delta E \Delta t \geq h$

Thus, we become aware that *the product of the uncertainties in the energy and the time interval involved is always at least as large as Planck's constant h.*

Second, with regard to the wave aspect of a photon or a material particle, the associated wavelength is expressed by $\lambda = h/p$. It follows that any uncertainty in the wavelength results in the following amount of uncertainty in the momentum:

$$p_2 - p_1 = \frac{h}{\lambda_2} - \frac{h}{\lambda_1} = \frac{h\lambda_1 - h\lambda_2}{\lambda_2 \lambda_1}$$
$$= \Delta p = \frac{h \Delta \lambda}{\lambda^2}$$

and

$$\Delta \lambda = \frac{\Delta p \lambda^2}{h}$$

Substituting in Eq. (17.11):

$$\Delta s \Delta \lambda = \frac{\Delta s \Delta p \lambda^2}{h} \geq \lambda^2$$

and

(17.13) $\qquad \Delta s \Delta p \geq h$

Thus, we become aware that *the product of the uncertainties in the displacement and the momentum in a physical process is always at least as large as Planck's constant h.*

Equations (17.12) and (17.13) are important expressions of the well-known *uncertainty principle* which Werner Heisenberg introduced in 1927. It places a fundamental limitation on the certainty of measurements of energy and time, or of position and momentum. For instance, if a photon is expressed in terms of an energy state E and it is known to have existed for a time interval Δt during measurement, then the energy is uncertain by at least the amount $h/\Delta t$.

An illustration of the position and momentum limitation is found in attempting to measure the wave and particle properties of a moving particle. In this situation the quantity Δs can be interpreted as the uncertainty in the position of the particle. The uncertainty principle shows it is impossible to specify simultaneously and with infinite precision the linear momentum and the corresponding position of the particle. The uncertainty in the position and momentum, as measured in a given direction, is equal to or greater than Planck's constant. These limitations do not reach important values when related to macroscopic objects, but lead to important consequences when brought to bear upon atomic and subatomic particles. For example, expressing momentum in terms of mass times velocity, Eq. (17.13) can be expressed:

$$\Delta s \Delta v \geq \frac{h}{m}$$

Then, let us compute the intrinsic uncertainty in the speed of an electron within a hydrogen atom. The electron mass is 9.1×10^{-31} kg; its range of displacement would be about that of the atomic radius, 10^{-10} meters. Planck's constant is 6.625×10^{-34} joule-sec. On this basis the intrinsic uncertainty in the speed of the electron is 7,200,000 meters per second—a very sizable velocity variation.

$$\Delta v \geq \frac{h}{m \Delta s}$$

$$\geq \frac{6.625 \times 10^{-34} \text{ joule-sec}}{9.1 \times 10^{-31} \text{ kg} \times 10^{-10} \text{ meters}}$$

$$= 7.2 \times 10^6 \text{ meters/sec}$$

By way of comparison, let us also compute the intrinsic uncertainty in the speed of a marble of mass 10 grams (10^{-2} kg). The center of gravity of a marble can be measured with a meter stick to within 10^{-3} meters. On this basis the intrinsic uncertainty in the speed of the marble is 6.625×10^{-29} meters per second—a completely negligible variation.

$$\Delta v \geq \frac{h}{m \Delta s} \geq \frac{6.625 \times 10^{-34} \text{ joule-sec}}{10^{-2} \text{ kg} \times 10^{-3} \text{ meter}}$$

$$= 6.625 \times 10^{-29} \text{ meters/sec}$$

ATOMIC CLASSIFICATION

The logical development of modern science places important limitations upon the available precision of certain observations. It also bestows important extensions of meaning to the principles of conservation of mass-energy and of conservation of momentum. At first it may seem to threaten to dissolve the carefully laid axioms upon which all the principles and laws that we have adopted in previous explanations seem to be based. It might appear as if our logic has revealed facts which are subject to completely different principles and laws. This is not true. The uncertainty principle and the relationships expressed by the relativity theory define the limitations within which the Newtonian concepts are valid. This adds stability to our knowledge and removes the frustration of uncertainty. In every situation, the previously confirmed laws are valid to a high degree of approximation when systems large in mass are involved, and when the range of motion or the size of the system is large. The principles of conservation of mass-energy and conservation of momentum remain as decisive concepts for interpreting observations and speculations of all dynamic processes in nature.

The quantization of atomic characteristics

Let us recall the conditions described in Chapter 2 in explanation of resonance of sound in a resonance tube. In a tube of a given length, only certain frequencies could excite resonant oscillations. The allowed frequencies are those for which the length of the tube is an odd number of quarter wavelengths. In these allowed states standing waves exist, in which the waves moving in one direction exactly counteract the effects of the waves moving in the opposite direction. These waves cannot be observed within the tube, but can be detected outside it. If energy were not emitted from the end of the tube, a resonating tube could in principle continue oscillation without loss of energy for an indefinite period of time. If now we imagined the tube bent into a closed circular loop, no emission could take place and the waves would join smoothly onto themselves and oscillate without energy loss. A similar action could be imagined for any form of wave phenomenon.

The de Broglie wave of electrons is such a phenomenon for which the concept of standing waves could define the quantized electron orbits in an atom. The de Broglie formula describes the wavelength as $\lambda = h/mv$. Thus, the conditions for the standing waves produced by an electron's motion in a circular orbit would be limited to those orbits in which the circumference $(2\pi r)$ is some integral multiple of the electron wavelength. A circular graph of the wave phenomenon is shown in Fig. 17.8. The energy in the standing waves of the electron remains constant. The atom does not radiate energy while in one of these stationary states. This concept establishes a firm basis for atomic stability. The stationary orbits for which there is no radiation are those in which

$$n\lambda = 2\pi r$$

where $n = 1, 2, 3, \ldots$ successively. The whole-number integer n is called the *principle quantum number.* Substitute the de Broglie expression of particle wavelength in the above equation:

$$n\left(\frac{h}{mv}\right) = 2\pi r$$

This is equivalent to the Bohr atom formula:

(16.8) $$mvr_n = n\left(\frac{h}{2\pi}\right)$$

Since the electron radius is restricted to certain permitted values, the energy is also restricted to certain discrete values. But in view of the uncertainty principle, precise knowledge of the electron radius is denied. Consequently, the quantity of energy is determined on the basis of electron and quantum constants such as were used in Eq. (16.11):

(16.11) $$\frac{1}{n_1^2} \times \frac{2\pi^2 k^2 e^4 m}{h^2} = -E_1$$

where n_1 = the principal quantum number (for E_1, $n_1 = 1$)

Figure 17.8 A circular graph of a standing wave. The energy in a standing wave remains constant.

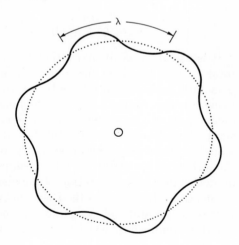

k = coulomb force constant
(9×10^9 newton-meters² per coul²)

e = electron charge
(1.602×10^{-19} coul)

m = electron mass
(9.108×10^{-31} kg)

h = Planck's constant
(6.625×10^{-34} joule-sec)

$-E_1$ = total energy of the lowest state, quantitatively equal to the ionization energy

It follows from Eq. (16.11) that the energy of other states of the hydrogen atom is:

$$E_n = \frac{-E_1}{n^2}$$

where E_1 is the ionization energy and n is the principal quantum number for the successive energy states. It is useful to recall that the total energy described for a particle in planetary motion depends only on the value of the major axis of the ellipse and not on the eccentricity of the orbits. The quantum relationships do not change this energy description. But whereas the Newtonian concepts place no restriction on the possible energy levels, *the quantum theory restricts the allowable energies of an atom to those indicated by the principal quantum number* n; *and determining these values of energy does not require knowledge of the orbit displacement radius.*

The angular momentum p_θ arising from the orbital motion of the electron is specified by Eq. (16.8). When we recall the value of the intrinsic uncertainty in the speed of an electron within a hydrogen atom, we realize that it is *not* proper to visualize the electron as moving in any specific orbit. This is why the Bohr model of the atom could not represent reality.

Calculations involving the concepts of wave mechanics show that the magnitude of the orbital angular momentum is quantized as described by the following equation:

$$(17.14) \qquad p_\theta = \frac{h}{2\pi} \sqrt{l(l+1)}$$

where l is an integer called the *orbital angular momentum quantum number*. The possible values of l are restricted by the value of the principal quantum number. The values of l range from zero to $(n-1)$ by integers; that is,

$$l = 0, 1, 2, 3, \ldots (n-1)$$

Here, again, precise knowledge of radius or velocity is *not* needed in defining these values. Thus, when the principal quantum number n equals one, the angular momentum equals zero. This would be a disastrous idea in terms of the Bohr atom because it would imply that the electron orbit passed through the nucleus. The uncertainty principle makes such precision in knowledge of orbital path unattainable and unnecessary.

The integral values of the orbital angular momentum quantum number l are often represented by letter symbols as follows:

$$l = 0, 1, 2, 3, 4, 5 \ldots$$
$$\text{symbol} = S, P, D, F, G, H \ldots$$

It is useful to recall that although the total energy described for a particle in planetary motion depends only on the value of the major axis, the angular momentum of the system remains constant throughout a given orbit but its value depends upon the eccentricity of the orbit. The quantum relationships do not change this description of angular momentum. But whereas the Bohr model describes the state of an atom by the quantum number n, which specified the *radius* of a circular orbit, *the relationships described by wave mechanics specify the state of an atomic system completely by including the values of all the appropriate quantum numbers.*

In view of these relationships, let us consider again the second postulate of the Bohr theory which held that when an electron undergoes a transition from an upper energy state to a lower energy state, the difference in the energies is transformed into a photon of energy $h\nu$. Fig. 17.9 shows the states of the hydrogen atom identified according to allowed transitions between quantum levels of energy and of angular momentum. Notice that only those transitions are allowed which connect the different energy levels in adjacent momentum columns. In other words, the only allowed transitions are those from a given energy state to another allowed energy state which also changes the orbital momentum quantum number by 1. We conclude that for the allowed transitions, the *selection rule* is:

$$\Delta l = \pm 1$$

All other combinations are highly unlikely but not absolutely impossible.

One effect of the selection rule is that the orbital angular momentum of the atom must change when a photon is emitted or absorbed. This could take place only if the photon carries angular momentum. The principle of conservation of angular momentum cannot be violated. Thus we recognize that a photon carries energy, linear momentum, and angular momentum, each in specific quantum amounts.

Our experiences at the outset of this chapter centered around four characteristics which described the energies and the angular momentum characteristics

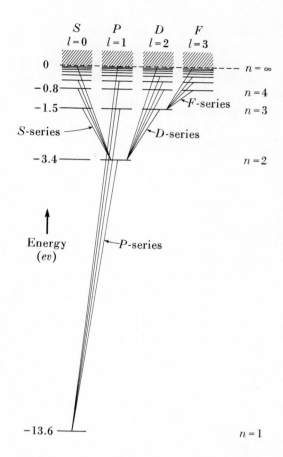

Figure 17.9 Energy-level diagram for hydrogen. The allowed transitions are between adjacent momentum columns.

of planetary systems. We have found that the first two relationships must be quantized in describing atomic phenomena. This does not mean that quantization does not take place in more massive phenomena. Just as the relativistic effects are too small to be detected at speeds far below the speed of light, so also the levels of quantization are too small to be detected in massive objects moving at the ordinary speeds of the everyday world. It is a fact, however, that when a baseball pitcher winds up before delivering a pitch, the energy and momentum changes imparted to the ball, while it is being accelerated in a curved path, increases not smoothly but in step-wise quantum jumps. The steps, however, are so tiny the phenomenon seems to be smooth.

We turn now to the third characteristic emphasized in describing planetary motion—the spatial components of angular momentum. Our reference to the Foucault pendulum led to the conclusion that components of the axial angular momentum directed anywhere in space are a constant depending only upon the angular momentum p_θ and the angle between the vector directions of p_z and p_θ. Space components of atomic phenomena involve magnetic force effects as well as electric force effects.

Recall Oersted's discovery of the magnetic effects of electric currents and Ampere's description of the directional qualities of the current-induced magnetic field—the right-hand rule for motion of positive charges and the left-hand rule for motion of negative charges. Study Fig. 17.10(a). The electron of negative charge moving in a circular orbit comprises an electric current loop. The

left-hand rule explains the direction of the magnetic field within the loop. The figure also shows how the magnetic field induced by the orbiting electron resembles and is equivalent to the magnetic field produced by a permanent magnet. Because the magnet has a north-seeking and a south-seeking pole, it is conveniently described as a magnetic *dipole*. In describing the magnetic effects of a current loop, it is useful to define a *magnetic dipole moment M* in terms of the magnitude of electric current i (a flow of 1 coulomb of charge per second equals 1 ampere) and the area A of the plane enclosed by a current loop:

(17.15) $$M = iA$$

The value of M does not depend upon the shape of the loop. The description has a counterpart in terms of a permanent magnet. The magnetic dipole moment of a permanent magnet is expressed as the product of the magnetic pole strength and the distance between the magnetic poles:

$$M = ul$$

where M = magnetic dipole moment
u = magnetic pole strength
l = distance between the poles of the magnet

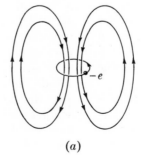
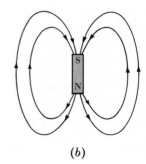

Figure 17.10 Magnetic fields. The magnetic field induced by the motion of the electron is equivalent to that of a permanent magnet.

(a) (b)

The magnetic dipole moment is a vector quantity directed perpendicular to the plane of the coil and in the direction indicated by the left-hand rule. Notice that the magnetic dipole moment is directed parallel and opposite to the angular momentum. The relationship does not end with this significant fact.

If we look upon an electron moving in a circular orbit as an electric current, then the current expressed as the time rate of transmitting charge is given by $i = ef$, where i is the current, e is the electronic charge, and f is the frequency of revolution of the electron in revolutions per second. Since the area of a circle is given by $A = \pi r^2$, Eq. (17.15) becomes:

$$(17.15) \quad M = iA = (ef) \times (\pi r^2)$$

Recall that angular velocity may be expressed in radians per second, and that there are 2π radians per revolution. Hence, the electron in the above example has an angular velocity of $\omega = 2\pi f$ radians per second. The moment of inertia of the electron in orbit is given by $I = mr^2$. Therefore, the orbital angular momentum of the electron is:

$$p_\theta = I\omega = (mr^2) \times (2\pi f)$$

Solving the equations of magnetic dipole moment M and of orbital angular momentum p_θ for the common factors $\pi r^2 f$ gives:

$$\pi r^2 f = \frac{M}{e} = \frac{p_\theta}{2m}$$

and

$$(17.16) \quad M = \left(-\frac{e}{2m}\right) p_\theta$$

where M = magnetic dipole moment of the electron in orbit

e = electronic charge

m = electronic mass

p_θ = angular momentum of the electron in orbit

The minus sign is introduced because the magnetic dipole moment is directed oppositely to the angular momentum.

Eq. (17.16) shows M to be directly proportional to p_θ and to be quantitatively determined without reference to electron velocity or the dimensions of its orbit.

The importance of the magnetic effect is brought into focus by recalling that the forces between the electric current and a magnetic pole are not directed along the line connecting the two, but are perpendicular to that line. These crosswise forces upon a magnetic dipole may produce a torque. This is the explanation of the turning magnet in Oersted's experiment. (See Fig. 16.2.) A torque which turns an object through an angle θ does work. Energy is transformed. If a restoring torque exists, the energy is transformed into potential energy. In this sense, when a magnetic dipole moment is oriented at an angle θ with respect to an external magnetic field, the dipole has potential energy because of the existing torque.

A magnetic field at any point can be described in terms of *magnetic intensity*. It is represented by the symbol B. The magnetic intensity may be defined by the equation

$$B = \frac{\tau}{M}$$

where B = magnetic intensity in newtons per ampere meter

if τ = torque in newton-meters upon a dipole moment set at right angles to the field

M = magnetic dipole moment in ampere-meters^2

Proper calculation indicates that the potential energy of a magnetic dipole oriented at an angle θ with respect to an external magnetic field is given by:

(17.17) $\Delta E_m = -MB \cos \theta$

Thus, when the north-seeking pole of the equivalent permanent magnet would be *aligned* with the magnetic field direction, angle θ is zero, and $\Delta E_m = -MB$, *a minimum value.* When the north-seeking pole would be anti-aligned with the magnetic field direction, angle θ is 180°, and $\Delta E_m = +MB$, *a maximum value.*

The quantum relationships indicated by Eq. (17.16) do not change this description of energy potentials. But whereas the Newtonian concepts of potential energy in rotating systems place no restrictions on the possible levels of energy within the range of orientations of the magnetic dipole moment in space, the quantum theory restricts the allowable magnetic energies to those orientations for which the component of p_θ along the direction of the magnetic field is an integral multiple of $h/2\pi$ as determined by:

(17.18) $p_z = m_1 h/2\pi$

where m_1 is *the orbital magnetic quantum number,* which can assume, for a given value of l, the integral values:

$m_1 = l, (l-1), (l-2) \ldots, 0, \ldots, -l$

This phenomenon is called *space quantization.* For example, in a zero state with $l = 2$, the possible values of m_1 are $+2$, $+1$, 0, -1, or -2. In this state, therefore, p_z can have the possible values h/π, $h/2\pi, 0, -h/2\pi$, and $-h/\pi$. When $l = 2$,

$$p_\theta = \frac{h}{2\pi} \sqrt{2(2+1)} = \frac{h\sqrt{6}}{2\pi}$$

In Fig. 17.5, we find $p_z = p_\theta \cos \theta$. Hence, the rule governing the orientation of the p_θ vector is:

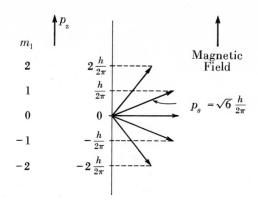

Figure 17.11   Space quantization of the orbital angular momentum vector. The orbital angular momentum vector is never completely aligned along the direction of an external magnetic field.

(17.19) $\cos \theta = \dfrac{p_z}{p_\theta} = \dfrac{m_1}{\sqrt{l(l+1)}}$

Eq. (17.19) is the rule for space quantization. Notice that the maximum component of p_θ along the direction of space quantization occurs when $m_1 = l$. Along this orientation $p_z = \dfrac{lh}{2\pi}$ and is always less than the magnitude of $p_\theta = \dfrac{h}{2\pi} \sqrt{l(l+1)}$. This proves that the orbital angular momentum vector is *never* completely aligned along the direction of an external magnetic field. (See Fig. 17.11.)

Precise knowledge of the rotational axis direction in space is *not* required for precisely specified knowledge of the magnitude of p_θ. Although its direction is not specified, it is useful to regard p_θ as having precession around the p_z axis. In this regard, just as the earth's axis is known to have a precession because of the torque produced by the gravitational effects of the sun and moon on the equatorial bulge, so also the torque acting on the p_θ vector by the forces inherent in the magnetic potential energy for an allowed value of m_1 is generally regarded to produce a precession of p_θ around the p_z axis at a constant angle θ.

These quantized magnetic effects explain the splitting of spectral lines into discrete components by an external magnetic field, as discovered by Zeeman in 1896.

There remains now only one of the four characteristics which have guided our inquiry—the relationship of particle spin to the total angular momentum of the planetary system. This will introduce the fourth and final quantum number which is associated with concept of *electron spin*. When spectral emissions are examined under high resolution, each spectral line exhibits a *fine structure* in that for each transition there are actually two or three lines separated from one another by no more than a very few angstroms in wavelength. The fine structure bears a resemblance to the Zeeman effect, but it does *not* require the presence of an *external* magnetic field for its observation. The resemblance suggested the possibility of an *internally* induced Zeeman effect. This concept was first developed by S. A. Goudsmit and G. E. Uhlenbeck in 1925. An intrinsic angular momentum was associated with the rotation of the charge cloud about an axis of rotation fixed with the electron. Again, the model cannot be visualized; the idea developed as an analogy to the rotation of a planetary particle about its axis. Because of this analogy, the intrinsic angular momentum of the electron is named *electron spin*. The rotating charge cloud produces a magnetic field and a magnetic dipole moment M_s, oppositely directed to the spin angular momentum

p_s. Thus, the electron produces not only an orbital magnetic moment M_1, but also a spin magnetic moment M_s. The spinning electron is pictured as being immersed in the magnetic field produced by M_1. Therefore, the energy of the system will differ slightly depending on the orientation of the spin magnetic moment with respect to the field of M_1.

Spectroscopic evidence indicates the spin quantum number s has the *single value* $\frac{1}{2}$. This spin is as basic a characteristic of an electron as is its charge and mass. The spin angular momentum is expressed by a formula analogous to that for orbital angular momentum. The magnitude of p_s is:

$$(17.20) \quad p_s = \frac{h}{2\pi} \sqrt{s(s+1)} = \frac{h}{4\pi} \sqrt{3}$$

In the presence of the magnetic field, the electron spin is space-quantized such that p_{sz}, the component of the spin angular momentum along the direction of the magnetic field, is:

$$p_{sz} = m_s \frac{h}{2\pi}$$

Figure 17.12 Space quantization of electron spin angular momentum. The orientation of the spin vector is restricted to two possible states.

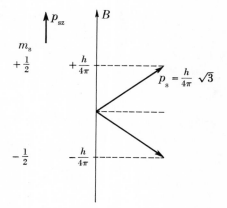

where m_s = the *spin magnetic quantum number*, which has two possible values:

$$m_s = +\tfrac{1}{2} \text{ or } -\tfrac{1}{2}$$

Fig. 17.12 illustrates the effect of space quantization of the electron spin angular momentum. The orientation of the spin vector is restricted to the two possible states in which the component m_s of the angular momentum along the component vector axis is $\dfrac{+h}{4\pi}$ or $\dfrac{-h}{4\pi}$. Because the magnetic potential energy arising from the orientation of the spin magnetic moment is greater for the state where $m_s = +\tfrac{1}{2}$ than where $m_s = -\tfrac{1}{2}$, the fine line structure is explained.

The Pauli exclusion principle The nonnuclear properties of an atom are specified by the complete analysis of the energy, angular momentum, and space quantization of each electron in the atomic structure. While this analysis is possible *in principle*, in practice a full theoretical prediction from quantum theory of *all* the atomic properties is not easily carried out because of the difficulties arising from many particled systems. In fact, the only atom which has been completely described using the relativistic-quantum theory is hydrogen. For hydrogen, there is essentially perfect agreement between prediction and experimentally observed events. But even though the other atomic elements have not been completely described, the quantum theory does provide insight into explanation of the chemical and physical properties of the atoms of the various elements. Many of these properties can be conveniently organized within the framework of the periodic table of the elements.

During the middle of the nineteenth century, the remarkable periodic recur-

Figure 17.13 Energy states available to the electron in the hydrogen atom. There are two states for each dash, corresponding to the two electron spin orientations.

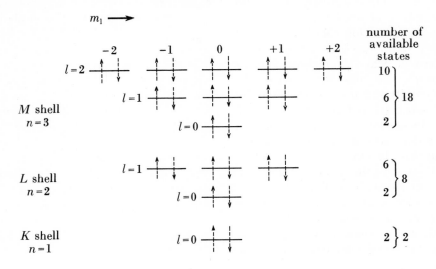

rence of certain properties describing the elements had been revealed by simply listing the elements in the order of their atomic weights. Many concepts were proposed in explanation. None were completely satisfactory and none were based on unified theory. The key to understanding the periodic listing is one of the greatest achievements of the relativistic-quantum theory. Spectroscopic evidences from all elements show that atoms never have two electrons occupying the same quantum state. In 1924 Wolfgang Pauli formalized this experimental fact into his celebrated *exclusion principle*: *No two electrons in an atom can have the same set of quantum numbers.* No exceptions to the exclusion principle have been found.

THE PERIODIC TABLE OF THE ELEMENTS

Let us review the rules governing the possible values of the quantum numbers. First, for a given n, which selects the energy state, the possible orbital angular momentum states are:

$l = 0, 1, 2, \ldots, (n-1)$ (*n possibilities*).

Second, for a given l, the possible orbital magnetic moments are:

$m_l = l, l-1, \ldots, 0, \ldots, -(l-1), -l$

$$(2l + 1 \; possibilities)$$

Third, for a given m_l, the possible spin magnetic moments are:

$$m_s = +\tfrac{1}{2} \text{ or } -\tfrac{1}{2} \quad (2 \; possibilities)$$

Fig. 17.13 illustrates the energy states available to the electron in the hydrogen atom within the first three principal energy states. The four quantum num-

bers which describe the states are n, l, m_l, and m_s. It is not necessary to indicate the electron spin number s because its value is always $\tfrac{1}{2}$.

The ground state The ground state of a hydrogen atom, often called the *normal state*, is achieved when the single electron is at its lowest energy. This occurs when $n = 1$, $l = 0$, $m_l = 0$, and $m_s = -\tfrac{1}{2}$. Fig. 17.14 is an energy-level diagram showing this state. Using letter symbols

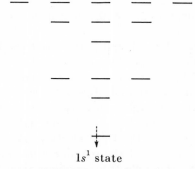

$1s^1$ state

Figure 17.14 Hydrogen atom in its ground state.

to represent the orbital angular momentum number l, the electron configuration for the ground state of hydrogen is $1s^1$, where the number 1 represents $n = 1$, the s represents $l = 0$, and the superscript 1 gives the number of electrons having these values of n and l.

Atoms with more than one electron have their electrons distributed among the possible energy states so as to achieve the lowest possible total energy. Thus, helium, which has two electrons, has the electrons arranged as shown in Fig. 17.15(a). The electron configuration for the ground state of helium is $1s^2$, repre-

Figure 17.15 (a) Helium atom in its ground state. (b) Lithium atom in its ground state.

senting $n = 1$, $l = 0$, $m_l = 0$, $m_s = -\frac{1}{2}$ and $+\frac{1}{2}$.

The element with the next higher atomic number is lithium $_3$Li. Fig. 17.15(b) represents its electron configuration in the ground state. Of the three electrons in this atom, two are in the $n = 1$ states; the exclusion principle requires that the third electron must go to the lowest of the remaining available levels. The electron configuration for the ground state of lithium is $1s^2 2s^1$ representing, first, $n = 1$, $l = 0$, $m_l = 0$, $m_s = -\frac{1}{2}$ and $+\frac{1}{2}$, and second, $n = 2$, $l = 0$, $m_l = 0$, and $m_s = -\frac{1}{2}$. The first energy level, called the K shell, is closed; and one electron is found in the incomplete $l = 0$ subshell of the second energy level, called the L shell.

Rules of electron configuration The rules of electron configuration, based on the exclusion principle, require the addition of one electron for each nuclear charge beginning with the lowest energy levels and proceeding to successively available lowest energy levels. Since no two electrons within an atom can have

the same set of quantum numbers, the electron configuration pattern is assured of an orderly development from one element to the next. Table 17.1 gives

TABLE 17.1 Electron configuration of the first 11 elements

Element	Electron configuration for the ground state			
$_1$H	$1s^1$			
$_2$He	$1s^2$			
$_3$Li	$1s^2$	$2s^1$		
$_4$Be	$1s^2$	$2s^2$		
$_5$B	$1s^2$	$2s^2$	$2p^1$	
$_6$C	$1s^2$	$2s^2$	$2p^2$	
$_7$N	$1s^2$	$2s^2$	$2p^3$	
$_8$O	$1s^2$	$2s^2$	$2p^4$	
$_9$F	$1s^2$	$2s^2$	$2p^5$	
$_{10}$Ne	$1s^2$	$2s^2$	$2p^6$	
$_{11}$Na	$1s^2$	$2s^2$	$2p^6$	$3s^1$

the electron configurations and the occurrence of closed shells and subshells representing the first eleven elements.

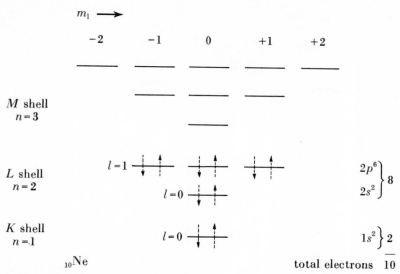

$m_1 \longrightarrow$

$$-2 \qquad -1 \qquad 0 \qquad +1 \qquad +2$$

M shell
$n = 3$

L shell
$n = 2$

$l = 1$

$l = 0$

$2p^6$
$2s^2$ $\Big\}$ 8

K shell
$n = 1$

$l = 0$

$1s^2 \Big\}$ 2

$_{10}$Ne

total electrons   10

Figure 17.16   Neon atom in its ground state.

Fig. 17.16 represents the electron configuration of neon $_{10}$Ne: $1s^2 2s^2 2p^6$. The orbital angular momenta as well as the spin angular momenta in each of the closed subshells are paired off; hence, the total angular momentum and total magnetic moment arising from these completed subshells equal zero. Atoms having this configuration of electrons in their ground state are chemically inert. All the electrons are strongly bound; thus, the ionization energy is particularly high.

In contrast observe the electron configuration of sodium $_{11}$Na: $1s^2 2s^2 2p^6 3s^1$, as represented by Fig. 17.17. This configuration shows a single electron outside the closed *L* shell. The inner electron shells are inert; hence, the single electron in the outermost shell moves around the inert shells in a manner similar to the single electron of hydrogen. The single electron in the so-called valence shell is a characteristic of elements

which are electron donors. It is clear why sodium has many of the chemical characteristics of hydrogen and other hydrogenlike atoms.

The periodic table of chemical elements is shown in Fig. 17.18. For each element the electron configuration of the outer electrons, the atomic number, and the chemical symbol are shown. Notice that there is a continuous stepwise filling of the sublevels in the expected order, $1s^1$, $1s^2$, $2s^1$, $2s^2$, etc., up through $3p^6$. At this point it would be logical to expect that the succeeding elements would fill in sequence the 10 available states of the $3d$ subshell of the quantum states in $l = 2$; but this action does not take place. Evidence from spectroscopic and chemical sources indicate the $4s$ subshell is filled first. The electrons of the first two states of the $4s$ subshell have greater binding energy than the $3d$ electrons. This is explained by the fact that zero angular momentum signifies a relatively

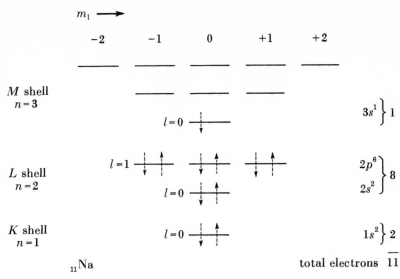

Figure 17.17 Sodium atom in its ground state.

short displacement from the nucleus during parts of the orbital motion which allows for the greater binding energy. Other factors of this sort change the order in which subshells are filled. Experimental evidence substantiates the following general order in which the electrons fill atomic subshells:

$1s$, $2s$, $2p$, $3s$, $3p$, $4s$, $3d$, $4p$, $5s$, $4d$, $5p$, $6s$, $4f$, $5d$, $6p$, $7s$, $6d$, $5f$

Organization of the table The arrangement in the periodic table is such that each vertical column contains the elements which have a common orbital state and which also have the same number of electrons in this orbital state. The elements in each column have similar chemical properties. The fundamental basis for the chemical properties of the elements is the electron configuration of the outermost subshells. Since the configuration is explained by the relativistic-quantum theory, the chemical and physical properties of materials can be predicted. These predictions form a basic and fruitful guide for research in all fields of science which involve chemical, electrical, and other atomic phenomena.

SUMMARY

The Bohr atomic model is valid only for certain features of hydrogen and hydrogenlike atoms. Inherent uncertainties in the possible observations needed for required relationships make any real attempt at alignment with

Figure 17.18 Periodic table of the chemical elements.

Main table (rows labeled by s-shell on the left, p-columns on the right):

1s	1 H $1s^1$						2 He $1s^2$						2p
2s	3 Li $2s^1$	4 Be $2s^2$		5 B $2p^1$	6 C $2p^2$	7 N $2p^3$	8 O $2p^4$	9 F $2p^5$	10 Ne $2p^6$				3p
3s	11 Na $3s^1$	12 Mg $3s^2$		13 Al $3p^1$	14 Si $3p^2$	15 P $3p^3$	16 S $3p^4$	34 Se $4p^4$					
4s	19 K $4s^1$	20 Ca $4s^2$	21-30 see (a)	31 Ga $4p^1$	32 Ge $4p^2$	33 As $4p^3$	34 Se $4p^4$	35 Br $4p^5$	36 Kr $4p^6$				4p
5s	37 Rb $5s^1$	38 Sr $5s^2$	39-48 see (b)	49 In $5p^1$	50 Sn $5p^2$	51 Sb $5p^3$	52 Te $5p^4$	53 I $5p^5$	54 Xe $5p^6$				5p
6s	55 Cs $6s^1$	56 Ba $6s^2$	57-80 see (c)	81 Tl $6p^1$	82 Pb $6p^2$	83 Bi $6p^3$	84 Po $6p^4$	85 At $6p^5$	86 Rn $6p^6$				6p
7s	87 Fr $7s^1$	88 Ra $7s^2$	89-102 see (d)										

(17 Cl $3p^5$, 18 Ar $3p^6$ in the 3p column)

(a) Transition elements: the ten 3d states follow the 4s states.

3d	21 Sc $3d^1$	22 Ti $3d^2$	23 V $3d^3$	24 Cr $4s^1 3d^5$	25 Mn $3d^5$	26 Fe $3d^6$	27 Co $3d^7$	28 Ni $3d^8$	29 Cu $4s^1 3d^{10}$	30 Zn $3d^{10}$

(b) 4d elements: the ten 4d states follow the 5s states.

4d	39 Y $4d^1$	40 Zr $4d^2$	41 Nb $5s^1 4d^4$	42 Mo $5s^1 4d^5$	43 Tc $4d^5$	44 Ru $5s^1 4d^7$	45 Rh $5s^1 4d^8$	46 Pd $5s^0 4d^{10}$	47 Ag $5s^1 4d^{10}$	48 Cd $4d^{10}$

(c) Rare earths and 5d elements: the ten 5d states and fourteen 4f states follow the 6s states.

5d	57 La $5d^1$	72 Hf $5d^2$	73 Ta $5d^3$	74 W $5d^4$	75 Re $5d^5$	76 Os $5d^6$	77 Ir $5d^7$	78 Pt $6s^1 5d^9$	79 Au $6s^1 5d^{10}$	80 Hg $5d^{10}$

4f	58 Ce $5d^1 4f^1$	59 Pr $5d^0 4f^3$	60 Nd $5d^0 4f^4$	61 Pm $5d^0 4f^5$	62 Sm $5d^0 4f^6$	63 Eu $5d^0 4f^7$	64 Gd $5d^1 4f^7$	65 Tb $5d^0 4f^8$	66 Dy $5d^0 4f^{10}$	67 Ho $5d^0 4f^{11}$	68 Er $5d^0 4f^{12}$	69 Tm $5d^0 4f^{13}$	70 Yb $5d^0 4f^{14}$	71 Lu $5d^1 4f^{14}$

(d) Actinides and transuranic elements: the 6d and 5f states follow the 7s states.

6d	89 Ac $6d^1$	90 Th $6d^2$											

5f	91 Pa	92 U	93 Np	94 Pu	95 Am	96 Cm	97 Bk	98 Cf	99 Es	100 Fm	101 Md	102 No	103 Lw

Newtonian principles untenable in describing and explaining atomic events. The language of science, however, has deep roots in Newtonian concepts, and the basic meanings of this language are not changed by the logical developments leading from the relativity and quantum theories.

Four characteristic aspects of energy and momentum describe planetary systems: the angular momentum of the planetary particle moving in an elliptical orbit remains constant; the total energy of a planetary system is independent of the eccentricity; the component of angular momentum about any axis directed towards a zenith in space remains constant; the total angular momentum of the system includes also the angular momentum of the rotation of each of the individual bodies involved.

Quantization of these characteristics of planetary systems leads to successful interpretations of atomic events. First, the quantum theory restricts the allowable major energy levels of an atom to those indicated by the principle quantum number n; determination of these values of energy does not require knowledge of an orbital displacement radius. Second, the quantum theory restricts the allowable magnitudes of the orbital angular momentum to those indicated by the orbital angular momentum quantum number l; determination of these values of momentum does not require knowledge of a radius or velocity of the planetary particle. Third, in view of the magnetic dipole moment of the electron in orbit, energy potentials are available because of the space components of the magnetic orientation. The quantum theory restricts the allowable magnetic energies to those orientations for which the space component of angular momentum for the system is indicated by the orbital magnetic quantum number m_l; determination of this value does not require knowledge of a rotational axis direction for the angular momentum of the system. Fourth, the electric charge characteristic of the electron produces a magnetic moment with reference to a spin angular momentum for the electron as a planetary particle. The quantum theory restricts the allowable magnetic spin energies to two orientations for which the space components of the electron spin angular momentum are indicated by the spin magnetic quantum number m_s having two possible values: $+\frac{1}{2}$ or $-\frac{1}{2}$.

The Pauli exclusion principle formalized the experimentally determined fact that no two electrons in an atom can have the same set of quantum numbers.

PROBLEMS

1 Why can there be no angular acceleration of a planetary particle moving in an elliptical orbit?

2 Why could the Newtonian cause-and-effect relationship not adequately explain atomic events when they explained the events of the macroscopic world with great accuracy?

3 Compute the kinetic energy of the earth at perihelion. (Eccentricity of the earth's orbit is 0.017.)

4 What changes may be expected in measurements of length, time, and mass in accord with Einstein's theory of special relativity?

5 A given object is moving at a relative velocity of 0.8 the speed of light with respect to an observer. If the object's length in the direction of motion were 2 meters as measured by an observer accompanying the object, what would be the apparent length of the object as observed by the stationary observer? (See Eq. (17.1).)

6 If the rest mass of the object in Problem 5 were 10 kg, what would be its relativistic momentum and kinetic energy in the situation described in Problem 5? What steps did you use in solving this problem and why?

7 What was the scientific importance of the discovery of the Compton effect?

8 Compute the de Broglie wavelength of a neutron ($m_n = 1.675 \times 10^{-27}$ kg) moving with 2 million ev kinetic energy? What steps did you use in solving this problem and why?

9 According to Eq. (17.10) what would be the uncertainty of the frequency if no beats were heard during a period of 1 minute?

10 Make an electron configuration diagram similar to Figure 17.17 for potassium $_{19}$K.

11 Prepare a specific comparison between the relativistic-quantum model of the atom and the Bohr atomic model.

18

STABLE AND UNSTABLE

NUCLEAR PARTICLES

The fundamental concepts of forces and the attending conservation principles of mass-energy and momenta, both linear and angular, seem to be also destined to become the basis for understanding nuclear phenomena. However, a fundamentally valid theory for interpreting nuclear events has not yet been formulated. A tremendous amount of time has been spent on speculation and experimentation in search of clues toward understanding what holds the nucleus together, but the problem is still largely unsolved. Some of the most ingeniously designed equipment and experimental techniques ever created are being used in nuclear studies. Significant progress has been made. Much has been learned about measuring and recording the events which reveal nuclear forces and nuclear energies. Relativistic-quantum theory has been used as a guide in designing techniques of inquiry and in interpreting the results.

Our inquiry in Chapter 14 into unstable nuclei, as they pertained to age-dating of geological events, introduced many of the terms used in describing nuclear processes. The major particles of the nucleus are called *nucleons*. There are two kinds: *protons* which carry a single positive electronic charge, and *neutrons* which are electrically neutral. The number of protons in a given nucleus is called the *atomic number*. This nuclear characteristic identifies each element. The term *mass number* is used to designate the total number of nucleons in an atomic nucleus. The mass number is roughly equivalent to the atomic mass of the isotope being described. The mass of an atom or atomic particle is generally listed in *atomic mass units* (amu). In defining amu, the atom of oxygen-16 ($_8O^{16}$) is listed at precisely 16 amu. The mass of all other particles are given in ratio to the mass of $_8O^{16}$.

(Recently, a new set of units based on carbon-12 ($_6C^{12}$) has been introduced which will change somewhat the value of the atomic mass unit. However, until the new units have reached a status of universal application, we shall adhere to the $_8O^{16}$ units.)

Table 18.1 lists the rest mass and rest energy values for the constituent particles of the atom. The precision of these measurements of mass have an uncertainty of about 3 parts per million. (By way of comparison, recall the uncertainty stipulated for the measurement of the astronomical unit in Chapter 8.)

NUCLEAR FORCES AND ENERGIES

The fact that positively charged protons are bound together in nuclei with binding

TABLE 18.1 Mass and energy of atomic particles (mass-energy conversion factor: 1 amu = 931.14 mev)

Proton rest mass	1.007596 amu
Proton rest energy	938.213 mev
Neutron rest mass	1.008986 amu
Neutron rest energy	939.507 mev
Electron rest mass	0.000549 amu
Electron rest energy	0.5112 mev

energies of several million electron volts shows that the nuclear forces of attraction are far stronger than the Coulomb forces of repulsion between the protons of like charge. Experimental measurements show that nuclear forces extend over a very short and well-defined range; at displacements beyond this, Coulomb forces predominate. The onset of the nuclear force between a pair of protons occurs at a distance of about 3 fermis (3×10^{-15} meters). The *fermi* is the natural unit of length pertaining to nuclear sizes, as the angstrom is the natural unit of length pertaining to atomic-sized measurements. One fermi is equal to 10^{-15} meters or 10^{-5} A. The nuclear force between a neutron and a proton becomes operative at about 2 fermis distance. *The nuclear forces increase as the displacement between nucleons decrease, but at extremely short displacements* (0.7 fermi or less) *the forces reverse and become forces of repulsion.*

It is quite obvious that if we cannot observe directly atoms of 1 A size, the events taking place within the space of 0.00001 (or 10^{-5}) A must be observed indirectly. The experimental techniques involving scattering are most effective. The method used is essentially the same as that suggested by Rutherford over 50 years ago.

Scattering experiments As was described for the Rutherford experiments, the method of scattering involves shooting one nucleon at high speed toward a group of other nucleons. If during its flight the high-speed nucleon makes a very close encounter with a second nucleon, the nuclear force takes effect. During the brief encounter the projectile nucleon swerves from its original path and the target nucleon is pulled out of position. By analyzing the pattern of deflections, the force relationships can be deduced.

Picturing the nucleons as particles moving in specifically determined paths is, of course, an impossible means of describing the events of scattering. The uncertainty principle makes precise descriptions of position and velocity untenable. The only reliable means of predicting and interpreting the effects of nucleon interactions is by applying the rules of quantum theory where wave aspects of energy and angular momentum simplify the interpretations. Let us inquire, therefore, into quantized characteristics.

An important property intrinsic to both the proton and the neutron is a quantized angular momentum, often referred to as *nuclear spin*. This term is misleading. The angular momentum is a property of each particle by itself; it does not depend on any orbital motion. The quantum number I defines the nuclear spin angular momentum. The magnitude of the nuclear spin angular momentum is:

(18.1) $$p_I = \frac{h}{2\pi} \sqrt{I(I + 1)} = \frac{h}{4\pi} \sqrt{3}$$

where I for both proton and neutron equals $\frac{1}{2}$. Quantitatively, the magnitude of the nuclear spin angular momentum is equal to the magnitude of the electron spin angular momentum. But the similarity does not end there.

Experiments involving external magnetic fields reveal the nuclear spin angular momentum to be space quantized. As was found with electron spin, the permitted components of nuclear spin along the direction of the magnetic field are $\frac{+h}{4\pi}$ and $\frac{-h}{4\pi}$. This was an especially surprising development with regard to the neutron which is neutral in charge.

It should be pointed out, however, that the magnetic moments of protons and neutrons are irregular and do not seem to fit smoothly into any of the present theories. It may be that the nucleons have a compound structure with a variety of constituents. The fact that theoretical explanation is still forthcoming does not prevent the use of those aspects of existing theories which do aid in interpretation. The knowledge that nuclear spin angular momentum is quantized and that these values are also space quantized has led to important inquiries concerning the energy relationships of the nuclear force between nucleons.

In quantum relationships between interacting nucleons, the total spin angular momentum is found by adding the angular momenta of the constituent particles. Remember that the quantum number I is $\frac{1}{2}$ and the available magnetic components are $\frac{+h}{4\pi}$ and $\frac{-h}{4\pi}$. Thus, when the intrinsic spins of two nucleons are parallel, the total spin is 1; when the spins are antiparallel, the total spin is zero. The effect of this relationship is that when two nucleons have parallel spins, they exhibit a non-central component in their interaction which suggests the presence of orbital effects. They act as if the nucleons were revolving in orbits about a fictitious force center. This sets up a situation similar to the electron energy level of $n = 2$ where l can equal $+1$, 0, and -1; the total angular momentum vector can have three, and only three, directions with respect to the orbital angular momentum vector: the two can be parallel, perpendicular, or antiparallel.

When the total spin angular momentum is the sum of antiparallel spins, the interaction is as if the nucleons were not spinning at all and the action produces no orbital effects.

In the scattering system, the interacting projectile and target nucleons conform to quantized orbital angular momentum rules. That is, the orbital angular momentum can have only integral values, $l = 0, 1, 2, 3, \ldots$. The fact that the orbital angular momentum can equal zero again underscores the fact that no visual model in terms of particle motion can mimic atomic events; zero angular momentum would mean that the approach of the centers of mass of the two nucleons would be zero. This would mean that the projectile nucleon passed directly through the target nucleon—a situation

which could not represent reality. Rather, the scattering at zero angular momentum can be explained best in terms of diffraction of particle waves.

In practice the Rutherford experimental technique is used. The distribution of scattered particles is determined by counting or recording on film the particles scattered out at different angles with regard to the direction of the incident projectile beam. This record is significantly simplified by techniques involving apparatus which allow double-scattering. The scattered particles of the first encounter are passed through a second group of scattering nucleons. When properly designed these instruments provide greater discrimination between the various quantum effects. The final records of particles scattered at different angles are then analyzed by theoretical physicists with regard to what kind of force would produce the recorded distributions.

Mass-energy experiments Extremely accurate measurements can be made of

Figure 18.1 Schematic diagram of a mass spectrograph. The action of the electrical and magnetic fields is to disperse the various ions of different mass-to-charge ratios and cause those of equal ratio to focus upon given points of the photographic plate.

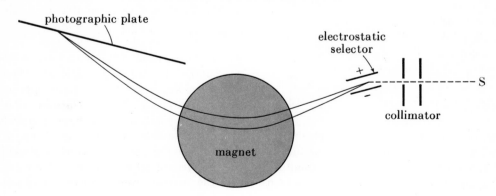

the masses of the nuclei of atoms by studying their motion in electrical and magnetic fields. The experimental apparatus and techniques are an elaboration of the Thomson apparatus (Fig. 16.9) used to determine the mass-to-charge ratio of cathode rays. Fig. 18.1 is a schematic diagram of a mass spectrograph. Essentially the action of the electrical and magnetic fields cause the ions of different mass-to-charge ratios to disperse and to come to a focus at different points on the photographic plate. Improvements in instrument design and experimental techniques have made it possible to measure masses with great enough precision to evaluate the conservation of mass-energy relationships in the various nuclear isotopes.

The simplest nucleus containing more than one nucleon is the *deuteron*, the nucleus of the deuterium atom, also called heavy hydrogen. The deuteron consists of a proton and a neutron. Its rest mass is 2.014194 amu. Let us compare this value to the total mass of the proton and neutron.

Proton rest mass . . . . 1.007596 amu
Neutron rest mass . . . . 1.008986 amu

Total mass of proton and
  neutron . . . . 2.016582 amu
Deuteron rest mass . . . . . 2.014194 amu

Mass difference . . . . 0.002388 amu

This mass difference interpreted in terms of relativistic conservation of mass-energy represents the amount of energy which must be added to the nucleons in the deuteron to separate them into a free proton and neutron beyond the range of the nuclear force. This energy is the binding energy. Making use of the mass-energy conversion factor listed in Table 18.1, the binding energy E_b of the proton-

neutron to form a deuteron is 2.224 mev.

$$E_b = 0.002388 \text{ amu} \times \frac{931.14 \text{ mev}}{\text{amu}}$$

$$= 2.224 \text{ mev}$$

The binding energy of the proton and electron to form a hydrogen atom has been given as 13.6 ev. Because the binding energy of the hydrogen atom is so small, it is not possible in practice to determine its quantized energies directly from the difference between rest masses of constituent particles and the mass of the bound system. This would require uncertainties of less than 1 part in 100 million. But the large binding energies of nucleons in nuclear systems, due to the great nuclear force, can be determined by measurement of mass differences.

Consider the nucleus of carbon-12, the atom destined to become the basis for improved atomic mass listings. The nucleus $_6C^{12}$ has 6 protons and 6 neutrons. Let us first calculate the *total* binding energy, the energy required to separate all of the nucleons of $_6C^{12}$ beyond the range of nuclear forces. We use the nuclear mass values given in Table 18.1 and the mass 12.000521 amu for the $_6C^{12}$ nucleus.

6 protons
  = 6 × 1.007596 . . . . . . 6.045576 amu
6 neutrons
  = 6 × 1.008986 . . . . . . 6.053916 amu

Total nucleon masses . . . . 12.099492 amu
Rest mass of $_6C^{12}$ nucleus 12.000521 amu

Mass difference . . . . 0.098971 amu

Total binding energy = 0.098971 amu

$$\times \frac{931.14 \text{ mev}}{\text{amu}} = 92.152 \text{ mev}$$

The *average* binding energy with which each of the 12 nucleons is bound is 92.152 mev/12 nucleons or 7.679 mev per nu-

A highly sensitive mass spectrograph of improved experimental design, used to evaluate the conservation of mass-energy relationships in the various nuclear isotopes. [*Courtesy of the University of Minnesota.*]

cleon. Compare this to the 1.112 mev per nucleon for the deuteron binding energy. The 7.679 mev per nucleon for carbon-12 does not mean that each of the 12 nucleons is bound by this amount of energy. The energy needed to separate the first nucleon from the remaining 11 is significantly greater than the average value.

Using the nuclear masses measured by the mass spectrograph allows a similar computation of the average binding energy per nucleon for all stable nuclei. When this was done, the values of *average*

binding energy per nucleon for each nucleus were plotted against their corresponding *mass numbers*. Fig. 18.2 shows the resulting curve. The curve fits fairly smoothly along the plotted points. As we would expect after comparing carbon and deuterium, the curve rises rapidly at the start. It tapers off to the horizontal at about mass number 20. The maximum is reached near the isotope of iron-56, and then the average binding energy per nucleon decreases slowly toward the heaviest stable nuclei. This curve will have far-reaching implications

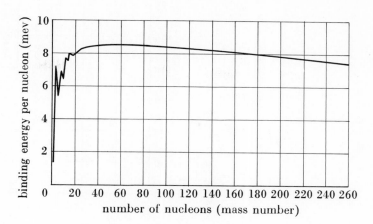

Figure 18.2 Average binding energy per nucleon.

in the explanation of energy released by fission and fusion.

STABLE NUCLEI

The term *nuclide* is used to designate the nuclei having specified values of atomic number and mass number. It is customary to indicate the atomic number by a subscript preceding the symbol of the element and to indicate the mass number by a superscript following the symbol. The nuclide $_6C^{12}$, for example, has atomic number 6 and mass number 12. This indicates the nuclei has 6 protons and 12 nucleons; thus it must have $12 - 6 = 6$ neutrons.

Nuclides having the same atomic number are called *isotopes*. Nuclides having the same mass number are called *isobars*. Nuclei having the same number of neutrons are called *isotones*.

The stability line   A graph can be plotted on the basis of the location of stable nuclides placed on a grid corresponding to the number of neutrons and the number of protons in each nuclide. Fig. 18.3 shows the resulting group of points for stable nuclei found with some abundance in nature. A smooth line drawn through the average positions of the points would indicate the general region in which most of the stable nuclides are found. This line is referred to as a *stability line*. The dashed line across the graph shows the location of equal neutrons and protons.

For the light nuclides, the stability line indicates a close adherence to the line of equal values. This would be expected in view of the fact that the protons and neutrons each have spin momentum values of $\frac{1}{2}$ which are restricted to space-quantized values of $\frac{+h}{4\pi}$ and $\frac{-h}{4\pi}$. Therefore the Pauli exclusion principle operates in building up stable nuclides where each closed sublevel has a pair of protons or a pair of neutrons in the lowest available quantum level.

For the heavier nuclides, the stability line deviates increasingly from the equal

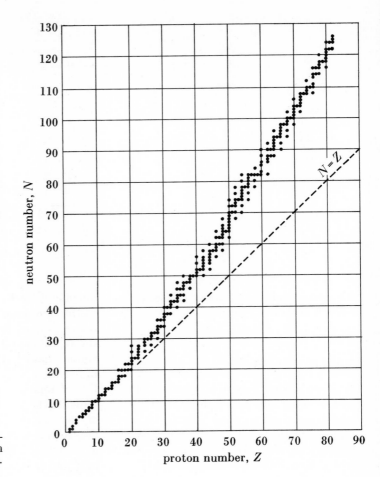

Figure 18.3 Graph of neutron number versus proton number for stable nuclides.

value line. The number of neutrons becomes greater than the number of protons. Two factors should be evaluated in interpreting this fact—the exclusion principle and the Coulomb force of repulsion between protons. The rule of the exclusion principle allows 2 protons to occupy a given energy and spatial state only if their nuclear spins are anti-aligned. The same rule applies to neutrons. Except for the effects of the Coulomb forces between protons, the states available to

protons and to neutrons should have nearly the same values. But as the number of protons increases in the heavy nuclides, the net effect of the combined Coulomb forces increases and competes noticeably with the nuclear force. The effect upon the available quantum states is shown schematically in Fig. 18.4; the spacing between the available proton levels increases as higher levels are reached, while the spacing between neutron levels remains nearly equal. A

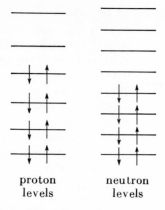

proton
levels

neutron
levels

Figure 18.4 Schematic representation of the proton and neutron states of oxygen-16.

theoretical basis for this speculation is still an unsolved problem, but the empirically determined facts seem to substantiate it in principle.

Following this line of speculation for the general trend of the stability line, we find general agreement. The first proton level and the first neutron level are filled when a nucleus is formed having 2 protons and 2 neutrons. This is, of course, the very stable alpha particle $_2\text{He}^4$. Some scientists believe that the alpha particles may represent stable units which interact as subunits within the larger nuclei. For our purposes we shall hold to a more direct system of filling energy levels. In line with quantum rules, the most stable nuclides will form when the lowest energy levels available to the protons and neutrons are filled. In view of the fact that as the number of protons increases the spacing between available proton energy levels also increases, the frequency of neutron filling becomes greater than that of protons. The quantum rules would require an excess of neutrons. The general trend of the stability line bears this

out without recourse to specific knowledge of the energy amounts involved between the supposed quantum levels.

Nuclear density Scattering experiments with very high-energy neutrons and electrons have confirmed the belief that the total volumes of the various nuclei are merely the sum of the volumes of the nucleons comprising each nucleus. Because all nucleons have nearly the same mass (the neutron mass exceeds the proton mass by less than 0.1 percent), we conclude that all nuclei have equal mass densities. Since the radius of a proton is approximately 1.4×10^{-15} meters and the proton mass is about 1.67×10^{-27} kg, the density of nuclei is 1.5×10^{17} kg per cubic meter or about 1 billion tons per cubic inch.

$$\text{density} = \frac{\text{mass}}{\text{volume}}$$

$$\text{volume of a sphere} = \frac{4}{3}\pi r^3$$

$$D = \frac{3m}{4\pi r^3} = \frac{3 \times 1.67 \times 10^{-27}\,\text{kg}}{4\pi\,2.7 \times 10^{-45}\,\text{meter}^3}$$

$$= 1.5 \times 10^{17}\,\text{kg/meters}^3$$

Can electrons exist in the nucleus of atoms? Recall how the beta particle emitted from radioactive nuclei proved to be an electron. It might seem logical, therefore, that electrons are present within the nucleus. But in order that an electron be confined within the nucleus, its de Broglie wavelength must be no greater than the nuclear dimension. To achieve this wavelength an electron must have an energy of 500 mev. Therefore, if electrons are contained in the nucleus, they must attain a potential energy of at least -500 mev. There is no evidence of nuclear attractive forces on electrons strong enough to achieve this.

We must, therefore, conclude that electrons cannot exist as a constituent particle within a nucleus.

THE ELEMENTARY PARTICLES

When the projectile nucleons in scattering experiments achieve energies near 300 mev, the nucleons do not simply interact by orbiting at available quantum levels to produce scattering; instead new particles are created in the interaction. A large group of new particles have been studied since the invention of machines capable of imparting high energies to projectile particles. Some of these particles were predicted on theoretical bases; others have come as a surprise. These newly discovered events must surely figure strongly in the theoretical explanations yet to come. Meanwhile, ever more powerful machines, built to impart as much as 25 bev to projectiles, will add

many new and important measurements and discoveries to the speculations of those who attempt to produce valid explanations. Although high-energy machines like the 6-bev synchrotron at Berkeley, California have been in operation since the 1950's, high-energy cosmic ray phenomena have been used for study since the turn of the century. Cosmic ray experiments are not as easily controlled as the manmade accelerators. However, cosmic ray experiments have usually laid the groundwork for those of the manmade machines. Energies as high as 10^{10} bev have been recorded for some cosmic ray particles. As improved techniques for recording cosmic ray events have been devised, many strange and mystifying nuclear reactions have been recorded.

Cosmic radiation Even the most highly insulated electroscopes slowly lose their charge. This loss of charge is attributed

The Brookhaven cosmotron, a synchrotron of the billion electron volt class, used in studies of nuclear structure and nuclear energies. When in operation, the cosmotron is surrounded by heavy concrete shields in order to protect personnel from radiation hazards. [*Courtesy of the Brookhaven National Laboratory.*]

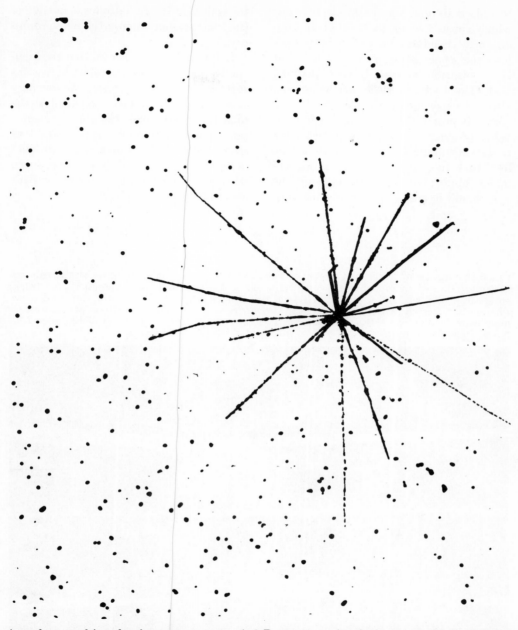

A nuclear emulsion showing a star event. A 2 Bev neutron (producing no track) has hit and exploded a nucleus into 17 different track-forming particles. The heavy lines are made by relatively slow particles, such as protons; the lighter lines are made by lighter particles, such as mesons. [*Courtesy of Brookhaven National Laboratory.*]

to ionized air molecules in the electroscope which cause the air to be slightly conducting. Sending charged electroscopes into the upper atmosphere proved that the ionization increased with altitude. V. F. Hess, who in 1911 carried out the altitude experiments by using balloons, correctly proposed that the ionization was being produced by a highly penetrating radiation coming from outer space. The fact that the intensity of radiation remains almost constant throughout the year made it reasonable to assume that the source of the radiation was outside of the solar system—hence the name *cosmic ray*.

Later studies have shown that the high-energy particles which reach the earth's surface are of two types: *the primary cosmic radiation* which constitutes the high-energy particles reaching the earth's atmosphere from outer space, and the *secondary radiation* which is the product of high-energy nuclear reactions produced when the primary rays enter the earth's atmosphere.

Cloud chamber photographs of a photon-initiated shower taken simultaneously with two cameras to permit three-dimensional analysis of the tracks. A 700 Mev photon (producing no track) enters from the top, and a positron-electron pair is created at the uppermost thin lead plate. Photons are created at the lower plates by *Bremsstrahlung* collisions, and these photons create more pairs, leading to a shower of electrons, positrons and photons. [*Courtesy of Professor J. C. Street, Harvard University.*]

The primary cosmic ray particles constitute a sampling of the interstellar materials in our galaxy. It is interesting to note that the abundances of the various heavy nuclides in the primary cosmic rays are in close agreement with the relative abundances of the elements in the sun, the stars, and the earth. This is further evidence of the hypotheses based on the idea of a common source of planetary and solar materials. In the cosmic radiation the particles are ionized. The most abundant particles are protons (hydrogen nuclei) and alpha particles (helium nuclei). These have abundance ratios of 77 percent and 21 percent, respectively. The remaining portion constitutes the evidence cited above.

These charged particles are believed to be accelerated by the changing magnetic fields known to exist within the galaxy. After a long period of continued acceleration within the magnetic fields of the galaxy, the particles achieve escape velocity and begin traveling outward through space. Some of these particles collide with the earth.

The secondary radiation springs from three general types of nuclear events which may occur when the primary rays interact with atmospheric nuclei. First, a nucleus in the atmosphere might absorb the enormous energy of the incoming particle and disintegrate into a large number of smaller particles. The emerging particles carry away the high energies and may cause similar events of their own. These events are called *star events* because of the appearance of the record in photographs. Second, the energy of the interaction might produce high-energy gamma rays. Often the gamma ray when passing near a nucleus gives rise to an electron-positron pair. These newly created particles interact with other nuclei giving rise to more gamma radiation and more electron-positron pairs. This chain reaction spreads outward rapidly. The record of these events appear as isolated rain showers and are called *cascade showers*. Third, the energies of the interaction produce entirely new kinds of particles. The most abundant of these are the *pions* of mass about 273 times the electron mass for the charged pions and $264m_e$ for the electrically neutral type. Heavier particles also have been observed in collision events. In this category are the *hyperons* which have greater mass than the nucleons. The third type of event holds the most interest since the particles produced have enriched the concepts which must be included in interpretations of nuclear events.

Before inquiring further into the high-energy particles, let us do a simple exercise in algebra which illustrates the problems involved in theoretical explanation.

Particles and antiparticles Consider again the relativistic Eqs. (17.4) and (17.7):

(17.4) $\quad p = \dfrac{m_0 v}{\sqrt{1 - v^2/c^2}}$

(17.7) $\quad E = \dfrac{m_0 c^2}{\sqrt{1 - v^2/c^2}}$

Squaring these equations:

(17.4a) $\quad p^2 = \dfrac{m_0^2 v^2}{(1 - v^2/c^2)}$

(17.7a) $\quad E^2 = \dfrac{m_0^2 c^4}{(1 - v^2/c^2)}$

Solving these two equations for the common factors:

$$\frac{m_0^2}{(1 - v^2/c^2)} = \frac{p^2}{v^2} = \frac{E^2}{c^4}$$

Thus

$$v^2 = \frac{p^2 c^4}{E^2}$$

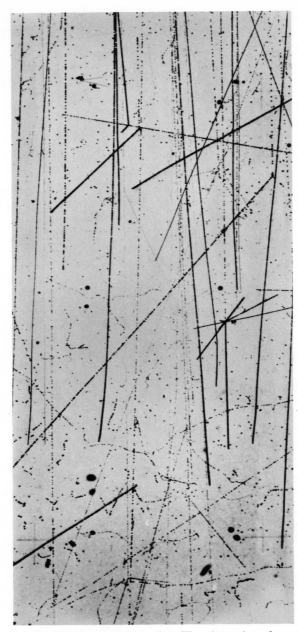

Bubble-chamber photograph. The incoming beam consists of protons and π-mesons; heavy tracks stopping in the chamber are protons, and light tracks passing through the chamber are π-mesons. A number of nuclear collisions can be discerned in this picture. [*Courtesy of Brookhaven National Laboratory.*]

Substituting this value of v^2 into Eq. (17.7a):

$$E^2 = \frac{m_0^2 c^4}{1 - \dfrac{p^2 c^4}{E^2 c^2}} = \frac{m_0^2 c^4 E^2}{E^2 - p^2 c^2}$$

Solving for E^2:

(18.2) $E^2 = p^2 c^2 + m_0^2 c^4$

But the quadratic nature of Eq. (18.2) leads to the problem of explaining the dilemma brought on by the fact that a particle of rest mass m_0 moving in free space with a momentum p can have a total energy expressed in both positive and negative terms. That is:

$$E_{\text{T}} = +\sqrt{p^2 c^2 + m_0^2 c^4} \text{ or } -\sqrt{p^2 c^2 + m_0^2 c^4}$$

At first thought, the second of these two expressions seems to require the existence of matter having negative mass; but phenomena indicating negative mass effects are never observed.

Many physicists have had a hand in developing an explanation of these relationships. Some of the suggested hypotheses seemed utterly fantastic at the time they were first offered. But fantastic ideas have a way of leading the speculations of science. None of the resulting theories have been completely successful in their interpretations, but many have inspired noteworthy insights into particle phenomena. We consider briefly two of the suggested theories. The first was proposed in 1928 by P. A. M. Dirac of England; it made possible the prediction of antiparticles. The second was proposed in 1935 by Hideki Yukawa of Japan; it predicted the existence of mesons.

The Dirac proposal expressed the idea that the electric force between charged particles may be described in terms of the exchange of electromagnetic quanta or,

particles. The proposed photons are undetectable and hence are called *virtual photons*. But if enough energy is added from the outside, as, for example, by accelerating particles in a cyclotron, the interaction can transform the photons from the virtual state to real particles. One means of partially visualizing this is to postulate that what is ordinarily regarded as empty space—a true vacuum—is really not empty but represents the condition where all quantum states for the negative mass particles have been filled, leaving only states for the positive mass particles available. For instance, with regard to negative mass electrons, the exclusion principle would limit the quantum states of negative mass electrons in the same manner as positive mass electrons. The negative mass quantum states merely represent states of lower energy than those of the positive mass states. Thus, the negative mass electrons when provided with enough energy to jump to an available positive mass state would also achieve a positive mass, leaving behind an unfilled negative mass state. In other words, the supposed vacuum would now have two detectable states: the electron in a positive mass state, and an imperfect background state. This last situation would be interpreted as creating a *manifestation* of the absence of a negative mass electron, that is, the *presence* of the mirror object, a particle of charge $-(-e) = +e$ and of mass $-(-m) = +m$. Thus was made possible the prediction of the *positron*. The over-all effect of the energy transformation would be the creation of a pair of particles having equal rest masses and equal but opposite electric charges. Furthermore, according to the theory, if the positron and electron collide they would annihilate each other and their mass would be converted into photons having an equivalent amount of energy. The least energy which could be involved in either the creation or annihilation of the particles would be $2m_0c^2$, the rest mass energy of the two particles involved.

It should be pointed out that the Dirac theory held such broad implications for the quantum theory that the above predictions were not actually made until after Carl D. Anderson of the California Institute of Technology discovered the positron in 1932. With that remarkable event, further prediction of antiparticles also were found feasible for the proton and neutron. These antiparticles have been detected and the predictions confirmed.

In order to conserve momentum for the conversion of high-energy photons into particle pairs, it is essential that the event take place in association with an interacting nucleus.

Yukawa's proposal also was based on the hypothesis that the nuclear force could be described in terms of exchange of quanta, or particles. In view of the extremely short range of the nuclear force, Yukawa predicted the existence of particles having a mass intermediate between the electron mass and nucleon mass as the agents exchanged in accounting for the nuclear force. The charged π-*mesons* were discovered in records of cosmic-ray interactions in 1947 and an uncharged π^0-meson was discovered in similar records in 1950. These *pions* fulfill the requirements of the Yukawa proposal.

From the viewpoint of the nuclear force hypothesis, pion emissions also must be undetectable, virtual processes where the quanta can be transformed into real particles only when enough outside energy is available to materialize them. Because the nuclear force is so strong, a nucleon must emit virtual pions very frequently, and there usually must be more than one outside the nucleus at the same time. Thus, the charge and quantum-cloud picture presented in explanation of certain atomic and molecular effects also might be applied to the pion-nucleon processes. Charged pions also materialize as particles of negative and positive

TABLE 18.2   Particles less massive than nucleons

	Particle	Spin	Rest mass (m_e)	Mean life (sec)	Principal mode of decay
Leptons	Neutrino ν ($\bar{\nu}$)	$\frac{1}{2}$	0	Stable	
	Electron e^- ($\overline{e^+}$)	$\frac{1}{2}$	1	Stable	
	Muon μ^-	$\frac{1}{2}$	206.84	2.22×10^{-6}	$\mu^- \to e^- + \nu + \bar{\nu}$
	$\overline{\mu^+}$	$\frac{1}{2}$	206.84	2.22×10^{-6}	$\overline{\mu^+} \to \overline{e^+} + \nu + \bar{\nu}$
Mesons	Pion π^0	0	264.4	$\sim 10^{-15}$	$\pi^0 \to \gamma + \gamma$
	π^+	0	273.23	2.54×10^{-8}	$\pi^+ \to \overline{\mu^+} + \nu$
	$\overline{\pi^-}$	0	273.23	2.54×10^{-8}	$\overline{\pi^-} \to \mu^- + \bar{\nu}$
	K-Mesons K^0 $\overline{(K^0)}$	0	966	$\sim 10^{-10}$	$K^0 \to \pi^+ + \overline{\pi^-}$
	K^+	0	967	1.2×10^{-8}	$K^+ \to 2\pi^+ + \overline{\pi^-}$
	$\overline{K^-}$	0	967	1.2×10^{-8}	$\overline{K^-} \to 2\overline{\pi^-} + \pi^+$

charge. As would be expected in view of the proton's charge, in this process the negatively charged pion is the antiparticle of the positively charged pion. The three different pions (π^+, $\overline{\pi^-}$, and π^0) allow for the charge independence of the nuclear forces between any pair of nucleons. (The bar above the symbol of a particle signifies an antiparticle.)

ons. These comparatively newly discovered particles and the *hyperons* listed in Table 18.3 have yet to be incorporated into a generally accepted theory of matter. For this reason, they are often called *strange particles*. There seems to be nothing to prevent discovery of even more massive particles. Some scientists would prefer to think of these as compound par-

TABLE 18.3   The heavy particles (baryons)

Particle	Spin	Rest mass (m_e)	Mean life (sec)	Principal mode of decay
Proton P^+ ($\overline{P^-}$)	$\frac{1}{2}$	1836.1	Stable	
Neutron n^0 ($\overline{n^0}$)	$\frac{1}{2}$	1838.6	Stable	
Lambda Λ^0 ($\overline{\Lambda^0}$)	$\frac{1}{2}$	2182	2.6×10^{-10}	$\Lambda^0 \rightarrow P^+ + \overline{\pi^-}$ or $n^0 + \pi^0$
Sigma Σ^0 ($\overline{\Sigma^0}$)*	$\frac{1}{2}$	2326	$\sim 10^{-18}$	$\Sigma^0 \rightarrow \Lambda^0 + \gamma$
Σ^+ ($\overline{\Sigma^-}$)*	$\frac{1}{2}$	2328	8×10^{-11}	$\Sigma^+ \rightarrow P^+ + \pi^0$ or $n^0 + \pi^+$
Σ^- ($\overline{\Sigma^+}$)*	$\frac{1}{2}$	2342	1.5×10^{-10}	$\Sigma^- \rightarrow n^0 + \overline{\pi^-}$
Xi Ξ^- ($\overline{\Xi^+}$)	$\frac{1}{2}$	2585	$\sim 10^{-10}$	$\Xi^- \rightarrow \Lambda^0 + \overline{\pi^-}$
Ξ^{0}* ($\overline{\Xi^0}$)*	$\frac{1}{2}$	?	?	$\Xi^0 \rightarrow \Lambda^0 + \pi^0$ (postulated)

* Never experimentally observed.

Properties of elementary particles   Table 18.2 summarizes the properties of the less massive particles, and Table 18.3 those of the more massive particles.

In Table 18.2, notice that all of the particles except electrons and neutrinos are radioactive, and in many cases would form a decay series to the stable electron and positron. The *mean life* given in these tables is *not* the same as half-life used in Chapter 14. You will recall that the half-life $T_{1/2} = 0.693/\lambda$, where λ is the decay constant. The mean life $T_{\rm AV} = 1/\lambda$; therefore, $0.693 T_{\rm AV} = T_{1/2}$.

Very little is known about the *K-mes-*

ticles of some sort, rather than to classify them clearly as elementary particles.

The *pion* is given the same function in explaining the nuclear force as the photon is in explaining the force between electric charges. As might be expected, the $\overline{\pi^-}$ is attracted to the nucleus and can be absorbed by it. The capture of a $\overline{\pi^-}$ by a nucleus and the subsequent release of its rest mass energy to the nucleons disrupts the nucleus, producing a *star event*.

The *muons* are not agents of nuclear force and, hence, interact very weakly with nucleons. As a consequence, muons are very penetrating. They constitute

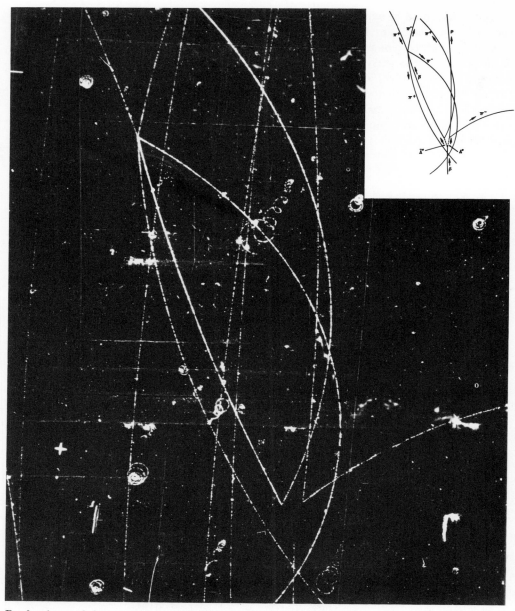

Production and decay of neutral lambda and anti-lambda baryons.   See the insert for mode of decay.   Notice that the total charge, the number of baryons, and the number of leptons are conserved.   [*Courtesy of Lawrence Radiation Laboratory, University of California.*]

about 75 percent of the secondary cosmic radiation which reaches the earth's surface at sea level, as compared to 1 percent for pions.

The particles marked with asterisks (*) in Table 18.3 have not yet been reported as having been experimentally observed, but certain inescapable theoretical arguments justify including them in this summary. In Table 18.3, there is also evidence of radioactive decay of extremely short mean life.

One final observation should be made in reference to Tables 18.2 and 18.3. A study of the principal modes of decay reveals that in any given reaction: (1) the total charge is conserved; (2) the number of baryons is conserved; and (3) the number of leptons is conserved. In (2) and (3) the antiparticles are taken to be negative. Thus, when pair production or pair annihilation takes place, the above-mentioned principles of conservation are preserved.

SUMMARY

The major particles of the nucleus are called nucleons. The proton and the neutron are the two kinds of nucleons. For a given nucleus, the atomic number lists the number of protons and the mass number lists the total number of nucleons. Short-range nuclear forces hold the nucleons together in the nucleus. The nuclear forces are opposed by the Coulomb forces between the positively charged protons.

Quantized levels of energy, angular momentum, and magnetic space orientations are evident also in nuclear descriptions. The Pauli exclusion principle operates for quantized proton levels and quantized neutron levels.

The binding energies of nuclear particles are determined by accurate mass determinations of the various nuclei. The mass differences are interpreted in terms of the relativistic law of conservation of mass-energy. The values of average binding energy per nucleon for the known nuclei increase rapidly for the nuclei of small mass numbers, reach a maximum near mass number 56, and decrease slowly as mass numbers increase beyond that value.

The preponderance of neutrons in the heavy nuclei is explained on the basis of increased Coulomb forces between large numbers of protons. This would increase the energy spacing between available proton quantum levels while the neutron levels would remain about equally spaced.

A large number of particles are created in the energy interactions between nuclei and high-energy projectile nucleons. A satisfactory hypothesis has not yet been devised to explain totally the functions of these particles. The conservation principles which are evident in these events include conservation of total charge, of number of baryons, of number of leptons, of total mass-energy, and of angular and linear momenta.

PROBLEMS

1 Why cannot the quantized energies of electron systems in atoms and molecules be determined by measurement of mass differences?

2 What evidences indicate that electrons cannot exist as constituent particles within a nucleus?

3 What nuclear characteristics are used to distinguish between the following classes of nuclides: isotopes, isobars, and isotones?

4 Explore the probable reason for the preponderance of neutrons in the heavier nuclides.

5 Calculate the average binding energy per nucleon for the nucleus of iron $_{26}Fe^{57}$ (mass = 56.939234 amu).

6 The nuclear density is said to be about 1 billion tons per cubic inch. Check the accuracy of this statement. What computational steps did you make and why?

7 Calculate the frequency of the radiation in the photons produced by the annihilation of a positron-electron pair producing two photons of equal energy.

8 What are some possible relationships between atomic particles and their antiparticles?

9 Find the most recent list of verified atomic particles and compare it to Tables 18.2 and 18.3.

10 Describe an example illustrating each of the conservation principles indicated in the concluding paragraph of the summary of Chapter 18.

19

ENERGY SOURCES—

THEIR DEVELOPMENT AND USE

For the United States, adequate sources of low-cost energy are a problem not of the dim future but of today. Even now our imports of petroleum are quite substantial. In another decade they almost certainly will be huge if, in fact, foreign oil is still available then in sufficient quantity. We shall have competitors. The energy problems of other nations are somewhat worse on the average than for the United States. We do have substantial reserves of coal and oil, but our most accessible supplies have been depleted. The cost of extraction will materially reduce the energy yield. Much of this cost is in terms of energy used in the processes of extraction and delivery to the consumer.

In the United States the primary sources of energy during the past century have been petroleum, coal, natural gas, water power, and wood. The last one might seem out of place as a primary source to many urban readers.

However, a century ago fuel wood contributed over 75 percent of this nation's energy requirement. By 1900, its contribution had been reduced to 25 percent; by 1950, to less than 4 percent, and at the present time it may be less than 2 percent. These figures are cited to show how rapidly patterns of fuel consumption can change. During that same century, petroleum contributions have gone from about 1 percent to about 35 percent. Coal has been the most consistent energy source. Its contribution reached a peak of about 75 percent of the total in about 1920; today it is somewhat less than 50 percent. These figures do not necessarily mean a cut-back in coal production. Our national consumption of energy has been increasing with giant strides. By way of comparison, estimates of the energy potential in the fuels used a century ago were about 8.5×10^{11} kilowatt-hours per year. Similar estimates for today are about 1.5×10^{13} kilowatt-hours per year —an eighteen-fold increase. And there seems to be no indication of cessation of increased demand.

We in the United States derive a somewhat unwarranted satisfaction from the statistics showing our unchallenged position in the world of energy consumption.

There are those who remind us that the measure of progress in a civilization is not how much energy is used but, rather, how much useful work and space heating is achieved per capita. The question should not be simply how to develop new ways to use energy, but should include more thought as to how well it can be used in the service of mankind.

There is no doubt that energy is the basis of our way of life. Without abundant energy our standard of living would be reduced to that of the Stone Ages. Therefore, our people may very soon be forced to think more realistically about problems of energy supply. No one can predict what the solutions will be, but we can seek to understand what some of them could be. Solutions will not come without realistic investment of research and capital. National foresight would recognize that solutions require time for development and a good measure of effective social direction.

NUCLEAR SOURCES OF ENERGY

For many laymen, nuclear energy has provided a wave of overconfident expectation that our energy resources will re-

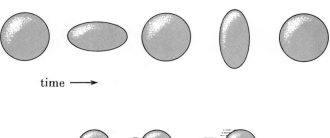

time $\longrightarrow$

Figure 19.1 Deformations of an oscillating nucleus leading to nuclear fission.

main unlimited and at reasonably low cost. Nuclear energy in abundance is still a dream of tomorrow. Nuclear energy of considerable proportions can be released in two types of nuclear reactions —nuclear fission and nuclear fusion. The reaction in these two sources is directly opposite. In fission, heavy nuclides are each split into two or more nuclides having comparable mass. In fusion, two light nuclides are joined to form a heavier nuclide. In both types of reaction, energy is released because the resulting nuclides have a lower mass per nucleon than the initial nuclides.

Fission The identification of the nuclear-fission reaction was first made in 1939 by the German scientists O. Hahn and F. Strassman. They had found elements such as barium and krypton among the products resulting from neutron bombardment of substances containing uranium. The discovery was correctly interpreted by Lise Meitner as products of fission of uranium nuclei by neutrons.

One possible explanation of nuclear fission involves the disruptive action in large nuclei of the competing influences of the Coulomb forces and the nuclear forces. Such an action takes place when a very-low-energy neutron is captured by the very heavy nucleus of uranium-235. By virtue of this capture the unstable nucleus of uranium-236 is formed with an excitation energy of 6.4 mev. In terms of the theoretical explanation, the excited nucleus of a very heavy nuclide oscillates as a whole. The competing forces tend to increase the amplitude of oscillation and to distort the shape of the nucleus (Fig. 19.1). The deformation may cause the heavy nucleus to assume periodically the shapes of a sphere, prolate ellipsoid,

sphere, oblate ellipsoid, sphere, etc. The short-range nuclear forces tend to return the nucleus to its spherical shape, while the more extended range Coulomb forces of repulsion between the protons tend to increase the ellipsoidal shapes. This would be particularly true in the prolate ellipsoidal shape (cigar shape) because the positive charges at the two ends repel each other while being beyond the effective range of the nuclear forces. When the degree of excitation is great enough, as is true in uranium-236, the Coulomb forces deform the nucleus into a dumbbell-like shape, whereas the nuclear forces tend to form separate spheres at the two ends rather than to pull the entire nucleus back into total sphericity. The Coulomb forces increase the separation until the two parts split into distinct nuclei, usually of unequal size. The newly formed nuclei are then accelerated apart by the Coulomb forces, thus gaining kinetic energy at the expense of the potential energy formerly held by the protons in the heavy nucleus. Being of much smaller size, the newly formed nuclides have too many neutrons for stability. Almost instantaneously two or three neutrons are released from these nuclides. Further stability is achieved by beta decay, changing some of the remaining neutrons into protons within the new nuclei.

Uranium-235 is the only *natural* nuclide which undergoes fission with low-energy neutrons. Many known fission reactions result from neutron capture in uranium-235. One example is shown here.

$$_0n^1 + {}_{92}U^{235} \rightarrow {}_{92}U^{236*} \rightarrow$$

$$_{56}Ba^{144} + {}_{36}Kr^{89} + 3{}_0n^1$$

Both barium-144 and the krypton-89 are radioactive and proceed through a series

The world's first privately financed nuclear power plant. This pioneer venture was developed at Pleasanton, California. The domed cylinder houses a water reactor which supplies the energy for this historic 5000-kilowatt plant. [*Courtesy of the General Electric Company.*]

of beta decays to stable nuclides. For the barium-144 the series is:

$$_{56}\text{Ba}^{144} \xrightarrow{\beta-} {}_{57}\text{La}^{144} \xrightarrow{\beta-}$$

$$_{58}\text{Ce}^{144} \xrightarrow{\beta-} {}_{59}\text{Pr}^{144} \xrightarrow{\beta-} {}_{60}\text{Nd}^{144}$$

The series for krypton-89 is:

$$_{36}\text{Kr}^{89} \xrightarrow{\beta-} {}_{37}\text{Rb}^{89} \xrightarrow{\beta-} {}_{38}\text{Sr}^{89} \xrightarrow{\beta-} {}_{39}\text{Y}^{89}$$

The stable nuclides formed from these reactions are neodymium-144 and yttrium-89, respectively.

If we now refer to the curve of average binding energy per nucleon shown in Fig. 18.2, we find that for the very heavy nuclides of atomic mass number near 235 the average binding energy per nucleon is approximately 7.6 mev per nucleon. In the middle-mass range nuclides of atomic mass number near 117, the average nucleon has a binding energy increased to about 8.5 mev per nucleon. This means that the product nuclides have decreased their potential energy per

nucleon by 8.5 − 7.6 = 0.9 mev per nucleon. At this rate, the total energy released per nuclide of uranium-235 in the fission process would be about 235 nucleons × 0.9 mev per nucleon, or 210 mev. The resulting energy would be found largely as the kinetic energy of the nuclides and emitted particles (neutrons, beta particles, and neutrinos). In order to compare energies, recall the typical radioactivity reaction:

$$_{92}\text{U}^{238} \rightarrow {}_{90}\text{Th}^{234} + {}_2\text{He}^4 + Q \ (4.21 \text{ mev})$$

The alpha decay of uranium-238 releases 4.21 mev per reaction as compared to 210 mev per reaction for the fission of uranium-235. The fission releases about 50 times as much energy per reaction. Furthermore, whereas the rate of alpha decay cannot be controlled in any manner, the fission reaction can be controlled in a useful manner by the conditions achieved in a *nuclear reactor*.

In short, reactor operation provides

that neutrons from one fission reaction initiate other fission reactions with attending release of energy and continued neutron capture until all the fissionable material is consumed. This self-perpetuating action is called a *self-sustained chain reaction*. The problems of control and safety are formidable.

In the fission of uranium-235, each decay reaction produces, on the average, 2.5 neutrons. Therefore, on the average, no more than 1.5 neutrons can be lost without stopping the chain reaction. On the other hand, on the average, no more than 1 neutron per reaction can be allowed to produce further fission without causing a runaway reaction. Of great importance to reactor design is the greater probability of low-energy neutron capture by uranium-235 than of high-energy neutron capture. The loss of neutrons from the reactor is reduced by increasing the size of the reactor in order that the greater volume of material insures adequate possibility of neutron capture. The slowing down of neutrons to increase the probability of capture is the function of the *moderator*. The material of the moderator must slow down the neutrons without capturing them. The lightest weight, us-

Interior view of a full-scale mock-up of the pressurized water reactor installed at the Shippingport, Pa. atomic power station. The men are moving a wooden model of a fuel element into position in this nuclear reactor which combines the qualities of a breeder reactor and heat exchanger in a single unit. [*Courtesy of Westinghouse Electric.*]

able moderator materials are deuterium oxide (heavy water), beryllium, and graphite. The conditions for a self-sustained chain reaction are met by properly arranging blocks of uranium within a moderator. The power level of the reactor can be controlled by inserting *control rods* of materials such as cadmium which absorb neutrons readily.

When, on the average, each fission reaction produces at least one more fission reaction, the reactor is said to go *critical*. The fission reaction is then self-sustained. If it is not self-sustained, a reactor is said to be *subcritical*. If each fission reaction produces more than one further fission, the reactor is said to be *supercritical*. The so-called atom bomb is an example of an extremely high supercritical state. The first self-sustained nuclear fission chain reaction was achieved in December 1942, under the direction of Enrico Fermi under the West Stands of Briggs Stadium, Chicago.

The large kinetic energy of the fission products in a nuclear reactor is transformed into heat. With the addition of a *heat exchanger*, the resulting energy can do useful work such as generating electric energy. Installations of this type are being used to power submarines and surface ships. Experimental installations also have been made to provide electrical power for communities which may be far removed from more economical sources of fuel. The nuclear reactor cannot at the present time compete economically with other more abundant and easily procured energy fuels.

Nuclear reactors have other uses than producing power. They are used as neutron sources, for production of radioisotopes, and as *breeder reactors*. The first two uses provide conditions and materials for scientific experiments and provide irradiated materials for industrial and medical purposes. The breeder reactor produces fissionable materials from the more abundant uranium-238 and thorium-232.

The reactions given below show the action of a breeder reactor:

$$_0n^1 + {}_{92}U^{238} \longrightarrow {}_{92}U^{239} \xrightarrow[23 \text{ min}]{\beta-}$$

$$_{93}Np^{239} \xrightarrow[2.3 \text{ da}]{-} {}_{94}Pu^{239}$$

$$_0n^1 + {}_{90}Th^{232} \longrightarrow {}_{90}Th^{233} \xrightarrow[23 \text{ min}]{\beta-}$$

$$_{91}Pa^{233} \xrightarrow[27 \text{ da}]{\beta-} {}_{92}U^{233}$$

The nuclides uranium-238 and thorium-232 do *not* undergo fission with capture of low-energy neutrons, but undergo reactions which lead, respectively, to the nuclides plutonium-239 and uranium-233. *The product nuclides do undergo fission with capture of low-energy neutrons.* Thus, the breeder reactor provides for two fuel materials, one which is fissionable and the other which is said to be *fertile* in that it can be converted into a fissionable material. In the fission of plutonium-239, there are, on the average, three neutrons released. When more than one of these neutrons are captured by fertile nuclides like uranium-238, it becomes possible for more fissionable material to be produced than consumed. Thus, the breeder reactor may produce both useful power and the replenishment of its supply of fissionable material.

In spite of these optimistic developments, nuclear energy produced by fission reactors will not greatly improve the energy resources of the United States or of the world. Commercially usable concentrations of uranium and thorium are very limited. At best the process of extracting these materials from their minerals is costly and not economically competitive with other fuels except in cases of high transportation costs for the more bulky conventional fuels.

Fusion

Combining nuclei of very light elements to form heavier and more tightly bound nuclei can result in significant release of nuclear energy. It is widely accepted by scientists that fusion reactions are responsible for the enormous energy release in the sun and other stars. There are two different ways in which such a fusion reaction is believed to occur. The first was proposed independently by Hans Bethe and von Weizacher and involves a so-called carbon cycle; the second is referred to as a proton-proton chain.

In the stellar carbon cycle, the suggested sequence of fusion events is:

$$_1H^1 + _6C^{12} \rightarrow _7N^{13} + \gamma \quad + Q$$
$$_7N^{13} \rightarrow _6C^{13} + _1e^+ \quad + \nu + Q$$
$$_1H^1 + _6C^{13} \rightarrow _7N^{14} + \gamma \quad + Q$$
$$_1H^1 + _7N^{14} \rightarrow _8O^{15} + \gamma \quad + Q$$
$$_8O^{15} \rightarrow _7N^{15} + _1e^+ \quad + \nu + Q$$
$$_1H^1 + _7N^{15} \rightarrow _6C^{12} + _2He^4 + Q$$

In total: $4 _1H^1 \rightarrow _2He^4 + 2 _1e^+ + Q$
$$(26.7 \text{ mev})$$

For interpreting the proton-proton chain, recall that the proton is a hydrogen nucleus. The sequence of reactions is believed to be ($_1H^2$ represents a deuteron):

(1) $_1H^1 + _1H^1 \rightarrow _1H^2 + _1e^+ \quad + \nu + Q$
(2) $_1H^1 + _1H^2 \rightarrow _2He^3 + \gamma \quad + Q$
(3) $_2He^3 + _2He^3 \rightarrow _2He^4 + 2 _1H^1 + Q$

In total: $4 _1H^1 \rightarrow _2He^4 + 2 _1e^+ + Q$
$$(26.7 \text{ mev})$$

In evaluating the total reaction, recall that steps (1) and (2) take place twice before step (3) is possible.

Stellar temperatures determine the probability of which of the two processes is possible. In stars like our sun having temperatures of about 20 million°C., the two processes are believed possible with equal probability. In stars at lower temperatures, the proton-proton chain is held to be more probable; in those at higher temperatures the carbon cycle is more probable.

The particles participating in these reactions taking place in the interior of the stars are completely ionized; all of the electrons have been separated from the atoms. In this state the mixture of electrons and nuclei is called a *plasma*. Under these conditions of high temperature and high pressure, the nuclei make frequent collisions with one another. The high-energy nuclei overcome the Coulomb repulsion forces and move within range of the nuclear force. Because of the required high thermal energy of the interacting nuclei, the process of fusion is called a *thermonuclear reaction*.

Controlled thermonuclear fusion has not yet been achieved. Several important advances have been made toward this goal, but the problems are of enormous difficulty. The tremendously high temperatures required to overcome the Coulomb repulsion and the need to confine the plasma for comparatively long periods of time are the fundamental barriers to the achievement of fusion under controlled conditions. Under equivalent conditions, deuterium undergoes fusion at a much faster rate than hydrogen. This fact was referred to in giving proof that the original materials of the earth had never taken part in the thermonuclear reactions of the sun. Deuterium occurs in the earth with an abundance of about 1 part in 6000 of hydrogen. The total amount of deuterium in the oceans

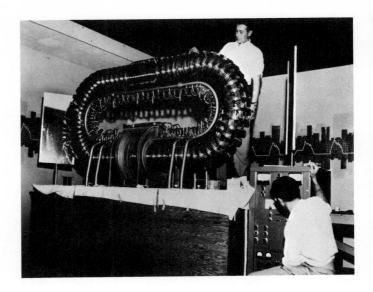

The stellerator, one of the first experimental devices used to study problems of plasma confinement for controlled nuclear fusion. [*Courtesy of Science Service, Inc.*]

is estimated to be about 10^{17} lb. If scientists succeed in achieving controlled fusion of deuterium, an energy source virtually without limit will be available.

Because of its ready abundance in water, the cost of deuterium is negligible. The cost of extraction is about 32 cents per gram. Its energy content per gram is equivalent to about 2400 gallons of gasoline. Man's dream of unlimited, low-cost energy is now more than a dream. It has reached the levels of applied research in the nuclear laboratories throughout the world.

Can you help but be excited by the prospect of being a part of such an adventure? By encouraging and understanding interest gained from identifying yourself vicariously, if not in actual participation, with the endeavors in this regard, you might take part in man's greatest revolution. The steam engine brought on the industrial revolution.

After this, civilization made giant steps forward. What might energy unlimited bring?

One of the major stumbling blocks is finding a usable means of plasma confinement. The confinement is necessary so that the plasma particles may travel the almost unbelievable distance of 100,000 kilometers within the plasma before undergoing fusion. The most promising method of plasma confinement being studied at present is the use of magnetic fields.

Let us apply our knowledge of forces produced between moving charges and a magnetic field. Consider, first, the random motion of the charged particles in a tube without a magnetic field. As illustrated in Fig. 19.2(a), the particles move in straight lines between collisions and make frequent collisions with the walls of the container. The energy transmitted to the walls cools the plasma.

Next, consider the effect of forces (right-hand rule for positively charged particles) between a magnetic field and a charged particle moving across the magnetic lines of force (Fig. 19.2(b)). With sufficient force the particles move in a circular path, such that the inertial reaction to the change in direction is just counteracted by the magnetic force upon the moving particle. Therefore, if a uniform magnetic field is applied as indicated in Fig. 19.2(c), the paths of the particles moving across the lines of force become tight helixes, providing the magnetic field is of sufficient intensity. The stronger the field, the smaller is the radius of curvature of the particle path. Significantly, the particle so involved cannot move outward to the walls of the container. The possible use of magnetic relationships is extremely significant because it shows how a hot plasma might be confined in a stable and controlled way by application of a suitable magnetic field. Vexing problems have developed in the early trials of magnetic confinement.

Undoubtedly the next few years will bring new and improved techniques in the attempt to solve these problems. It is not within the province of this book to explain the intricacies of the several projects which have been reported. The reader should feel obligated to use his knowledge in attempting to interpret current reports. References to the important problems and achievements of science are frequently found in magazines and newspapers. An educated person will be more than mildly interested in the progress being achieved.

Figure 19.2 Motion of charged particles in a magnetic field. (*a*) Random motion without a magnetic field. (*b*) Particles in a magnetic field. (*c*) Particles traveling in a helical orbit within a uniform magnetic field.

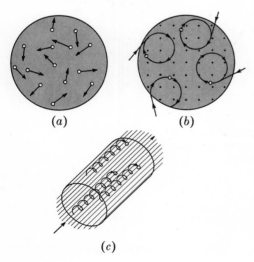

(*a*)   (*b*)

(*c*)

SOLAR ENERGY

In the search for new and more abundant sources of energy, we might be prone to overlook the most potent source of all—that of the perpetually available energy from the sun. Any thinking person must realize his total dependence upon solar energy. It is estimated that if man were to stockpile all of the available sources of energy now in general use, he would have the equivalent energy of but three or four days of the solar contribution toward making the earth a habitable place for man.

In our dreams of energy abundance, we in the United States tend to narrow our view too drastically toward the fields of industrial power, transportation, and communication. In fact, more energy is required for heating and lighting our homes and places of work than for any other use. But for most of us this requirement is taken for granted. In many places of the world, heating problems are paramount. In the United States, nearly a third of the total energy used is for heating and cooling homes and places of work and recreation. From the standpoint of the world's population the ratio would be much larger. Much of the energy is used wastefully. In solving space heating problems, the individual householder is supreme. Herein each of us can use his intelligence and knowledge in solving his unique problems of energy utilization. Perhaps we should all look to the sun.

Society seems destined to become more and more dependent upon the sun for all energy. To make intelligent choices we must inquire into the physical principles which might aid us in making greater use of solar energy. Herein our knowledge touches upon problems of personal economies as well as explanation.

Solar heating Significantly, sunlight is somewhat more easily adapted to space heating than to industrial motive power. Solar heating of houses is not new. At the dawn of civilization man was wholly dependent on the sun for heat. Without adequate knowledge of energy principles, the early man used solar energy wastefully and ineffectively. With today's knowledge and engineering skill, solar heating has an economic efficiency comparable to modern standards for fuel or electric heating. The incidence of sunlight is beyond our control, so we must accept it when it is available. Proper utilization of solar energy requires a greater degree of knowledge of basic principles than required for energy sources that can be placed largely under automatic controls. The challenge is great, but the rewards are gratifying.

A basic relationship in solar heating is that ordinary window glass is a radiant

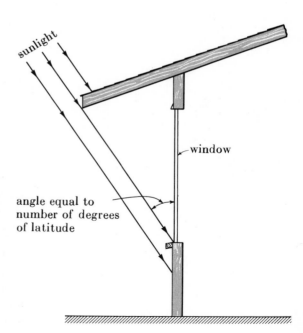

Figure 19.3 Seasonal control of solar heating. From March 21 to September 21 the south window will be shaded from the midday sun.

energy filter. Glass is transparent to nearly the full range of solar radiation except the ultraviolet regions. Clean window glass allows about 90 percent of the visible and infrared radiation from the sun to pass through. On the other hand, glass is almost opaque to the long-wave infrared reradiated by low-temperature objects which have absorbed the incident radiation. This is why the interior of an automobile becomes so hot when left in the sunlight with the windows closed. The solar energy can enter through the glass, but the radiation from inside cannot be transmitted outward through the glass. Therefore, the materials within the automobile absorb and hold the energy as heat.

Glass is not only a good heat filter; it is also a good insulator. That is, heat is not conducted readily through the material. Because of the thin sheets of glass used in windows, however, much heat is conducted through the window panes. This is because the amount of heat conducted through a material is inversely proportional to the thickness of the material and directly proportional to the areas of the surfaces through which heat can enter and leave. The insulating qualities of window openings can be enhanced greatly and at a very moderate cost by using two sheets of glass across the opening and separating the two by an air space. Dry air is a particularly good insulation. The double-pane glass window allows the inner sheet of glass to remain warm while the outer sheet remains cool.

Window glass is no longer a luxury.

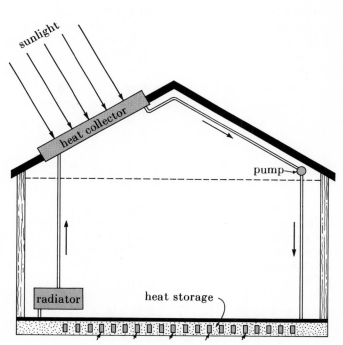

Figure 19.4 Schematic diagram of solar heating assembly. Heat is stored as heat of fusion without great increase of temperature in the circulating liquid.

cans of heat-storing compound

Glass is cheap enough to be used extensively in modern construction. Many houses are now designed with south walls almost completely of glass. It is not unusual to find glass comprising 75 to 80 percent of the entire wall area of some homes.

Control of energy intake through windows is accomplished by selective shading of the light. Draperies may be used to control energy intake. Drawing the draperies at night also increases the insulation of window openings, thereby holding the heat in the living space. Overhanging eaves constructed for seasonal shade are effective and automatic. Recall from Chapter 5 that the dimensions of the overhang are determined from the latitude of the location. To provide shade from the noonday sun from Mar. 21 until Sept. 21 in the northern hemisphere, the overhang is constructed so that the angle between the vertical window and a line from the bottom of the window to the edge of the overhang is equal to the degrees latitude of the location. (See Fig. 19.3.)

A homeowner should not overlook the possible use of deciduous trees in providing seasonal shade control. The summer foliage provides shade; the lack of foliage in winter allows the radiation to reach the window openings. Furthermore, if the warm weather season is delayed, the foliage also is delayed. If cold weather should arrive unseasonably early, the foliage falls off early. By careful planning of home construction and landscaping, the homeowner can do much to make optimum use of direct solar heating of his living space.

One problem of immediate interest is the provision for storage of energy from periods of abundance to be used during periods of energy lack. The familiar phenomenon of melting and solidifying which involves the heat of fusion of materials is most useful in this regard. We have previously studied the various energy characteristics of water. The low-temperature freezing point of water makes it unusable for storing energy in heat of fusion for heating homes. Other chemicals are more ideal for this purpose. Table 19.1 summarizes the fusion properties of several compounds which may be usable. Most of these materials can be produced cheaply and in abundance, and

TABLE 19.1   Fusion properties of selected compounds

Name	Formula	Melting point, °F.	Heat of fusion, BTU/lb*
Sodium carbonate	$Na_2CO_3 \cdot 10H_2O$	90–97	115
Sodium orthophosphate	$Na_2HPO_4 \cdot 12H_2O$	97–118	114
Sodium sulfate	$Na_2SO_4 \cdot 10H_2O$	88–90	104
Calcium nitrate	$Ca(NO_3)_2 \cdot 4H_2O$	104–108	90
Sodium hyposulfite	$Na_2S_2O_3 \cdot 5H_2O$	120–126	90
Calcium chloride	$CaCl_2 \cdot 6H_2O$	84–102	75
Water	H_2O	32	144

* 1 calorie = 3.97×10^{-3} BTU; 1 calorie/gram = 1.8 BTU/lb

Solar Batteries. One of the first experimental applications of solar cells was to obtain energy for the telephone system at Americus, Georgia. [*Courtesy of Bell Telephone Laboratories.*]

their melting points are in the temperature range where usable heat for space heating can be exchanged between the materials and the home heating facilities.

Fig. 19.4 shows schematically how heat collection and heat storage might be designed. The heat collector consists of a multipaned glass window behind which is placed a black sheet of copper to insure maximum absorption of the transmitted radiation. The heat exchanger consists of water or other liquid which can be pumped through tubes connected to the black sheets. After being warmed the liquid flows through radiators within the house, providing energy for space heating. Surplus heat is exchanged in the concrete floor of the house where the selected "fusion" compound is stored in imbedded cans. When sufficiently high temperatures are reached, the heat is stored by melting quantities of the canned compound. At a later time, when radiation absorption is reduced, the stored heat of fusion is restored to the circulating

liquid as the compound begins to solidify.

From the standpoint of engineering and available radiation, it is feasible to provide from solar radiation most of the heat required for winter comfort in all but the northernmost regions of the United States. Everywhere it could be used to supplement conventional heating systems. Experimental houses have been maintained in several localities to test the performance of solar heat installations. It is still too early to give proved economic performance figures in comparison with other forms of heating. A conservative estimate is that the use of solar heating in most localities of the nation would reduce household electrical and fuel bills by at least one-half to three-fourths depending upon climatic conditions. Savings of this magnitude should make it economically worth inquiring with increased vigor into the feasibility of solar heating under the conditions found in every climatic locality. Solar heating is worth investigating not only for homes,

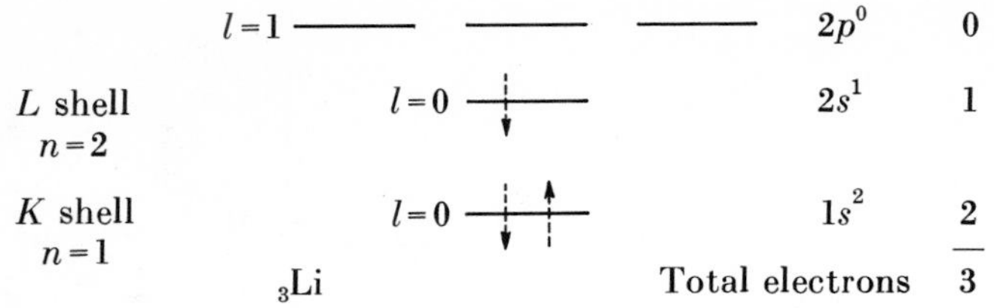

Figure 19.5 Electron configuration of lithium. Each lithium atom has its own particular set of available energy levels as revealed by its spectral lines.

L shell
$n = 2$

K shell
$n = 1$

$_3$Li

$l = 1$ ——— ——— ——— $2p^0$ 0

$l = 0$ ——— $2s^1$ 1

$l = 0$ ——— $1s^2$ 2

Total electrons $\overline{3}$

but also for industrial and commercial space.

The solar battery The space program has rapidly brought the solar battery into general use. This energy source is composed of a series of photovoltaic cells which operate at fairly high light intensities. The photovoltaic action is explained by principles of theoretical quantum characteristics in solids. The end result of the action is direct conversion of radiant energy to electricity.

Regardless of whether the radiant energy is converted to heat or electricity, the absorption of photons by a solid material is explained by the *energy band* theory. Energy bands are closely related

to electron quantized energy levels of atoms. To initiate our inquiry into the band theory of solids, let us consider again the electron configuration of lithium as shown in Fig. 19.5. Each lithium atom has its own characteristic set of available energy levels as revealed by its line spectra. The permitted states of any one atom of a group of lithium atoms are identical to those of any other lithium atom. In other words, the energy-level diagrams of all lithium atoms are identical. Similar identifying energy diagrams would be uniquely true of all isolated atoms of any given element. The number of energy levels and available states shown in Fig. 19.5 are summarized schematically in Fig. 19.6(a). If N identical isolated atoms of lithium are

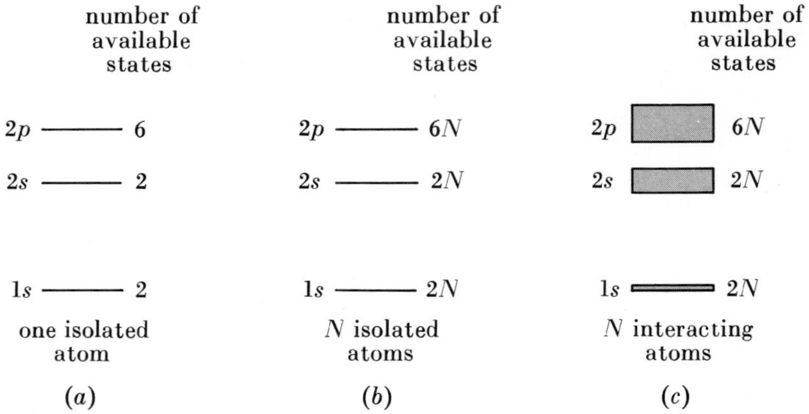

Figure 19.6 Schematic summary of the energy levels and states of lithium. The interaction between closely-packed atoms produces a band of energy levels for the available states.

	number of available states		number of available states		number of available states
$2p$	——— 6	$2p$	——— $6N$	$2p$	$6N$
$2s$	——— 2	$2s$	——— $2N$	$2s$	$2N$
$1s$	——— 2	$1s$	——— $2N$	$1s$	$2N$
one isolated atom		N isolated atoms		N interacting atoms	
(a)		(b)		(c)	

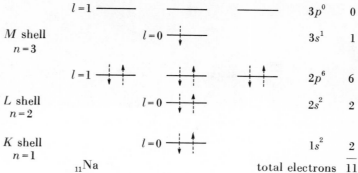

Figure 19.7 Electron configuration of sodium. All of the electron shells of the atom are filled except the $3s$ shell, which contains 1 electron.

M shell
$n = 3$

L shell
$n = 2$

K shell
$n = 1$

$_{11}$Na

$l = 1$ ———— ———— ———— $3p^0$ 0

$l = 0$ —⥮— $3s^1$ 1

$l = 1$ —⥮— —⥮— —⥮— $2p^6$ 6

$l = 0$ —⥮— $2s^2$ 2

$l = 0$ —⥮— $1s^2$ 2

total electrons $\overline{11}$

considered, the number of available states for each quantized level is increased by a factor of N, as shown in Fig. 19.6(b). As shown for a single atom, the number of available states for electrons in an s energy level is 2 and in a p energy level, 6. But with N isolated atoms the s levels can each accommodate $2N$ electrons and the p level, $6N$ electrons.

Next, we must consider the fact, expressed near the end of Chapter 3, that when atoms are held close together as in a solid, interactions and interference between the closely packed atoms prevent them from emitting their characteristic frequencies of radiation. The consequence of the interaction is to broaden the discrete energy levels of the system into a band of energy levels having slightly different energies. This result is shown schematically in Fig. 19.6(c). The effect of bringing together in a crystalline solid a large number of the originally isolated atoms is to spread out the discrete energy levels into energy bands. The number of available states has not been increased; the only change is that the energy states are spread (essentially) in a continuum throughout each energy band. Not all energy levels

are available. Just as the regions between available energy levels of isolated atoms cannot be occupied by a planetary electron, so also the regions between the available energy bands cannot be occupied by any electron.

Now let us consider again the electron configuration of sodium $_{11}$Na: $1s^2 2s^2 2p^6 3s^1$, as represented by Fig. 19.7. All of the electron levels of the atom are filled except in the $3s$ state which contains 1 electron. When sodium atoms are com-

Figure 19.8 Schematic summary of the energy bands occupied by electrons in sodium. The dark regions correspond to occupied states.

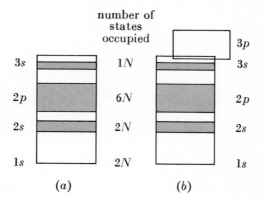

number of states occupied

$3s$	$1N$	$3p$ / $3s$
$2p$	$6N$	$2p$
$2s$	$2N$	$2s$
$1s$	$2N$	$1s$

(a) (b)

A portion of the band spectrum of cyanogen (CN) in the ultraviolet. [*Courtesy of RCA Laboratories.*]

bined to form a solid, the sodium crystal has an energy band for each of the electron energy states of the atom. To illustrate the distribution of the electrons among the various energy bands, consider Fig. 19.8(a) for sodium at its ground state. The 1s, 2s, and 2p bands are completely filled, as indicated by the dark regions. The 3s band having 2N available states is only half filled.

Sodium is a very good conductor of electricity. The fact that the uppermost energy band is only partially filled is responsible for this high electrical conductivity. All materials having similar partially filled energy bands are good conductors. When an external electric force is applied to these materials, the electrons at the top of the partially filled band gain small amounts of energy by the action of this external force and are promoted upward to the continuum of higher available energy states. Thus, the electrical charges flow under the influence of very small energies. In sodium not only is the 3s band partially occupied, but in addition the 3p band overlaps the 3s band, as shown in Fig. 19.8(b). Thus, the number of continuously available unoccupied states is greatly increased.

The nature of the crystalline linkages in solids may also affect the size and energy distribution of available states in the energy bands. An excellent example of the effect of linkages is found in the different characteristics of carbon atoms when linked in diamond as compared to

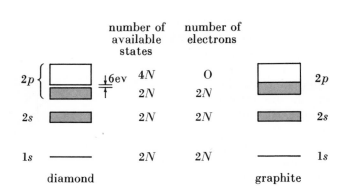

	number of available states	number of electrons	
2p	4N	0	2p
	2N	2N	
2s	2N	2N	2s
1s	2N	2N	1s
diamond			graphite

Figure 19.9 Schematic representation of the energy bands and states in diamond and graphite.

the linkage in graphite. Diamond is an insulator; graphite is a conductor. The electron configuration of carbon $_6$C in its ground state is $1s^2 2s^2 2p^2$. Fig. 19.9 is a schematic representation of the energy bands as found in diamond and graphite. The tetrahedral arrangement of atoms in diamond is such that two atoms mutually share an *electron pair* in much the same manner as was described in Chapter 11 for the oxygen atoms in the silicates. The *exchange interaction* of the paired $2p$ electrons in diamond increases the binding energy of these electrons. This loss of potential energy gives rise to two $2p$ energy bands for diamond. The two bands are separated from each other by a region of 6 electron volts, as shown in Fig. 19.9. The lower $2p$ band is filled completely with $2N$ electrons in the $2N$ available states. The thermal energy at room temperature is very small; hence, there are virtually no electrons in the upper $2p$ band of diamond. Thus, when an external electric force is applied, the electrons cannot gain enough energy to move to the upper $2p$ band. No electric charge flows; therefore, diamond is classified as a good insulator.

As for diamond, any substance which has a sizable forbidden energy region between a filled band and the next available empty energy band is an insulator. In the above description, the filled band is called the *valence band*. The next higher energy band available is called the *conduction band*.

The hexagonal arrangement of atoms in graphite is such that bonding electrons of the crystals are not fixed to a single atom or to a pair of atoms but are in continual transition from one quantum state to another without alliance to any one atom. The effect is shown in Fig. 19.9. Since a continuum of available states lie immediately above the occupied levels, an external electric force will provide the energy necessary to promote electrons to the upper levels. Hence, graphite crystals are conductors.

In terms of photon absorption by a material, unless the energy of the photon is greater than the gap between the valence band and the conduction band of an insulator, the electrons in the valence band cannot absorb the energy of the photons. This accounts for the transparency of pure diamond. All visible-light photons which enter the crystal are transmitted. Analogously, good conductors are opaque. The continuum of available energy states immediately above the occupied levels makes it possible for the electrons in conductors, like graphite, to be promoted upward by absorbing photons of a wide range of frequencies. Hence, the dark appearance of graphite and other conductors can be explained.

In Chapter 11 we found that *impurity atoms* within crystalline structures often changed materially the characteristics of the crystals. This can also be true with regard to the conductivity of crystalline solids. Because of the influence of impurity atoms, certain insulators may become *semiconductors*. For example, let us inquire into the effect of arsenic atoms as an impurity in a silicon crystal. The electron configuration of the outermost levels (see Fig. 17.18) of silicon $_{14}$Si is: $3s^2 3p^2$; that of arsenic $_{33}$As is: $4s^2 4p^3$. Thus, a neutral atom of arsenic has one more electron in its outer levels than a neutral atom of silicon. This extra electron does not take part in the electron pair sharing of the tetrahedron structure of silicon crystals. Consequently, this extra electron is weakly bound and adds energy levels of its

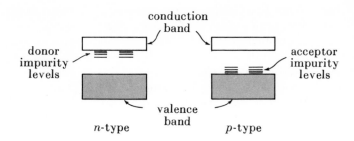

Figure 19.10 Energy-level diagram showing the effects of *n*-type and *p*-type impurities in silicon.

conduction band

donor impurity levels

acceptor impurity levels

valence band

n-type   *p*-type

own within the energy gap of the energy band regions for silicon crystals. In effect the arsenic donates a carrier of negative charge which has energy levels deeply spaced into the forbidden zone of the crystal. Impurity atoms of this type are called *donors* and lead to semiconductors of *n-type*.

On the other hand, had the impurity atom been gallium $_{31}$Ga, its outermost electron configuration of $4s^2 4p^1$ would have left one incomplete electron pair in the crystal structure for each impurity atom in the crystal. This would produce a vacancy in the valence band for each impurity atom. The impurity atom,

The Telstar communications satellite. The satellite is covered by 3600 solar cells which obtain energy from the sun to power the microwave relay in space. [*Courtesy of the American Telephone and Telegraph Company.*]

therefore, tends to accept an electron to complete the electron pair structure but this electron is less strongly bound because of the ionized nature of the action. A hole, or positive charge, is left at the location from which the electron came.

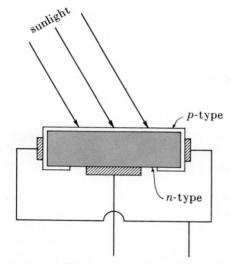

Figure 19.11 Diagram of a solar cell.

This hole keeps moving about the location of the impurity atom, as electrons keep falling into the charge void. In effect this adds energy levels to the valence band in the region of the impurity atoms. Impurity atoms of this type are called *acceptors* and lead to semiconductors of *p-type*.

Fig. 19.10 is an energy-level diagram showing the effects of *n*-type and *p*-type impurities in silicon. If the *n*-type semiconductor is joined to a *p*-type one, the junction region exhibits the combined energy level characteristics of both types. A very small amount of excitation energy at the junction can promote electrons across the remaining energy gap at the locations of the impurities. Illuminating the junction with light of proper frequency can promote electrons across properly prepared junctions, thereby absorbing the energy of the absorbed photons. This is the principle used in the *solar battery*.

Silicon solar batteries are made by diffusing boron into the surface layer of *n*-type silicon. The diffused surface layer becomes *p*-type. The boron layer is removed from the "shade" side of the cell and an electrical contact made with the *n*-type silicon. Electrical contact with the *p*-type material is made at the edges of the cell, leaving a major portion

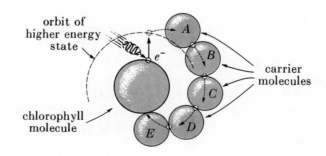

Figure 19.12 Cyclic photosynthetic energy exchange. The energy absorbed by the "carrier" molecules is converted to chemical energy in synthesis of carbohydrate molecules.

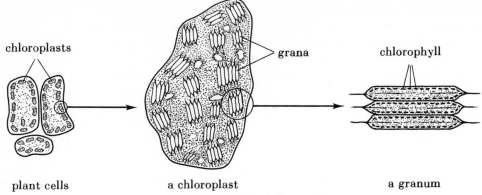

chloroplasts   grana   chlorophyll

plant cells   a chloroplast   a granum

Figure 19.13   Diagrams of successive enlargements of plant cell structure.

of the cell to be exposed to sunlight. Because of the thin surface layer, sunlight penetrates easily to the junction. A diagram of a photovoltaic cell is shown in Fig. 19.11.

Many applications have been found for the photovoltaic cell. The efficiency of the best units yet devised is about 6 percent for the silicon solar cells. This is comparable to the utilization efficiency of solar energy by photosynthesis in many living plants.

Photosynthesis Not completely unlike the energy conversion process in the solar battery, the photosynthetic process absorbs photons by raising an electron of a chlorophyll molecule to available high-energy states from which it is captured by a chain of "carrier" molecules. These molecules provide an external circuit within the living plant cell where the absorbed energy is converted to chemical energy before the electron returns to the chlorophyll. (See Fig. 19.12.) The level of chemical energy is increased in synthesizing carbohydrate molecules out of

water and carbon dioxide molecules. Thus, the energy of sunlight is stored in the electron configuration of the newly formed molecules. The quantum energy levels, or energy bands, which mediate this "carrier" process are not fully understood, largely because the molecules involved have not yet been fully identified. Riboflavin (vitamin B_2) and vitamin K are thought to be links in the chain.

The structure of the living cell also suggests, in miniature, the organization of photovoltaic cells in a solar battery. The chloroplast is the site of photosynthesis which keeps the life cycle of plants and animals supplied with energy. Fig. 19.13 shows diagrams of successive enlargements of plant cell structures. Notice the orderly arrangement of the structures. The chlorophyll molecules have a very flattened oblate form. They in turn are arranged in layered stacks within the granum, giving it the appearance of the crystalline structure of the semiconductors in a photovoltaic cell. Each granum might be looked upon as a photovoltaic cell. The several grana form the "solar battery," represented by the chloroplast. The chloroplasts also contain the "carrier" molecules which provide the circuit for fixing the energy absorbed from sunlight into the carbohydrate molecules. Each chloroplast seems to be self contained. It can carry out the photosynthetic process even when separated from the rest of the cell.

In contrast to man-made photovoltaic cells, the plant structure is subminiature. The cross section of a granum has a radius of about 7×10^{-7} cm. That is, about a million cells could be stacked in the space of 1 cm.

Although the over-all efficiency of energy conversion for a field of sugar cane, for instance, may be less than 5 percent, the efficiency of each individual cell can be about 75 percent. This is most impressive in contrast to the theoretical 20 percent held possible in solar batteries of optimum efficiency.

Periodically the suggestion is made that we make use of our agricultural surpluses by converting the grain and other products of photosynthesis into alcohol to be used as fuel. This could and is being done, particularly in those regions of the world where petroleum has to be imported and an abundance of sugar from sugar cane is available. As a supplementary fuel supply it might have useful value. If attempted on a scale equal to the present petroleum output,

the cost of processing would be fantastic. The cheapest fuel alcohol is now made from ethylene obtained as a by-product in petroleum refinery gases. The cheapest fermentation alcohol is produced from blackstrap molasses. The most expensive is from wood and other forms of cellulose. On the average, fermentation alcohol cannot be produced for less than twice the cost of gasoline and its energy value per gallon is only about two-thirds that of gasoline. The synthesis of gasoline from agriculture wastes could compete economically with the production of alcohol. However, for proper soil management, agricultural wastes may be more valuable when returned to the soil than when converted to fuel.

The scientists who know most about vegetation, its improvement, and use are inclined to predict that the best that modern application of science will be able to do is to provide a sufficient amount of food for the burgeoning population growth. We cannot look to increased utilization of natural photosynthesis for industrial energy. The study of the process of photosynthesis might, of course, lead to an understanding and duplication of the processes involved. If economically useful, this could lead to more direct utilization of sunlight for industrial power. Dreams more fantastic than this have been realized during the past century of scientific progress.

SUMMARY

Adequate sources of low-cost energy are a present-day problem for nearly all nations of the world, including the United States. The full impact of atomic energy potentials have not yet been felt. Fissionable materials are costly to extract and are not of unlimited abundance. Nuclear fusion, if the problems of controlling the reaction are solved, could make fuel abundance a reality. However, the cost of energy transformation depends upon the manner of control and the yield of useful energy.

Solar energy promises to be an important field of research in supplying present and future energy needs for individual and corporate enterprises. Solar space heating is an accomplished fact in research facilities and is being used more extensively as better understanding of techniques for absorption and storage are put to use.

Space-age use of the solar battery has focused attention upon the energy band theory of quantum levels in solids.

Photosynthesis is the natural process of solar energy conversion and storage accomplished in living plants. Continued research into this process might give clues to similar processes for energy conversion of more directly usable types for our industrial world.

PROBLEMS

1 Describe a possible explanation of the fission process in heavy nuclei.

2 What are the essential conditions for a controlled chain reaction and for a breeder reactor?

3 A mass of uranium-235 of 235 grams (a little more than $\frac{1}{2}$ lb) contains 6.025×10^{23} nuclides. If half of the nuclides react in the fission process of a reactor, how many joules of energy are transformed?

4 Describe the essential features of radiant energy which make solar heating possible.

5 If 1600 kg of sodium sulfate used in a solar heating system is melted for heat storage, how many calories of heat are transformed into heat of fusion? If heating requirements averaged 15,000 BTU per hour, how many hours of heating would the stored energy provide?

6 The sun transforms 2.28×10^{28} joules per minute through fusion of nuclei. How much mass is converted to provide this energy?

7 Find some recent library references about projects involving controlled fusion reactions. Summarize your findings and interpret the possible effect upon the problem of energy supplies.

8 Compare the effects of the *valence band* and the *conduction band*.

9 Describe the quantum effects which produce *n*-type and *p*-type semiconductors.

20

LIVING INTELLIGENTLY IN
THE WORLD OF SCIENCE

Since the dawn of science, man's progress in understanding nature's processes has been an unbroken history of continued enlightenment. Man has gained the opportunity to live more wisely with increasing freedom to adapt his life to the realities of nature rather than to live in ignorant fear of imagined superstitions. Science in a certain sense is embraced by all of society. This is not to infer that each person participates in it. But the application of scientific knowledge to practices in industry, the home, transportation, and communication has periodically remade man's mode of living in terms of his actual adaptation to or control of the realities of nature. Each person's stake in civilization is continually being enhanced.

A problem becoming more acute of late is that society has become more attached to the special products of applied science than to the adventurous sense of action which comes from relating oneself to living in a civilization which can focus its vision upon successful choices in dealing with natural events. The problems of society will not be solved by the professional scientists. Science is but a guide to action. It outlines that on which society might act with great probability of success. But the action must be conducted within society as a whole. With regard to this action, it is true that society's leaders reflect the collective choices made by society. This is the rub. The leaders of society; the persons in authority; the spokesmen of government, industry, labor, merchandising, the professions, religion; the leaders which we the people, having the freedom to choose, place at our command are incredibly ignorant of the most basic principles of science. A man, no matter how intelligent and forceful, is not free to choose that of which he has no knowledge. We proclaim that we live in the age of science. Should we not act as if we believed it? It becomes one's individual responsibility as a free citizen, no matter what one's walk of life, to identify oneself to a greater extent with the adventure of scientific activities. In this sense all people can participate in science to share with the professional scientist some of the feeling of adventure—the exuberance, the satisfaction, and the security which new knowledge brings. In this sense also, a free people can choose to follow those leaders who exhibit the common-sense skills and knowledge to use scientific principles in choosing and attempting to solve the truly critical problems of society. These choices are yours and mine. It is really more than a simple matter of choice; it is our responsibility as educated persons to use our intelligence and our increasing knowledge to this end.

Freedom is an opportunity but not a reality unless it is being used. From the first chapter on through each chapter of this book you have been challenged to clarify for yourself certain relationships which have stimulated the growth of scientific knowledge. Each of you now knows how his own task of self-enlightenment has progressed. No one has gained everything he possibly could. But each is more free to make certain choices now than before starting this adventure. It is hoped that each reader has experienced the thrill of knowing and has accepted the true freedom which is within the grasp of all men—the freedom to inquire, to be guided by his own curiosity and imagination.

FREEDOM TO INQUIRE

Freedom to inquire means freedom from fear of the unknown. No longer is the lack of complete understanding an obstacle to progress. Science develops because of uncertainty rather than reliance upon absolute knowledge. The strength of science is its self-corrective method of evaluating and solving problems. This is the history of scientific advancement. The temporary solution of one problem marks the rebirth of inquiry into the questions which have been generated by the ongoing investigation. There can be no end to the cyclic processes of scientific inquiry. This is the adventure of science. Valid understandings gained in one area prepare the way for further ventures into the world of the unknown; and each person may choose his own frontier to investigate.

You can choose your own frontier, but you are not alone in your venture. All scientists who have gone before you have left records of their inquiries such that you can make use of their discoveries in planning and executing your own inquiries. Who can help but get a thrill from working hand in hand with Brahe, Kepler, Newton, Lyell, Curie, Rutherford, Einstein, Bohr, Fermi, and the many, many others who have ventured into the unknown? With men and women like these showing us the way how can one help but be inspired to choose the way of inquiry?

Intellectual honesty Scientists have learned by experience that it pays to stop and think. Each person must face his own prejudices and personal beliefs with open-mined awareness of that which one honestly would like to believe and why he so believes. When you face these facts of personal bias, it is a factor of personal honesty to suspend these wishes and prejudices while you try to find out what the reliable facts are in any given situation. If the newly discovered facts which have been determined by understandably controlled conditions run contrary to one's wishes, one must face and accept with honesty the pathway of scientific fact. Nature does not lie. Nature is orderly and reasonable, although to the neophyte it might appear that nature delights in saying no to our traditional ways of interpreting its phenomena. Nature makes no choice. It is neither capricious nor animated. It is but a phenomenon. To be successful in dealing with nature, one must interpret each situation in terms of the known laws and principles found in organized knowledge about similar natural processes. This is where curiosity and intelligent imagination come into play. Man must relate his anticipations to the realities of nature and check upon the outcomes to determine whether his choices were valid.

One must continually test one's knowledge and interpretations or one has lost the freedom of inquiry.

Intellectual immaturity How delightful it is to enter fantasy-land when one realizes that the performance is fantasy. How free from restraint is one's imagination when engrossed in a good book of fiction, listening to good music, or enjoying good art. These excursions are refreshing and should have a place in everyone's life. But how tragic it is when a person no longer can distinguish between truth and fantasy—when fantasy is accepted as truth or truth as fantasy. These persons no longer have the freedom of inquiry.

We have stated before in this book that a mark of the immature intellect, particularly in this day of pseudo-scientific advertisements and "thrilling science-adventure" type of movies and TV programs, is that he finds the careful cross-check system of scientific speculation and confirmation prosaic and unworthy of his attention. It seems like a lot more fun to remain ignorant. But how boring it must be to wait for the next show! In ignorance there can be no choice. It is a life rigged completely from outside the individual. He has no freedom who fails to use it.

Personal curiosity and reasoned search activities lead to a possibility of choices of meanings for a given situation. Among the choices are the more intelligent pathways to freedom and progress that only awareness can bring. It is a mark of prudence to ask what understandable relationships among observed evidences are used to support a given explanation. If no crucial test has been made with regard to the premises made, the conclusions must be looked upon with extreme caution and disbelief until reliable and understandable tests have been made. Testimonials, no matter how convincingly given, cannot take the place of truth. Surely educated persons must learn to use evidence in forming their conclusions and not simply follow every suggestion without question.

The immature and illiterate are more to be pitied than censured. The censure should be given to those who prey upon the misfortunes of the ignorant. In this sense, the educated must in truth be his brother's keeper. The thinly veiled fantasy, misrepresentation, and downright untruth which are paraded as truth in some of today's pronouncements by advertisers and others who seek to influence public opinion should be recognized for what they are and censured. Only the intellectually immature are fooled. A great number of persons are mildly annoyed by these bizarre events, but they do nothing about it. Among those who are educated there should arise a censure to a degree which those who use these means cannot mistake. We can choose to patronize only those who have proved themselves intellectually honest. Intellectual maturity is all we ask of those who lead the public.

Nonconformity Nonconformity is not the pathway of the masses, it arises from the freedom of inquiry held by individuals. It is a virtue widely talked about but rarely observed. We live in a security-conscious age. But few realize that one must risk his personal security to gain it. Those who use personal knowledge as a guide know that true security is an inner quality of satisfaction with oneself. Its foundation is freedom of choice. Its vitality is the fearless spirit and open-faced adherence to the principles of scientific inquiry. One does not consciously and deliberately break with conformity any more than one consciously and deliberately changes his physical stature or intellectual maturity. One does not begin thinking new thoughts and making independent judgments that count, as if by the flip of a coin. New and fresh interpretations come only after deliberate experimentation with one's ideas to find if they have basis in fact. They are not formed by discovering that the ideas are approved by the general public. Can you imagine, for instance, the ideas of relativity coming from a public opinion poll? Only by using knowledge based upon facts can one bring forth enduring innovations. These spring forth only by firm self-honesty and continued enterprise in the inquiries which raise those questions which are crucial tests of one's knowledge and which at the same time hold promise for extending one's understanding of the phenomena involved. This is often the path to frustration, but it is also the path to truth. One does not have to be a professional researcher or scientist to gain this independence. The spirit is gained by identification with some phase of the pursuit of new knowledge based on fact. This identification might show itself in continued interest and growth of personal knowledge in some phase of science.

FREEDOM TO DISCUSS AND COMMUNICATE

It is most natural for us as human beings to become curious about the world in which we live. From early childhood we have had the urge to know more about the events of the universe. Our recent experiences have reaffirmed that there is only one method of gaining *reliable* knowledge about natural events—that which includes observation, speculation, and experiment. These self-corrective activities are one in science.

It is vitally true that our experiences would be most meager were we restricted to our own devices. The discussions in this book and the inquiries which have been communicated were made possible because the experiences of others have been formulated into agreed upon terms and symbols which have been given meaning through a common fund of everyday experiences and a deliberate organizing of generalizations and principles out of analyses of our growing fund of experiences. You should recall your most strenuous efforts at clarifying for yourself a scientific meaning. Your problems very likely were not caused by an inability to read and write the words and symbols used; your lack of understanding was caused by the lack of background experiences. As individuals we are not prone to analyze the universe, organizing it into solar systems, crystals, molecules, atoms, and the like, each system described by a universal core of scientifically acceptable meanings for explanation. Only through discussion and communication with others were we made aware of the explicit properties which truly describe the universe we hold in common.

Every communication involves at least two persons. Communication of meaning depends upon usable and recognized similarities in the interpretations used by both of the persons for the words and symbols used in expressing ideas. Herein we must each be patient with each other. Stating a word by itself does not convey meaning. Meanings must be made clear. We must allow time for thought and inquiry to take place in order that the self-corrective verification aspects of scientific method can operate. We might even have to invite inquiry from some people. We must not equate nimbleness of expression with thoroughness of inquiry. Lack of expression may not mean lack of thought and inquiry and then again it may. But, if one wishes to continue freedom of discussion and communication with the widest group of persons, one must allow time for the formulation of original ideas from *all* who wish to communicate, else one has closed the door upon an essential freedom. Unfortunately, college classroom situations are not always conducive to the widest interplay of ideas. Fortunately, however, discussion and communication are not restricted to the classroom. The classroom may serve primarily to trigger more widespread communication and inquiry elsewhere. The freedom to discuss and communicate is, again, an individual's possession. One either uses it or he loses it.

Originality The process of living in the modern world can be a dynamic experience or a series of submissions to suggestion. The difference lies within the spirit of an individual's outlook. Exploration, invention, and expression are experiences which enrich the lives of all who partake. These are the active, exciting, forward-looking and tenacious activities which bring out a person's originality. These are not the passive, leisurely, self-indulging activities so often pictured as the "good life" by magazine and TV ads. An exploration of scientific meanings in any significant depth cannot be completed in an hour or two, or even in days. At best it is the continuing activity of a lifetime.

One cannot predict from what source the most successful insights may arise, but it is quite certain that they will not arise without the challenge of communication. You should be elated when ideas are used which to you seem unusual because in them may lie a key to a rapid advancement in understanding if they represent reality. Testing ideas for their true meanings calls for originality. A true test of one's originality is to convey to others the meaning of that which is unfamiliar in terms of the familiar. This art must be practiced to be appreciated. It often involves the invention of models wherein an action or resulting outcome can have none but the intended meanings; but the limitations of the model must also be apparent. It often involves using the logic of mathematical formulas to express relationships which can later be analyzed by measuring outcomes; but the communicators must know the fundamentals of mathematical expression. It involves organizing the familiar into unfamiliar patterns which lead to questions which are crucial tests of meaning; but the questions must be mutually understood. Always, it involves the crucial test of provoking anticipations which link given meanings to present situations in such a manner as to make predictions of future events a possibility. Only thus can the validity of the anticipated meanings be interpreted in terms of observed facts. This is the strength of science. It is not the world of tell me; it is the world of show me.

Critical thought The successful attainments of scientific concepts lie in the self-corrective nature of basing meanings *only* upon interpreting that which is observed fact. This eliminates searching for ghosts. It is a sad commentary on contemporary life that decisions today are made more on the basis of slogans than upon evaluation of facts. There may be nothing wrong with the ideas behind a slogan. It is the acting upon suggestion which is questioned. We who are supposed to be the most highly educated people on this earth find it too easy to sit back and to denounce some action or advocate some other action by simply shouting the "proper" words without any basis in fact upon which to defend our actions. Of course, not all problems might warrant detailed analysis. A part of the success of science is that it seeks out the crucial problems by critical judgment of purpose. Where important problems are being judged without fact, judgment should be suspended until the facts are known. It takes courage to stand up for truths which are not yet known; but if it is not done in pertinent problems, your freedom to discuss and communicate will be lost. Science can do nothing in and of itself. You cannot support science with money and laboratories in the hope that it will solve your problems. As far as your judgments are concerned only you can do things with science, because it is you who makes decisions, not science.

Before making decisions concerning situations of natural processes, it is wise to consult more than one source of scientific discussion. This is not so much in the prospect that more than one concept or hypothesis will be proposed, but rather as a check upon your interpretations of the communications by comparing the meanings which are conveyed. Science rarely accepts the conclusions of a single source. Tests are made for verification in several critically structured situations. It also is prudent for the individual to give critical thought to the meanings conveyed by several sources before reaching a decision. Should conflicting explanations be found, it is well to recall that all scientific explanations must be looked upon as tentative and subject to change. Therefore, the more recent interpretations coming from reliable sources—the scientists working closest to the area of concern—should be studied most carefully in order to improve one's understanding. Having made your interpretation, then use your freedom of discussion and communication toward those who can help you to bring any revolutionary changes of meaning into harmony with your fund of basic principles of science.

FREEDOM OF PURPOSEFUL ACTION

Science is the capacity for action. It is the power of thinking constructive thoughts which have never been thought before; but someone must do the thinking. It is the power of analyzing and solving present and future problems; but someone must do the solving. It is the power of doing things that have never been done before; but someone must start the doing. The most exciting prospect is that no one can set limits as to the ultimate achievements of the actions based on science.

Lack of action on modern-day problems cannot be attributed to the lack of scientific knowledge. The problems are not being acted upon because we lack the someone to do the thinking, analyzing, solving, and doing which puts science into action. Science provides the freedom of purposeful action for all those who have scientific knowledge. This freedom is the right and potential possession of every person living in this age of science, but the right and the potential possession mean nothing if they are not put to use.

We who have been concerned with the inquiries of this book have placed our faith in the powers of education. The major problem in American education at this instant is how to make adults—the school administrators, school board members, teachers, labor leaders, industrial leaders, parents, everyone now controlling public opinion—realize that they are living in an age of science and that they have the freedom of purposeful action through using science. We need a great ground swell of enthusiasm as was felt in the great American westward movement, when people in all walks of life readjusted their mode of living in order to provide greater freedom for themselves and their children to live and control their own destinies in their own life span. *We can live in a similar age.* Our problem is to communicate to the American public what science is. The western movement would not have taken place had it only been talked about and written about. It took place *only* because people lived it; the people used the freedom which was theirs. Today we can bring our neighbors to realize the power of science *only* by living it; that is, by using our freedom of purposeful action. We need an enthusiastic public. This is not the task only of scientists; there would have been no western movement had only the trail guides moved west. The task is for newspapermen, novelists, playwrights, historians, teachers, politicians, lawyers—the non-scientists—who along with the scientists must evolve a new cultural age which can strive to reach beyond the present progress of science, not trail far behind it or oppose it. This is your task and your duty to your nation.

Purposeful action in the home A factor of great concern is that so many school children and adults in our society have come to feel that science is alien to the "common man" and is something they neither *can* nor *care* to understand. Those readers who have completed the inquiries of this book know that this is a false pretention. Each of you is a living symbol of the truth. The concepts of science make common sense when analyzed with understanding. True, you have not the skill and the depth of knowledge needed to be a professional scientist. But no one pretends that you have to be a professional baseball player to play sand-lot baseball. In the same manner, you can enjoy the adventure and enthusiasm of science without having to be a scientist. Every day brings opportunities for purposeful action in your home and neighborhood.

Children are natural born scientists. Awareness of the world begins very soon after birth. The child begins to interpret his world a long time before he can talk about it or associate his understandings with words. It is easy for adults to overlook the really significant science learning that the child experiences in the early months of life. For example, the child learns about gravitation from its own falls, the things that he drops, the tipping up of its formula bottle. Words to express these experiences come weeks or months later. But in the same sense as your scientific vocabulary has been enriched by references to personal experi-ences, so the careful observation and aid provided by parents can assure that experience meanings be attached to the *proper* words of a child's vocabulary, so that meaningful communication can begin at an early age.

By the time your child begins the elementary school, you can have helped him gain meaningful concepts (although the identifying words may be quite different from those of the adult world) of weight, push-pull (force), speed, acceleration, inertia, shininess, dullness, sharpness, smoothness, roughness, solid, liquid, gas, and many other qualities in the things of his growing world of observations. Adults must encourage the purposeful curiosity of children. It is impossible to predict what may arouse a child's curiosity and cause him to seek an explanation. A child's explanation might seem very crude by adult standards. But the adult might do well to recall mankind's history of efforts at explanation when a child is attempting to make sense out of this amazing world. Some children exhibit vivid imaginations in creating their explanations for observed events. You must be patient in letting them express their meanings as they see them at the time without restraint or prompting except when asked. Remember, imagination is needed in developing future scientific theories, and the only way for the child to clarify his ideas is to express them in his own way. It would be ideal if you could begin the practice of open-minded self appraisal at an early age; not by condemnation or ridicule of ideas but by self-learning to distinguish between the imaginary accounts and the ones based on reliable information. It might be begun as simply as asking with a quizzical smile of genuine interest, "How much of what you have just said do you know to be true?" or "How can we find out about what you said?" If it turns out to be imagination, we just accept it as such, even praise it if it shows originality; but then we face reality, if possible, to show that it is also fun to find out how things really are. This can be done at another appropriate time, but be related back to the first. In other words, at the child's level we are making inquiry and using critical thought in reaching conclusions on the basis of observed facts. Detailed opportunities such as these do not occur every day of the child's life, so we must be ready to welcome and make use of every opportunity. There is no set age when these inquiries begin or flourish. Adults should be naturally interested in what children are doing and trying to express. They must patiently allow the children to lead the way in the initiation of these inquiries.

The hobbies and interests of adults profoundly influence children. Your identifying yourself with some aspect of science by continued interest and growth in understanding, even though in a purely amateur way, makes for conversation between parents and friends of the family which soon sets a pattern for the listening child. The child may not understand what is said, but he grasps phrases here and there which he remembers. When, later, the child adds more direct experiences to these phrases from observing the parents enjoying their hobbies, and from contacts in school, museums, TV programs, and among his friends, his interest in learning about truth is much enhanced. He is proud to be a part of this adult world.

We can learn much from observing the pre-school child. If encouraged just a little, the child shows purposeful curiosity, shows initiative, and is a natural experimenter. These are attributes we have held before us as vital to scientific inquiry. The child is continually checking to see if the world is really the way it seems to be. He is not dismayed if it turns out to be different than he expected. In fact, you often find children repeating an unusual experience over and over again in sheer delight at the new discovery.

We need not regiment a child's life for learning to take place. He generates his own interests and needs for continued growth in understanding. The adult plays the role of interest stimulator, safety guide, and source of materials, communication, and aid. It is a sorry commentary on our schools, that as the child progresses through the school his learning is taken more and more away from his own initiative, away from his natural curiosity, and away from the guidance of his parents.

Purposeful action in the schools If we wish science to serve as a dominant factor in the intellectual life of society, we must first endeavor to procure for scientific action a central place in education. The science curriculum should be designed for unbroken development from the kindergarten through the general education phases of our colleges. Your experiences while making the inquiries of this book should serve you well in showing creative interest and action toward the programs of science education in the schools.

But well planned science curricula are not enough. Before science can achieve the central place in education for the age of science, the total school curriculum must be infused with the spirit and principles of scientific inquiry. The fact that this may not be found in our present-day schools might as often be the fault of science instruction as of instruction in other fields. Too often, instruction in science creates the impression that the other fields of learning have no relation to science. Nothing could be further from the truth. All fields of learning are the products of man's creative reaction to his environment. All fields of learning have evolved together from common roots in a changing society. Only changes of emphasis mark the branching into the several fields of learning. In our recent inquiries, we have attempted to show that the adventure of knowing is in its enhancement of the total enjoyment and purpose of life.

The crux, however, is the complete lack of any real understanding of science among those who should initiate science-centered curricula. Even those who may be willing to make changes are not free to choose that of which they have no personal knowledge. Education of all teachers and, particularly, of the educational administrators should be based upon adequate experiences in the sciences and in mathematics at an adult level. Only thus can the leadership be capable of critical evaluation of curriculum development for the age in which we live.

Public spirited citizens can do much to hasten the day of educating students for the age in which they will live. You have the power to act. You can show creative interest in the criteria used by school boards in selecting school administrators. Is required preparation and demonstrated interest in science and mathematics included in the criteria? You can show creative interest and support for adequately prepared supervisory service staffs to aid schools in planning science-centered curricula with a diversity of approaches usable by teachers having a variety of backgrounds. Is maximum use being made of community resources, science materials and equipment, and the experience backgrounds of individual teachers, science and non-science, to produce a science-integrated total program of instruction? You can show creative interest and support for science-centered curricula planned to provide useful and stimulating instruction for pupils of a wide range of age, abilities, and career interests. We need more scientists; but we also need a science-oriented public. Is adequate use being made of the natural abilities and interests of pupils in self-motivating their own inquiries into natural processes at their own levels of understanding? You can show creative interest and support for an increasing utilization of mathematics as a tool for the examination of the structures and predictable relationships wherever found in the material of the curriculum. Mathematics is not for science and mathematics alone; it has universal application as does reading and writing of English. Is mathematics being shunned in favor of less critical models in analyzing processes and functions within the phenomena presented in the experience program of your schools?

These actions are not based upon slogans and "battle cries" for a return to the schools of yesteryear, or to make any unnecessary changes just for the sake of change. We ask only that you recognize the age in which you live. The actions you take must come after proper evaluation and inquiry into the status of your schools in order that you can support *constructive action*. Remember, your freedom of action is lost if you have not made an evaluation of the probable consequences of your choices, and if you do not follow up on the outcomes to determine the results. Freedom of choice is not found in blind submission to suggestion.

One final statement—man is free and responsible for his actions. The final test for freedom can be made only by one's own satisfaction of doing what he sets out to do. No one from outside can evaluate this freedom, because no one but you knows what your true intentions are. But whatever your intentions are, your actions are the only purposeful contacts you can have with human society. In the final analysis, your actions will determine the degree of freedom you will have attained in this age of science.

SUGGESTED READINGS

The Nature of Sound and Light

BEISER, ARTHUR, *Basic Concepts of Physics*, pp. 90–106, 199–249. Reading, Mass.: Addison-Wesley Publishing Co., Inc., 1961.

KRAUSKOPF, KONRAD B., *Fundamentals of Physical Science*, pp. 150–167, 277–296. New York: McGraw-Hill Book Co., Inc., 1959.

PRIESTLY, HERBERT, *Introductory Physics*, pp. 103–126, 284–299, 322–366. Boston: Allyn and Bacon, Inc., 1958.

WHITE, HARVEY E., *Modern College Physics*, pp. 246–318, 352–367. Princeton, N. J.: D. Van Nostrand Co., Inc., 1962.

The Solar System—Its Mechanics and Origins

ASHFORD, THEODORE A., *From Atoms to Stars*, pp. 15–84. New York: Holt, Rinehart and Winston, Inc., 1960.

BAKER, ROBERT H., *An Introduction to Astronomy*, pp. 20–67, 110–157, 176–208. Princeton, N. J.: D. Van Nostrand Co., Inc., 1957.

CHRISTIANSEN, G. S. AND PAUL H. GARRETT, *Structure and Change*, pp. 17–65, 145–170. San Francisco: W. H. Freeman and Co., 1960.

HOYLE, FRED, *Frontiers of Astronomy*, pp. 66–126. New York: Harper and Brothers, 1955.

JEAN, F. C., E. C. HARRAH AND F. L. HERMAN, *Man and His Physical Universe*, pp. 1–27, 82–125, 139–145. Boston: Ginn and Co., 1958.

PRIESTLEY, HERBERT, *Introductory Physics*, pp. 54–87. Boston: Allyn and Bacon, Inc., 1958.

Atmosphere and Hydrosphere

CABLE, E. J., R. W. GETCHELL, W. H. KADESCH, AND W. J. POPPY, *The Physical Sciences*, pp. 92–141. Englewood Cliffs, N. J.: Prentice-Hall, Inc., 1951.

CHRISTIANSEN, G. S. AND PAUL H. GARRETT, *Structure and Change*, pp. 237–249. San Francisco: W. H. Freeman and Co., 1960.

JEAN, F. C., E. C. HARRAH, AND F. L. HERMAN, *Man, and His Physical Universe*, pp. 505–556. Boston: Ginn and Co., 1958.

KRAUSKOPF, KONRAD B., *Fundamentals of Physical Science*, pp. 456–474. New York: McGraw-Hill Book Co., 1959.

The Earth's Crust—Its Structure and Processes

CHRISTIANSEN, G. S. AND PAUL H. GARRETT, *Structure and Change*, pp. 226–237. San Francisco: W. H. Freeman and Co., 1960.

CRONEIS, CAREY AND WILLIAM C. KRUMBEIN, *Down to Earth*, pp. 13–43, 129–214. Chicago: The University of Chicago Press, 1936.

GREGG, DONALD C., *College Chemistry*, pp. 84–198, 271–275. Boston: Allyn and Bacon, Inc., 1961.

JEAN, F. C., E. C. HARRAH, AND F. L. HERMAN, *Man and His Physical Universe*, pp. 561–572, 598–623. Boston: Ginn and Co., 1958.

KRAUSKOPF, KONRAD B., *Fundamentals of Physical Science*, pp. 433–455, 476–535. New York: McGraw-Hill Book Co., 1959.

Growth of the Atomic Theory

ASHFORD, THEODORE A., *From Atoms to Stars*, pp. 174–255, 285–455. New York: Holt, Rinehart and Winston, Inc., 1960.

BEISER, ARTHUR, *Basic Concepts of Physics*, pp. 131–196, 227–309. Reading, Mass.: Addison-Wesley, Inc., 1961.

CHRISTIANSEN, G. S. AND PAUL H. GARRETT, *Structure and Change*, pp. 253–307, 447–561. San Francisco: W. H. Freeman and Co., 1960.

PRIESTLEY, HERBERT, *Introductory Physics*, 179–214, 248–276, 368–486. Boston: Allyn and Bacon, Inc., 1958.

TAYLOR, LLOYD W., *Physics, the Pioneer Science*, pp. 577–643, 761–847. Boston: Houghton Mifflin Co., 1941.

WHITE, HARVEY E., *Modern College Physics*, pp. 380–401, 420–439, 476–526, 556–717. Princeton, N. J.: D. Van Nostrand Co., Inc., 1962.

GLOSSARY

A

ABSOLUTE TEMPERATURE The temperature recorded in terms of the Kelvin scale on which the freezing point of pure water is 273°K and the boiling point is 373°K at standard pressure. Absolute temperature equals centigrade temperature plus 273°.

ALPHA PARTICLE A particle often emitted by radioactive nuclei. It is a helium nucleus consisting of two protons and two neutrons.

ANGSTROM UNIT An atomic sized unit measure of displacement equal to 10^{-10} meter.

ANION A negatively charged ion which moves toward the anode during electrolysis.

ANODE The positive electrode of a voltaic or electrolytic cell.

ATOM The smallest chemical unit consisting of a positively charged nucleus of radius about 10^{-14} meter around which is an electron cloud of radius about 10^{-10} meters. The atom of a given element is identified by its atomic number, i.e., the number of protons in the nucleus.

ATOMIC NUMBER The number of protons in the nucleus of an atom and, therefore, the number of electrons surrounding the nucleus. The elements are characterized by their atomic numbers and are classified by it in the Periodic Table.

445

ATOMIC WEIGHT   The relative weight of an atom as compared with the weight of one atom of carbon 12 which is taken as 12.0000.

B

BETA PARTICLE   A high-speed electron emitted by some radioactive nuclei.   The small mass of the electron, when given kinetic energies of about a million electron volts, moves at speeds near that of light, 3×10^8 meters per second.

BINDING ENERGY   The property of constituent parts of a system held together by forces at a distance.   The energy is measured in terms of the work necessary to move a given part to a point which is beyond the influence of the system.

BOILING POINT   The temperature at which the vapor pressure of a liquid is equal to the external pressure.

B.T.U., BRITISH THERMAL UNIT   The amount of energy required to raise the temperature of one pound of water 1° Fahrenheit.

C

CALORIE   One hundredth of the energy required to raise the temperature of one gram of water from 0° to 100° centigrade.

CATHODE   The negative electrode of a voltaic or electrolytic cell.

CATION   A positively charged ion which moves toward the cathode during electrolysis.

CENTIGRADE TEMPERATURE   The temperature scale on which the freezing point of pure water is 0° and the boiling point is 100° at standard pressure.

COMPOUND   A homogeneous substance composed of two or more elements, the proportions of which by weight are fixed and invariable.

COSINE (of an angle θ)   In a plane right triangle the cosine θ is the ratio of the length of the side adjacent to the angle and the length of the hypotenuse of the triangle.

COULOMB   The unit quantity of electricity equivalent to one ampere flowing for one second.

COSMIC RAYS   High energy particles which bombard the earth from outer space.   The particles reaching the upper atmosphere are mostly protons, but in the collision with nuclei of air molecules other forms of radia-tion are produced with a wide range of energies and penetrating power.

CRITICAL TEMPERATURE   The temperature above which a gas may not be liquefied irrespective of the pressure.

CRYSTAL   A solid in which the component parts (molecules, atoms, or ions) are oriented in a definite pattern or geometric design.

CYCLE   A sequence of events which are repeated during certain types of processes.

D

DAUGHTER PRODUCT   The nucleus left when a radioactive nucleus emits a particle.   In many instances the daughter product is also radioactive.

DECAY   Synonymous with *disintegration*—The spontaneous emission of a particle from a radioactive nucleus.

E

ECCENTRICITY   In an ellipse or an elliptical orbit, the fractional part of the semimajor axis (mean displacement) by which the foci are displaced from the common center.

ELECTROLYSIS   A process of bringing about a chemical change through the action of an electrical current.

ELECTROLYTE   A substance which in solution is a conductor of the electrical current.

ELECTRON   A fundamental particle with negative charge.   The mass of the electron is 9.11×10^{-32} kilogram, its charge is 1.602×10^{-19} coulomb.

ELECTRON VOLT   The energy gained by an electron being accelerated through a potential difference of one volt.   One electron volt is equivalent to 1.602×10^{-19} joule.

ELEMENTARY CHARGE   The unit electrical charge carried by the electron (negative charge) and the proton (positive charge). It is equivalent to 1.602×10^{-19} coulomb.

ELEMENT (chemical)   A substance consisting of atoms having identical chemical properties.

EQUILIBRIUM (mechanical)   A state in which there are no unbalanced forces and no unbalanced torques.

F

FAHRENHEIT TEMPERATURE   The temperature

scale on which the freezing point of pure water is 32° and the boiling point is 212° at standard pressure.

FERMI UNIT   The nuclear sized unit measure of displacement equal to 10^{-15} meter.

FUSION   The process of melting; change of solid to liquid.

G

GAMMA RAY   A penetrating radiation emitted by some radioactive nuclei. It is of the same nature as x-rays and ordinary light. Its energy is usually in the order of a few million electron volts as compared to energies of less than ten electron volts for visible light.

GRAM   A unit of mass often used in scientific work. It is very nearly the mass of one cubic centimeter of water.

GRAM ATOMIC WEIGHT   The atomic weight of an element expressed in grams.

H

HALF-LIFE   The time during which a radioactive nucleus has a 50:50 chance of disintegrating. In a collection of nuclei of the same isotope, the half-life is the time during which half of them will undergo disintegration and change into the daughter product.

HEAT   A form of energy characteristic of molecular motion.

I

INERTIA   The quality in objects to resist rapid changes in their states of motion.

INTERFERENCE   The diminishing of wave effects by subtraction between two or more waves which are out of phase.

ION   An atom or group of atoms possessing an electrical charge.

IONIZATION   The process in which an electron is separated from or added to a neutral atom or group of atoms thereby giving these particles, respectively, a positive charge or a negative charge.

ISOTOPE   Nuclei having the same number of protons but differing numbers of neutrons, i.e., having the same atomic number but different atomic weights.

J

JOULE   A unit of energy equivalent to doing the work of lifting an object weighing one newton to a height of one meter.

K

KILOGRAM (1000 grams)   A unit of mass often used in scientific work. It is very nearly the mass of one liter of water, about 1.06 quarts.

M

MASS   A measure of the inertial qualities of an object in terms of dividing the amount of an unbalanced force acting on the object by the amount of acceleration it produces for the object.

MOLECULAR WEIGHT   The sum of the atomic weights of the atoms which make up a molecule.

MOLECULE   The smallest unit of an element or a compound which can exist by itself in the free state.

MOMENTUM   The quantity of motion which is the property of objects moving linearly or rotating. It is measured by the product of multiplying the constant opposing force applied to the object times the time necessary for it to bring the object to rest from a linear motion and the product of multiplying the constant opposing torque times the time necessary to stop the rotation.

N

NEUTRON   Along with the proton, a basic building block of the nucleus. It has about the same mass as the proton but is uncharged. Free neutrons decay to protons and beta particles with a half-life of 12 minutes.

NEWTON (force)   A unit of force defined by its effect of accelerating a one kilogram mass at the rate of one meter per second per second.

NUCLEAR FISSION   The nuclear process in which a nucleus splits in two and releases energy.

NUCLEAR FUSION   The nuclear process in which two light nuclei join together to form a heavier one. It occurs most readily with hydrogen and hydrogen isotopes. Fusion is the process by which the sun and stars transform mass to other forms of energy.

NUCLEON   A proton or a neutron.

NUCLEUS   The massive core of the atom. Its radius is of the order of 10^{-14} meter; it consists of neutrons and protons, is positively charged, and contains almost all of the mass of the atom; its density is in the order of a million tons per cubic inch.

NUCLIDE   A nucleus of a specific isotope.

P

PERIOD   The average time required for completing one cycle of a cyclic (reoccurring) process.

PHASE   In cyclic events, the time stage in the period of the cycle measured in relation to a standard or designated instant of starting.

PHYSICAL CHANGE   A change which does not involve a change in the chemical composition of a substance.

PROTON   A nuclear particle carrying a positive charge; the hydrogen 1 nucleus. Its mass is 1.67×10^{-27} kilogram.

Q

QUANTUM   An elemental unit of energy, the smallest change in energy possible under a given set of conditions.

R

RADIOACTIVITY   The unstable condition of nuclides which cause them to spontaneously emit energetic particles.

REINFORCEMENT   The intensification of wave effects by the addition of two or more waves which are in phase or nearly so.

S

SINE (of an angle θ)   In a plane right triangle the sine θ is the ratio of the length of the side opposite the angle and the length of the hypotenuse of the triangle.

SPECIFIC HEAT   The quantity of heat in calories necessary to raise the temperature of one gram of a substance one degree centigrade.

SPECTRUM   The series of images formed when radiant energy is dispersed and focused on a screen or photographic film so that the component waves are arranged in the order of their wavelengths.

STANDARD CONDITIONS   Temperature of 0°C and pressure of one atmosphere (760 mm of mercury).

SUBSTANCE   Any homogeneous material.

T

TEMPERATURE   A measure of heat intensity indicating the possible direction of spontaneous heat flow from higher to lower temperatures.

TETRAHEDRON   A figure or solid enclosure formed by four intersecting faces.

V

VALENCE   A number which represents the combining capacity of an atom or submolecular group of atoms referring to hydrogen as a standard.

VAPOR PRESSURE   The partial pressure exerted by a vapor in equilibrium with a liquid or solid.

VERNAL EQUINOX   The point where the sun seems to cross the celestial equator on about March 21. The tropical year is the interval of time between successive vernal equinoxes.

VIRTUAL IMAGE   An illusion brought about by seeing or representing the reflection and refraction of characteristics from objects so situated that a real image cannot be formed.

VISCOSITY   Resistance to flow, the opposite of fluidity.

X

X-RAY   Artificially produced radiation of energy similar to gamma rays. Its penetrating power depends on the energy of the radiation which ranges from about 10^4 to 10^5 electron volts.

INDEX

Ellipse, characteristics of, 164
Elliptical orbits, of planets, 110, 128–131; of electrons, 374
Elongation, 165
Emissions, radioactive, 294–295
Energy, 135–137; in atmospheric circulation, 203; conservation principle of, 9; electric potential of, 344; equivalence of mass, 367; gravitational potential of, 139; heat, 142; kinetic, 10; light, 39; nuclear, 393; potential, 10; sound, 18
Energy-level diagrams, 375, 381–384
Epicycle, 85
Equant, 86
Equatorial bulge, of earth, 271; of Jupiter, 174
Equilibrium, 2
Equinoxes, 96; precession of, 101
Equivalence of mass and energy, 367
Erosion and deposition, 303–305
Eros, 161
Escape velocity, 140; from planets, 160; from solar system, 141
Ether of space (luminiferous), 76
Exclusion principle (Pauli), 380–381
Extrusion, volcanic, 261

Falling bodies, 123–131
Families of elements, 385
Faraday, Michael, 324
Faraday's laws of electrolysis, 325
Faults, 277–278
Feldspars, 234, 236
Fermi (unit), 390
Ferrel cell, 198, 206
Ferromagnesians, 238
Field, electric, 150; electromagnetic, 149, 329–331; gravitational, 112; magnetic, 149
Fission, 411–414; breeder reactor, 414; fissionable elements in, 411, 414; nuclear reactor, 412
Fixed stars, 85
Floatation of mountains, 281–283
Fluorescence, 338
Foot-pound (unit), 8
Force, between molecules, 230; centripetal, 128; defined, 117; of elasticity, 6–7; electrical, 150, 229; gravitational, 112–113; magnetic, 149; nuclear, 390; tectonic, 284
Foucault, Jean, 51, 90
Foucault pendulum, 90–92
Fracture, surfaces of, 241
Franklin, Benjamin, 322
Fraunhofer lines, 342
Freezing point, 260
Frequency, 4; of light, 52; of sound, 24–25; threshold in photoelectric effect, 59; of vibrating systems, 3–4
Fuels, 409–410, 429
Fusion, latent heat of, 420; latent heat of storage salts in solar heating, 420–421; nuclear, 415–417

Galvani, Luigi, 323
Gamma rays, 295, 339
Gas, 30; force between molecules of, 255; properties of, 254–256
Geocentric universe, 85
Geometrical optics, 42–44, 49–51
Geosyncline, 302
Gram atomic weight, 236, 242
Gram formula weight, 236–237
Granite, 237–238
Graphite, 425
Gravitation, law of, 112–113
Gravitational, constant, 113; mass, 112; potential, 139–140; separation, 249–250
"Greenhouse" effect, 193
Ground state, 381

Hadley, George, 197
Hadley cell, 198, 202
Half-life, 296–297
Halo, 71
Hardness, 241
Heat, 142; exchanges in atmosphere, 203; of fusion in ice, 258; of fusion in heat storage salts, 420; of vaporization, 258; work equivalent of, 142
Heat capacity, 257
Heat conduction, 147
Heat convection, 147
Heat equator, 195
Heisenberg, Werner, 371
Heisenberg uncertainty principle, 371
Heliocentric universe, 88–90
Herschell, William, 177
Horizon, 92
Horizontal eddies, in atmosphere, 200, 203; in ocean, 219
Horse latitude, 189, 198
Huygens, Christian, 46
Huygens' principle, 46–47
Hydrogen, 315; spectral series, 342–343; stellar fuel, 415
Hydrogen spectra, 342; Balmer series, 342–343; Lyman series, 343; Paschen series, 343
Hyperons, 401

Ice, 257, 258; on planets, 175, 176, 177
Igneous intrusions, 264
Igneous rocks, 276
Images, virtual, 43
Independence of motions, principle of, 124–131
Index of refraction, 49
Inert gases, 228, 383
Inertia, 7
Inertial forces, 126
Inertial mass, 116
Inertial system, 8
Infrared light, 57, 193, 343
Insulators, electrical, 322, 425

Interference, of light, 48; of waves, 47–48, 216; of X-rays, 233, 362
Interferometer, 52–53
Intermolecular forces, 230
Intrusions, 264
Inverse-square relationship, 31; for electricity, 230; for gravitation, 113
Ions, 229
Ionosphere, 192
Iron, in earth's interior, 249; in meteorites, 249
Isobars, 395
Isostasy, 281–284
Isotones, 395
Isotopes, 395
Isotopic age determination, 297–300

Jet streams, 203
Joule (unit), 135

K capture, 295
Kelvin temperature scale, 142
Kepler, Johannes, 107–108
Kepler's laws of planetary motion, 108–111
Kinetic energy, 137
Kinetic theory of gases, 13, 254–255
Kinetic theory of matter and heat, 147
Kuiper, Gerard P., 181

Laccoliths, 264
Laplace, Pierre Simon, 181
Latent heat, of fusion and vaporization, 258; of heat storage salts, 420
Laue, M. T. F. von, 361
Lavas, 262–264
Lavoisier, Antoine Laurent, 315
Law, combining weights, 318; conservation of energy, 9; conservation of momentum, 122; Coulomb's, 344; definite proportions, 316; equivalence of mass and energy, 367; Faraday's, 325; Gay-Lussac's, 320; gravitation, 113; Kepler's, 108–111; multiple proportions, 317; Newton's, 114–119; periodic, 383–385; planetary motion, 108–111
Lead isotopes, 299
Leptons (table), 404
Light, 39–61; aberration of, 97; diffraction, 48, 71; dispersion, 54; interference and reinforcement, 47–48; as particles, 367–368; photons of, 59; quantum of, 59; reflection of, 42–44; refraction of, 49–51; speed of, 49; spectra, 55–56; wavelength, 51; waves, 48
Lightning, 322–323
Line absorption spectra, 56
Line emission spectra, 56
Liquids, characteristics of, 257; electrical conduction in, 325–326
Lithium, 181
Longitudinal waves, 21
Looming, 75
Loudness, 31–32

Lowell, Percival, 179
Luster, 240
Lyell, Charles, 291
Lyell's principle of uniformitarianism, 292, 300, 305
Lyman series, 343, 351

Magma, 262, 264
Magnetic dipole, 376–378
Magnetic effect of electric currents, 330
Magnetic energy, 377–378
Magnetic fields, 149; force on an electric current, 331; origin of solar, 152–153; in sunspots, 151
Magnetic side thrust, 330
Major planets, 172
Mass, atomic, 236, 242; of atomic particles, 390; center of, 112; defect, 393; of earth, 134, 270; energy-equivalence of, 367, 390; gravitational, 112; inertial, 116; number, 390; of planets, 160; relativistic, 366; rest, 366; standard of, 120; of sun, 134
Mass-energy, conservation of, 367
Mass-equivalence of energy, 390
Mass number, 390
Mass spectrograph, 392, 393
Mass-to-charge ratio, 335
Mass unit, atomic, 390
Mass-velocity relationship, 367
Matter, structure of, 254–257
Matter waves, 368
Mean-life, 405
Melting point, of heat storage salts, 420; of ice, 258
Meson properties (table), 404
Metamorphic rocks, 276, 302
Meteorites, 172, 249
Metric units of weights and measures, 120–121
Michelson, interferometer, 52–53
Michelson-Morley experiment, 76
Mid-ocean fracture zones, 306
Mid-ocean ridges, 280
Millikan, Robert A., 337
Millikan's oil drop experiment, 337
Minerals, defined, 234
Mineral, silicate groups, 234
Mirage, 73–74
Mixtures, 225
Moderator, reactor, 413
Mohorovicic discontinuity, 265, 275, 285
Moh's scale, 241
Molecular weight, 321
Molecules, 226, 254; Avogadro's hypothesis, 320; collisions between, 256; motion of, 310–312
Momentum, in atmospheric circulation, 206; conservation of, 119–122; in ocean currents, 218–220; in protoearth theory, 249; in protoplanet theory, 185–186; relativistic, 367
Month, lunar, 80–81; sidereal, 80; synodic, 81
Moon, origin of, 246, 250; phases, 81; spiralling away from earth, 250–251; surface gravity, 112

Motion, constant acceleration, 116; constant speed, 128; Newton's laws of, 114, 182; retrograde, 84; rotational, 181–185
Mountains, ancient and present-day belts, 302; building of, 303, 305; floatation theory, 281–283; theory of roots of, 283; types of, 278–281
Multiple proportions, law of, 317
Musical phenomena, 66–70; beats, 67; diatonic scale, 69–70; instruments of, 68; tempered scale, 70

Naturally radioactive elements, 293, 297
Nebular hypothesis, 181, 185
Neptune, mathematical discovery of, 178
Neutrino, 295
Newton, Isaac, 111
Newton's hypothesis of gravitation, 112; laws of motion, 114, 182; *Principia*, 111; rules of reasoning, 111
Nonconductors, electrical, 322, 425
Nuclear, binding energy, 393–394; charge, 293; density, 397; discovery of, 339; disintegration, 293–296; energy of particles, 390; fission, 411–414; forces, 390; fusion, 415–417; mass of particles, 390; spin, 391; spontaneous reaction equations, 295; stability line, 395; reactor, 412–414
Nucleon, 292
Nuclides, 395

Ocean currents, 217
Ocean gyres, 218
Ocean waves, size, 215–216; speed of propagation, 216; theoretical model, 214; of translation, 212; wavelength, 216
Oersted, Hans Christian, 329
Oil-drop experiment, 337
Olivine, 235
Orbits, characteristics of, 165; of electrons in Bohr atom, 348
Oxygen, in atmosphere, 192, 262; discovery of, 315; in earth's crust, 226; as ozone, 192; as standard of atomic weight, 321
Ozone, 192

Paired electrons, 234, 425
Pair formation and annihilation, 403
Palmen, E., 202
Palmen's model of atmospheric circulation, 202–208
Partial pressure, Dalton's law of, 259
Paschen series, 343, 351
Paths, elliptical, law of, 110
Pauli, Wolfgang, 381
Pauli's exclusion principle, 381
Pendulum, conservation of energy of, 137; Foucault, 90–92; gravitational acceleration of, 272
Perception, depth of, 41

Perihelion, 99
Period, definition of, 4
Periodic motion, 4–6
Periodic system of the elements, 355–385
Photoelectric effect, 57–59
Photon, 59; absorption and emission, 349–352; angular momentum of, 375; interactions, 368; linear momentum of, 367; in photoelectric effect, 59; spectrum, 55–56
Photon-wave dilemma, 59
Photosynthesis, 428–429
Photovoltaic cell, 422–428
Planck, Max, 59
Planck's constant, 59, 345
Planck's quantum hypothesis, 59
Plane wave fronts, 19
Planetary motion, characteristics of, 356–360; elliptical orbits of, 110, 128–131; energy relationships, 138–139; laws of, 108–111
Planetary electrons, 228
Planets, data of, 160, 165; Earth, 170; Jupiter, 174; Mars, 170; Mercury, 167; Neptune, 178; Pluto, 178; Saturn, 176; Uranus, 171; Venus, 169
Plasma, 415
Pluto, discovery of, 179
Plutonic rocks, 276, 302
Plutonium, 414
Polar front, 203
Polarization of light, 71–72; in scattering, 72, 144; in sunspots, 151
Pole, magnetic, 149
Positron, 404
Precession, of the earth, 101; of the equinoxes, 101; of the perihelion of Mercury, 131
Prediction and verification, 122
Pressure, in compressional waves, 23–25; explained by molecular motion, 13; standard of, 255
Pressures, law of partial, 259
Prevailing winds, 197–198
Principal quantum numbers, 373
Principia, 111
Probability of survival law, 294
Proportions, multiple, law of, 317
Prominences of sun, 144
Protoearth theory, 246
Protoplanet theory, 180–186
Proton-proton cycle (fusion), 415
Ptolemaic astronomy, 85–88

Quanta, 59, 227, 254, 312, 348, 351
Quantization of atomic characteristics, 372–380
Quantum concept, 58–59; excited state, 351; ground state, 381; hypothesis, Planck's, 59; in photoelectric effect, 59
Quantum numbers, 373–380; electron spin, 379; in energy band theory, 422–427; nuclear spin, 391; orbital angular momentum, 374; orbital magnetic, 374; principal, 373

69; heat of fusion of heat storage salts, 420; index of refraction, 49; intensity and loudness of sounds, 33; isotopes used in measuring geologic time, 297; leptons and mesons, 404; Moh's scale of hardness, 241; periodic, of chemical elements, 385

Tangential components, of force, 128, 183, 351; of velocity, 357

Tectonic deformation, 284–285

Temperature, absolute, Kelvin scale of, 142; in chromosphere and corona, 148; in interior of earth, 266; in interior of sun, 143; kinetic theory of interpretation, 29, 146; radiation, 147; on solar surface, 142

Tempered scale, 70

Terrestrial planets, 166

Tetrahedral distribution of bonds, 234–235

Theory, Bohr's atomic, 348; catastrophic, of geologic change, 292; Dalton's atomic, 319; Dirac's, of electrical forces, 403; energy band, 422; geocentric, of universe, 85; heliocentric, of universe, 88; infall, of the sun, 154; kinetic molecular, 30; magnetic field, of the sun, 152; nuclear atom, Rutherford, 341; Palmen's, of atmospheric circulation, 202; photon, 58; protoplanet, 180; relativity, 76; relativistic-quantum, of the atom, 372; Rutherford-Soddy, of radioactive transformation, 339; uniformitarianism, of geologic change, 292; vertical cell, of atmospheric circulation, 197; Yukawa's, of nuclear forces, 404

Thermal units, 142

Thermonuclear reaction, 415

Thomson, J. J., 335

Thomson's atomic model, 337

Threshold frequency, 58

Tides, moon-earth, 250; protoplanets, 186, 250

Time, mean solar, 96; in relativity, 365; sidereal, 99; tropical, 102

Torque, 181, 183

Transformations, of energy, 9–10; of radioactive nuclides, 294–295

Total reflection, 74

Transverse waves, 21

Triads, in musical scales, 69

Triple point, 260

Troposphere, 191

Ultraviolet light, 192, 247, 262

Uncertainty principle, 370–372

Uniformitarianism, 292

Uranium-238 series, 298

Uranus, discovery of, 177

Vacuum, in antiparticle theory, 403; of space, 154

Valence band, 425

Vaporization, latent heat of, 258

Vapor pressure, 259

Vapor pressure curve, 259

Vector analysis, addition, 115; resolution of components, 118

Vector quantities, 115

Velocity, average, 114; distinction from speed, 114; of earthquake waves, 274; instantaneous, 114; of light, 52; tangential, of earth's surface, 270; of wave propagation, 213

Vibration, 2–12; molecular, 257

Virtual image, 43

Visible light, 56

Volcanic activity, 251–267

Volcanism, extrusions, 261; intrusions, 264; in mountain formation, 264–265

Volcanoes, 253

Volta, Alessandro, 323

Voltaic cell, 323

Water, composition of, 316; decomposition of, 324; vapor-pressure temperature curve, 259; waves, diffraction of, 216; waves of translation, 212

Wavelength, de Broglie, 369; definition of, 24; of light, determination of, 52–53; of sound, determination of, 33–34

Waves, earthquake, types of, 273–274; frequency of, 53; gravitational, 21; interference, 215; longitudinal, 21; speed of propagation of, 52; sound, 21–22; transverse, 21

Weathering of rocks, 239

Weight, 112

Weights, combining, 317

Westerlies, prevailing winds, 189, 198

Winds, in atmospheric circulation, 197, 202, 204; in formation of ocean currents, 218; prevailing, 197–198; in wave formation, 215

Work, definition of, 7; function in photoelectric effect, 59; involved in vibrational systems, 8

X-rays, 233; diffraction analysis by, 361–364; discovery of, 338

Year, International Geophysical, 190

Year, sidereal, 81; tropical, 102

Young, Thomas, 47

Young's double-slit experiment, 47–48

Yukawa, Hideki, 403

Zeeman, Pieter, 151

Zeeman effect, 151; explained by quantum theory, 379

Zenith, 92

Zero, absolute, 142

Zodiac, 101

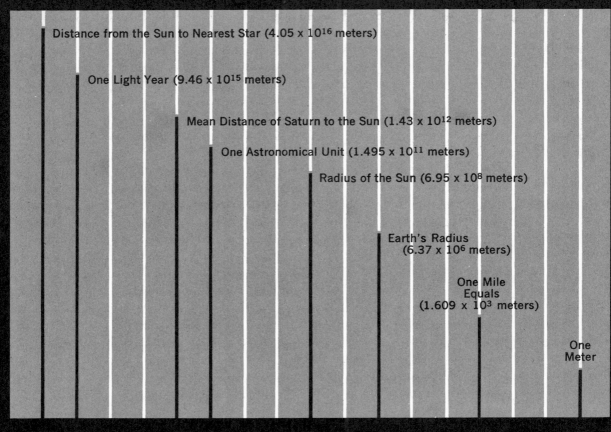

COMPARISON OF SIZES AND DISTANCES
USING AN EXPONENTIAL SCALE